PREFACE TO THE SEVENTH EDITION

In the second edition of this volume (1907) an appendix on the Principles of the Stadia Method was added. In the third edition (1908) the section on Public Lands Surveying was revised by Professor W. C. Hoad; the Mine Survey chapter was revised by Mr. Blamey Stevens; and an appendix on the Planimeter was added. In the fourth edition (1915) this volume was reduced to pocket size and bound in flexible covers. This change was made without reducing the size of type, making it practicable to carry in the pocket a book that is easy to read. A new chapter on the Stadia Method and a Stadia Reduction Table were added. The chapter on Mine Surveying was revised again. In the fifth edition (1923) Chapter VIII on Observations for Meridian and Latitude, Chapter X on City Surveying, and Chapter XIV on the Calculation of Traverses were revised completely. In the sixth edition (1931) Chapters I to V, VII and X were largely rewritten and a brief treatment of the Plane Table was added to Chapter VII.

In this, the seventh edition, the entire volume has been thoroughly reviewed, and no pains spared to make all desirable revisions and improvements. Numerous problems have been added to nearly every chapter. All page references and illustrative examples have been checked. Chapter I has been expanded to include a more complete discussion of errors in measurement and their adjustment. The description of foreign instruments in Chapters III and IV has been modified and brought up to date. The article on Convergence of Meridians in Chapter V has been made more complete. Much of Chapter VII, the Stadia Method, has been rewritten to give a more logical approach to this subject. In Chapter VIII the description of the celestial sphere has been revised and new figures added; all astronomical tables and examples have been brought up to date. Chapter XIV on Traverse Computations has been completely rearranged to obtain a more logical sequence in the presentation of these calculations. The section on reproduction of plans in Chapter XV has been modified to include present practice.

We are deeply indebted to Professor J. W. Howard, of Massachusetts Institute of Technology, for his valuable suggestions based upon a reading of the entire text. Appreciation is also due Professor A. J. Bone and Mr. H. J. Shea, of M.I.T., and to Professor J. M. Robbins of Newark College of Engineering for their valuable assistance.

C. B. B.

Cambridge, Mass., *January*, 1938.

PREFACE TO THE FIRST EDITION

In the preparation of this volume, it has been the authors' chief purpose to produce a text-book which shall include the essentials of a comprehensive knowledge of practical surveying and at the same time be adapted to the use of teachers and students in technical schools. In this book, which is essentially an elementary treatise, such subjects as stadia, plane table, hydrographic and geodetic surveying, are entirely omitted, these subjects being left for a later volume.

Considerable stress is laid upon the practical side of surveying. The attempt is made not only to give the student a thorough training in the fundamental principles and in approved methods of surveying, computing, and plotting, but also to impress upon him the importance of accuracy and precision in all of his work in the field and the drafting-room. In carrying out this purpose it has seemed necessary to lay particular stress upon some points which to the experienced engineer or the advanced student may appear too obvious to require explanation, but which teaching experience has shown to be most helpful to the beginner. The most common errors and mistakes have therefore been pointed out and numerous methods of checking have been explained. Every effort has been made to inculcate right methods even in minor details, and for this purpose a large number of examples from actual practice have been introduced.

In arranging the subject matter of the work, the four parts are presented in what appears to be a logical sequence. First, the use, adjustment, and care of instruments are taken up ; then the next three parts, surveying methods, computations, and plotting, are taken in the order in which they are met in the daily practice of the surveyor. To show more clearly the steps in the process, the notes which are used as illustrations in surveying methods are calculated in the computation section, and are treated again under the methods of plotting, finally appearing as a completed plan.

While the authors recognize fully their indebtedness to those who have preceded them in this field, they hope that they have made some useful contributions of their own to the treatment of the subject. Thus in the section on Surveying Methods, many practical suggestions have been inserted which they have found of value in their own work and which, so far as they are aware, now appear in a text-book for the first time. On the subject of Computations, much emphasis is laid upon the proper use of significant figures and the arrangement of the work, matters which heretofore have not been adequately treated in books on surveying. The section on Plotting contains many hints referring particularly to surveying drafting, which are not given in the published books on drawing and lettering. It is hoped also that the complete set of original illustrations which have been introduced throughout the book will aid materially in making the text clear.

A comprehensive cross-reference system giving the page as well as the article number has been adopted : this, together with the complete index at the end of the book and the many practical hints throughout the volume will, it is hoped, render it useful to the practical surveyor as a reference book.

The authors desire to acknowledge their indebtedness to their various associates in the teaching and engineering professions who have kindly responded to requests for information and assisted in the preparation of this work, particularly to Blamey Stevens, M. Sc., of Ellamar, Alaska, who supplied the entire chapter on Mining Surveying. They are also under obligations for the use of electrotype plates of tables : to W. H. Searles for Tables IV, V, and VI ; to Professor J. C. Nagle for Tables II and III ; and to Professor Daniel Carhart for Table I ; all of these plates were furnished by John Wiley & Sons. The authors are under special obligation to Professors C. F. Allen, A. G. Robbins, and C. W. Doten of the Massachusetts Institute of Technology, and to H. K. Barrows, Engineer U. S. Geological Survey, who have read the entire manuscript and who have offered many valuable suggestions in preparing the work for the press.

The authors also desire to express their appreciation of the excellent work of W. L. Vennard, who made the drawings for illustrations.

No pains has been spared to eliminate all errors, but the authors cannot hope that their efforts in this line have been completely successful, and they will consider it a favor if their attention is called to any which may be found.

C. B. B.

G. L. H.

Boston, Mass., *September*, 1906.

CONTENTS

PART I

USE, ADJUSTMENT, AND CARE OF INSTRUMENTS

CHAPTER I. — GENERAL DEFINITIONS — MEASUREMENT OF LINES — ADJUSTMENT OF ERRORS

ADJUSTMENTS OF THE COMPASS.

CHAPTER III. — MEASUREMENT OF ANGLES

THE TRANSIT.

USE OF THE TRANSIT.

ADJUSTMENTS OF THE TRANSIT.

Chapter IV. — Measurement of Differences of Elevation

THE LEVEL.

LEVELING RODS.

USE OF THE LEVEL AND ROD.

ADJUSTMENTS OF THE LEVEL.

I. ADJUSTMENTS OF THE WYE LEVEL

II. ADJUSTMENTS OF THE DUMPY LEVEL

PART II

SURVEYING METHODS

CHAPTER V. — LAND SURVEYING

SURVEY OF FIELD WITH TRANSIT AND TAPE.

THE UNITED STATES SYSTEM OF SURVEYING THE PUBLIC LANDS.

CONTENTS   xiii

Chapter VI. — Traverse Lines — Location of Buildings
Miscellaneous Surveying Problems

TRAVERSE LINES.

LOCATION OF BUILDINGS FROM TRANSIT LINE.

MISCELLANEOUS SURVEYING PROBLEMS.

CHAPTER VII. — THE STADIA METHOD — THE PLANE-TABLE METHOD

THE PLANE TABLE.

Chapter VIII. — Observations for Meridian and Latitude

Observations for Meridian.

Observations for Latitude.

Chapter IX. — Leveling

CHAPTER X. — CITY SURVEYING — LINES AND GRADES FOR CONSTRUCTION — SURVEY OF CITY LOTS, BUILDINGS AND PARTY WALLS

ESTABLISHING AND STAKING OUT CITY LINES AND GRADES.

SURVEY OF CITY LOTS.

RECTANGULAR COÖRDINATE SYSTEM OF SURVEYING CITIES.

CHAPTER XI. — CONTOURS — MISCELLANEOUS TOPOGRAPHICAL SURVEYING METHODS

CHAPTER XII. — MINE SURVEYING

MINING INSTRUMENTS.

PART III

COMPUTATIONS

Chapter XIII. — General Principles — Miscellaneous Problems — Earthwork Computations

Chapter XIV. — Calculations Relating to Traverses

PART IV

PLOTTING

Chapter XV. — Drafting Instruments and Material — Process Prints

Chapter XVI. — Methods of Plotting

TABLES

APPENDICES

THE PRINCIPLES AND PRACTICE OF SURVEYING.

PART I.

USE, ADJUSTMENT, AND CARE OF INSTRUMENTS.

CHAPTER I

GENERAL DEFINITIONS
MEASUREMENT OF LINES — ADJUSTMENT OF ERRORS

1. DEFINITION. — Surveying is the art of measuring and locating lines and angles on the surface of the earth. When the survey is of such limited extent that the effect of the earth's curvature may be neglected it is called *Plane Surveying*. When the survey is so large that the effect of curvature of the earth must be taken into account to secure appropriate accuracy as, for instance, in the survey of a state or a country the refinements are made by applying the principles of *Geodetic Surveying*.

2. Purposes of Surveys. — Surveys are made for a variety of purposes such as the determination of areas, the fixing of boundary lines, and the plotting of maps. Furthermore, engineering constructions, such as waterworks, railroads, mines, bridges, and buildings, all require surveys.

3. Horizontal Lines. — In surveying, all measurements of lengths are **horizontal** or else are subsequently reduced to horizontal distances. As a matter of convenience, measurements are often taken on slopes, but the horizontal projection is afterward computed. The distance between two points as shown on a map then is **always** this horizontal projection.

INSTRUMENTS FOR MEASURING LINES

4. THE CHAIN. — Formerly two kinds of chain were used by surveyors, but these have been almost wholly superseded by steel tapes. The *Surveyor's (or Gunter's) Chain* is 66 ft. long; its use was confined chiefly to land surveying on account of its simple relation to the acre and to the mile, as shown below.

$$1 \text{ Gunter's Chain} = 4 \text{ Rods} = 100 \text{ Links.}$$
$$1 \text{ Mile} = 80 \text{ Chains.}$$
$$1 \text{ Acre} = 10 \text{ Square Chains.}$$

Each link of the surveyor's chain is $\frac{66}{100}$ of a foot (or 7.92 inches).

These units of measurement are employed today in the surveys of the public lands (U. S. Land Office) but a tape graduated to chains and links is used in the fieldwork instead of a chain.

The *Engineer's Chain* is 100 ft. long and is divided into 100 links of 1 ft. each. Each end link is provided with a handle, the outside of which is the zero-point, or end, of the chain. In these chains, every tenth link counting from either end is marked by a brass tag having one, two, three or four points corresponding to the number of tens which it marks. The middle of the chain is marked by a round tag. In the engineer's chain then the 10-ft. and 90-ft. points, the 20-ft. and 80-ft. points, etc., are marked alike; hence it is necessary to observe on which side of the 50-ft. point a measurement falls in order to read the distance correctly. Distances measured with the surveyor's chain are recorded as *chains and links* (or in *chains and decimals*); while those measured with the engineer's chain are recorded as *feet and decimals*.

5. Metric Chain. — The *Metric Chain* is usually 20 meters long and is divided into 100 links, each 2 decimeters long.

6. TAPES. — Cloth — Metallic. — There are three kinds of tape in common use — *cloth, metallic,* and *steel.* Cloth tapes stretch so easily that they are of little use in surveying. The so-called metallic tapes are cloth tapes having very fine brass wires woven into them to prevent stretching. They are usually graduated into feet, tenths, and half-tenths and are made in lengths of 25 ft., 50 ft., and 100 ft. When precise results are required a steel tape should be used.

7. STEEL TAPES. — Steel tapes are almost universally used for accurate measurements of length. They may be obtained in lengths up to 1000 ft., but the most common are the 50-ft., 100-ft., 200-ft., and 300-ft. lengths. In metric units they may be obtained in lengths from 10 meters to 30 meters. While the shorter tapes are usually made of thin steel ribbon, the longer ones are of sufficiently large cross-section to withstand rough usage. Some of these heavy tapes are marked every 10 ft., the 10-ft. length at the end of the tape being marked every foot, and the last foot divided into tenths. Others are marked every foot throughout their length, the end foot being divided into tenths and hundredths. The light tapes are graduated throughout their length into feet, tenths, and hundredths, each line being etched on the steel. The numbering is continuous from the zero-point to the end. (Fig. 1.) In order to facilitate rapid reading of the tape and also to avoid mistakes in reading the foot-mark

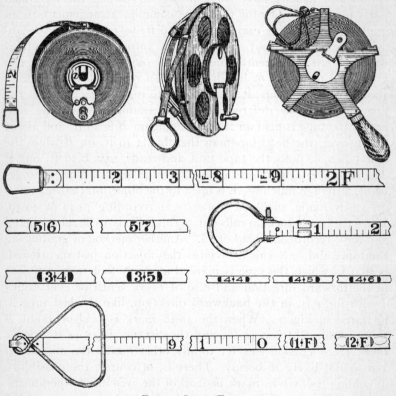

FIG. 1. STEEL TAPES.

some tapes have the number of the foot repeated at each tenths division; for instance, at the 55.1 mark there is a large figure 1 and a small figure 55.

Many of the light tapes have the zero-point at the extreme end of the brass loop instead of on the steel, as in the first tape shown in Fig. 1. This is convenient in taking measurements, but there is danger that the loop may become flattened and the relation of the zero to the other graduations changed. The Bureau of Standards will not place its identification number on a tape unless the graduations are all on the steel ribbon.

Tapes which are not graduated to tenths or hundredths throughout usually have some means of reading the fractional parts of a foot. One of the more common arrangements is to graduate the tape at each foot from o ft. to 100 ft. and then to subdivide the first foot (o ft. to 1 ft.) into tenths or into hundredths; not infrequently the last foot (99 ft. to 100 ft.) is also graduated to tenths or hundredths. To read a distance (under 100 ft.) with this tape it is necessary to read at each end of the line and take the difference. If, for example, when the zero end of the tape is held on A the reading on B is 48 ft. and about 0.4 ft. over, the head tapeman then holds 49 ft. on B while the rear tapeman pulls the tape taut and reads, say, 0.56 ft. on A. The distance is therefore $49 - 0.56 = 48.44$ ft. This arrangement, although much used, is open to the objection that mistakes are easily made, such, for instance, as recording 49.44 or 49.56. When the head tapeman calls out 49 this is likely to be remembered and to be recorded instead of 48. Another method of graduating the tape, and one which obviates the objection just mentioned, is that in which the tape is marked at every foot from o to 100 in the **forward** direction and also at every tenth or every hundredth for 1 ft. in the **backward** direction, like the last tape illustrated in Fig. 1. When the 48-ft. mark is held on point B the reading on A is 0.44 ft., and the distance is 48.44 ft. Since there is no occasion to refer to any other marks the mistake of 1 ft. is not likely to occur. There is, of course, the possibility of holding the -1-ft. mark instead of the zero mark when measuring a full 100 ft. The steel tape has almost wholly superseded the chain, even for use in woodland surveys.

Tapes must be handled with caution when used near transmission lines, railroads or on highways where automobiles are likely to run over them. Standardized tapes should always be wound on the reel. **All tapes should be cleaned at the end of every day. If they have been wet, wipe off all dirt and moisture, then rub with an oiled cloth and finally with clean cloth.**

The surveyor's measurements are usually in feet and decimals. The inch is not used in surveying fieldwork. But for the use of mechanics in construction work it is frequently necessary to convert decimals of a foot into inches and fractions. The following table of equivalents shows certain relations which it is convenient to remember, and which enable the surveyor to convert rapidly from one unit to the other.

TABLE 1

DECIMALS OF FOOT IN INCHES.

DECIMAL OF FOOT.		INCHES.	DECIMAL OF FOOT.		INCHES.
.01	=	$\frac{1}{8}$ −	.25	=	3 (exact)
.08	=	1 −	.50	=	6 (exact)
.17	=	2 +	.75	=	9 (exact)

Decimals of a foot can easily be converted mentally into inches by use of the equivalents in the above table, for example, 0.22 ft. $= 0.25 - 0.03 = 3'' - \frac{3}{8}'' = 2\frac{5}{8}''$.

Invar Tapes. — Invar (nickel-steel) tapes having a coefficient of expansion of about $0.000\ 0002$ per $1°$ F. (one-thirtieth that of steel) may now be obtained in lengths of 100 ft., 300 ft., 50 meters, and 100 meters. These are coming into more general use in engineering work. They have for many years been used for measuring geodetic base-lines, to the exclusion of all other apparatus. (See Vol. II, Chapter I.)

8. THE STADIA. — Where it is desired to measure distances with great rapidity but not with very great accuracy the *stadia* method is frequently employed. The distance is obtained by sighting with a transit instrument at a graduated rod held at the other end of the line and noting the space on the rod included between two special cross-hairs set in the instrument at such a distance apart that the horizontal distance to the rod is 100 times the space on the rod. From this observed interval on the rod the distance from the transit to the rod can be easily calculated. Another form of stadia instrument (European make) is that in which a glass prism, having a small angle, is placed in front of the objective so as to cover but half of it. This produces two images of the rod, one part (marked with a vernier) being displaced with reference to the other part (marked with a scale) by one per cent of the distance of the rod from the transit. By reading the scale and vernier the distance may be obtained with unusual precision. One of the uses to which the stadia is frequently put is to check the measurements made by the tape. (See Chap. VII, Vol. I, and Chap. IV, Vol. II.)

9. OTHER INSTRUMENTS. — *Wooden Rods* are used in certain kinds of work for making short measurements, usually less than 15 ft.

The *Two-Foot Rule* divided into tenths and hundredths of a foot is very convenient for short measurements.

The *Odometer* is an instrument which may be attached to a vehicle in such a manner as to register the number of revolutions of one of the wheels. The circumference of the wheel being known the approximate distance traversed is easily determined. This instrument measures the slope distances.

The *Pedometer* is a small instrument, about the size of a watch, which records the distance traveled by the person carrying the instrument. The mechanism requires that it should be carried vertically in the pocket. The instrument must be adjusted for the length of pace of the person using it if reliable results are to be obtained.

MEASUREMENT OF DISTANCES

10. MEASUREMENT ON LEVEL GROUND WITH A TAPE. — In measuring long distances (over 1000 ft.) when the intermediate points are not needed for side measurements or for angles the most important matter is to keep correct count of the number of tape lengths.

One man, the head-tapeman, takes the forward end of the tape and ten marking pins and goes ahead along the line to be measured, while the rear-tapeman, with one pin, takes his position at the stake marking the beginning of the line. The rear-tapeman, with his eye over the point, places the head-tapeman in line with some object, such as a lining pole, which marks the other end of the line to be measured. When the head-tapeman is nearly in line he takes a pin and, standing to one side of the line, holds it upright on the ground a foot or so short of the end of the tape and the rear-tapeman motions him to the right or left until his pin is on the line. When the head-tapeman has the pin in line he stretches the tape taut, seeing that there are no kinks and that no obstructions cause bends in the tape. The rear-tapeman at the same time holds the zero-point of the tape at his pin and when he calls out, " All right here," the head-tapeman, stretching the tape past his line pin, removes this line pin, places it at the end graduation of the tape, and presses it vertically into the ground. When the tapemen are experienced the pin may be set for both line and distance at the same time. When the pin is in place the head-tapeman calls, " All right," the rear-tapeman takes the pin left at his end of the line and they proceed to the next tape-length. The pin that the rear-tapeman has is a record of the first tape-length. Just before reaching the second pin the rear-tapeman calls out, " Tape," to give the head-tapeman warning that he has nearly reached a tape-length. The process of lining in the head-tapeman and measuring a tape-length is then repeated. After the third pin has been stuck in the ground the rear-tapeman pulls out the second pin; in this way the number of pins the rear-tapeman holds is a record of the number of tape-lengths measured. There is always one pin in the ground which marks the distance but is not counted. When 10 tape-lengths have been measured the head-tapeman will be out of pins and calls to the rear-tapeman, who brings forward 10 pins. The pins are then counted by **both men.**

It can be shown (Art. 21) that if a pin is placed a few tenths of a foot to the right or left of the line at the end of a tape-length the resulting error in the **distance** is very small and consequently " lining in " by eye is accurate enough, so far as the **distance** is concerned. But when any side measurements or angles are to be taken the points should be set accurately on line by means of a transit instrument. It is obvious that any error in lining in the pin produces a greater error in a short measurement than in a full tape-length.

In most engineering surveys the lines are comparatively short, and the intermediate (100-ft.) points on the lines are needed for side measurements, such as ties, offsets, etc. In all such surveys the accuracy is comparatively high and it is necessary to employ more exact means of marking the points. Sometimes **stakes** are driven into the ground and **tacks** or **pencil marks** used to mark the points. A short galvanized **nail** with a large head, pressed into the ground so that the center of the head is in the proper position makes a good temporary mark, but of course is easily lost. In measuring on the surfaces of hard roads heavy steel **spikes** are used for permanent marks.

Measurements of important lines which are not checked by some geometric test, like the closure of a traverse, should be checked by repeating the measurement, and in such a way as not to use the same intermediate points on both of the measurements.* In fact, it is good practice to do this on all lines. If the distance is not checked by a duplicate measurement it may be checked by means of the stadia.

Where distances are to be measured continuously from the initial point of a line without regard to angles in the line, as in railroad surveys, it is customary to establish the 100-ft. points. Mistakes will often be avoided by setting the 100-ft. points as follows. Suppose an angle to occur at 870.1 ft. from the point of beginning; this would be called " **station 8 + 70.1**." To set " station 9 " the 70.1-ft. point of the tape should be held on stake 8 + 70.1 and the stake at station 9 placed at the 100-ft. point of the tape. This is better than making a measurement of 29.9 ft. from the zero end of the tape.

Pacing furnishes a Convenient Means of obtaining Approximate Distances. — In measuring a long line much time can be saved if the head-tapeman will **pace** the tape-length and then place himself very nearly in the line by means of objects which he knows to be on line as, for example, the instrument, a pole, or the last pin. While no great accuracy is to be expected from pacing, its importance to the surveyor should not be underestimated. It is often necessary to know a distance roughly and to obtain it quickly. Furthermore in all surveys the accuracy should be

* In measuring with the tape some prefer to make a series of measurements between points set in the ground a little less than 100 ft. apart, summing up the partial measurements when the end of the line is reached. This guards against the mistake of omitting a whole tape-length. Another advantage is that it is easier to read the distance to a fixed point than to set a point accurately at the end of the tape; this is especially true in measurements where plumbing is necessary. This method takes less time than the usual method, but it is not applicable when it is necessary to mark the 100-ft. points on the line.

direction, the vertical angle being $-2° 30'$ and the distance 80.21 ft. Then

$$AB = 98.74 - 98.74 \times \text{vers } 4° 31'$$
$$= 98.74 - 98.74 \times .00311$$
$$= 98.74 - .31$$
$$= 98.43$$

Similarly, $BC = 80.13$, and $AC = 178.56$.

13. Another way of taking the slope measurement is to measure the slope distance from point to point as before, and then to calculate the horizontal distance by using the difference in elevation of the ends of the tape as determined by leveling. The taped distance is the hypotenuse of a right triangle and the difference in elevation is the short (vertical) side. The long side, or the horizontal distance, usually may be calculated with sufficient accuracy by the approximate formula derived in Art. 21.

On city streets, where grades are uniform, the tape may be laid flat on the surface, and the distance reduced to horizontal either by means of the difference in elevation, or by means of the vertical angle, obtained by sighting at a point on a rod or a plumb string which is as far above the surface as the telescope itself is above the surface.

For further details regarding tape measurements see Chapter X.

14. COMMON SOURCES OF ERROR IN MEASUREMENT OF LINES. —

1. Not pulling tape taut.
2. Careless plumbing.
3. Incorrect alignment.
4. Effect of wind.
5. Variation in temperature.
6. Erroneous length of tape.

15. COMMON MISTAKES IN READING AND RECORDING MEASUREMENTS OF DISTANCES. —

1. Failure to observe the position of the zero-point of the tape.
   ((1) End of ring; (2) end of steel band; (3) on steel band.)
2. Omitting a whole tape-length.
3. Transposing figures, e.g., 46.24 for 46.42 (mental); or reading tape upside down, e.g., 6 for 9, or 86 for 98.
4. Reading wrong foot-mark, as 48.92 for 47.92.
5. Subtracting incorrectly when using tape graduated on first foot only.

16. AVOIDING MISTAKES. — Mistakes in counting the tape-lengths may be avoided if more than one person keeps the tally. Mistakes of reading the wrong foot-mark may be avoided by noting not only the foot-mark preceding, but also the next following foot-mark, as, " 46.84 . . . 47 feet," and also by holding the tape so that the numbers are **right side up** when being read.

In calling off distances to the note keeper, the tapeman should be systematic and always call them distinctly and in such terms that they cannot be mistaken. As an instance of how mistakes of this kind may occur, suppose a tapeman calls, " Forty-nine, three "; it can easily be mistaken for " Forty-nine feet." The note keeper should repeat the distances aloud so that the tapeman will know that they were correctly understood. Frequently it is useful in doubtful cases for the note keeper to employ different words in answering, which will remove possible ambiguity. For example, if the tapeman calls, " Thirty-six, five," the note keeper might answer, " Thirty-six and a half." If the tapeman had meant 36.05 the mistake would be noticed. The tapeman should have called in this instance, " Thirty-six O (pronounced " oh ") five." The following is a set of readings which may be easily misinterpreted unless extreme care is taken in calling them off.

40.7 — " Forty and seven."
47.0 — " Forty-seven O (oh) " or " forty-seven flat."
40.07 — " Forty, — O (oh) seven."

All of these might be carelessly called off, " Forty-seven."

In **all** cases the tapemen should make **mental estimates** of the distances when measuring, in order to avoid making serious mistakes.

17. ACCURACY REQUIRED. — The accuracy demanded in different kinds of surveys varies from one part in 400 or 500, in farm or woodland surveys, to one part in 20 000 or 30 000 in city survey work; in geodetic surveys the accuracy is much higher than this. An accuracy of about one in 500 may be obtained by the use of the chain or by the stadia method. For a better grade of work such as would be expected in railways, highways, and various kinds of construction, an accuracy of about one part in 5000 would be suitable. To reach this degree of accuracy a steel tape should be used and it is important to give careful attention to the **pull,** the **plumbing,** and the error in the **length of tape.** Small differences in temperature may be neglected, but any very large variation of temperature from the standard should be allowed for. The tension may be estimated with sufficient accuracy. For an accuracy greater than about one in 10 000, that is, for all the finer grades of city work, it is necessary to measure the temperature and the tension. (Art. 267, p. 319.)

When making use of the measure of accuracy mentioned above, as $\frac{1}{5000}$, or when using the " error of closure " of a traverse as a measure of its accuracy it should be remembered that such measures of accuracy do tell us something about the amount of accidental error that has affected the work, but that they tell us nothing about systematic errors affecting all the measurements. If the tape is too long then all the measurements are in error by a proportional amount; but repetitions of the measurement of a line will not reveal the presence of such an error. Nor will the " error of closure " of a traverse show whether the tape has a constant error of length.

18. Amount of Different Errors. — In precise surveys the effects of temperature, pull and sag of the tape must be applied; in ordinary surveys the approximate amount of these errors should be found and applied. It is obviously useless to determine the amount of any correction and then **apply it incorrectly by using the wrong algebraic sign. Tape corrections are important.**

19. Pull. — At the tension ordinarily used the light steel tapes will stretch between 0.01 and 0.02 ft. in 100 ft. if the pull is increased 10 lb. The heavy tapes will stretch much less than this. The amount of this increase in length may be calculated by the formula

$$C_p = \frac{L(t - t_0)}{SE}$$

in which L is the length of the tape, t is the actual tension in pounds, t_0 is the tension at which tape is of standard length, S is the cross-section of the tape in square inches, and E is the modulus of elasticity. (E = about 28 000 000 to 30 000 000, expressed in lbs. per sq. in.) C_p will be in the same units as L. The amount of the correction may also be measured directly by varying the amount of the tension (using a spring balance) and noting the resulting changes in length.

20. Temperature. — The average coefficient of expansion for a steel tape is nearly .000 006 45 for 1° F. Hence a change of temperature of 15° produces nearly 0.01 ft. change in the length of a 100-ft. tape. Tapes are usually manufactured to be of standard length at 68° F. and under a tension of 10 lb. while supported throughout their length. When great accuracy is demanded the temperature of the tape must be determined and the corresponding temperature correction applied to the measurements. Small tape thermometers are made especially for this purpose. The thermometer bulb should be in contact with the tape so as to obtain as nearly as possible the temperature of the steel. Even under these conditions it is difficult to determine the true temperature if the tape is exposed to sunlight.

Some tapes have a temperature scale graduated on the steel at the 100-ft. end. When measuring full tape-lengths the head tapeman holds on the point that graduation which corresponds to the actual temperature at the time, instead of holding the 100-ft. mark. The length actually measured is a true 100-ft. distance automatically corrected for temperature.

21. Alignment. — The error in length due to poor alignment can be calculated from the approximate formula

$$c - a = \frac{h^2}{2\,c}\ *$$

---

* In the right triangle,

$$c^2 - a^2 = h^2,$$
$$(c + a)\,(c - a) = h^2,$$

assuming $c = a$ and applying it to the first parenthesis only,

$$2\,c\,(c - a) = h^2 \text{ (approximately)}$$

$$c - a = \frac{h^2}{2\,c} \text{ (approximately)}$$

Similarly $$c - a = \frac{h^2}{2\,a} \text{ (approximately)}$$

It is evident that the smaller h is in comparison with the other two sides the more exact will be the results obtained by this formula. This formula is correct to the nearest $\frac{1}{100}$ ft. even when $h = 14$ ft. and $a = 100$ ft., or when $h = 30$ ft. and $a = 300$ ft.

where h is the perpendicular distance of the end of the tape from the line, c is the length of the tape, and a is the distance along the straight line. For example, if one end of a 100-ft. tape is held 1 ft. to one side of the line the error produced in this tape-length will be $\dfrac{1^2}{2 \times 100} = 0.005$ ft. (about $\frac{1}{16}$ inch). The correction to be applied to the distance when the two ends of the tape are not at the same level, as when making slope measurements, is computed in the same way.

22. Sag. — When the tape is suspended it will hang in a ' catenary " curve. Consequently the horizontal distance between the end-points of the tape is less than the tape reading. This shortening due to sag depends upon the weight of the tape, the distance between points of support, and the pull exerted. If the pull is 10 lbs. the sag effect on a full 100-ft. tape length is 0.01 ft. to 0.02 ft. for light-weight tapes; it may be 0.06 ft. to 0.08 ft. for heavy tapes. The amount of error in recorded distance due to sag may be computed for a single suspended section of the tape by the formula (1).

$$C_s = \frac{w^2 l^3}{24\, t^2} \quad (1) \qquad\qquad C_s = \frac{L}{24}\left(\frac{wl}{t}\right)^2 \quad (2)$$

in which,

w is the weight of the tape in pounds per foot of tape.

l is the distance between supports in feet.

t is the tension in pounds.

If the tape is supported at one or more uniformly spaced intermediate points, then formula (2) applies, in which,

l is the length of one suspended section.

n is the number of sections.

$nl = L$, the whole tape length.

A practical way to eliminate the effect of sag is to determine by actual test the length between the end marks of the suspended tape as follows. First, while the tape is supported its whole length, mark the positions of its end-points while a pull of 10 lb. is being exerted. Then establish two new points, by means of the transit or a plumb-line, at the same distance apart, but in such positions that the tape may be tested while supported at the ends only. Then determine the pull necessary to bring the end marks of the suspended tape to coincide with these new reference marks. If this tension is always applied then the two ends of the suspended tape will be the same distance apart as the ends of the supported tape were under a 10-lb. pull. If the supported tape is not of standard length when a 10-lb. pull is used this error should be allowed for in all measurements. Or, if preferred, the reference marks just mentioned may be placed exactly 100 ft. apart and the amount of pull required to make the suspended tape correct may be determined.

If the wind is blowing hard during the measurements the tape tends to bend into a horizontal curve, and the effect on the measurement is similar to the effect of sag. This may be remedied by supporting the tape at one or more intermediate points, or by making some allowance for its effect if the amount of the middle-ordinate of the curve can be estimated. For very accurate results the measurement had better not be attempted in high winds. (Further treatment of tape corrections will be found in Vol. II, Arts. 28-32, pp. 38-42.)

23. PRECISION AND ADJUSTMENT OF ERRORS OF MEASUREMENTS. — While the cost of any survey is influenced by the prevailing physical difficulties such as obstructions along the measured lines, distance from the survey office and weather conditions, it is also greatly influenced by the precision required. The grade of precision sought should depend upon the value of the land, present purpose of the survey and its future use. Many surveys are made with a precision not justified by these conditions; on the other hand, they are also made where an increase in precision would have paid well. Herein lies a phase of the art of surveying, namely, **intelligent selection of degree of precision for every one of the processes that comprise the entire survey.** It should be much higher for the basic survey lines than for the details which are to be attached to these lines by measurements.

The surveyor should distinguish carefully between errors which are of such a nature that they tend to balance each other and those which continually accumulate. The latter are by far the more serious. Suppose that a line 5000 ft. long is measured with a steel tape which is supposed to be correct but is really 0.01 ft. too long and that the error (uncertainty) in measuring a tape-length is, say, 0.02 ft., which may of course be a + or a − error. This latter is an "accidental" error. There will then be 50 tape-lengths in the 5000-ft. line. A study of the laws governing the distribution of accidental errors (Method of Least Squares) shows that in such a case as this the number of errors that will probably remain uncompensated equals the **square root of the total number of opportunities for error,** i.e., in the long run this would be true. Hence the total number of such uncompensated errors left in the measurement of the line is 7; and 7 × 0.02 = 0.14 ft., which is the total error due to inaccuracy in marking the tape-lengths on the ground. Since the error due to erroneous lengths of tape increases directly as the number of tape lengths, and since these errors are not compensating, the total error in the line due to the fact that the tape is 0.01 ft. too long is 50 × 0.01 = 0.50 ft. The small (0.01) **accumulative error** (systematic or constant error) is therefore seen to have far greater effect than the larger (0.02) **compensating error** (accidental error).

The usual accumulative errors in taping are those which are due to error in tape-length, temperature, sag and tension on the tape, the amounts of which may be computed by the formulas given in the previous articles. No attempt should be made at distributing compensating errors until the effect of accumulative errors has first been applied to all measurements.

The following articles deal primarily with the precision and adjustment of distances; the same principles apply to the adjustment of angles or of level circuits. See Art. 146, p. 125 for a discussion of the accuracy of angle measurements; Art. 265b, p. 313, for distributing errors in a level circuit; and Art. 387, p. 471 for the relation between the precision required for consistent angle and distance measurements.

23a. Probability of Errors. — The theory of probability is based upon the following assumptions relative to the occurrences of errors:

1. Errors of small magnitude are more frequent than errors of large magnitude.

2. Positive and negative errors of equal magnitude are equally likely to occur.

3. The probability of very large errors occurring is small.

4. The mean of an infinite number of observations is the true value.

The purposes of the adjustment of observation are: first, to derive the most probable value of a set of observations; and second, to provide results free from inherent discrepancies. It must be understood that the results of such adjustments are not the true values, but are the most probable values derivable from the given observations, as, for example, a simple mean obtained from a series of observations. In these adjustments, only accidental or compensating errors are considered; accumulative errors may be still present in the adjusted results.

23b. — Adjustment of Compensating Errors. — Assume that corrections for all accumulative errors have been made. Then, if the measurements are taken under like conditions, the most probable value (adjusted result) of a set of corrected observations is a simple mean; and this adjusted result should have the same number of significant figures as are present in any single observation. The following measurements were made of a line A to B.

(1) 615.42 ft.,   (2) 615.36 ft.,   (3) 615.44 ft.

If the mean, 615.4067 feet, were carried to four decimal places and published as such, a false impression of the precision of the mean measurement would be obtained; 615.41 ft. gives a more nearly correct idea of the degree of precision attained.

If n direct observations, M_1, M_2, M_3, . . . M_n are made of the value of a quantity, M, and all are taken under like conditions, the most probable value, M_0, is the arithmetical mean of the observations.

$$M_0 = \frac{M_1 + M_2 + M_3 + \cdots M_n}{n} = \frac{\sum M}{n}$$

The *Residual* (v) of an observation is the difference between an observed value of a measured quantity and the value of the mean.

The *Probable Error* (r) of an observation is an error such that one-half the errors of the series are greater than it and the other half are less than it; that is, the probablity of making an error greater than r is just equal to the probability of making an error less than r.

From the Method of Least Squares, the following formulae may be derived:

The probable error of an observation, $r = \pm0.6745 \sqrt{\dfrac{\Sigma v^2}{(n-1)}}$

and the probable error of the mean, $r_0 = \pm0.6745 \sqrt{\dfrac{\Sigma v^2}{n(n-1)}}$.

From the above measurements of the line A to B, we have

	M	v	v^2
1.	615.42 ft.	-0.01	0.0001
2.	615.36 ft.	$+0.05$	0.0025
3.	615.44 ft.	-0.03	0.0009
Mean	615.41 ft.	$\Sigma v = +0.01$	$\Sigma v^2 = 0.0035$

While Σv should equal 0, the values in this example have only been carried to hundredths, and the $\Sigma v = \pm0.01$ is a small discrepancy due to rounding off the mean values.

$$r = \pm0.6745 \sqrt{\frac{0.0035}{2}} = \pm0.03 \text{ ft.}$$

$$r_0 = \pm0.6745 \sqrt{\frac{0.0035}{2 \times 3}} = \pm \frac{0.03}{\sqrt{3}} = \pm0.02 \text{ ft.}$$

Final expression for length A to B is 615.41 ±0.02 ft., which is the most probable value of the length and the most probable value of the error in that length. This is sometimes called the *precision measurement* of this line. The degree of precision is commonly expressed as a fraction (with unity in the numerator) as follows:

$$\text{Precision} = \frac{0.02}{615.41} = \frac{1}{30,000}$$

Whenever any quantity is made up of the algebraic sum of several other independent quantities each being subject to accidental errors, the combined probable error can be found by the relation

$$R = \pm\sqrt{r_1{}^2 + r_2{}^2 + \cdots}$$

An illustration of this would be a distance of 400 ft. made up of short sections, say, each 100-ft. tape-length long. If the accidental error in measuring a tape-length is ±0.008 ft., then for the total distance

$$R = \pm\sqrt{0.008^2 + 0.008^2 + 0.008^2 + 0.008^2} = \pm0.016 \text{ ft.}$$

This principle was stated in words in the second paragraph of Art. 23.

If two or more precision measurements of an observed value are known, a more nearly accurate value can be obtained. If the probable error of a precision measurement is small, it indicates that this precision measurement probably has a high degree of accuracy, because there was so close agreement in the individual measurements that made up the set. If, however, the probable error of a precision measurement obtained from a set of measurements of the same line is relatively large then there is indication of a lack of precision in that set. Hence, in combining two or more precision measurements to obtain the more accurate value, it is logical to give greater weight to that set which had a small error than to a set that had a larger error, and it is customary to apply the weight inversely proportional to the square of the error. For example, if the probable error in one set was ±.01 and in another it was ±.03, nine times the weight would be given to the first as compared with the second precision measurement.

The probable error of the final value may be computed from the formula

$$R = \pm\sqrt{\frac{w_1{}^2 r_1{}^2 + w_2{}^2 r_2{}^2 + w_3{}^2 r_3{}^2 + w_4{}^2 r_4{}^2}{(\sum w)^2}}$$

in which r is the probable error of each set and w is the corresponding weight.

The weighted mean (M_0) is found from the relation

$$M_0 = \frac{w_1 M_1 + w_2 M_2 + w_3 M_3 + w_4 M_4}{w_1 + w_2 + w_3 + w_4} = \frac{\sum w \times M}{\sum w}$$

and the check on the calculation of the weighted mean is the fact that $\sum w \times v = 0$.

For example, the line A to B has been measured on four different days with the following precision measurements

	M	r	Weighting of Measurements*	w	$W \times M$ for decimal part only	$w^2 r^2$
I	615.41 ± 0.02 ft.		$\dfrac{M \times .0036}{.0004} = 9\,M$	9	3.69	0.0324
II	615.40 ± 0.03		$\dfrac{M \times .0036}{.0009} = 4\,M$	4	1.60	0.0144
III	615.42 ± 0.03		$\dfrac{M \times .0036}{.0009} = 4\,M$	4	1.68	0.0144
IV	615.41 ± 0.02		$\dfrac{M \times .0036}{.0004} = 9\,M$	9	3.69	0.0324
			Totals	26	10.66	0.0936

Weighted $M_0 = 615 + \dfrac{10.66}{26} = 615.41$ ft.

$$R = \pm\sqrt{\frac{w_1^2 r_1^2 + w_2^2 r_2^2 + w_3^2 r_3^2 + w_4^2 r_4^2}{(\sum w)^2}} = \pm\sqrt{\frac{0.0936}{(26)^2}} = \pm 0.01 \text{ ft.}$$

Final expression for A to B: 615.41 ± 0.01 ft.

$$\text{Precision} = \frac{0.01}{615.41} = \frac{1}{62,000}$$

If all the probable errors are equal, however, the final value may be obtained by finding a simple mean of the observations, and by finding the probable error of this mean. The latter may be found by dividing the probable error of one determination by the square root of the number of precision values.

---

* In the above problem the inverse square of each probable error is multiplied by such a factor (0.0036) as will give weights of integral whole numbers. Thus the weight given to the first set is $\dfrac{1}{0.0004} \times 0.0036 = 9$, and for the second the weight is $\dfrac{1}{0.0009} \times 0.0036 = 4$, etc. The factor 0.0036 is the least common multiple of the squares of the probable errors.

If all the probable errors of the above series had been ±0.02 ft., the probable error of the final value would be $\pm \dfrac{0.02}{\sqrt{4}}$ or ±0.01 ft.

Thus it will be observed that the probable precision reached in a series of sets of measurements of the same distance is more refined than the probable precision reached in one set of measurements.

In the case illustrated above four sets of observations gave a probable error of one-half the probable error for one set of observations. Since the probable error of the mean varies inversely as the square root of the number of observations, additional measurements beyond a certain number not only have little effect on the resultant probable error, but also greatly increase the cost of the survey.

Errors may not always remain accumulative or compensating, i.e., an accidental error may become a systematic error and *vice versa*. There is in reality no fixed boundary between the systematic and the accidental errors. Every accidental error has some cause, and if the cause were perfectly understood and the amount and sign could be determined, it would cease to be an accidental error, but would be classed as systematic. On the other hand, errors which are either constant or systematic may be brought into the accidental class, or at least made partially to obey the law of accidental error, by so varying the conditions, instruments, etc., that the sign of the error is frequently reversed. If a tape is 0.01 ft. different from the standard, this produces a constant error in the result of a measurement. If, however, we use several different tapes, some of which are 0.01 ft. too long and others 0.01 ft. too short, this error may be positive or negative in any one case. In the long run these different errors tend to compensate each other like accidental errors.

23c. Accuracy and Precision. — In determining the length of a line, or, in fact, in making any observation (linear or angular) it is customary to repeat the measurements. In plane surveying these repetitions are not always for the purpose of obtaining a more precise result, but for insuring accuracy within the limits of the precision desired. **Precision** implies **refinement of measurements** or **closeness in agreement** between several measurements, whereas **accuracy** implies **correctness** or freedom from mistakes or carelessness. Precision is of no significance unless accuracy is also obtained. Consider, for example, that a tape measurement is made on a smooth pavement which is on a grade where the tape is supported upon the pavement and every tape length is marked off with the utmost precision. In this case the precision is of a high order but the measurement is inaccurate because the tape was not level when the measurements were made.

Another example may be cited in which mistakes have been introduced; a distance is measured three different times with close agreement to the nearest .01 ft.; the results were 5280.16, 5282.18 and 5281.17 ft. These three measurements were precise because they were observed to within about 0.01 ft., yet they were not accurate because they had different values in the whole foot digit. In other words, this was a precise but an inaccurate survey. No amount of adjusting will eliminate the effects of such mistakes and observations having obvious blunders must be disregarded.

Now, suppose the measurements had been made to the nearest foot only and the three results were 5280, 5282 and 5281 ft., indicating reasonably accurate work for the precision attempted, because it was obviously free from error, but it was not a very precise series because the closeness of agreement required for the three independent measurements was 1 ft.

A surveyor may attempt to obtain a precision which the method he employs does not warrant. In such a case, after he has determined the mean of his measurements, he must use the figures only within the degree of precision that is indicated by the agreement between the independent measurements, which will clearly indicate to him the degree of precision probably obtained by the method employed.

For example, a line 287.16 ft. long can be measured with a 300-ft. tape without difficulty to the nearest .01 ft. In this case the probable error contemplated in the single tape-length is ±0.005 ft. in 300 ft. which is a precision of $\frac{1}{60000}$. If the same tape is used to measure a line about 6000 ft. long there will be more opportunities for error since the tape-length must be marked off

20 times with the probability of an error of ±0.005 ft. being made at each 300-ft. interval. Several measurements of this line each recorded to the nearest 0.01 ft. may show by computation a probable error of ±0.03 ft. This is equivalent to a precision of $\frac{1}{200,000}$; i.e., although the probable amount of error in the longer line was 6 times as great as that in the shorter line, the degree of precision obtained in the longer line was greater than that in the shorter line. The surveyor should keep clearly in mind that the true measure of precision is the ratio of the probable error to the length measured and is not determined by a definite value, such as the nearest 0.01 ft.

PROBLEMS

1. A distance is measured with an engineer's chain and found to be 796.4 ft. The chain when compared with a standard is found to be 0.27 ft. too long. What is the actual length of the line?

2. A metallic tape which was originally 50 ft. is found to be 50.14 ft. long. A house 26 ft. × 30 ft. is to be laid out. What measurements must be made, using this tape, in order that the house shall have the desired dimensions? Using the same tape what should the diagonals read?

3. A steel tape is known to be 100.000 ft. long at 68° F. with a pull of 12 lbs. and supported its entire length. Its coefficient of expansion is 0.000 006 4 for 1° F. A line was measured and found to be 142.67 ft. when the temperature was 8° below zero. What is the true length of the line?

4. In chaining down a hill with a surveyor's chain the head-chainman held his end of the chain 1.5 ft. too low. What error per chain-length would this produce?

5. In measuring a line with a 100-ft. tape the forward end is held 3 ft. to the side of the line. What is the error in one tape-length?

6. A certain 100-ft. steel tape was tested by the Bureau of Standards and its length given as 100.015 ft. at 68° F. when supported throughout its length and a 10 lb. tension applied. The tape was afterward tested with a 10 and then a 20 lb. pull and found to stretch 0.016 ft. (or 0.0016 per lb.). To obtain the length when supported at the ends only a 12 lb. pull was used and the full length between end graduations was marked off on tripods, the tape being supported throughout its length. The intermediate supports were then removed. The tape was found to sag 0.77 ft. and was 0.017 ft. shorter than when supported full length, the tension remaining at 12 lbs. Compute the true (chord) length of the tape for 12 lb. pull, 68° F. supported at ends only.

7. A distance measured with a 50-ft. steel tape is recorded as 696.41 ft. The tape is known to be 49.985 ft. long. What is the correct length of the line?

8. Two measurements of a line were made with the same tape on different days. The first length was 510.02 ft., the temperature being 65° F. The second length was 510.06, the temperature being 50° F. The tape is standard at 60°; coefficient = .000 006 45. Compute the length of the line from each of the two measurements and explain any difference in the reduced readings.

9. A distance is measured on slope with a 300-ft. tape and found to be 299.79 ft. If the difference of level of the two points is 15.10 ft. what is the horizontal distance?

10 If the slope distance is 201.61 ft. and the vertical angle is 4° 21′ what is the horizontal distance?

11. With transit set up at B, a slope distance of 182.42 ft. is measured with a 200-ft. tape from the horizontal axis of the transit to a tack in the top of stake A; similarly to tack in stake C (on the other side of B), the slope distance was 191.16 ft. Vertical angle to point A was +7° 12′ and to point C, −6° 47′. The tape used was 0.01 ft. too long at temperature 68° F. While this work was being done the tape temperature was 80° to 86° F. The suspended tape was given sufficient pull in both cases so as to offset the shortening due to sag.

(a) What is the corrected horizontal distance ABC to 1/100 ft.?

(b) Had the vertical angles been +7° 13′ and −6° 46′, how much difference (to the nearest 0.01 ft.) would this have made in the length of ABC?

12. A slope distance of 172.62 ft. is measured from the horizontal axis of a transit to a drill hole in a ledge, vertical angle +4° 33′.

(a) How many minutes of error must there be in this vertical angle to effect the computed horizontal length by 0.005 ft.?

(b) Had the angle been −1° 27′, how much error in the angle would cause an error of 0.005 ft. in the horizontal distance?

13. With a 300-ft. tape the slope distance measured from the horizontal axis of the transit to a point on a stake was 283.73 ft.; the vertical angle was read +6° 15′ (to the nearest 05′ only).

(a) What error may there be in the horizontal distance due to the fact that the angle was read to the nearest 05′?

(b) Had the vertical angle been +2° 25′ (to nearest 05′), how large an error in horizontal distance may have been introduced by the approximation in reading the vertical angle?

(c) The maximum error computed in (a) might be caused by how much change in temperature of this tape from its standard temperature of 68° F.? Use result of (a) to nearest 0.01 ft.

(d) If the tape temperature was 77° F. and the vertical angle +6° 15′ (to nearest 05′) can you be certain of the exact horizontal distance within 0.01 ft.?

14. A 100-ft. steel tape is 0.005 ft. too short at 68° F. with 12 lbs. pull while supported. A rectangle is measured with this tape (supported). The sides were recorded as 601.72 ft. and 437.15 ft. The temperature of the tape was 81° F. at the start and 85° F. at the end of the job, with pull 12 lbs.

(a) If the recorded measurements are used will the square feet in the field be too great or too small?

(b) What is the error (in sq. ft.)?

(c) If the land is worth 80¢ per sq. ft., how does this error in dollars and cents compare with the wages paid a surveying party for a day's work?

15. Using a 300-ft. tape a distance is measured as 286.42 ft. but the tape was bent out of line to the right 0.7 ft. at about the 60-ft. point and to the left of the line 1.0 ft. at about the 200-ft. point.

(a) What was the correct length of the line?

(b) What would have been the correct length if both the 0.7 ft. and 1.0 ft. were to the right of the line?

(c) What would be the correct length had it been bent 0.7 ft. to the right of the line at the 20-ft. point and 1.0 ft. to the left at the 270-ft. point?

(d) Explain fully why (a), (b) and (c) give different values.

16. A line 4500 ft. in length was measured with a 100-ft. steel tape. The uncertainty in the length of the tape was ±0.005 ft. per tape-length. The uncertainty in determining a representative value for the temperature of the tape caused an error per tape-length of ±0.004 ft. The error in marking each tape-length was ±0.005 ft. The uncertainty introduced in each tape-length by not holding the tape exactly horizontal was 0.01 ft. Determine the probable error in the length of the line introduced by each source of error and the probable error from all sources combined.

17. A base-line is measured in one operation and found to be 5282.76 ± 0.10 feet. It is then measured in two sections, the resulting lengths being 2640.35 ± 0.07 and 2642.36 ± 0.07 ft. It is then remeasured in three sections, the resulting values being 1761.27 ± 0.06, 1761.39 ± 0.05, and 1760.15 ± 0.06 ft. All the measurements are made under the same conditions.

(a) What is the probable error of the base-line as computed from each of the three determinations and which is probably the most accurate?

(b) Computing a simple mean from the separate measurements, what is the final expression for the length of the base-line?

(c) If the tape used in determining these lengths were 0.01 ft. too long in 100 ft., what would be the effect of disregarding this accumulative error on the recorded measurement of the base-line?

18. A length from Sta. 1 to Sta. 2 is measured with the following results:

1. 3254.65 feet	3. 3254.72 feet	5. 3254.70 feet
2. 3254.69 feet	4. 3254.66 feet	

(a) What is the probable error of an observation?

(b) What is the probable error of the mean?

(c) What is the final expression for the most probable length from Sta. 1 to Sta. 2?

19. A distance was measured with a 100-ft. steel tape and found to be 400.00 ft. The tape weighed 2.2 pounds. It was of standard length under a 15 pound pull, when fully supported, at a temperature of 70° F. The line was measured with the tape supported on stakes at the ends only, the applied tension being 15 pounds. All stakes for tape supports were set at full tape intervals. The difference in elevation between the top of stakes 1 and 2 was 1.5 ft.; between 2 and 3, 3.2 ft.; between 3 and 4, 2.8 ft.; between 4 and 5, 1.9 ft. The temperature at the time of measurement was 34° F. The coefficient of the tape was 0.000 006 45 per degree F. Compute the true length of the line.

20. A 300-ft. steel tape is used to set a point on a pier from a point on the shore, both points being at the same elevation. The tape is compared with a standard and found to be 300.003 ft. long when supported throughout at the standard conditions (temperature, 68° F.; tension, 20 lbs.). The weight of the tape is 3.6 lbs. and the area of the cross-section is 0.0026 square inches. The modulus of elasticity is 30,000,000 lbs. per square inch.

(a) What is the true horizontal distance between the end divisions when the tape is supported only at the ends and is at the standard conditions?

(b) What would the horizontal distance be if the tension were increased to 40 lbs., the temperature remaining at 68° F.?

(c) What effect would an increase of temperature from 68° to 78° F. have on (a) and (b)?

CHAPTER II

MEASUREMENT OF DIRECTION

24. THE SURVEYOR'S COMPASS. — The surveyor's compass (Fig. 3) is an instrument for determining the horizontal direction of a line with reference to the direction of a magnetic needle. The needle is balanced at its center on a *pivot* so that it swings freely in a horizontal plane. The pivot is at the center of a horizontal circle which is graduated to degrees and half-degrees, and numbered from two opposite zero-points each way to 90°. The zero-points are marked with the letters N and S, and the 90° points are marked E and W. The circle is covered with a glass plate to protect the needle and the graduations, the part enclosed being known as the *compass-box*. A screw is provided for raising the needle from the pivot by means of a lever. The needle always should be raised when the compass is lifted or carried, to prevent dulling the pivot-point; a dull pivot-point is a fruitful source of error. Both the circle and the pivot are secured to a brass frame, on which are two vertical sights so placed that the plane through them also passes through the two zero-points of the circle. This frame rests on a tripod and is fastened to it by means of a ball-and-socket joint. On the frame are two spirit levels at right angles to each other, which afford a means of leveling the instrument. This ball-and-socket joint is connected with the frame by means of a spindle which allows the compass-head to be revolved in a horizontal plane, and to be clamped in any position.

The magnetic needle possesses the property of pointing in a fixed direction, namely, the *Magnetic Meridian*. The horizontal angle between the direction of this meridian and of any other line may be determined by means of the graduated circle, and this angle is called the *Magnetic Bearing* of the line, or simply its *Bearing*. If the bearings of two lines are known the angle between them may be computed. Bearings are counted from

0° to 90°, the 0° being either at the N or the S point and the 90° either at the E or the W point. The quadrant in which a bearing falls is designated by the letters N.E., S.E., S.W., or N.W. For example, if a line makes an angle of 20° with the meridian

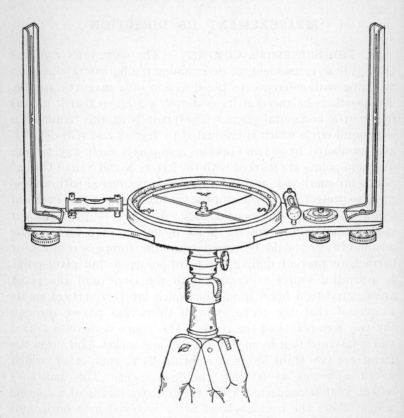

FIG. 3. SURVEYOR'S COMPASS.

and is in the southeast quadrant its bearing is written S 20° E. Sometimes the bearing is reckoned in a similar manner from the geographical meridian, when it is called the *true bearing*. In general this will not be the same as the magnetic bearing. True bearings are often called *azimuths*, and are commonly measured from the **south** point right-handed (clockwise) to 360°;

i.e., a line running due West has an azimuth of 90°; a line due North an azimuth of 180°; a line due East an azimuth of 270°. Sometimes, however, the azimuth is measured from the **north** as, for instance, when observing the azimuth of the Pole-Star (Art. 232b, p. 261b).

25. THE POCKET COMPASS. — The *pocket compass* is a small hand instrument for obtaining roughly the bearing of a line. There are two kinds, the *plain* and the *prismatic*. The former is much like the surveyor's compass, except that it has no sights. In the prismatic compass the graduations, instead of being on the compass-box, are on a card which is fastened to the needle (like a mariner's compass) and which moves with it. This compass is provided with two short sights and the bearing can be read, by means of a prism, at the same instant that the compass is sighted along the line.

26. METHOD OF TAKING A MAGNETIC BEARING. — The surveyor's compass is set up (and leveled) at some point on the line whose bearing is desired. The needle is let down onto the pivot, and the compass sights pointed approximately along the line. While looking through the two sights the surveyor turns the compass-box so that they point exactly at a lining pole or other object marking a point on the line. The glass should be tapped lightly over the end of the needle to be sure that the

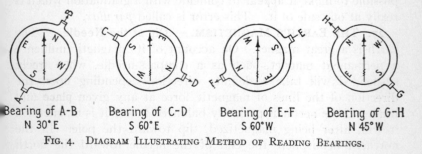

Bearing of A-B   Bearing of C-D   Bearing of E-F   Bearing of G-H
    N 30° E   S 60° E   S 60° W   N 45° W
FIG. 4. DIAGRAM ILLUSTRATING METHOD OF READING BEARINGS.

latter is free to move. If it appears to cling to the glass this may be due to the glass being electrified, which condition can be removed at once by placing the moistened finger on the glass. The position of the end of the needle is then read on the circle and recorded. Bearings are usually read to the nearest quarter of a degree although it is possible to estimate somewhat closer.

Since the needle stands still and the box turns under it, the letters E and W on the box must be reversed from their natural position so that the direct reading of the needle will give not only the angle but also the proper quadrant.   Reference to Fig. 4 will show the following rule to be correct.   **When the north point of the compass-box is toward the point whose bearing is desired, read the north end of the needle.**   When the south point of the box is toward the point, read the south end of the needle.   If a bearing of the line is taken looking in the opposite direction it is called the *reverse bearing*.   **Reverse bearings should be taken.**

Since iron or steel near the instrument affects the direction of the needle, great care should be taken that the tape, axe, or marking pins are not left near the compass.   Small pieces of iron on the person, such as keys or iron buttons, also produce a noticeable effect on the needle.   Electric currents are a great source of disturbance to the needle and in cities, where electricity is so common, the compass is practically useless.   Vehicles standing nearby or passing will attract the needle.

In reading the compass-needle, the surveyor should take care to read the farther end of the needle, always looking **along** the needle, not across it.   By looking at the needle sidewise it is possible to make it **appear** to coincide with a graduation which is really at one side of it.   This error is called *parallax*.

27. THE EARTH'S MAGNETISM. — Dip of the Needle. — The earth is a great magnet.   On account of its magnetic influence a permanent magnet, such as a compass-needle, when freely suspended will take a definite direction depending upon the direction of the lines of magnetic force at any given **place** and **time.**   If the needle is perfectly balanced before it is magnetized it will, after being magnetized, dip toward the pole.   In the northern hemisphere the end of the needle toward the north pole points downward, the inclination to the horizon being slight in low (magnetic) latitudes and great near the magnetic pole.   In order to counteract this dipping a small weight, usually a fine brass or silver wire, is placed on the higher end of the needle at such a point that the needle assumes a horizontal position.

28. DECLINATION OF THE NEEDLE. — The direction which the needle assumes after the counterweight is in position is called the magnetic meridian and this rarely coincides with the true meridian. The angle which the needle makes with the true meridian is called the *declination of the needle.* When the north end of the needle points east of the true, or geographical, north the declination is called *east;* when the north end of the needle points west of true north it has a *west* declination.

29. Variations in Declination. — The needle does not constantly point in the same direction. Changes in the value of the declination are called *variations of the declination.* [*] The principal variations are known as the *Secular, Daily, Annual,* and *Irregular.*

The *Secular Variation* is a long, extremely slow swing. It is probably periodic in character but its period covers so many years that the nature of it is not thoroughly understood. The following table shows the amount of secular variation as observed in Massachusetts during two centuries.

TABLE 2

(Latitude 42° N, Longitude 70° W.)

YEAR	DECLINATION	YEAR	DECLINATION	YEAR	DECLINATION
1750	7° 48′ W.	1860	11° 17′ W.	1915	14° 31′ W.
1780	7° 11′ W.	1880	12° 18′ W.	1920	14° 50′ W.
1800	7° 33′ W.	1900	13° 12′ W.	1925	15° 15′ W.
1820	8° 27′ W.	1905	13° 31′ W.	1930	15° 35′ W.
1840	9° 48′ W.	1910	14° 01′ W.	1935	15° 55′ W.

Northeast of the line of " no change " the north end of the needle is moving westward, and southwest of that line it is moving eastward at the rates shown in Fig. 5.

The *Daily Variation* consists of a swing which averages about 7 minutes of arc from its extreme easterly position at about 8 A.M. to its most westerly position at about 1.30 P.M.

---

* The *Declination* is usually called *Variation* by navigators.

† See p. 11 of U. S. Coast and Geodetic Survey Serial 592, " Magnetic Declination in the United States 1935;" also Special Publication No. 117, " The Earth's Magnetism."

It is in its mean position at about 10 A.M. and at 5 or 6 P.M. The amount of daily variation is from 3 to 12 minutes according to the season and the locality.

The *Annual Variation* is a periodic variation so small (about one minute a year) that it need not be considered in surveying work.

Irregular Variations in the declination are due chiefly to magnetic storms. These variations are uncertain in character and cannot be predicted. They are, however, usually observed whenever there is a display of the Aurora Borealis. Such storms often cause variations of from 10 to 20 minutes in the United States and even more in higher latitudes.

30. Isogonic Chart. — If lines are drawn on a map so as to join all places where the declination of the needle **is the same at a given time,** the result will be what is called an *isogonic chart.* (See Fig. 5.) Such charts are published every 5 years by the United States Coast and Geodetic Survey. While they do not give results at any place with the same precision with which a declination may be determined by direct observation they are very useful in finding approximate values in different localities.

These isogonic lines are drawn for each whole degree of declination. The dotted lines show the annual rates of change in the declination.

An examination of the isogonic chart of the United States shows that in the eastern states the needle points west of north while in the western states it points east of north. The line of no declination, or the *agonic line,* passes (in 1937) through South Carolina, Kentucky, Indiana and Michigan.

31. OBSERVATIONS FOR DECLINATION. — For any survey where the value of the present declination is important, it should be found by special observations. The value found at one place may be considerably different from that at a place only a few miles distant. The method of finding the meridian by observation on the Pole-Star is described in Art. 232b, p. 261b. The solar observation for meridian is described in Art. 238, p. 271.

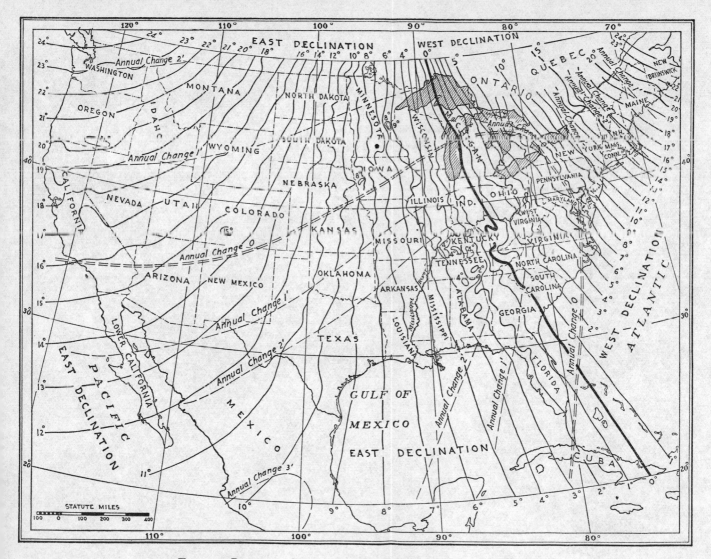

FIG. 5. ISOGONIC CHART OF THE UNITED STATES FOR 1935.

From U. S. Coast and Geodetic Survey.

The lines of equal magnetic declination, or isogonic lines, apply to Jan. 1, 1935. East of the line marked 0° (Agonic Line) the north end of the compass needle points west of north; west of that line it points east of north.

The north end of the compass needle is moving to the westward for places north of the line of no change and to the eastward for places south of that line at an annual rate indicated by the lines of equal annual change (dash lines).

ADJUSTMENTS OF THE COMPASS

32. The three adjustments which need to be most frequently made are (1) adjusting the bubbles, (2) straightening the needle, (3) centering the pivot-point.

33. ADJUSTMENT OF THE BUBBLES. — To make the Plane of the Bubbles Perpendicular to the Vertical Axis. — Level the instrument in any position. Turn 180° about the vertical axis and, if the bubbles move from the center, bring each one half-way back by means of the adjusting screws; repeat the process until the desired fineness of adjustment is secured.

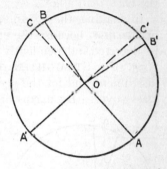

FIG. 6.   BENT COMPASS-NEEDLE.

34. DETECTING ERRORS IN ADJUSTMENT OF THE NEEDLE. If the readings of the two ends of the needle are not 180° apart, this may be due to the needle being bent, to the pivot point not being in the center of the graduated circle, or to both. If the difference of the two readings is the same in whatever direction the compass is turned, it follows that the needle is bent but the pivot-point is in the center of the circle. (See Fig. 6.) The bent needle is represented by the line AOB and the position of a straight needle shown by the line AOC. In the two positions shown it is seen that the difference in readings will be the same, i.e., arc $CB =$ arc $C'B'$. If the difference of the readings varies as the compass is turned around it follows that the pivot-point is not in the

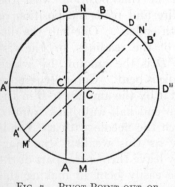

FIG. 7.   PIVOT-POINT OUT OF CENTER.

center, and the needle may or may not be bent. Suppose the needle is straight but the pivot is not in the center, then the effect in different parts of the circle is shown in Fig. 7. When the needle is in the position AD, perpendicular to CC' (where C is the true center and C' is the position of the pivot-point), then the error is a maximum. If B is a point 180° from A then the difference of the two readings is BD. When the needle is at $A'D'$ the error is less than before and equals $B'D'$. When the needle is in the line CC'', i.e., in the position $A''D''$, the ends read alike.

In making these adjustments it is better to straighten the needle first, because the error due to the needle being bent can be detected independently of the error of the pivot.

35. To Straighten the Compass-Needle. — Level the instrument and let the needle down on the pivot. Remove the glass cover. By means of a brass wire or a light stick of wood

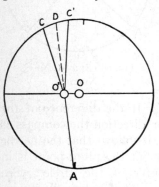

FIG. 8. STRAIGHTENING THE COMPASS-NEEDLE.

steady the needle so that one end of it, say the south end, is opposite some graduation on the circle as A in Fig. 8. Note the position of the north end of the needle C. Now, without moving the compass itself, turn the needle around so that the north end is at the graduation A. Hold it in this position with the brass wire and read the position of the south end C'. One-half the difference of the readings, or, the distance $C'D$ is the amount by which the needle is bent. Carefully remove the needle from the pivot and bend it by the amount $C'D$ in the direction which will move the south end half-way back from C' toward C. It is better not to touch the needle with the hands more than is absolutely necessary as this weakens the magnetism. Instrument makers usually leave the central part of the needle quite soft so that it can be easily bent in making this adjustment. Since the amount by which the needle is bent is a matter of estimation it should be replaced on the pivot and the test repeated until it is found that reversing the needle does not change the readings.

36. To Center the Pivot-Point. — If the difference of readings of the two ends of the needle varies in different parts of the circle it is due to the pivot-point being out of center. Take readings of the two ends of the needle in various positions of the compass and find the position of the needle in which the difference of the two readings is greatest (Art. 34, p. 27). The pivot is to be bent at right angles to this direction an amount equal to half this difference. Remove the needle and bend the pivot by means of a pair of small flat pliers. Replace the needle and see if the difference of end readings is zero. If not, the pivot must be bent until this condition is fulfilled. As the pivot may become bent somewhat in a direction other than that intended, a complete test for adjustment must be made again, and the process continued until the difference in the readings of the ends of the needle is zero in all positions of the compass. The metal at the base of the pivot is left soft so that it can be easily adjusted.

37. To Remagnetize the Needle. — Rub each end of the needle from the center toward the end several times with a bar-magnet, using the N end of the magnet for the S end of the needle and *vice versa*. (The N end of the magnet attracts the S end of the needle and repels its N end.) When the magnet is drawn along the needle it should move in a **straight line,** parallel to the axis of the needle. Do not stop at the end of the needle but continue moving the magnet in the same direction until it is several inches beyond the needle. When returning the bar from the end of the needle toward the center, lift it a foot or more **above** the needle.

38. Common Sources of Error in Compass Work. —

    1. Iron or steel, or electric current, near compass.
    2. Parallax in reading needle.

39. Common Mistakes. —

    1. Reading wrong end of needle.
    2. Not letting needle down on pivot.
    3. Reading the wrong side of the 10th degree, viz., reading 61° instead of 59°.

40. DETECTING LOCAL ATTRACTION OF THE NEEDLE. — As

the needle is always affected by masses of iron near the compass
it is important that the bearings in any survey should be checked.
This is most readily done by taking the bearing of any line from
both its ends or from intermediate points on the line. If the two
bearings agree it is probable that there is no local magnetic disturbance. If the two do not agree it remains to discover which
is correct.

In Fig. 9 suppose that the compass is at A and that the
bearing of AB is N $50°\frac{1}{4}$ E, and with the compass at B the

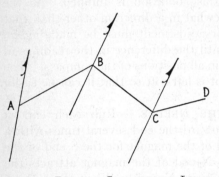

bearing BA is found to be
S $49°$ W. It is evident
that there is local attraction at one or both points.
In order to ascertain the
correct magnetic bearing,
turn the compass toward
a point C which is apparently free from magnetic
disturbance, and observe
the bearing of BC, which is,
say, S $72°$ E. Now move
the compass to C and observe the bearing CB. If

FIG. 9. DIAGRAM ILLUSTRATING LOCAL
ATTRACTION AT A.

this is N $72°$ W it indicates that there is no local attraction at C or B, hence S $49°$ W is the correct bearing of line
BA, and there is $1°\frac{1}{4}$ error in all bearings taken at A. If the
bearings of BC and CB had not agreed it would have been
necessary to take the bearing and reverse bearing of a new
line CD. This process is continued until a line is found whose
bearing and reverse bearing differ by exactly $180°$. In order
to be certain, however, that these latter bearings are really
free from attraction several other stations should be occupied.
Since local attraction drags the needle a **fixed** amount from the
magnetic meridian it follows that **the angles at any one point
computed from the bearings are not affected by local attraction.**

41. CALCULATING ANGLES FROM BEARINGS. — In calcu-
lating the angle between two lines it is necessary only to re-

member that the bearing is always counted from the meridian, either N or S, toward the E and W points. In Fig. 10,

AOB = difference of bearings.
AOC = 180° — sum of bearings.
AOD = 180° — difference of bearings.
AOF = sum of bearings.

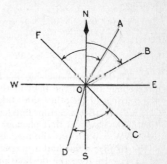

For example: if the magnetic bearing of OA = N 35° 15′ E and that of OD = S 18° 30′ W, the angle AOD = 180° − (35° 15′ − 18° 30′) = 163° 15′.

For a discussion of the methods of calculating bearings see Art. 419, p. 502.

FIG. 10. ANGLES MARKED WITH ARCS ARE BEARINGS

41a. Remarks on the Use of the Compass. — Great accuracy cannot be expected from the magnetic compass, and it is no longer used on surveys of importance. It is, however, quite important that the surveyor of the present day should understand the instrument, its peculiarities and its limitations. (1) The subdivision of nearly all of the land in the older states was made by means of the compass. Since the surveyor who is making re-surveys must re-trace the old lines as nearly as possible he should know the changes in the declination and the possibilities of the compass as a surveying instrument. (2) The methods now used for carrying out the calculations for area, rectangular coördinates, etc., from bearings or azimuths, are the same as those used when the compass was employed for measuring the bearings. These calculations are better understood if the surveyor is familiar with the compass. (3) In spite of its lack of precision the compass is still much used for obtaining rough checks on angles or azimuths taken with the transit, so it is likely to hold its place indefinitely in spite of the fact that it cannot be depended upon for precise work.

PROBLEMS

1. Compute the angles *AOB*, *COD*, *EOF* and *GOH* from the given magnetic bearings.

(a) *OA*, N 39°¼ E.
    OB, N 76°¾ E.
(b) *OC*, N 35° 15′ E.
    OD, S 88° 00′ W.

(c) *OE*, N 15° E.
    OF, S 36° E.
(d) *OG*, N 40° 15′ E.
    OH, N 66° 45′ W.

2. The bearing of one side of a field in the shape of a regular hexagon is S 10°¼ E proceeding around the field in the left-hand (counter-clockwise) direction. Find the bearings of the other sides taken around the field in order.

3. (a) In 1859 a certain line had a magnetic bearing of N 21° W. The declination of the needle at that place in 1859 was 8° 39′ W. In 1902 the declination was 10° 58′ W. What was the magnetic bearing of the line in 1902?

(b) In 1877 a line had a magnetic bearing of N 89° 30′ E. The declination was 0° 13′ E. In 1902 the declination was 1° 39′ W. Find the magnetic bearing of the line in 1902.

4. Magnetic bearings of a closed field are as follows. Short side is *DE*.

Sta.	Forward Bearing	Reverse Bearing	Sta.	Forward Bearing	Reverse Bearing
A	due N.	S 85° ¾ W.	*D*	N 86° ½ W.	N 2° E.
B	N 87° ½ W.	due S.	*E*	S 10° E.	S 89° E.
C	S 1° ¼ W.	S 87° ¼ E.	*F*	N 82° ¾ E.	N 12° W.

Bearing error may be caused by local magnetic attraction or by errors in observation.

(a) Will the former affect the interior angles computed from the bearings?

(b) In the above survey of a closed figure first compute the interior angles from the forward and reverse bearing at each station and adjust the interior angles, i.e., make them equal to the proper number of right angles, placing the error adjacent to the short side. Then start at a station free from local attraction and compute the correct bearings thus producing a closed figure in which the local attraction has been eliminated from the bearings and the other errors have been adjusted.

5. Magnetic bearing of line *AB* is N 48° 15′ E. Angle *ABC* is 99° 50′, *C* being south of *AB*. Compute the bearing of *BC*. The deflection angle at *C*, i.e., angle between *BC* produced and line *CD* is 31° 10′ Right. Compute the bearing of *CD*.

6. Determine from the Isogonic Chart the approximate declination in 1938 at a place in latitude 30° N, longitude 100° W.

7. In 1935 a land surveyor near Boston, Massachusetts, wished to rerun a compass line 1530 feet long originally surveyed in 1775. (a) Find the amount and direction of the resulting divergence in the magnetic meridian between these dates. (Table 2 and Fig. 5.) (b) If the bearing of the line in 1775 had been S 54° 30′ W, what would the bearing be in 1935?

8. A 4-sided piece of land in Western Pennsylvania in latitude 40° N and longitude 80° W was surveyed in 1840, and the bearings recorded as follows: N 30° 15′ E, N 89° 30′ E, S 5° 45′ E, and S 88° 00′ W. Magnetic declination in 1840 = 0° 17′ E. What bearings should be used to retrace the lines in 1935 (to nearest ¼°)?

CHAPTER III

MEASUREMENT OF ANGLES

THE TRANSIT

42. GENERAL DESCRIPTION OF THE TRANSIT. — The engineer's transit is an instrument designed primarily for measuring horizontal and vertical angles. A section of the transit is shown

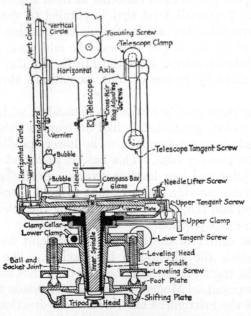

FIG. 11. SECTION OF TRANSIT.

in Fig. 11. Two spindles, or centers, one inside the other, are each attached to a horizontal circular plate, the outer spindle being attached to the lower plate and the inner one to the upper plate. Except in some older instruments, the lower plate carries the graduated circle and the upper plate carries the *verniers* for reading the angles on this circle. On this upper plate are two uprights or *standards* supporting a horizontal axis. At the center of the horizontal axis is a telescope attached at right angles to it. The length of the telescope and the height of the standards are commonly such as to allow the telescope to make a complete rotation on its horizontal axis. The motion of the telescope and the horizontal axis is controlled by means of a clamp and a *slow-motion screw* called a *tangent screw*. This screw acts against an opposing spring.

For leveling the instrument, there are two spirit levels on the upper plate, one parallel and the other at right angles to the horizontal axis. The spirit level that is parallel to the axis is the more important one because it controls the position of the horizontal axis of the telescope; it should be and generally is made somewhat more sensitive than the other. In the transit, the leveling is done by means of four (sometimes three) leveling screws.

The upper plate usually carries a compass-box with a magnetic needle and a circle graduated to half degrees, so that the transit may be used also as a compass. The lower spindle fits into a socket in the leveling base. This base is provided with a ball-and-socket joint and four leveling screws. Both the upper and lower plates are provided with clamps to hold them in any desired position and tangent screws for setting the telescope or the circles in an exact position.

Under the center of the ball-and-socket joint hangs a short chain to which the plumb-line is attached. The plumb-bob used with the transit is generally heavier than that used in taking tape measurements. Modern transits are so made that the entire head of the instrument can be shifted a fraction of an inch laterally with reference to the tripod and thus can be readily placed exactly over a point on the ground.

The horizontal circle is usually graduated either to half-degrees or to 20-minute spaces. The graduations are often numbered from 0° to 360° by two rows of figures running in opposite directions. In some transits they are numbered from 0° to 360° in a right-hand direction and, by a second row of figures, from 0°

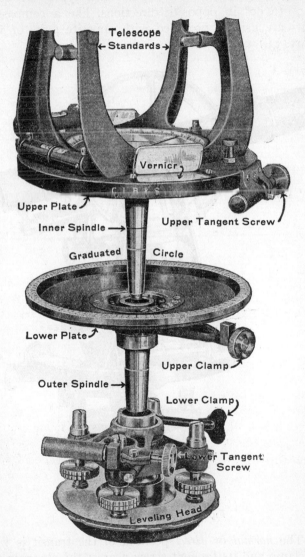

FIG. 12. ENGINEER'S TRANSIT.

each way to 180°; and still others (older types) are numbered from 0° to 90° in opposite directions, like a compass circle. Transits are usually provided with opposite pairs of verniers. (See Art. 53.)

FIG. 13.   ENGINEER'S TRANSIT.

43. The *normal* or *direct* position of the transit is with the upper clamp and its tangent screw nearest the observer and the focusing screw of the telescope on the right-hand side (in some instruments, on top) of the telescope.   When the instrument is turned 180° in azimuth from the direct position and the telescope is *inverted* (turned about its horizontal axis) it is said to be in the *reversed* position. This is often spoken of as " plunging " the telescope.

If the telescope is provided with a long level tube and a vertical circle, or arc, it is called an *Engineer's Transit*, or *Surveyor's Transit*. (Figs. 12 and 13.) If it does not have these attachments it is called a *Plain Transit*.

44. THE TELESCOPE. — The essential parts of the telescope are the *objective*, the *cross-hairs*, and the *eyepiece*. (See Figs. 14 and 14a.)

The line of sight, or *line of collimation*, is the straight line drawn through the optical center of the objective and the point of intersection of the cross-hairs. When light from any point X falls on the objective, the rays from X are bent and brought to a focus at a single point Y called the *image*. Points X, Y, and the optical center of the lens are nearly in a straight line, and are often considered to be exactly so. (See Art. 46.) The only exception to this is when X is on the optical axis; the ray which coincides with the optical axis is **not** bent. The cross-hairs are placed in the telescope tube near where the image is formed, as shown in Figs. 14 and 14a, where the fine lines representing rays of light intersect. The objective is screwed into a tube, which is inside the main tube, and which can be moved by means of a rack-and-pinion screw so as to bring the plane of the image of the object into coincidence with the plane of the cross-hairs.

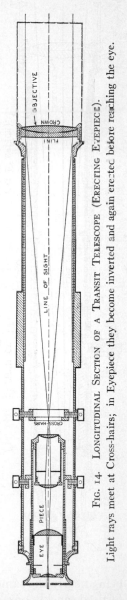

FIG. 14. LONGITUDINAL SECTION OF A TRANSIT TELESCOPE (ERECTING EYEPIECE).

Light rays meet at Cross-hairs; in Eyepiece they become inverted and again erected before reaching the eye.

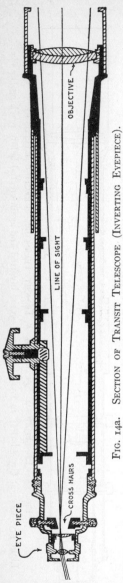

FIG. 14a. SECTION OF TRANSIT TELESCOPE (INVERTING EYEPIECE). Light rays meet at Cross-hairs and become inverted in Eyepiece.

The instrument is so constructed that the motion of this tube is **parallel** to the line of sight. This is of the utmost importance in a transit telescope. The eyepiece is simply a microscope for viewing the image and the cross-hairs. When the plane of the image coincides with the plane of the cross-hairs, both can be viewed at the same instant by means of the eyepiece. The adjustment of the eyepiece and the objective, so that the cross-hairs and the image can be seen clearly at the same time, is called *focusing*.

In focusing, first the eyepiece tube is moved in or out until the cross-hairs appear distinct; then the objective is moved until the image is distinct. If it is found that the cross-hairs are no longer distinct after moving the objective, the above process is repeated until both image and cross-hairs are clearly seen **at the same instant.** The focus should be tested for parallax by moving the eye slightly from one side to the other; if the cross-hairs appear to move over the image the focus is imperfect. In focusing on objects at different distances it should be remembered that the nearer the object is to the telescope, the farther the objective must be from the cross-hairs; and that for points near the instrument the focus changes rapidly, i.e., the objective is moved considerably in changing from a focus on a point 10 ft. away to one 20 ft. away, whereas for distant objects the focus changes very slowly, the focus for 200 ft. being nearly the same as that for 2000 ft. An instrument can be focused quickly on a distant point if the objective is moved in as far as it will go and then moved out slowly until the image is distinct. The objective should not be moved rapidly as it may pass the correct position before the eye can detect the image. If an instrument is badly out of focus it may be pointing directly at an object and yet the image may not be visible.

45. Interior Focusing Telescopes. — Interior focusing telescopes are now in frequent use. These telescopes are similar to those previously described with the exception that an additional lens is placed between the cross-hairs and the objective. This lens is usually a concave (negative) lens. In this type of telescope both the objective and the cross-hairs are fixed in position in the telescope tube. The negative lens is assembled in a tube which fits inside the telescope. The telescope is focused by mov-

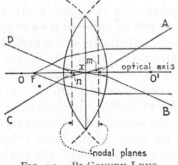

FIG. 15. BI-CONVEX LENS.

ing this interior tube back and forth by means of a rack and pinion; thus the image is brought into the plane of the cross-hairs. This arrangement has two advantages: (1) the barrel of the telescope is in one piece, closed at one end by the objective and at the other by the eyepiece and therefore there is little likelihood of dust getting into the telescope; (2) the telescope is better balanced on its horizontal axis when sighting short distances because the objective is not moved in focusing.

46. The Objective. — The objective might consist of a simple bi-convex lens, like that shown in Fig. 15, which is formed by the intersection of two spheres. The line OO' joining the centers of the two spheres is called the *optical axis*. If rays parallel to the optical axis fall on the lens those near the edge of the lens are bent, or refracted, more than those near the center, so that all the rays are brought to a focus (nearly) at a point F on the optical axis called the *principal focus*. If light falls on the lens from any direction there is always one of the rays such as AC or BD which passes through the lens without permanent deviation, i.e., it emerges from the other side of the lens parallel to its original direction. All such rays intersect at a point x on the optical axis which is called the *optical center*. It should be noted that the vertex of the angle formed by rays from A and B is not point x but a point (m) nearer to the surface of the lens. This is called the " Nodal Point." Rays from C and D intersect at (n) the other nodal point, to the left of x. The planes through these points perpendicular to the optical axis are called " Nodal Planes."

A simple bi-convex lens does not make the best objective because the rays do not all come to a focus at **exactly** the same point. This causes indistinctness (spherical aberration) and also color (chromatic aberration) in the field of view, particularly near the edges. This difficulty is overcome by using a combination of two lenses, one of " crown " and one of " flint " glass (having different indexes of refraction) as shown in Fig. 14; this arrangement very nearly corrects these imperfections.

The position of the image of any point is located on a straight line (nearly) through the point and the optical center; it will be seen therefore that the image formed by the objective is inverted.

47. Cross-Hairs. — The cross-hairs consist of two very fine spider threads stretched across a metallic ring at right angles to each other and fastened by means of shellac. The cross-hair ring, or diaphragm (Fig. 16) is held in place by four capstan-headed screws which permit of its being moved vertically and horizontally in the telescope tube. The holes in the tube through which the screws pass are elongated enough to allow a slight rotary motion of the ring in adjusting.

The cross-hairs are not invariably made of spider threads. A disadvantage of the spider thread is that it will slacken when moist. It requires some skill to mount it with just the right tension. Platinum wires and tungsten wires have been much used, but it is difficult to draw them fine enough for use under very high-power eyepieces. Lines ruled on a thin plate of glass have also been much used. This arrangement has the advantage that short lines and other marks may be ruled (or photographed) on the glass for special purposes. It also permits carrying several spare ruled glasses to be used in emergencies. The disadvantages of the glass are the loss of light in the field of view and the liability to collect dust and film, which fog the image. Recent experiments with spun glass indicate that threads can be drawn having a diameter of from one to four ten-thousandths of an inch. These threads are very satisfactory and seem to have no disadvantages.

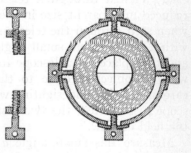

FIG. 16. CROSS-HAIR RING, OR DIAPHRAGM.

48. Eyepiece. — The eyepiece may be either of two kinds, that which shows an inverted image (Fig. 14a) or that which shows an erect image (Fig. 14). In the inverting type all objects appear to be upside down and those on the right appear to be on the left. An erecting eyepiece requires two more lenses than the inverting eyepiece, which add to its length and also absorb light; yet the erecting eyepiece is generally used on ordinary transits. With the same length of telescope, however, a greater magnifying power and a clearer definition of the image can be obtained by the use of the inverting eyepiece. These advantages are so important and the disadvantage of seeing objects inverted is so slight that inverting eyepieces should be used more generally than they are at present.

49. Magnifying Power. — The magnifying power of a telescope is the amount by which an object is increased in apparent size. It is equal to $\dfrac{\tan \frac{1}{2} A}{\tan \frac{1}{2} a}$, $\left(\text{or nearly equal to } \dfrac{A}{a}\right)$, A being the angle subtended by an object as seen through the telescope and a the angle as seen by the unaided eye.

The magnifying power may be measured in two ways.

(1) The dimensions on a graduated rod will appear magnified when viewed through a telescope. If, with one eye at the telescope, the rod is viewed directly with the other eye it will be noticed that one space as viewed through the telescope will appear to cover a certain number of spaces as seen with the naked eye. This number is approximately the magnifying power of the telescope; it is expressed as so many " diameters."

(2) Viewed through a telescope wrong-end-to, an object is reduced in apparent size in the same ratio that it is magnified when seen through the telescope in the usual manner. Measure with a transit some small angle A between two distant points and then place the telescope to be tested in front of the transit, with its objective close to the objective of the transit. By careful focusing and sighting with the transit through the telescope to be tested, the two distant stations will be observed in the field of view.

Measure this small angle a between the stations with the transit. Then the Magnifying Power $= \dfrac{\tan \frac{1}{2} A}{\tan \frac{1}{2} a}$. The magnifying power of the ordinary transit telescope is between twenty and thirty diameters.

50. Field of View. — The field of view is the angular space that can be seen at one time through the telescope. It is the angle subtended at the optical center of the objective by the opening in the eyepiece. In the ordinary transit this angle is about one degree, but in some instruments it is considerably more.

51. EUROPEAN THEODOLITES* (transits) are being used to a limited extent on this continent. Some of these instruments are radical departures from the type of transit commonly used in the United States.

In the older types of theodolite the telescope was so long that it could not be rotated about its horizontal axis 360°. In late years the design has been changed and this feature eliminated. Of several modern types, two common ones will be described. One of them (Fig. 16a) is similar to the ordinary transit except that the horizontal circle is read through two prismatic micro-

---

* In the United States the term theodolite is often applied to transits that may be read to 10 seconds or less.

scopes attached above the circle at places 180° apart thus providing a convenient means of reading opposite points of the circle.

Instead of the usual metal vernier adjacent to the horizontal circle to aid in reading it, there is introduced into the reading microscope a vernier scale ruled on glass by means of which the circle may be read to the nearest 20 seconds of angle. The vertical circle, however, has the usual metal verniers and in addition attached reading glasses.

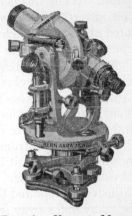

The second type of theodolite (Fig. 16b) has additional optical devices. By means of an auxiliary telescope placed at one side of the observing telescope, opposite points of the horizontal circle are made to appear to coincide, and

FIG. 16a. VERNIER MICROSCOPE TRANSIT (4¾ INCHES).

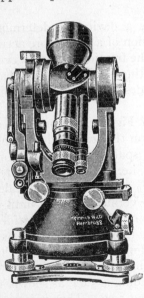

FIG. 16b. UNIVERSAL THEODOLITE (⅓ ACTUAL SIZE).

the angle of displacement is read on a drum; then by changing the position of a prism the horizontal circle disappears from view and the opposite points on the vertical circle may then be simultaneously read. A micrometer device permits the reading of both the horizontal and vertical circles to the nearest second of arc. The instrument in Fig. 16b has no lower motion. For a desired initial circle setting it is necessary to move the lower circle by means of a disk with milled circumference (or edge). If, for example, a traverse is being run using azimuths, transporting the instrument between set-ups disturbs the circle setting; it is then necessary to reset the circle reading, and it is often difficult to do this exactly.

Many of these instruments have no provision for a plumb-line, but are equipped with optical collimators for setting over the point. While this is an advantage when a strong wind is blowing, nevertheless for work where very few angles are to be measured at a set-up, such as a traverse, the time consumed in using the optical collimator is often excessive.

Most of these foreign instruments have very small horizontal circles (about 2 inches in diameter in some instruments) and the circle graduations are usually ruled on glass. The telescopes are short, have interior focusing and are provided with various stadia intervals. They are very light and compact.

These small instruments are capable of producing very precise results. Any transit having complicated optical devices has the obvious disadvantage, however, that it cannot be readily cleaned, adjusted, or repaired by the surveyor in the field who is likely to be many miles away from the factory where such work must be done.

52. THE VERNIER. — The vernier is a device for determining the subdivision of the smallest division of a scale more accurately than can be done by estimating the fractional part by eye. These fractional parts are read by noting the number of that division line on the vernier which coincides with some line on the scale, as explained below.

A simple form of vernier, shown in Fig. 17, is constructed by taking a length equal to 9 divisions on the scale and dividing this length into 10 equal parts. One space on the vernier is then equal to $\frac{9}{10}$ of a space on the scale, i.e., it is $\frac{1}{10}$ part shorter than a space on the scale, hence $ab = \frac{1}{10}$ of a space on the scale, $cd = \frac{2}{10}$ of a space, etc. Now, if the vernier is raised until a coincides with b, i.e., until the first line on the vernier coincides with the next higher line on the scale, then the index line has moved over $\frac{1}{10}$ of a space and the reading will be 5.01. If the vernier is moved $\frac{1}{10}$ space higher then line 2 coincides with the next higher line on the scale and the reading is 5.02, as shown in Fig. 18. Similarly Fig. 19 shows reading 5.26. Thus it is seen that the number of the line on the vernier which coincides with a line on the scale is the number of tenths of the smallest division of the scale that the index point (zero) lies above the next lower division on the scale. Furthermore it will be seen from its construction that it is impossible to have more than one coincidence at a time on a single vernier. The kind of vernier just described is used on leveling rods.

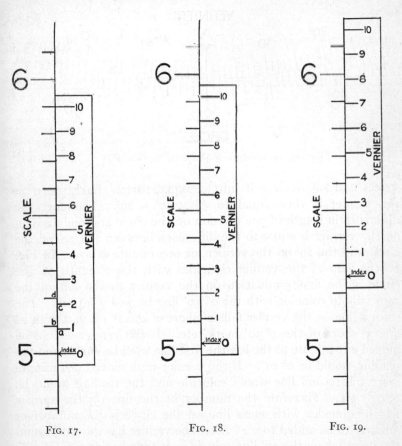

FIG. 17.   FIG. 18.   FIG. 19.

53. Verniers used on Transits. — Since a transit may be used to measure angles in either direction, the verniers are usually double, i.e., a single vernier is placed on each side of the index line, one of which is to be used in reading angles to the right, and the other in reading angles to the left.

The vernier most commonly found on the transit reads to

one minute of arc (Fig. 20). When this vernier is used the circle is divided into degrees and half-degrees. The vernier scale is made by taking a length equal to 29 of the half-degree

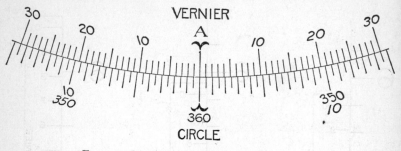

FIG. 20.   ONE-MINUTE VERNIER SET AT 0°.

spaces and subdividing it into 30 equal parts. Each space on the vernier is then equal to $\frac{29}{30} \times 30' = 29'$. Therefore the difference in length of one division on the circle and one division on the vernier is equal to the difference between the 30' on the circle and the 29' on the vernier, or one minute of arc. In Fig. 20 the zero of the vernier coincides with the 0° mark on the circle. The first graduation on the vernier to the left of the zero fails to coincide with the 0° 30' line by just 1' of arc. The second line on the vernier falls 2' short of the 1° mark, the third line 3' short of the 1° 30' mark, etc. If the vernier should be moved one minute to the left the first line would coincide and the reading would be 0° 01'. If the vernier were moved one minute more the second line would coincide and the reading would be 0° 02', etc. Therefore the number of the line on the vernier which coincides with **some** line on the circle is the number of minutes to be added to 0°. After the vernier has moved beyond the point where the 30' line coincides, it then begins subdividing the next space of the circle, and we must then add the actual vernier reading to 0° 30'.

The following figures show various arrangements of verniers commonly used on transits.

Fig. 21. — Double vernier reading to 1'. Circle divided into 30' spaces. 29 divisions of the circle divided into 30 parts to make one division of the vernier.

Reading, outer row of figures, 9° 16'.
Reading, inner row of figures, 350° 44'.

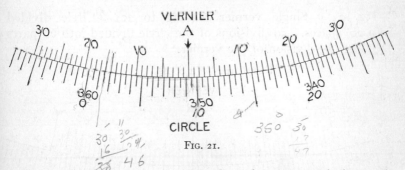

FIG. 21.

Since the vernier moves with the telescope, **read the angle on the circle in the same direction that the telescope has moved (clockwise or counter-clockwise).** Read the number of degrees and half-degrees the index has passed over and estimate roughly the number of minutes beyond the last half-degree mark. Then follow along the vernier in the **same** direction and find the coincidence. The number of this line is the number of minutes to be added to the degrees and half-degrees which were read from the circle. An **estimate** of the number of minutes **should always be made before reading the vernier** as a check against large mistakes in reading the vernier or in reading the wrong vernier.

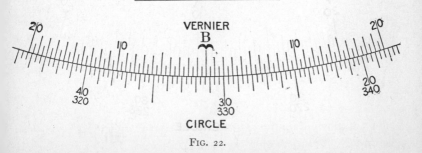

FIG. 22.

Fig. 22. — Double vernier reading to 30″. Circle divided into 20′ spaces. 39 divisions of the circle divided into 40 parts to make one division of the vernier.

Reading, inner row of figures, 31° 17′ 30″.
Reading, outer row of figures, 328° 42′ 30″.

Fig. 23. — Single vernier reading to 20″. Circle divided into 20′ spaces. 59 divisions of the circle divided into 60 parts to make one division of the vernier.

Reading, 73° 48′ 40″.

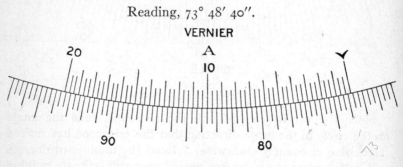

CIRCLE

Fig. 23.

On account of the length of this vernier it is impracticable to use a double vernier. Where it is desirable to read the angles in either direction the circle and the vernier have two rows of figures as shown in Fig. 24.

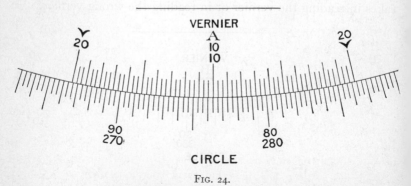

CIRCLE

Fig. 24.

Fig. 24. — Reading, inner row of figures, 73° 48′ 40″.
Reading, outer row of figures, 266° 31′ 20″.

It is evident that if angles are to be read " clockwise " the index at the right end of this vernier should be set at 0°. If angles are to be measured in the opposite direction the index at the left end should be set at 0°. To avoid this inconvenience of resetting, some surveyors set the middle line (10′ line) of the vernier on 0° and disregard the numbering on the vernier, reading it as explained under Fig. 26.

Fig. 25. — Single vernier reading to 10″. Circle divided into 10′ spaces. 59 divisions of the circle divided into 60 parts to make one division of the vernier.

Reading, 59° 15′ 50″.

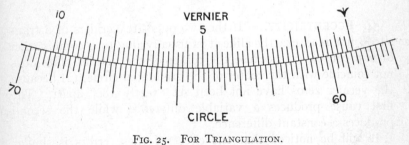

FIG. 25. FOR TRIANGULATION.

Fig. 26. — Single vernier reading in either direction to 1′. Circle divided into 30′ spaces. 29 divisions of the circle divided into 30 parts to make one division of the vernier.

Reading, 2° 23′.

This vernier is read like the ordinary 1′ vernier except that if a coincidence is not reached by passing along the vernier in the direction in which the circle is numbered, it is necessary to go to the other end of the vernier and continue in the same direction, toward the center, until the coincidence is found.

6538

This vernier is used on the vertical circles of transits and on plane-table alidades when the space between the standards is too small for a double vernier.

Another vernier has been designed in which the degree is divided into hundredths, but this never came into general use.

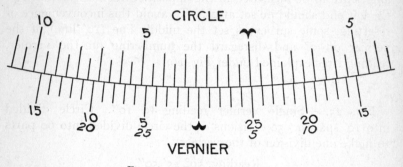

FIG. 26. "FOLDED" VERNIER.

54. ECCENTRICITY. — If the two opposite verniers of a transit do not read exactly alike it is usually due to a combination of two causes, (1) because the center of the vernier plate does not coincide with the center of the graduated circle, (2) because the vernier zeros have not been set exactly 180° apart. The first cause produces a variable difference while the second produces a constant difference.

It will be noticed that the effect of these errors is similar to that described in Art. 34, p. 27, on Adjustments of the Compass; the eccentricity of the circles of the transit corresponding to the bent pivot of the compass and the error in the position of the verniers of the transit corresponding to the bent needle of the compass.

With reference to the eccentricity of the plates, let C in Fig. 27 be the center of the vernier plate and C' the center of the circle. Let GF be a line through the two centers. When one vernier is at F and the other is at G the vernier readings will be the same as though C and C' were coincident, since the displacement of the center of the circle occurs in the direction of the lines of graduation at F and G. If the telescope is then turned at right angles to its former position, the verniers then being at D and E, the readings of opposite verniers will differ by the maximum amount. Suppose that the graduations are numbered from 0° right-handed to 360°. When the vernier is at an intermediate position, as at A, it will be seen that it reads too much by the amount AA'. The opposite vernier at B reads too little by the amount BB'. Since AB and $A'B'$ are parallel, BB' and AA' are equal. Consequently the mean of the two vernier readings will be the true reading and the eccentricity error has been eliminated. Since the effect of eccentricity is never more than a very few minutes it is customary

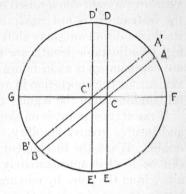

Fig. 27. ECCENTRICITY OF CIRCLE.

to read the degrees and minutes on one vernier and the minutes only on the other.

55. In spite of the fact that the two verniers are not 180° apart no error is introduced provided; (1) that the same vernier is always used, or (2) that the mean of the two vernier readings is always taken. But if vernier A is set and the angle is read on vernier B an error does enter. Where only one vernier is read **always read the vernier that was set at 0°.**

In good instruments both of these errors are very small, usually smaller than the finest reading of the vernier.

USE OF THE TRANSIT

56. SETTING UP THE TRANSIT. — In setting up the transit, first give the tripod sufficient spread to insure steadiness, keeping the plate of the instrument **approximately level,** the plumb-bob being nearly over the point. Then if the instrument is so far from the point that it cannot be brought into the correct position by pressing the legs into the ground the instrument should be lifted bodily and moved so that the plumb-bob is almost over the point; then press the legs firmly into the ground, doing this in such a manner as gradually to bring the plumb-bob accurately over the point. The nuts at the top of the tripod legs should be tight enough so that the legs are just about to fall of their own weight when raised from the ground. If they are loose the instrument is not rigid; if they are too tight it is not in a stable condition and may shift at any moment. Tripods having legs of adjustable length are much used where difficult set-ups are common such as in mines and tunnel surveys. While convenient for transportation in automobiles they require more careful handling than the regular tripod.

If the station point is on sloping ground it is often convenient, and insures greater stability, to set two legs downhill and one uphill. When the instrument is over the point the tripod head can be leveled approximately without moving the instrument away from the point by moving one, sometimes two, of the tripod legs in an arc of a circle about the point. Nothing but practice will make one expert in setting up the transit.

It is desirable to make the instrument nearly level by means of the tripod; this is a saving of time because it takes longer to level up by the leveling screws than by the tripod. It also saves time on the next set-up to have the leveling screws nearly in their mid position. If the transit is set by means of the tripod, say, within 0.01 or 0.02 ft. of the point, the exact position can be readily reached by means of the *shifting head*, which may be moved freely after any two **adjacent** leveling screws are loosened. When the transit has been brought accurately over the point, the leveling screws should be brought back to a bearing. In the first (rough) setting the plumb-bob should hang, say, an inch above the point, but when the shifting head is used it should be lowered to within about $\frac{1}{8}$ inch or less of the point.

57. In leveling the instrument, first turn the plates so that each plate level is parallel to a pair of **opposite** leveling screws. Then each level is controlled solely by the pair of leveling screws which is parallel to it. Great care should be used in leveling. The screws must not be loose, as this will cause the plates to tip and perhaps to move horizontally which would change the position of the plumb-bob over the point. On the other hand they must not be too tight, as this will not only injure the instrument but will cause errors due to strains in the metal. To level the instrument, grasp one pair of opposite screws between the thumbs and forefingers and turn so that the thumbs move either **toward** each other or **away from** each other, as illustrated in Fig. 28. In this way one screw is tightened as much as the other is loosened. The motion of both screws must be uniform; if they bind, the one which is being loosened should be turned

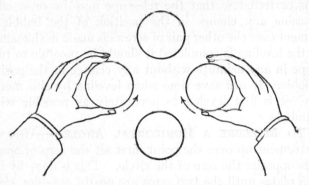

FIG. 28.   DIAGRAM SHOWING HOW FINGERS MOVE IN LEVELING.

faster. If this does not appear to remedy matters then the other pair of screws is binding and should be loosened slightly. Only experience will teach one to level an instrument quickly and correctly. It may be convenient for beginners to remember that in leveling the instrument the bubble will move in the same direction as the left thumb moves. After one bubble has been brought nearly to the center of its tube the other bubble is centered in a similar manner by its pair of leveling screws. Instead of trying to center one bubble **exactly** before beginning on the second one it is better to get both of them nearly level, after which first one bubble and then the other may be brought exactly to the center. After the instrument is leveled the plumb-bob should be examined to see that it has not been moved away from the point during the process of leveling.

It is always possible to level a transit by means of the long bubble attached to the telescope, and since this bubble is more sensitive than the plate bubbles, the result will be more accurate. The telescope is first turned so that it is over one pair of opposite leveling screws, the vertical arc reading zero, and the bubble is brought to the center of its tube by means of the leveling screws. The telescope is then reversed 180° about the vertical axis (without touching the clamp or the tangent screw on the standard). If the bubble is no longer central it should be moved half-way back by means of the tangent screw, the other half by means of the leveling screws. By additional trials the adjustment is perfected so that the telescope may be reversed without causing any change in the position of the bubble. The adjustment over the other pair of screws is made in the same way. When the leveling is completed it should be possible to turn the telescope in any azimuth without any change in the position of the bubble. It will save time when leveling by this method, if the transit is first leveled as accurately as possible with the plate bubble.

58. To Measure a Horizontal Angle. — After setting the instrument up over the point, first set the zero of one of the verniers opposite the zero of the circle. This is done by turning the two plates until the two zeros are nearly opposite, clamping the plates firmly together with the **upper clamp,** and then bringing the two into exact coincidence by means of the tangent screw which goes with the **upper clamp.** If a line on the vernier is coincident with a line on the circle then the two adjacent lines on the vernier will fail to coincide with the corresponding lines on the circle by **equal amounts** (Art. 53, p. 45). Hence the coincidence of any line on the vernier with a line on the circle can be more accurately judged by examining also the adjacent divisions and noting that they are symmetrical with respect to the coincident lines. A pocket magnifier, or "reading glass," is generally used for setting and reading the vernier. **Never touch the clamp after a setting has been made by means of the tangent screw.** In setting with the tangent screw it is better to do this by a **right-hand turn,** i.e., by turning the screw in the direction which **compresses** the spring against which it works. If the screw needs to be turned back, instead of turning it to the exact setting turn it back too far and then bring it up to the accurate setting with a right-hand motion, thereby insuring a firm bearing of the spring against the screw. The two plates which are now clamped in proper position are free to turn together about the vertical axis. Turn to the first object and point the telescope at it approximately by looking over the top of the telescope. When turning the instrument so as to sight the first point it is good practice to touch the lower plate only. Focus the telescope by moving the eyepiece until the cross-hairs are distinct and then moving the objective until the image is distinct. It is sometimes convenient to point the telescope at the object when focusing the cross-hairs so that they can be readily seen.* Test for parallax by moving the eye slightly from one side to the other. Move the telescope until the vertical cross-hair is very nearly on the point. It is better to use that part of the cross-hair which is near the center of the field of view. Clamp the lower plate by means of the **lower clamp,** and set exactly on the point by the **lower** tangent screw. The line of sight is now fixed on the first object. To measure the angle loosen the **upper clamp,** turn the telescope to the second point, and focus the objective if necessary. Set nearly on the point, clamp the **upper** plate, and set the vertical cross-hair exactly on the point by means of the **upper** tangent screw. The angle is then read by **using that vernier which was set at 0°.**

The tangent screws should **not** be used to move the plates over large angles. Acquire the habit of setting closely by hand and using the tangent screw for slight motions only.

59. To Measure an Angle by Repetition. — The eyepiece magnifies the image so much that it is possible to set the cross-hair on a point much more closely than the vernier will read. The graduation of the circle is very accurate and can be depended upon closer than the vernier can be read, consequently the full value of the instrument is not utilized by single readings of an angle. To obtain the value of an angle more accurately proceed as follows. After the first angle has been measured leave the two plates clamped together, loosen the **lower clamp** and turn back to the first point. Set on the first point, using

---

* If the eyepiece is focused on the cross-hairs with the telescope pointing at the sky, as is frequently done, they will be found to be nearly in focus when looking at the object; but for accurate work the eyepiece should be focused on the cross-hairs when the objective is in focus on the object.

the **lower clamp** and **its** tangent screw. Then loosen the upper clamp and set on the second point, using the **upper clamp** and **its** tangent screw, thus adding another angle, equal to the first one, to the reading on the circle. Repeat this operation, say, six times. The total angle divided by six will give a more precise result than the first reading. Suppose that the angle is actually 18° 12′ 08″; if a " one-minute " instrument is being used it is impossible to read the 08″ on the vernier, so the reading will be 18° 12′. Each repetition will add 08″ (nearly) and after the 6th repetition, the amount will be 48″ which will be read as 1′. After the sixth pointing the total angle will then be read 109° 13′ which divided by 6 gives 18° 12′ 10″, a result which is correct to the nearest 10″. To eliminate errors in the adjustment of the transit the above process should be repeated with the instrument reversed and the mean of the two values used. (See Art. 79, p. 71.) It is customary to take only the first and sixth readings, but as a check against mistakes it is well for the beginner to examine the vernier reading after each repetition and see that ½ the second reading, ⅓ the third, etc., nearly equals the first reading.

Repetition has also the advantage of eliminating, to a great extent, errors of graduation. If an angle is about 60° and is repeated 6 times it will cover a whole circumference. If there are systematic errors in the graduations the result is nearly free from them. The effect of accidental, or irregular, errors of graduation is decreased in proportion to the number of repetitions. In the best modern instruments, however, the errors of graduation seldom exceed a few seconds.

Little is gained by making a very large number of repetitions as there are systematic errors introduced by the action of the clamps, and the accuracy apparently gained is really lost on this account. Three repetitions with the telescope normal and three with the telescope inverted are sufficient for anything but very exact work.

It is desirable that as little time as possible should elapse between pointings, as the instrument cannot be relied upon to remain perfectly still. As a matter of fact it is vibrating and " creeping " nearly all the time from numerous causes. For example, when the instrument is set up on frozen ground, it will quickly change its position on account of the unequal settlement of the tripod legs. Changes of temperature, causing expansion or contraction of the metal of the instrument, and the effect of wind introduce errors. The more rapidly the measurements can be made, consistent with careful manipulation, the better the results will be. If the transit is set up on shaky ground the transitman should avoid walking around his instrument.

60. "Doubling" the Angle. — Repetition is useful not only to secure precision, but also as a check against mistakes. If a mistake is made on the first reading of an angle the vernier, on the second reading, falls in a new place on the circle so that the mistake is not likely to be repeated. It is common practice to repeat, or "double," all important angles and divide the second reading by 2 simply as a check on the first reading.

61. TO LAY OFF AN ANGLE BY REPETITION. — There is no direct method of laying off an angle by repetition as in measuring an angle, therefore the following indirect method is used. With the vernier set at 0° and the telescope sighted on the first point the angle is laid off carefully on the circle and the second point set in line with the new position of the telescope. Then this angle which has been laid off is **measured** by repetition as precisely as is desired as described in Art. 59. The resulting angle obtained by repetition is a more precise value than the angle first set on the vernier. The difference between this value and the angle desired is the correction which should be made at the second point. This can be readily done by measuring approximately the distance from the instrument to the second point, and computing the perpendicular offset to be laid off at the second point. (The offset for an angle of one minute at a distance of 100 ft. is nearly 0.03 ft.)

62. RUNNING A STRAIGHT LINE. — One Point Visible from the Other. — There are several ways in which a straight line may be fixed on the ground, depending upon the existing conditions. If the line is fixed by the two end points one of which is visible from the other, the method of setting intermediate points would be to set the transit over one point, take a "foresight" on the other and place points in line. For very exact

work the instrument should be used in both the direct and reversed positions (Art. 79, p. 71). This will eliminate errors of
adjustment such as failure of the telescope to revolve in a true
vertical plane, or failure of the objective tube to travel parallel
to the line of sight.

**63. RUNNING A STRAIGHT LINE. — Neither Point Visible
from the Other.** — If neither point can be seen from the other
then it is necessary to find some point, by trial, from which the
terminal points can be seen. The transit is set up at some intermediate point estimated to be on the line, a " backsight " is
taken on one of the points and the instrument clamped. The
telescope is then reversed on its horizontal axis. If the vertical
cross-hair happens to cut the second point, then the estimated
position happens to be on the line; if not, then the distance this
trial line is to one side of the second point can be estimated
(or measured) and from this the distance the transit is off line
can be computed mentally by proportion and the instrument
moved over (toward the line) by this amount. In this way, by
successive trials, the true point is attained. The final tests should
be made with the instrument in direct and reversed positions to
eliminate errors of adjustment of the line of sight and the horizontal axis. To eliminate errors in the adjustment of the plate
bubbles the plate level which is perpendicular to the line should
be re-leveled just before making the second backsight and while
the telescope is pointing in that direction. This can be more
readily done if, when the transit is set up, one pair of opposite
leveling screws is turned into the line; then the other pair will
control the level which is perpendicular to the line of sight.

The method of running a line between two points when
neither one is visible from an intermediate set-up is to run first
a trial line, called a *random line*, as described in Art. 199, p. 199.

64. Prolonging a Straight Line. — If a line is fixed by two
points A and B, Fig. 28a, not far apart, and it is desired to prolong this line in the direction AB, the instrument should be set
up at A, a sight taken on B and other points C, D and E set in
line beyond B. For the best results the transit should be used
in the direct and reversed positions and the mean result used;
this is especially important if the distances are such that it is

necessary to change the focus of the telescope. When running toward a foresight the points ahead tend to come nearer and nearer into line as the transit approaches the terminal point. If, however, there is any doubt about the objective slide's traveling parallel to the line of collimation it is advisable to use the instrument in the direct and reversed positions.

But when it is impossible to see beyond B from A, the transit should be set up at B and points ahead should be set by the method of backsighting and foresighting as follows. With the transit at B a backsight is taken on A with the telescope in its direct position and the plates clamped. The telescope is then

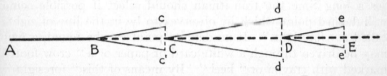

FIG. 28a. PROLONGING A LINE BY BACKSIGHTING AND FORESIGHTING.

inverted and a point c set ahead in line. The position of this point c is then verified by repeating the process, the backsight on A being taken with the telescope in the inverted position. If, when the telescope is again plunged point c is not on the cross-hair, set point c' beside point c. The true position of C is midway between c and c'. The transit is then moved ahead to the new point C and the whole process is repeated.

When prolonging a line by backsighting and foresighting, using the transit **in but one position** of the axis, the error in the sight line is always on the same side, the resulting line is curved, and the points lie farther and farther from the true line. **It is very important, therefore, to observe with the transit in the two positions and to use the mean result.**

65. Methods of Showing Sights. — If the point sighted is within a few hundred feet of the transit a pencil (held vertical) may be used to show a point for the transitman to sight on. Sighting-rods or range poles are used on long distances.* Where

---

* It is desirable that the object used for the foresight should be of such color that the cross-hair is clearly seen, and of such width that the cross-hair can easily bisect it. A yellow or light colored pencil against a dark background, or a dark pencil against the sky usually give good results.

only the top of the pole is visible an error will be introduced if
it is not held plumb. A plumb-line is much more accurate for
such work but may be difficult or impossible to see on long sights.
Under conditions where the plumb-line cannot be seen readily
some surveyors use for a sight an ordinary white card held with
one edge against the string or held so that the **center** of the
card is directly behind the string. If the edge of the card is
held against the string, the transitman must be **extremely** careful
that he is sighting on the proper edge.*

Whenever the instrument is sighted along a line which is to
be used frequently or along which the transit is to remain sighted
for a long time the transitman should select if possible some
well-defined point which he observes to be in the line of sight,
called a " foresight." If no definite point can be found, a nail
may be driven through a white card or paper or a " crow-foot "
marked with crayon or " keel." By means of this " foresight "
the transitman can detect if his instrument moves off the line,
and can reset the telescope exactly at any time without requiring
the aid of another man to show him the line.

---

* It is the practice among some surveyors to use a 2-ft. rule for a sight.
The rule is opened so that it forms an inverted V (Λ). The plumb-string is
jammed into the angle of the Λ by pressing the two arms of the rule together.
The rule is then held so that the plumb-string as it hangs from the rule appears
to bisect the angle of the Λ.

Another device involves attaching to the plumb-line an ordinary fish-line
float (shaped like a plumb-bob). This may be fastened so that its axis coincides with the string and so that it can be raised and lowered on the string.
It should be painted with such colors that it can be seen against any background,
say, the upper half white and the lower half red, or black.

The man showing the sight for the transitman should always try to stand so
that the sun will shine on the object he is holding; on long sights it is difficult
(sometimes impossible) to see an object in a shadow.

An effective way of setting a point on line in a place where there is poor
visibility such as in dense undergrowth or at twilight is by using an ordinary
flashlight in the following manner. With the corner of a file make a V-shaped
groove in the metal ring of the flashlight rim. In using the flashlight hold
its barrel at about 30° to the horizontal with the groove at the top. Over
this groove hang a plumb-line so that it will not touch the glass face of the
flashlight. Then put on the light. The transitman can readily see the light
and the vertical plumb-line in front of it. Another less accurate way is to
loop the plumb-line over the flashlight near the lighted end so that the plumb-
bob will hang under the flashlight over the point, and then the transitman will
sight directly on the light. In this case the flashlight barrel is held horizontal.

66. Signals. — In surveying work the distances are frequently so great that it is necessary to use hand signals. The following are in common use.

" *Right* " or " *Left* " when setting points. — The arm is extended in the direction of the motion desired, the right arm being used for a motion to the right and the left arm for a motion to the left. A slow motion is used to indicate that the point must be moved a long distance and a quick motion a short distance.

" *Plumb the Pole.*" — The hand is extended vertically above the head and moved slowly in the direction it is desired to have the pole plumbed.

" *All Right* " — Both arms are extended horizontally and moved up and then down; or, both hands shown at same time (without raising and lowering).

" *Give a Foresight.*" — The transitman, desiring a foresight, motions to the rodman, by holding one arm vertically above his head.

" *Take a Foresight.*" — The rodman desiring the transitman to sight on a point, motions the transitman by holding one arm vertically above his head and then he holds his lining-pole or pencil vertically on the point.

" *Give Line.*" — When the rodman desires to be placed " on line " he holds his lining-pole horizontally with both hands over his head and then brings it down to the ground in a vertical position. If the point is to be set carefully, as a transit point, the rodman waves the top end of pole in a horizontal circle above his head before bringing it to the vertical position or, he may wave the arm in a similar manner if a pole is not being used.

" *Pick up the Transit.*" — When the chief of the party desires to have the instrument set at another point he signals to the transitman by extending both arms downward and outward and then raising them quickly.

All signals should be distinct so as to leave no doubt as to their meaning. Care should be taken to stand so that the background will not prevent the signals being seen distinctly. The palms of the hands should be shown in making the signals; for distant signals a white handkerchief is often used. Where much distant signaling is to be done flags are attached to the lining-poles. Special signals may easily be devised for different kinds of distant work and for various conditions.

67. TO MEASURE A VERTICAL ANGLE. — In measuring a vertical angle with a transit, first point the vertical cross-hair approximately at the object, then set the horizontal cross-hair exactly on the point by means of the clamp and tangent screw controlling the vertical motion. Next read the vertical arc or circle. Then, **without disturbing the rest of the transit,** unclamp the vertical arc, and bring the telescope to the horizontal position by means of the level attached to the telescope, and the clamp and tangent screw of the vertical arc. When the telescope bubble is in the center read the vertical arc again. This gives the *index correction*, to be added or subtracted according to whether the vertical angle reading and the index correction reading are on opposite sides or the same side of the zero of the circle. The instrument is supposed to be adjusted so that the vernier reads zero when the telescope is level, and a circle reading gives the angle above or below the horizontal line. The index correction is seldom zero because, even though this adjustment were perfect, the plate is seldom exactly level.

In some forms of transit the vernier is placed on a separate arm which also carries a level. By bringing this vernier level to the center of its tube by means of its tangent screw the index correction is automatically reduced to zero each time and the true angle is then read directly. Instruments provided with this form of level often have no level attached to the telescope (See Fig. 91, p. 213.)

If the transit has a complete vertical circle errors in the adjustment of the bubble and the horizontal cross-hair may be eliminated by inverting the telescope, turning it through 180° in azimuth, and remeasuring the angle. The mean of the two results is free from such errors. It is not free, however, from errors in leveling the plates. If the transit is provided with only a portion of a circle the vernier will be off the arc when the telescope is inverted, consequently with a transit not having a full circle the elimination of errors cannot be effected.

68. PRECAUTIONS IN THE USE OF THE TRANSIT. — In the preceding text several sources of error and also precaution against mistakes have been mentioned, but in order that the beginner may appreciate the importance of handling the instrument carefully he should make the following simple tests.

1. Set the transit up with the three points of the tripod rather near together so that the instrument will be high and unstable. Sight the cross-hair on some definite object, such as the tip of a church spire, so that the slightest motion can be seen. Take one tripod leg between the thumb and forefinger and twist it strongly; at the same time look through the telescope and observe the effect.

2. Press the tripod leg laterally and observe the effect on the level attached to the telescope; center the bubble before testing.

3. Step on the ground about 1 or 2 inches from the foot of one of the tripod legs and observe the effect on the line of sight.

4. Breathe on one end of the level vial and observe the motion of the bubble.

5. Press laterally on the eyepiece and observe the effect on the line of sight.

These motions, plainly seen in such tests, are really going on all the time, even if they are not readily apparent to the observer, and show the necessity for careful and skillful manipulation. The overcoat dragging over the tripod, or a hand carelessly resting on the tripod, are common sources of error in transit work.

Before picking up the transit **center the movable head, bring the leveling screws back to their mid positions, loosen the lower clamp, and turn the telescope either up or down.**

ADJUSTMENTS OF THE TRANSIT

69. Some parts of a transit are fixed while other parts permit of adjustments. For example, the centers of the two vertical axes are solidly constructed perpendicular to the horizontal plates. If their relation should change, the instruments must be sent to the factory for repairs. As examples of the adjustable parts, (1) the plate bubble tubes are adjustable so that their axes may be made parallel to the horizontal plate, (2) the cross-hair ring is movable so that the line of sight may be made perpendicular to the horizontal axis, otherwise it would not rotate in a vertical plane, (3) one end of the horizontal axis is movable so that the axis may be made truly horizontal, for otherwise the line of sight will move in a plane oblique to the vertical when the telescope is raised or lowered, (4) the telescope bubble is movable so that the axis of the telescope bubble and the line of sight may be made parallel. The usual handling of the transit and the effect of temperature changes tend to alter these relations (1) to (4). The surveyor can readily make these adjustments in the field.

If an instrument is badly out of adjustment in several respects it is better not to try to make final adjustments of one part at a time but to make approximate adjustments of each part at the start, thus bringing the instrument as a whole gradually into adjustment.

Nearly all adjustments of surveying instruments are made to depend on the principle of **reversion.** By reversing the position of the instrument the effect of an error is doubled.

The adjustments described in Arts. 70-3 apply to all transits, whether they are "plain," or "engineers"; those described in Arts. 74-6 do not apply to plain transits.

70. ADJUSTMENT OF THE PLATE BUBBLES. — To adjust the Plate Levels so that Each lies in a Plane Perpendicular to the Vertical Axis of the Instrument. — Set up the transit and bring the bubbles to the centers of their respective tubes. Turn the plate 180° about its vertical axis and see if the bubbles remain in the center. If they move from the center, half this distance is the error in the adjustment of the tube. (See Figs. 29 and 29a.) The adjustment is made by turning the capstan-headed

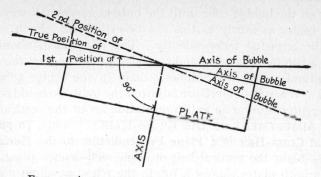

FIG. 29. ADJUSTMENT OF THE PLATE BUBBLES.

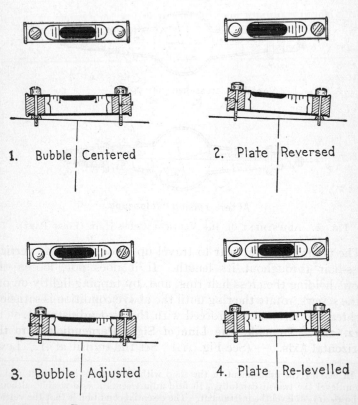

1. Bubble Centered

2. Plate Reversed

3. Bubble Adjusted

4. Plate Re-levelled

FIG. 29a. ADJUSTMENT OF PLATE BUBBLES.

screws on the bubble tube until the bubble moves half-way back
to the center as nearly as this can be estimated.   Each bubble
must be adjusted independently.   The adjustment should be
tested again by re-leveling and reversing as before, and the process continued until the bubbles remain in the center when reversed.   When both levels are adjusted the bubbles should remain
in the centers during an entire revolution about the vertical axis.

71. ADJUSTMENT OF THE CROSS-HAIRS. — 1st.   **To put the
Vertical Cross-Hair in a Plane Perpendicular to the Horizontal
Axis.** — Sight the vertical hair on some well-defined point, and,
leaving both plates clamped, rotate the telescope slightly about
the horizontal axis (see Fig. 30).

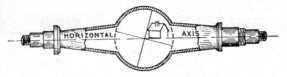

Vertical cross-hair on point

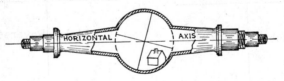

After raising telescope

FIG. 30.   ADJUSTMENT OF THE VERTICAL CROSS-HAIR (FIRST PART).

The point should appear to travel up or down on the vertical
cross-hair throughout its length.   If it does not, loosen the
screws holding the cross-hair ring, and, by tapping lightly on one
of the screws, rotate the ring until the above condition is satisfied.
Tighten the screws and proceed with the next adjustment.

**72. 2nd.   To make the Line of Sight Perpendicular to the
Horizontal Axis.*** — (See Fig. 31.)   Set the transit at *A*.   Level

---

* In making the adjustment in the shop with collimators instrument makers
seldom level the transit carefully.   In field adjustments it is desirable, although
not necessary, to level the instrument.   The essential condition is that the vertical
axis shall not alter its position.

up, clamp both plates, and sight accurately on B which is approximately at the same level as A. Reverse the telescope and set C in line with the vertical cross-hair. B, A, and C should be in a straight line. To test this, turn the instrument about the **vertical** axis until B is again sighted. Clamp the plate, reverse the telescope, and observe if point C is in line.

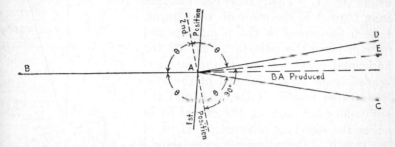

FIG. 31. ADJUSTMENT OF THE VERTICAL CROSS-HAIR (SECOND PART).

If not, set point D in line with the cross-hair just to one side of point C; then the cross-hair ring must be moved until the vertical hair appears to have moved to point E, which is set at **one-fourth** the distance from D toward C, since, in this case, a **double reversal** has been made.

The cross-hair ring is moved by loosening the screw on one side of the telescope tube and tightening the opposite screw. If D falls to the **left** of C then the cross-hair ring should be moved to the **left;** but if the transit has an erecting eyepiece the cross-hair will **appear** to move to the **right** when viewed through the telescope. If the transit has an inverting eyepiece the cross-hair appears to move in the same direction in which the cross-hair is actually moved.

The process of reversal should be repeated until no further adjustment is required. When finally adjusted, the screws should hold the ring firmly but without straining it.

73. ADJUSTMENT OF THE STANDARDS. — To make the Horizontal Axis of the Telescope Perpendicular to the Vertical Axis of the Instrument. — (See Fig. 32.) Set up the transit and sight the vertical cross-hair on a high point A, such as the top of a church steeple. Lower the telescope and set a point B in line, on the same level as the telescope. Reverse the telescope, turn the instrument about its vertical axis, and sight on B. Raise the telescope until the point A is visible and see if the cross-hair comes on A. If not, note point C in line and at same height as A. Then half the distance from C to A is the error of adjustment. Loosen the screws in the pivot cap and raise or lower the adjustable end of the horizontal axis by means of the capstan-headed screw under the end of the axis. Repeat the test until the high and the low points are both on the cross-hair in either the direct or reversed positions of the transit. The adjusting screw should be brought into position by a right-hand turn, otherwise the block on which the horizontal axis rests may stick and not follow the screw. The cap screws should then be tightened just enough to avoid looseness of the bearing.

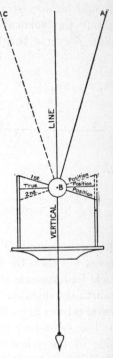

FIG. 32. ADJUSTMENT OF THE STANDARDS.

74. Adjustment of the Telescope Bubble. — This is adjusted by the " *peg* " *method*, or *direct method*, as explained in Art. 128, p. 99. After the " peg " test has been completed the true difference in elevation between the two turning points becomes known. Knowing the height of the transit above one of the turning points, and the true difference in elevation, a rod reading (at the other turning point) is then computed to give a point at the same elevation as the center of the instrument. This establishes a true horizontal line through the center of the instrument. After the telescope has been inclined (by means of the tangent screw) so that the horizontal hair is set at the computed reading, the bubble is brought to its zero position on the scale by means of the adjusting screw on the level case.

Adjusting the bubble will throw out the adjustment of the vernier of the vertical arc; this necessitates a readjustment of the vernier. If the error is but slight this may be avoided by moving the cross-hairs instead of the bubble. That is, center the bubble, and then move the upper and lower adjusting screws of the diaphragm until the horizontal hair shows the proper reading on the rod. It is not advisable to move the cross-hair ring very far, however, as it will then be out of the line of motion of the objective slide and an error will be introduced when very short sights are taken.

75. Adjustment of the Auxiliary Level on the Vernier of the Vertical Arc. — (See Art. 67, p. 62.) **To adjust the Level so that it is in the Center of the Tube when the Line of Sight is Level and the Vernier reads 0°.** — When there is no level attached to the telescope the auxiliary level is adjusted by the " peg method " (Art. 128, p. 99). The bubble is first brought to the center of the tube by means of its tangent screw. Then the telescope is moved until the vernier of the vertical arc reads 0°. The instrument is then in condition to be used as a leveling instrument and is adjusted by the " peg method."

If the telescope is provided with an attached level the auxiliary level could be adjusted by comparing it with the telescope level as follows. Level the telescope by means of its attached level, make the vernier read 0° by means of the tangent screw of the vernier, and then bring the bubble of the auxiliary level to the center by means of its adjusting screws.

76. Adjustment of the Vernier of the Vertical Arc or Circle. — **To make the Vernier read 0° when the Telescope Bubble is in the Center of Its Tube.** — Level the instrument first by means of the plate levels, and then by means of the long bubble on the telescope, so that it will remain central when the transit is revolved. Adjust the distance between the vernier and the circle so that the 30' lines coincide with the circle divisions. To make the vernier zero coincide with the circle zero loosen the screws holding the circle or arc and, by tapping the spokes lightly, perfect this adjustment. Then tighten the screws.

77. Adjustment of the Objective Slide. — **To make the Objective Slide move Parallel to the Line of Sight.** — If the tube holding the objective is adjustable it must be placed so that the direction of the line of sight will not be disturbed when the telescope is focused. The adjustment may be made as follows. Adjust the line of sight as in Art. 72, using very distant points. This will require the objective to be drawn in nearly as far as it will go and hence the position of the objective will be changed but little by any subsequent lateral adjustment of the tube. Next repeat the test for the adjustment of the line of sight by using two points which are very near the instrument, that is, about as near as the telescope can be focused. In sighting on these points the objective must be run cut and any error in its adjustment will change the direction of the line of sight so that it is no longer perpendicular to the horizontal axis of the instrument. If the instrument fails to stand this test the objective slide does not move parallel to the line of sight. The adjustment is made by moving the adjustment screws of the objective slide so as apparently to increase the error, making, by estimation, one-quarter the correction required. The adjustment of the line of sight should be tested again on two distant points and the cross-hairs moved if the second adjustment appears to have disturbed the first. This adjusts for the vertical hair.

To adjust the horizontal hair first carry out the peg adjustment as described in Art. 128. Then set the transit so that it is near one point and far from the other, so that there will be a large change of focus. Sight the horizontal hair on a division of the rod when held at the distant point; then read the rod when held on the near point. Invert the telescope and repeat the operation, setting the horizontal hair on the same division at the distant point. If the reading on the near point does not agree with that obtained before it indicates that the run of the objective is not in line with the horizontal hair; this must be corrected by moving the inner end of the objective slide up or down until the telescope will stand this test.

If the objective slide is not adjustable then this adjustment must be made by moving the cross-hairs until they are in the line of motion of the optical center of the objective. This adjustment cannot be made with the vertical hair because this would throw the line of sight off the perpendicular to the horizontal rotation axis. The horizontal hair may be moved up or down, however, until it is in the line of motion of the optical center. To test this, sight on a distant point and then set a point in line with it as close to the transit as it can be focused. Invert the telescope and repeat the test. If the second (near) point does not coincide with the first (near) point the horizontal cross-hair should be moved in that direction which appears to increase the error. It will require several trials to perfect this adjustment. After the horizontal hair is in the correct position the telescope level must be made parallel to the line of sight by moving the screws on the level case, not the cross-hair ring. This adjustment will seldom have to be made, but if the telescope has been taken apart for cleaning or for emergency repairs, or if it has met with an accident, this test should be made.

78. SHOP ADJUSTMENTS. — The adjustment of the objective slide and other adjustments such as centering the eyepiece tube and centering the circles are usually made by the instrument maker.

79. HOW TO ELIMINATE THE EFFECT OF ERRORS OF ADJUSTMENT IN THE TRANSIT. — Errors of adjustment in the plate bubble may be avoided by leveling up and reversing as when adjusting. Then, instead of altering the adjustment, simply move the bubble half-way back by means of the **leveling screws.** This makes the vertical axis truly vertical. Then the bubbles should remain in the same parts of their respective tubes as the instrument revolves about its vertical axis.

Errors of the line of sight and errors of the horizontal axis are eliminated by using the instrument with the telescope in the direct and then in the reversed position and taking the mean of the results whether the work is measuring angles or running straight lines.

Errors of eccentricity of the circle are completely eliminated by reading the two opposite verniers and taking the mean.

Errors of graduation of the circle are nearly eliminated by reading the angle in different parts of the circle or by measuring the angle by repetition.

80. Care of Instruments. — A delicate instrument like the transit requires constant care in order that the various parts may not become loose or strained. Care should be taken that the tripod legs do not move too freely, and that the metal shoes on the feet of the tripod do not become loose. The transit should be securely screwed to the tripod. In caring for the lenses a camel's-hair brush should be used for dusting them and chamois or soft linen with alcohol for cleaning them. The objective should not be unscrewed except when absolutely necessary, and when replaced it should be screwed in to the reference mark on the barrel of the telescope. Grease should never be used on exposed parts of an instrument, as it collects dust. Care should be taken not to strain the adjusting screws in making adjustments. The instrument should be protected as much as possible from the sun, rain and dust. If the instrument is carried in the box it is less likely to get out of adjustment than when carried on the shoulder, but the former is often inconvenient. It is customary in traveling by automobile or rail to carry the transit in its box. While being carried on the shoulder the lower clamp should be left unclamped, or clamped lightly, so that if the instrument strikes against anything, some parts can give easily and save the instrument from a severe shock. When the transit is being carried through a building it is good practice to keep the head of the transit forward in full view and the feet of the tripod almost touching the floor. In this manner the transitman may be sure that the head does not strike anything and that the tripod is not likely to break a window or strike a person in the building. When the transit is in use, be careful not to clamp it too hard, but clamp it firmly enough to insure a positive working of the tangent screws and so that no slipping can occur. Do not allow the hands to touch the vertical circle or vernier because the silver will tarnish quickly and make it difficult to read the scales.

In oiling an instrument use only the best refined watch oil. Under no circumstances should fine emery cloth or even the finest abrasive be used. The exposed vertical arc readily becomes tarnished and consequently has to be cleaned frequently. Clean it by applying watch oil; let it stand for a day, then wipe it dry with a fine linen cloth but do not rub the edges of the arc or vernier.

81. COMMON SOURCES OF ERROR IN TRANSIT WORK. —

1. Nonadjustment, eccentricity of circle, and errors of graduation.

2. Changes due to temperature and wind.

3. Uneven settling of tripod.

4. Poor focusing (parallax).

5. Inaccurate setting over point.

6. Irregular refraction of atmosphere.

82. COMMON MISTAKES IN TRANSIT WORK. —

1. Reading in the wrong direction from the index on a double vernier.

2. Reading the vernier opposite the one which was set.

3. Reading the circle wrongly, e.g., reading 59° for 61°. If the angle is nearly 90°, reading the wrong side of the 90° point, e.g., 88° for 92°.

4. Using the wrong tangent screw.

5. Neglecting to add 30' to a reading; such as 42° 16' for 42° 46'.

6. Where circle is graduated in both directions from 0° to 360°, reading wrong circle scale near 180°.

PROBLEMS

1. Is it necessary that the adjustments of the transit should be made in the order given in this chapter? Give your reasons.

2. A transit is sighting toward B from a point A. In setting up the transit at A it was carelessly set 0.01 ft. directly to one side of A, as at A'. What would be the resulting error, i.e., the difference in direction (in seconds) between AB and $A'B$ (1) when $AB = 40$ ft., (2) when $AB = 1000$ ft.?

3. An angle of 90° is laid off with a "one minute" transit, and the angle then determined by six repetitions, the final reading being $179° 58' + 360°$. The point sighted is 185 ft. from the transit. Compute the offset to be laid off in order to correct the first angle. Express the result in feet and also in inches.

4. An angle measured with a transit is $10° 15' 40''$. The telescope of a leveling instrument is placed in front of the transit (with its objective toward the transit) and the angle again measured and found to be $0° 18' 20''$. What is the magnifying power of this level telescope?

5. The line of sight of a transit is one minute to the right of its true position. If the cross-hair is sighted at a high point and then the telescope lowered and a point set in line with the cross-hair, what is the angular error in the position (bearing) of the last point if the vertical angle to the first point is 60° and to the second 0°?

6. If a transit is set up so that the horizontal axis is inclined one minute with the true horizontal direction, what will be the angular error in sighting on a point on a hill, vertical angle 20°, and then setting a point in line and on the same level as the instrument?

7. Design a vernier to read to 30″ for a circle divided into 15′ spaces.

8. Design a vernier to read to 5′ when the circle is divided into degrees.

9. Example of Triangulation Notes.

| Station | | High Head | | | | | Date, June 16, 1937 |
| Inst. B & B No. 1441 | | | | | | | Observer, J. B. Snow. |

Sta.	Time	Tel.	Rep.	Ver. A			B	Remarks
				°	′	″	″	
Gardner	10:30			0	00	00	10	
to	A.M.							
Chase			I	40	16	25		
		D	6	241	38	10	20	

Compute the mean angle.

10. In the transit having a graduated circle five inches in diameter, the centers do not coincide by 0.001 of an inch.

(a) What is the maximum error in seconds (on one vernier) due to this eccentricity?

(b) What would be the maximum error in a circle seven inches in diameter?

11. A line AU is to be laid out about 6000 feet long in 300-ft. intervals. At B, the end of the first 300-ft. interval, the transit is set up, sighted on A with telescope direct, and the telescope then plunged to give line for setting point C, 300 feet in advance of B. In exactly the same manner the entire line is laid out, the instrument being set up at every 300-ft. point. Stations A, B, C, etc., are approximately at the same elevation. The transit has a collimation error of 1′ 30″ to the right in a direct position.

(a) Compute the angular divergence between the last 300-ft. portion (TU) of the line and the first 300-ft. portion (AB).

(b) Compute the right-angle offset between the true prolongation of AB and the end of line at U (to 0.1 ft.).

(c) Had the backsight been taken with the telescope in direct position from Sta. B, D, F, etc. (alternate stations) and taken with the telescope inverted when backsighting from C, E, G, etc. (alternate stations), what would then be the right-angle offset between the true prolongation of AB and the end of line at U (to 0.1 ft.)?

CHAPTER IV

MEASUREMENT OF DIFFERENCE OF ELEVATION

93. LEVEL SURFACE. — A level surface is a **curved** surface which at every point is perpendicular to the direction of gravity at that point, such, for example, as the surface of still water. Any line of sight which is perpendicular to the direction of gravity at a given point is therefore tangent to the level surface at that point and is called a *horizontal line*.

94. The Spirit Level. — In nearly all instruments the direction of gravity is determined by means of either a plumb-line or a spirit level. A spirit level is a glass tube, the inside of which is ground to a circular curve longitudinally, and nearly filled with a liquid such as alcohol or ether, leaving enough space to form a bubble. The grinding is usually done only on the inside upper surface of the tube. The radius of the curve varies according to the use which is to be made of the level; a very short radius makes a slow moving bubble while a long radius makes a

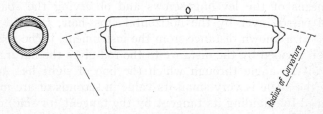

FIG. 33. LEVEL VIAL.

very sensitive bubble. It is important that the curve should be exactly circular so that equal distances on the tube subtend equal angles at the center of curvature. The level is provided with a scale of equal parts, which may be either a metallic scale attached to the brass case holding the glass bubble tube, or it may consist of lines etched on the glass itself. A point near the middle of the tube is selected as the *zero-point* and the graduations

73

are considered as numbered both ways from that point. The straight line tangent to the curve at the zero-point of the scale is called the *axis of the bubble*. The position of the bubble in the tube is determined by noting the positions of both ends. The

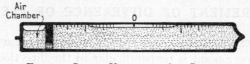

FIG. 34. LEVEL VIAL WITH AIR CHAMBER.

bubble will change its length with changes in temperature, consequently the reading of one end is not sufficient to determine the position of the bubble. On account of the action of gravity on the liquid the bubble will always move toward the higher end of the tube; hence, when the bubble is **central** the axis of the tube is **horizontal.**

95. Angular Value of One Division of the Level Tube. — The angular value of one division of a level tube is the angle, usually expressed in seconds, through which the axis of the tube must be tilted to cause the bubble to move over the length of one division on the scale. The simplest way of finding this in the field consists in moving the bubble over several divisions on the scale by means of the leveling screws and observing the space on a rod passed over by the horizontal cross-hair, the rod being placed at a known distance from the instrument. The space on the rod divided by the distance to the rod gives the natural tangent of the angle through which the line of sight has moved. Since the angle is very small its value in seconds of arc may be obtained by dividing its tangent by the tangent (or sine) of one second,* (log tan $1'' = 4.6855749 - 10$). Dividing the angle just found by the number of divisions of the scale passed over by the bubble in the experiment gives the average number of seconds corresponding to a single division.

In a properly constructed leveling instrument the value of one division of the level scale should have a definite relation to the

---

* Instead of dividing by tan $1''$ (= arc $1''$ = sin $1''$) it is often more convenient to multiply by 206 264.8, which is the reciprocal of arc $1''$, and therefore the number of seconds in one radian.

magnifying power of the telescope. The smallest angular movement that can be shown by the level bubble should correspond to the smallest movement of the cross-hairs that can be detected by means of the telescope.

THE LEVEL

96. The instruments chiefly used for the direct determination of differences of elevation are known as the *Wye Level*, the *Dumpy Level*, and the *Hand Level*. The *Geodetic Level* differs in its details from the others but does not really constitute a different type; it is essentially a wye level or a dumpy level, according to the principle of its construction. The engineer's transit, which has the long level attached to the telescope, is frequently used for direct leveling. All of these instruments are so constructed that the **line of sight is horizontal when the bubble of the attached spirit level is in the middle of its tube.**

97. THE WYE LEVEL. — In the wye level (Figs. 35 and 36) the spirit level is attached to the telescope tube which rests in two Y-shaped bearings from which it derives its name. Those parts of the telescope which bear

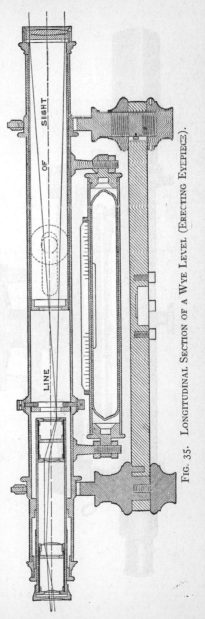

FIG. 35. LONGITUDINAL SECTION OF A WYE LEVEL (ERECTING EYEPIECE).

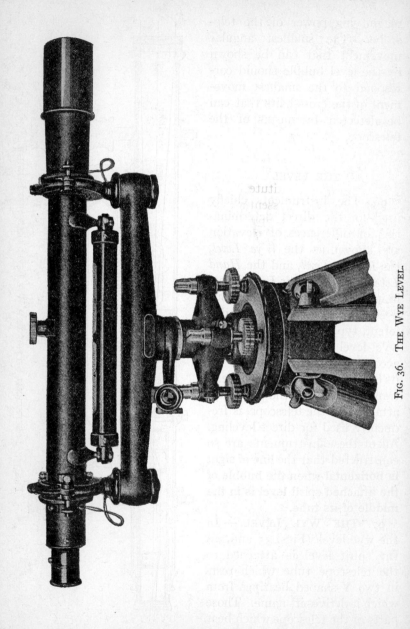

FIG. 36.   THE WYE LEVEL.

on the wyes are made cylindrical and are called *collars*, *rings*, or *pivots*. The telescope is held in the wyes by means of two *clips*, or *stirrups*. The level is attached to the telescope by means of screws which allow vertical and lateral adjustments. The two wye supports are secured, by means of adjusting screws, to a horizontal bar which is attached rigidly at right angles to a spindle, or vertical axis, similar to that of a transit. The instrument is provided with leveling screws, clamp, and tangent screw, but has no shifting head or plumb-line attachment. The whole upper portion of the instrument is screwed to a tripod. The telescope can be lifted out of its supports, turned end for end and replaced, each collar then resting in the opposite wye.

98. THE DUMPY LEVEL. — In the dumpy level (Fig. 37) the telescope, the vertical supports, the horizontal bar and the vertical spindle are all made in one casting or else the parts are fastened together rigidly. The spirit level is fastened to the horizontal bar and can be adjusted in the vertical plane; there is no other adjustable part except the cross-hair ring.

99. Comparison of Wye and Dumpy Levels. — Obviously the adjustment of the level in which the line of sight is made parallel to the axis of the bubble is all-important because this bubble axis is **always horizontal when the bubble is central.** The wye level has long been favored because, to perform this adjustment, all that is required is to reverse the telescope in the wyes, much as one turns an ordinary carpenter's level end for end to determine if the axis of its bubble is parallel to the bottom of the level frame. While this feature of the wye level is convenient when adjusting the instrument in the field it is based on the assumption that both pivots are *circular* and of *exactly the same diameter*, which may or may not be true. For, even if the pivots are perfect when new, they soon wear, and perhaps unevenly, and consequently the method of adjusting the wye level by reversing the telescope in the wyes will fail and the advantage therefore of the wye construction is lost. In that event the line of sight must be made parallel to the axis of the bubble by what is known as the " *peg* " *adjustment* or *direct* method. (See Art. 128, p. 99.)

The dumpy level is much more rigidly constructed than the wye level and will stand much rougher treatment; it has very

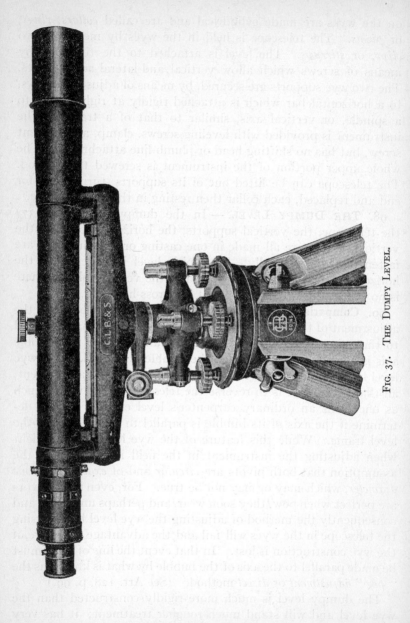

FIG. 37.   THE DUMPY LEVEL.

few movable parts, and consequently it does not easily get out of adjustment even when subjected to rough usage. Furthermore, the results of the geodetic leveling of the U. S. Coast and Geodetic Survey,* the U. S. Geological Survey, and others, indicate clearly the superiority of the dumpy form of level.

100. PRECISE TILTING LEVEL. — While it is possible to run levels of fairly high precision with the dumpy or wye level, there are certain disadvantages in using these instruments for

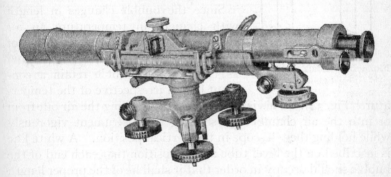

FIG. 37a. PRECISE TILTING LEVEL.
(Courtesy, C. L. Berger & Sons)

such work. With the ordinary wye or dumpy level it is not convenient for the observer to view the level bubble from the observing position and should the bubble be not central, he must shift from the observing position in order to center it. In changing his position the instrument man not only loses time but may also disturb the elevation of the instrument especially when leveling over marshes, sandy or frozen ground.

The Precise Tilting Level shown in Fig. 37a is of the dumpy type, usually supported on a base by means of three leveling screws. A spirit level equipped with an air chamber is mounted by brackets on the left side of and close to the telescope; thus it is alongside of the line of collimation. By means of a prismatic reading device attached above and to the left of the level

---

* See Special Publication 129, serial 376, U. S. Coast & Geodetic Survey, on "Geodetic Level and Rod," 13 pages.

vial casing, the level bubble is made to appear to be split longitudinally and also transversely so that it looks like Fig. 37b. The left half of Fig. 37b shows half of one end of the bubble and the right half shows half of the other end of the bubble, hence when the bubble is in the central position the two half-ends will appear to coincide. Without changing his position the observer can view the position of the bubble image with his left eye and the rod and cross-hairs with his right.

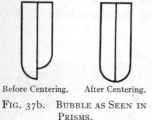

Before Centering.   After Centering.

FIG. 37b. BUBBLE AS SEEN IN PRISMS.

Since the bubble changes in length with changes in temperature an air chamber is introduced at one end of the bubble which can be so regulated as to make the bubble retain a constant length irrespective of the temperature (Fig. 34). This is accomplished by letting the air out from or into the air chamber by shaking the instrument vigorously while holding the telescope in the vertical position. A white line is inscribed on the level tube at the position that each end of the bubble should occupy in order that it shall be of the proper length to be seen reflected in the prismatic device.

By means of a micrometer screw bearing at a point directly beneath the eyepiece and connected by an arm of the cradle supporting the telescope, the telescope may be raised and lowered (tilted) about a horizontal axis directly above the vertical axis, thus insuring no change of the height of the telescope. To prevent undue wear, a cam is provided for lifting the telescope off the micrometer screw head when observations are not being taken. The micrometer screw is graduated for setting the telescope at any desired slight inclination from the level position in setting grade points on a slope. (See Art. 262, p. 309.)

The instrument is first made approximately level by the use of a small circular (or universal) level located to the right of the telescope. The telescope is then pointed at the rod and the ends of the level bubble are brought into coincidence in the prism by rotating the micrometer screw. At the moment the bubble ends are in coincidence all three hairs are read, the mean giving the final rod reading. It is important not to disturb the leveling screws between observations at a given set-up, since, with the usual three-leveling-screw base, motion of any one screw raises or lowers the height of the telescope.

Another form of precise tilting level is equipped with a mirror which is so placed that from the observing position the entire bubble may be seen with the left eye while the rod and cross-hairs are viewed with the right eye.

While these instruments are so designed as to be effective for most precise leveling yet their use is mostly on ordinary engineering work that requires rapidly obtaining a precision superior to that usually obtained with the ordinary dumpy or wye level.

100a. European Levels. — A number of European levels, the designs of which embody several unique features, mainly optical, have recently been used to some extent in the United States and Canada. These levels are mostly of the wye type; they are very small (telescope length is from 6 to 9 inches) and are equipped with prismatic devices for viewing the level bubble at the same instant that the readings are taken. They usually have three leveling screws on the base.

The level case (bubble) is usually placed at one side of the telescope and, unlike ordinary levels, the glass of the level vial has two curved (ground) surfaces, one at the upper and the other at the lower surface of the tube. Like the ordinary wye level, the telescope may be rotated 180° about its longitudinal axis so that the bubble may be centered either on the upper or on the lower bubble tube scale. If a sight is taken with the telescope normal and then another reading is taken with the telescope reversed (about the longitudinal axis), the bubble being centered at the instant when the sights are taken, the mean result is a reading referred to the mean axis of the level vial and is free from any error in the position of the cross-hairs, because if the first line of sight is inclined downward then the second sight is inclined upward by the same amount.

One of these instruments (Fig. 37c) is equipped with a tilting-screw under the eyepiece of the telescope for nice centering of the bubble after an approximate level position has been obtained through the use of a small circular level. The bubble is viewed through prisms so arranged that the two ends of the bubble appear to coincide only when the bubble is in the central position (Fig. 37b). This not only simplifies the reading but also increases the precision since the apparent motion of the bubble is doubled optically; in this process the observer does not have to step from his position.

Another feature of this type of level is a tilting glass plate placed in front of the objective of the level telescope; the sur-

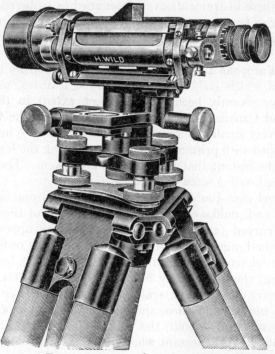

FIG. 37c. LEVEL ($\frac{4}{11}$ ACTUAL SIZE).

faces of this plate are exact planes and are parallel. By inclining this plate from the vertical, the image of the graduation on the level rod may be made to move up or down until the image of a graduation is exactly at the cross-hair. The amount of this vertical displacement of the line of sight which is read on a drum scale at the eyepiece, when applied to the reading of the graduation which has been displaced, results in a reading of the fraction of a division by which the cross-hair was originally away from the division displaced.

Another type of European level is equipped with two objectives, one at each end of the tube. The eyepiece is removable and may be placed before either one of the objectives; then the objective nearer the eyepiece will have no effect on the rays of light coming through the other objective. On the surfaces of these objectives are ruled lines which serve as cross-hairs. These lines are magnified by the eyepiece and are therefore only visible on the objective that is directly in front of the eyepiece; the lines on the far objective are so out of focus that they are not seen. By observing with the eyepiece first at one end of the telescope and then at the other end the errors of adjustment of cross-hair and level are eliminated completely at a single set-up of the instrument, because in principle the process eliminates all errors corrected by the " peg " adjustment. (See Art. 128, p. 99.)

They are equipped with the interior system of focusing. While these levels are light and can be handled rapidly, they present the same disadvantage as European transits in that having somewhat complicated optical devices, emergency repairs and adjustments cannot be made by the surveyor in the field.

100b. The precision specified by the Federal Board of Surveys and Maps for different classes of leveling are

1st Order — Error of closure of circuit in feet	= $0.017 \sqrt{\text{miles}}$
2nd " — " " "	= $0.035 \sqrt{\text{miles}}$
3rd " — " " "	= $0.05 \sqrt{\text{miles}}$

First order precision should be expected in geodetic and in city control leveling; third order would be such as could be readily obtained with the ordinary dumpy or wye level.

101. THE LOCKE HAND LEVEL. — The hand level has no telescope, but is simply a metal tube with plain glass covers at the ends and a spirit level on top (Fig. 38). When looking through the tube one sees the bubble and the cross-wire (reflected in a prism) in the left half and the landscape in the right half of the field of view. In order that the eye may see the bubble and the landscape simultaneously a half lens is placed in the sliding tube to permit focusing on the bubble. The cross-wire which defines the level line may be adjusted by means of two opposing screws. The instrument is held at the eye and the farther end is raised or lowered until the bubble is in the center of the tube.

FIG. 38. THE LOCKE HAND LEVEL.

At this instant a point on the ground in line with the horizontal wire is noted. In this way approximate levels may be obtained.

LEVELING RODS

According to their construction rods are either *Self-reading* or *Target* rods, or a combination of the two. Self-reading rods are those which can be read directly from the instrument by the levelman whereas target rods can be read only by the rodman. The commonest forms of leveling rods are known as the *Boston*, the *New York*, and the *Philadelphia* rods. (See Fig. 39.)

102. BOSTON ROD. — The Boston rod (Fig. 39) is a target rod of well seasoned wood about $6\frac{1}{2}$ ft. long, made in two strips, one of which slides in a groove in the other. A target is fastened rigidly to one of these strips about 0.3 ft. from one end. Clamps are provided for holding the two parts in any desired position. There is a scale on each side of the rod, one starting from either end, graduated to hundredths of a foot and each having a vernier placed at about the height of the eye and reading to thousandths of a foot. When the rod-reading is less than 5.8 ft. the rod is first placed on the ground with the target near the bottom. Then the strip carrying the target is raised to the proper height while the bottom of the other strip rests on the ground, as shown in Fig. 39. For readings over 5.8 ft. the rod is turned end-for-end so that the target is at the top and can be moved from 5.8 to 11.4 ft., the limit of readings on the rod. The terms " *short rod* " and " *long rod* " are used to distinguish these two positions.

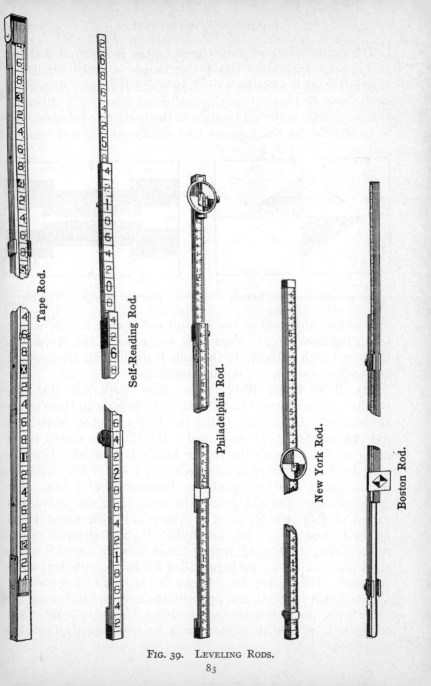

FIG. 39. LEVELING RODS.

Tape Rod.

Self-Reading Rod.

Philadelphia Rod.

New York Rod.

Boston Rod.

83

The common form of target used on the Boston rod is shown in Fig. 40. Instead of this target one of a design similar to that in Fig. 41 is sometimes used, in which the white strip in the center may be bisected by the horizontal cross-hair. Bisection is more precise under all conditions than setting on a single line or on the division line between two surfaces of different color.

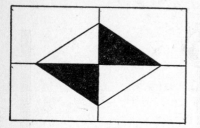
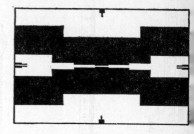

Fig. 40. Boston Rod Target.   Fig. 41. Bisection Target.

A serious objection to the Boston rod is that in reversing it (changing from long to short rod) any error in the position of the target with reference to the scale is doubled by the reversal, and such an error is not readily eliminated.

103. NEW YORK ROD. — The New York rod (Fig. 39) consists of two strips of wood, arranged similarly to those of the Boston rod. Unlike the latter the target on the New York rod is **movable.** For " short rod " the target is moved up or down on the rod until the proper height is reached. The face of the rod is graduated to hundredths of a foot. The vernier is on the target itself and reads to thousandths of a foot. The graduations on the rod cannot be read from the instrument except at short distances. For " long rod " the target is set at the highest graduation, usually 6.5 ft., and clamped to one of the sliding strips which is then raised until the target is in the right position. A clamp is provided for holding the two strips together. The reading for " long rod " is found on the side of the strip that is raised, and opposite the vernier which is on the other strip, the scale readings increasing downward. When the " long rod " is used the scale cannot be read directly from the instrument.

104. PHILADELPHIA ROD. — This rod has the graduations plainly painted on its face so that it can be used as a self-reading rod at long distances (Fig. 39). The Philadelphia rod is more extensively used than any other form. It has a target which in some rods is read to 0.001 ft. directly by means of a vernier, and in others is read directly to half-hundredths by means of a scale. The rod is extended (for "long rod") in the same manner as the New York rod, and can then be read by means of a scale on the back. When the rod is fully extended the graduations on the front face are continuous and readings up to 12 ft. or 13 ft. can be made directly by the levelman. On some rods the graduations are placed at every tenth of a foot, or at every half tenth, but the usual pattern is that having every hundredth of a foot marked; in this pattern the lines are 0.01 ft. wide, the upper edges of the black lines being the even numbered hundredths. The Philadelphia rod is also made in one piece either 12 ft. or 10 ft. long and without a target. This rod is very convenient except where it is necessary to carry it on conveyances; and it has the advantage that no error can be introduced through a loose joint at the middle, which is one of the disadvantages of the jointed pattern. The rigidity of this rod is increased by having a second strip of wood attached to the back so that its section is T shaped.

Philadelphia jointed rods are also made in very short lengths for use in mines and tunnels; some prefer them to the regular size for convenience in carrying in vehicles.

105. SPECIAL SELF-READING RODS. — There are a large number of self-reading rods of special design. The usual difference between them is in the design of the figures and markings on the face of the rods. One of the commonest types, shown in Fig. 39, is similar to the Philadelphia rod except that it has no target and is not graduated closer than tenths. The figures on the face of the rod are made of definite height (0.06 or 0.08 ft.) and of definite thickness (0.01 or 0.02 ft.) so that it is easy for the levelman to estimate the readings to hundredths of a foot. These rods are usually constructed so that they can be extended for "long rod" readings.

106. Tape Rod. — The tape rod (Fig. 39) is on a self-reading rod of radically different design from the Philadelphia rod. It is a wooden rod made in one piece with a metal roller set into it near each end. Passing over these rollers is a continuous steel band 20 ft. long and 0.1 ft. wide, on the outside of which for its entire length is painted a scale graduated to feet, tenths, and half-tenths, with the details of the numbers so designed that readings can be made readily to the nearest 0.01 ft. Unlike the other rods mentioned the scale reads **downward** on the face of the rod instead of upward. It is provided with a clamp so that the metal band, or tape, can be set at any desired reading and held firmly in that position. The use of this rod is limited to certain kinds of work, its advantage being the time saved in calculations as explained in Art. 254, p. 302.

106a. Flexible or Pocket Leveling Rod. — This consists of a specially prepared strip of oilcloth or canvas graduated the same as any other self-reading rod. When in use it may be tacked to a light board of convenient size. For transportation it may be rolled up and packed in a very small space. These rods are not so reliable as wooden rods because they are subject to stretching and shrinkage, but they are so convenient to transport that where accuracy is not of primary importance they have a decided advantage over the heavy rods for work requiring much traveling.

107. Geodetic Level Rod. — The rods used by the U. S. Coast and Geodetic Survey and the U. S. Geological Survey are of the non-extensible pattern. Those used by the Coast and Geodetic Survey are about 3.3 m. long and are made of flat pieces of wood on which are painted the meter and decimeter graduations, and to which are attached strips of invar on which are painted the centimeter divisions. The Geological Survey rod is graduated in yards and hundredths; otherwise it is similar to the Coast Survey rod. Each rod is provided with a spirit level for plumbing, and with a centigrade thermometer. The foot of the rod consists of a metal piece, with a flat end, connected rigidly (at the top) with the invar strip.

108. Advantages of the Self-Reading Rod. — While the advantage in the **speed** with which leveling can be accomplished by use of the self-reading rod is well understood, it is also true although not always recognized, that very **accurate** results can be obtained. For any single reading the error may be larger than with the target rod, but the errors of estimating fractional parts are **compensating,** so that in the long run the results are found to be very accurate. Geodetic leveling carried on by the U. S. Coast and Geodetic Survey and by European surveys has demonstrated the superiority of such rods. The self-reading rod has largely superseded the target rod in engineering work.

The sensitiveness of the bubble used on the ordinary leveling instrument is about 20″ of angle for a division one-tenth of an inch long on the level scale. This corresponds to an interval on the rod of about 0.01 ft. per 100 ft. or, say, about 0.02 ft. to 0.03 ft. for ordinary sights. It is probably fair to assume that, with the ordinary means of leveling, the bubble cannot be centered closer than a tenth of a scale division, and considering the instability of the instrument, seldom is centered closer than a fifth of a division at the instant of sighting. These errors correspond to errors of rod-reading of about 0.002 and 0.004 respectively, for a distance of 200 ft. At a distance of 200 ft. the 0.01 ft. division of the Philadelphia rod can be read to the *nearest* 0.005 without difficulty if the magnifying power of the telescope is consistent with the sensitiveness of the bubble. A rod-reading to 0.005 ft. is therefore about as fine as the sensitiveness of the bubble permits; and any reading of the target vernier smaller than 0.005 (on long sights) has the appearance of accuracy which does not really exist.

It would seem therefore that there is no advantage whatever in the target rod over a self-reading rod as regards accuracy. This statement, however, should not be construed as meaning that the target has no place in leveling. On very long sights, where the scale divisions of the rod are difficult to see, the target is almost indispensable. In thick woods where it is difficult to identify the graduations the use of the target will remove all uncertainty. In construction work, where the same rod-reading is to be used repeatedly (setting batter boards, for example) the target is a time saver. In this connection the use of the target lessens the liability to make mistakes.

109. Attachments to the Rod for Plumbing. — In accurate work it will be convenient to use some device for making the rod plumb. Spirit levels attached to brass " angles " which may be secured to a corner of the rod are very convenient. Two patterns are shown in Fig. 42. In some rods, such as those used for precise leveling, the levels are set permanently into the rod itself.

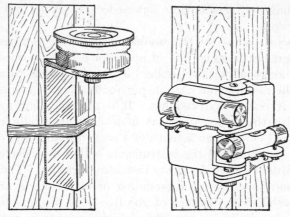

FIG. 42.   ROD LEVELS.

110. Errors in Length of Rod. — Changes of temperature do not affect seriously the length of the rod since the coefficient of expansion of wood is small. The effect of moisture is greater but is indeterminate. It is well known that rods vary in length, and consequently if very accurate leveling is to be done the length of the rod should be tested frequently with a steel tape. Rods which are accurate when manufactured may show errors, after a time, as great as 0.01 ft. in 12 ft. In accurate work the error of the rod should be determined and recorded, and the heights should be corrected for this error just as horizontal distances are corrected for the error of the tape.

USE OF THE LEVEL AND ROD

111. To obtain the difference in elevation between two points, hold the rod vertically at the first point and, while the instrument is level, take a rod-reading. This is the distance that the bottom of the rod is below the line of sight of the telescope. Then take a rod-reading on the second point; the difference between the two rod-readings is the difference in elevation of the two points.

112. To Level the Instrument. — Set up the instrument in such a position and at such a height that the horizontal cross-hair will strike somewhere on the rod when held on either point. Time will be saved if the habit is formed of doing nearly all of the leveling by means of the tripod legs, using the leveling screws only for slight motions of the bubble in bringing it to the middle of the tube. Turn the telescope so that it is directly over two opposite leveling screws. Bring the bubble to the center of the tube **approximately;** then turn the telescope until it is over the other pair of leveling screws and bring the bubble **exactly** to the center. Move the telescope back to the first position and level carefully, and again to the second position. Repeat until the bubble is exactly in the center in both positions. If the instrument is in adjustment and is properly leveled in both directions, then the bubble will remain in the center during an entire revolution of the telescope about the vertical axis. The instrument should seldom be clamped, but this may be necessary when a strong wind is blowing.

113. To Take a Rod-Reading. — The rodman holds the rod on the first point, taking pains to **keep it as nearly plumb as possible.** The levelman focuses the telescope on the rod, and brings the bubble to the center **while the telescope is pointing at the rod,** because leveling over both sets of screws will not make the bubble remain in the center in **all** positions unless the adjustment is perfect. If a target rod is used, the target should be set so that the horizontal cross-hair bisects it **while the bubble is in the center of the tube.** It is not sufficient to trust the bubble to remain in the center; it should be examined just before setting the target and immediately afterward, **at every reading.**

With the self-reading rod the levelman reads the feet and tenths and notes approximately the hundredths; then, **after verifying the position of the bubble,** he makes the final reading of the hundredths and half-hundredths.

If, however, the target is being used the levelman signals the
rodman to move the target up or down. When the center of the
target coincides with the horizontal cross-hair the levelman
signals or calls to the rodman " all right " and the rodman clamps
the target. Before the rodman reads the target he should
allow the levelman time to check the position of the target to be
certain that it has not slipped in clamping. The reading is then
recorded in the note-book. For readings to hundredths of a
foot it is not necessary to clamp the target or the rod; the rodman can hold the target in position or the two parts of the rod
firmly together while he reads the scale.

Most levelers prefer to have the rodman stand behind the rod,
facing the instrument, so that he can watch the levelman.
Other levelmen prefer that the rodman stand beside the rod and
plumb it at right angles to the line of sight, while the levelman
directs the rodman which way to plumb the rod so that it will
be parallel to the vertical cross-hair. **It is extremely important
that the rod be held plumb.** Vertical lines on buildings are a
great aid to the rodman in judging when his rod is plumb. If
there is no wind blowing he can often tell when the rod is plumb
by balancing it on the point. If the rodman promptly and
attentively holds the rod plumb it not only increases the accuracy
of the results but also the rapidity with which the work may be
carried on.

114. WAVING THE ROD. — Ordinarily there is no difficulty in
obtaining accurate results if the rodman follows the above
direction and has had some experience. But in some circumstances where difficulty is found in obtaining a reliable reading
when the " long rod " is used it may be plumbed in the direction
of the line of sight by **" waving the rod."** To do this the rodman
stands behind the rod and inclines it toward the instrument
not a large amount, but just sufficient to cause the reading
to increase one or two hundredths. He then **slowly** draws it
back, causing the reading to decrease to a minimum, after which
the reading increases if the rod is drawn further back. The
direct reading of the cross-hair on the scale will, of course, be
least when the rod is plumb. If the target is used, it must be
raised or lowered until there is found just one position where the

target rises as high as the line of sight (and no higher) while the rod is being waved.

The above process is slow and wastes time and therefore should not be used unless it appears necessary.

115. Signals. — While the rodman is seldom very far away from the levelman in this work still it is often convenient (in noisy city streets, for example) to use hand signals. The following are commonly used in leveling.

" *Up* " or " *Down.*" — The levelman motions to the rodman by raising his arm above his shoulder for an upward motion and dropping his arm below his waist for a downward motion. A slow motion indicates that the target should be moved a considerable amount and a quick motion indicates a short distance.

" *All Right.*" — The levelman extends both hands horizontally and moves them up and down, or, if not far away, he merely shows the palms of both hands.

" *Plumb the Rod.*" — The hand is extended vertically above the head and moved slowly in the direction it is desired to have the rod plumbed.

" *Take a Turning Point.*" — The arm is swung slowly in a circle above the head.

" *Pick up the Level.*" — When a new set-up of the level is desired the chief of party signals the levelman by extending both arms downward and outward and then raising them quickly.

Some surveyors use an improvised system of signals for communicating the rod-readings, but mistakes are liable to be made unless great care is used.

116. DIFFERENTIAL LEVELING. — Differential leveling is the name given to the process of finding the difference in elevation of any two points. In Art. 111 the simplest case of differential leveling is described. When the points are far apart, or when the difference in elevation is great, or when for any other reason the measurement cannot be completed from a single set-up of the instrument, the difference in elevation is found as follows: The instrument is set up and a rod-reading is taken on the first point; this is called a *backsight*, or *plus sight*, and is usually written *B. S.* or +*S* in the notes. Next the rod is taken to some well-defined point which will not change in elevation (such as the top of a firm rock, the top of a hydrant, or a spike in the root of a tree) and held upon it and a reading taken; this is called a *foresight,* or *minus sight,* and is written *F. S.* or −*S.* The difference between the two readings gives the difference in elevation between this new point and the first point. This second point is called a *turning point* and is written *T. P.* The level is next set up in a new position and a backsight taken on the same turning point. A new turning point further ahead is then selected and a foresight taken upon it.

This process is continued until a foresight is taken on the final point. The elevation of the last point above the first is equal to the sum of all the backsights minus the sum of all the foresights. If the result is **negative,** i.e., if the sum of the foresights is the **greater,** then the last point is **below** the first. One form of notes which may be used for this work is shown below, and the field-work is illustrated by Fig. 43.

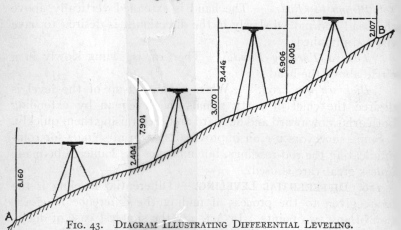

FIG. 43.   DIAGRAM ILLUSTRATING DIFFERENTIAL LEVELING.

.Point	+ S.	− S.	Remarks
A.	8.160	. . . . . .	Highest point on stone bound, S. W. cor. X and Y Sts.
T. P.	7.901	2.404	
T. P.	9.446	3.070	
T. P.	8.005	6.906	
B.	. . . .	2.107	N. E. cor. stone step No. 64 M St.
	33.512	14.487	
	14.487		
Diff.	19.025	B above A.	

117. The Proper Length of Sight. — The proper length of sight will depend upon the distance at which the rod appears distinct and steady to the levelman, upon the variations in readings taken on the same point, and also upon the degree of precision required. Under ordinary conditions the length of sight should not exceed about 300 ft. where elevations to the nearest 0.01 ft. are desired. " Boiling " of the air due to irregular refraction is frequently so troublesome that long sights cannot be taken accurately.

If the level is out of adjustment the resulting error in the rod-reading is proportional to the distance from the instrument to the rod. If the level is at equal distances from the rod the errors are equal and since it is the **difference** of the rod-readings that gives the difference in elevation, the error is eliminated from the final result if the rodman makes **the distance to the point where the foresight is taken equal to the distance to the backsight** by counting his paces as he goes from one point to the other.

118. Effect of the Earth's Curvature and of Refraction on Leveling. — Since the surface of the earth is very nearly spherical, any line on it made by the intersection of a vertical plane with the earth's surface is virtually circular. In Fig. 44 the distance

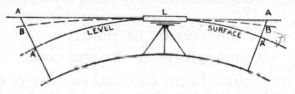

Fig. 44. Diagram Illustrating Effect of Earth's Curvature and of Refraction.

AA', from the horizontal line to the level line, varies nearly as $\overline{A'L}^2$ (see foot-note, p. 485). This is the amount by which the rod-reading is too large owing to the earth's curvature. The ray of light that enters the telescope horizontally at L, however, is that starting from B, not that from A because the ray from B is bent into a curve. The effect of the refraction of the atmosphere is to make this offset from the tangent appear to be $A'B$, which is about one-seventh part smaller than $A'A$.

This offset, corrected for refraction, is about 0.57 ft. in 1 mile and varies as the square of the distance. Corrections (in feet) for curvature and refraction are given in Table 2A for every 100 ft. of distance up to 1000 ft.

TABLE 2A

Distance in Feet.	Correction (in Feet) for Earth's Curvature and Refraction.	Distance in Feet.	Correction (in Feet) for Earth's Curvature and Refraction.
100	0.000	600	.007
200	.001	700	.010
300	.002	800	.013
400	.003	900	.017
500	.005	1000	.020

If the rod is equally distant from the instrument on the foresight and backsight the effect of curvature and refraction is eliminated from the result.

119. PRECAUTIONS IN LEVEL WORK. — Nearly all of the precautions mentioned in Art. 68, p. 62, for the transit instrument, are also applicable to the level. Care should be taken not to strike the rod on the ground after it has been clamped and before it has been read. It may cause the parts of the rod to slip, and it may also affect the elevation of the turning point.

ADJUSTMENTS OF THE LEVEL

I. ADJUSTMENTS OF THE WYE LEVEL

120. ADJUSTMENT OF THE CROSS-HAIRS. — (a) **To make the Horizontal Cross-Hair truly Horizontal when the Instrument is Leveled.** — This may be done by rotating the cross-hair ring, if the instrument is so constructed that the telescope cannot be rotated in the wyes. In many instruments the telescope can be rotated in the wyes, but only when the stirrup is raised. In some levels the telescope is always free to rotate in the wyes, while others are provided with a stop regulated by an adjusting screw, which prevents the telescope from rotating beyond a certain point.

The instrument is leveled and some point found which is covered by the horizontal cross-hair. The telescope is then turned slowly about the vertical axis so that the point appears to traverse the field of view. If the point remains on the cross-hair the adjustment is perfect. If it does not, then an adjustment must be made, the manner of doing this depending upon the

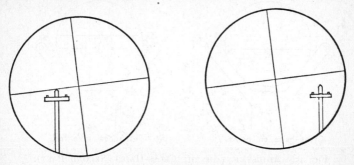

FIG. 44a. TESTING THE HORIZONTAL CROSS-HAIRS.

construction of the instrument. If the telescope cannot be rotated in the wyes the adjustment is made by rotating the diaphragm, similar to the adjustment described in Art. 71, p. 66. If the telescope has a stop-screw this must be moved until the instrument satisfies this test. If the telescope can rotate freely in the wyes it can be turned by hand until it satisfies the test. Since there is nothing to hold the telescope in this position the adjustment in the last case is likely to be disturbed at any time. Fig. 44a illustrates this test.

121. (b) When the preceding adjustment is completed **the Line of Sight should be made to Coincide with the Axis of Collars, or Parallel to it.** — (See Fig. 45.) Pull out the pins which hold the stirrups on the telescope and turn them back so that the telescope is free to turn in the wyes. Sight the intersection of the cross-hairs at some well-defined point, using the leveling screws for the vertical motion and the clamp and tangent screw for the horizontal motion. Then rotate the telescope 180° in the wyes, so that the level tube is above the telescope. The intersection of the cross-hairs should still be on the point. If it is not, move the horizontal cross-hair half-way back to its first position by means of the upper and lower adjusting screws of the cross-hair ring. Then move the vertical cross-hair half-way back to its first

position by the other pair of screws. Repeat the test until the adjustment is perfect.

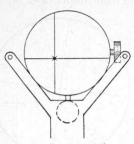
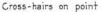
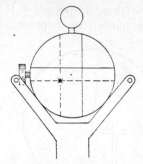

Cross-hairs on point   Telescope inverted

FIG. 45. ADJUSTMENT OF THE CROSS-HAIRS (SECOND PART).

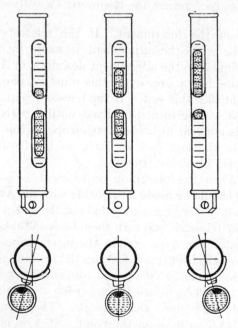

FIG. 45a. TESTING THE BUBBLE FOR PLANE OF AXIS.

122. ADJUSTMENT OF THE LEVEL TUBE. — To make the Line of Sight and the Level Tube Parallel to Each Other. — Two

methods are used, — the *direct*, or "*peg*," method and the *indirect* method. While the former is the only one applicable to the dumpy level either one can be used for the wye level, although the indirect method is the simpler.

123. ADJUSTMENT OF THE LEVEL TUBE BY INDIRECT METHOD. — (a) **To put the Axis of the Bubble Tube in the Same Plane with the Line of Sight.** — Bring the bubble to the center of the tube and rotate the telescope in the wyes for a few degrees (very little is necessary) first toward one side, then toward the other; if the bubble moves toward one end of the tube that end must be the higher, and indicates in which direction the adjustment should be made. (See Fig. 45a.) Move the lateral motion screws of the tube until the bubble does not change its reading when this test is applied. Test the final adjustment by rotating the telescope each way.

124. (b) To make the Axis of the Bubble Tube and the Line of Sight Parallel to Each Other. — First clamp the instrument, then bring the bubble to the center of the tube, lift the telescope out of the wyes, turn it end-for-end and set it down in the wyes, the

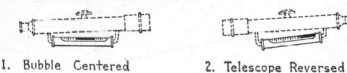

1. Bubble Centered   2. Telescope Reversed

3. Bubble Adjusted   4. Instrument Re-leveled

FIG. 46. ADJUSTMENT OF THE BUBBLE TUBE BY INDIRECT METHOD.

eye end now being where the objective was originally. (See Fig. 46.) This operation must be performed with the greatest care, as the slightest jar of the instrument will vitiate the result. If the bubble returns to the center of the tube, the axis of the tube is in the correct position. If it does not return to the center, the end of the tube provided with the vertical adjustment should be raised or lowered until the bubble moves half-way back to the center. This test must be repeated to make sure that the movement is due to defective adjustment and not to the jarring of the instrument.

125. ADJUSTMENT OF THE WYES. — To make the Axis of the Level Tube Perpendicular to the Vertical Axis of the Instrument. — Bring the two clips (stirrups) down over the telescope and fasten them with the pins. Level the instrument, bring the bubble precisely to the middle of the tube over one set of leveling screws, and then turn the telescope 180° about the vertical axis. If the bubble moves from the center bring it half-way back by means of the adjusting screws at the foot of one of the wye supports. (See Fig. 47.)

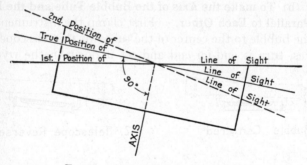

FIG. 47. ADJUSTMENT OF THE WYES.

Since the bubble is brought to the center of the tube each time a rod-reading is taken this last adjustment in no way affects the **accuracy** of the leveling work but it is a convenience and a time saver for it avoids the necessity for re-leveling at each new sight.

II. ADJUSTMENTS OF THE DUMPY LEVEL

126. ADJUSTMENT OF THE CROSS-HAIR. — If the horizontal cross-hair is not truly horizontal when the instrument is level it should be made so by rotating the cross-hair ring as described in the adjustment of the transit, Art. 71, p. 66, and Art. 120.

127. ADJUSTMENT OF THE BUBBLE TUBE. — To make the Axis of the Bubble Tube Perpendicular to the Vertical Axis. Owing to the construction of the dumpy level it is necessary to make this adjustment **before** making the line of sight parallel to the bubble tube. It is done by centering the bubble over one pair of leveling screws, and turning the instrument 180° about the vertical axis. If the bubble does not remain in the center of the tube, move it half-way back to the center by means of the adjusting screws on the level tube.

128. THE DIRECT, OR " PEG," ADJUSTMENT. — To make the Line of Sight Parallel to the Axis of the Bubble. — (See Fig. 48.) Select two points A and B, say, 200 ft. or more apart. Set up the level close to A so that when a rod is held upon it the eye-piece will be about a quarter of an inch from the rod. Look through the telescope **wrong-end-to** at the rod and find the rod reading at the cross-hair, if visible, otherwise the reading opposite the center of the field (see Art. 49). After a little experience it will be found that this can be done very accurately. Owing to the fact that only a small portion of the rod is visible it will be found convenient to set a pencil-point on the rod at the center of the small field of view. Turn the telescope toward B and take a rod-reading on it in the usual way, being certain that the bubble is in the middle of the tube. The difference between these two rod-readings is the difference of elevation of the two points **plus** or **minus** the error of adjustment. The level is next taken to B and the above operation is repeated. The result is the difference in elevation **minus** or **plus** the same error of adjustment. The mean of the two results is the true difference in elevation of points A and B. Knowing the difference in elevation between the two points and the height of the instrument above B the rod-reading at A which will bring the target on the same level as the instrument may be computed. The bubble is brought to the center of the tube and the horizontal cross-hair raised or lowered by means of the adjusting screws on the cross-hair ring until the line of sight strikes the target. In this method the small error due to curvature of the earth (nearly 0.001 ft. for a 200-ft. sight) has been neglected.

EXAMPLE.   (See Fig. 48.)

Instrument at A.
    Rod-reading on $A = 4.062$
    Rod-reading on $B = 5.129$

Diff. in elev. of A and $B = 1.067$

Instrument at B.
    Rod-reading on $B = 5.076$
    Rod-reading on $A = 4.127$

Diff. in elev. of B and $A = 0.949$

Mean of two diff. in elev. $= \dfrac{1.067 + 0.949}{2} = 1.008$ true diff. in elev.

Instrument is now 5.076 above B.
Rod-reading at A should be $5.076 - 1.008 = 4.068$ to give a level sight.

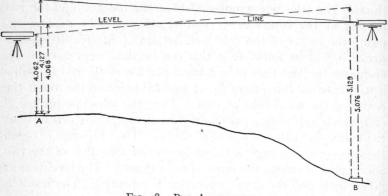

FIG. 48. PEG ADJUSTMENT.

The peg method may be used for adjusting the wye level or the transit, the difference being that in the dumpy level the axis of the bubble tube is first made horizontal and then the line of sight is brought parallel to it, while in the wye level and in the transit the line of sight is first made horizontal and then the axis of the bubble tube is made parallel to it. Consequently, in adjusting the dumpy level the cross-hair ring is moved, whereas with the transit, or the wye level the adjustment is made in the bubble tube. The peg adjustment in its simplest form is described in Art. 129.

128a. Alternate Procedure for Peg Adjustment. — Another way of making the peg adjustment is as follows. Set the level half-way between the two bench-marks and determine their difference in elevation. This difference will be correct, even though the level is not in adjustment, because the instrument is equally distant from the two bench-marks. Then set the level in line with the bench-marks and so that both points will be in front of the level, but one close to the level. Take readings on the two points. If they differ by the true difference in elevation the instrument is in adjustment. If they do not, then move the horizontal cross-hair so it will read on the distant rod the same

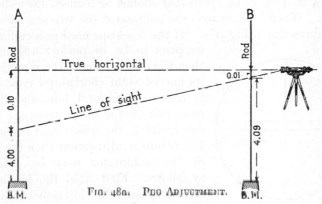

FIG. 48a. PEG ADJUSTMENT.

as the near reading plus or minus the difference in elevation. Then sight again on the near point. This time the reading will be changed slightly. Repeat the operation until the two readings differ by exactly the correct difference in elevation. When the near point is sighted merely note the change in reading. When the distant point is sighted move the cross-hair so that it sights the desired rod-reading.

Example. — Suppose that the two bench-marks are at the same elevation and that the instrument when sighting at A reads 4.00 ft., and when sighting at B reads 4.09 (Fig. 48a). If the cross-hair is now moved until it reads 4.09 on A, it will be found to read 4.099 ft. on B. If it is again raised until it reads 4.099 on A, it will read (nearly) 4.10 on B. The line of sight is now horizontal because the reading is 4.10 on each rod.

128b. Use of Collimator. — The " peg " adjustment may be made by using another instrument as a *collimator.** The two telescopes are placed about half an inch apart and facing each

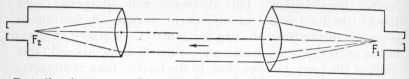

FIG. 48b. ADJUSTING BY MEANS OF COLLIMATOR (SHOWING RELATIVE POSITION
OF COLLIMATOR AND THE TELESCOPE TO BE ADJUSTED).

other, Fig. 48b. The collimator should be focused for a distant object. When looking into the collimator the two sets of cross-hairs appear as in Fig. 48c. If the telescope used as a collimator

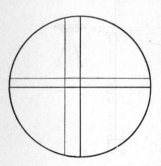

FIG. 48c. APPEARANCE OF
CROSS-HAIRS OF COLLIMA-
TOR. (LIGHT LINES ARE
CROSS-HAIRS OF COLLIMA-
TOR. HEAVY LINES ARE IN
THE TELESCOPE THROUGH
WHICH OBSERVER IS LOOK-
ING.)

happens to be in perfect adjustment then when it is leveled the direction of its line of sight (horizontal cross-hair) is a true horizontal line, and if the cross-hair of the other telescope coincides with it the adjustment is correct. If it is not in adjustment then the error of the collimator may be detected as follows. First sight the horizontal cross-hair of the instrument to be adjusted at the horizontal cross-hair of the collimator; this is done by moving the upper and lower capstan headed screws holding the diaphragm until the horizontal hairs coincide. The bubble should be in the center of its tube while this is being done. Next turn the collimator about and find a distant object in line with the horizontal hair, the bubble being central. Then turn the instrument to be adjusted so that this same object is in the field of view. The cross-hair of the telescope to be adjusted should now be sighting at this point. If it is not,

---

* See " The Use of the Collimating Telescope for Field Adjustments " by Professor George L. Hosmer, The Military Engineer, August, 1923.

then the point sighted by the collimator is as far above (below) the true horizon as the point sighted by the other telescope is below (above) it, and the point on the true horizon is exactly half-way between. If the cross-hair of the telescope to be adjusted is made to sight this midway point (by moving the diaphragm) then the line of collimation is horizontal and the instrument is properly adjusted.

When adjusting the dumpy level it should be observed that the horizontal hair should be in such a position that the line of sight is coincident with or parallel to the line of motion of the objective slide. Also, the level axis must be perpendicular to the vertical axis. Therefore when the level is to be made parallel to the line of sight the conditions conflict. One of the preceding adjustments must be disturbed. It is usually better to move the cross-hairs, because this can cause but little error except on very short sights, and here the error is not important.

In wye levels and transits the above difficulty can be avoided, since the relation of the telescope axis and the vertical axis is not fixed.

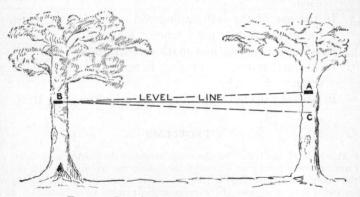

FIG. 49. PEG ADJUSTMENT FOR HAND LEVEL.

129. ADJUSTMENT OF THE LOCKE HAND LEVEL. — In adjusting the hand level the principle of the peg adjustment is used. The level is placed at a mark A (Fig. 49) and another mark B in line with the cross-hair is made, say, 100 ft. away, when the bubble is in the middle. The level is then taken to B, held so that its center is at the height of this mark, and sighted toward the first point. A third point C is marked in line with the cross-hair when the bubble is in the middle. The point midway between A and C is at the same level as B. The adjustment is made by screws which move the horizontal wire.

130. COMMON SOURCES OF ERROR IN LEVELING. —

1. Improper focusing (parallax).
2. Bubble not in middle of tube at instant of sighting.
3. Rod not held plumb.
4. Foresights and corresponding backsights on turning points not equally distant from the instrument.
5. Poor turning points selected. (See Art. 250, p. 298.)
6. Erroneous length of rod.

131. COMMON MISTAKES. —

1. Foresight and backsight not taken on exactly the same point.
2. Neglecting to set target accurately when " long rod " is used.
3. In the use of the self-reading rod neglecting to clamp the rod at the proper place when " long rod " is used.
4. Reading the wrong foot-mark or tenth-mark.
5. In keeping notes, — entering F. S. in B. S. column or *vice versa*.
6. In working up notes, adding F. S. or subtracting B. S.

PROBLEMS

1. A wye level was tested for the sensitiveness of the bubble, as follows: the rod was held on a point 200 ft. away; the bubble was moved over 13.6 divisions of the scale; the rod-readings at the two extreme positions of the bubble were 4.360 and 4.578. Compute the average angular value of one division of the level.

2. A dumpy level was tested by the peg method with the following results:

Instrument at A: —   Instrument at B: —
  + S. on A, 4.139   + S. on B, 3.900
  − S. on B, 4.589   − S. on A, 3.250

Find the rod-reading on A to give a level line of sight, the instrument remaining 3.900 above B. Was the line of sight inclined upward or downward? How much?

3. The target on a Boston rod has been disturbed and it is desired to find out

if the target is in the correct position with reference to the scale. Describe a method by which the amount of this error can be determined.

4. A New York rod is found to be 0.002 ft. short, due to wear on the brass foot-plate. Explain what effect this will have in finding the difference in elevation between two points.

5. (a). A level is set up and a +S. of 5.098 is taken on a point 400 ft. away, then a −S. of 3.260 is taken on a point 900 ft. away. What is the curvature and refraction correction? What is the difference in elevation of the two points?

(b). In another case a +S. of 8.266 was taken on a point 100 ft. away and a −S. of 6.405 taken on a point 600 ft. away. What is the curvature and refraction correction? What is the difference in elevation of the two points?

6. A level is set up near a hydrant and a backsight taken on the hydrant, the reading being 3.17. A foresight is taken to a stone bound and equals 5.29. The level is next set up close to the bound, the rod-reading upon it being 4.82. The second reading upon the hydrant is 2.66. What is the error of the sight line and which way must the cross-hairs be moved to correct this error?

7. In testing a level by the "peg method" the following rod-readings are taken: Instrument at $B.M._1$, + sight on $B.M._1$ = 4.01, − sight on $B.M._2$ = 4.29: Instrument at $B.M._2$, + sight on $B.M._2$ = 4.36; − sight on $B.M._1$ = 4.10. Which way should the cross-hairs be moved and how much?

8. The level bubble of a certain wye level is centered and the telescope then reversed in the wye, the bubble moving 4 divisions toward the eyepiece. If the angular value of 1 division of the level scale corresponds to 0.02 ft. on the rod per 100 ft. of distance, what is the error from this source alone in the elevation of $B.M._2$ above $B.M._1$ when the sum of the backsight (horizontal) distances taken with this level is 200 ft. greater than the sum of the foresight distances?

9. The line of sight of a level is found by the "peg adjustment" test to be inclined downward 0.011 ft. per 100 ft. in distance. What is the allowable difference in the backsight and foresight distances if readings are to be correct within 0.002 ft.?

10. Levels are run between $B.M._1$ and $B.M._2$ with a recorded difference of elevation of +84.19 feet. The error in reading the rod is ±0.003 ft. and the error in the rod-reading due to the bubble not being in the middle of the tube at the instant of sighting is ±0.005 ft. 16 set-ups were required to run the levels.

(a) What is the probable error of the difference of elevation?

(b) Assuming that a 12-ft. rod is used and that the rod is 0.008 ft. too long, what is the corrected difference of elevation?

(c) If the difference of elevation had been −84.19 ft., what would be the corrected difference?

11. A rod which is 2 inches square on its base is held on the flat top of a stone step which is used as a bench-mark. If the rod is held on a rounded surface and waved toward and from the levelman, and the levelman records the shortest reading, this is the vertical rod-reading. But if the rodman waves the rod on a flat surface obviously as the rod is waved backward from the vertical position it is supported on the back edge of its base and when in that position the least rod-reading is obtained. This reading was 0.48 ft. (a very short reading). What is the correct rod-reading?

12. If a 12-foot rod is 1 foot out of plumb at the top, what is the error in a 7.50-ft. reading? What is the corrected reading?

13. A line of differential levels was run between two bench-marks 8 miles apart, sights averaging 250 feet in length. The measured difference in elevation was 1746.24 feet. On comparison with a standard it was found that the rod, having

a nominal length of 12 feet, was actually 12.000 feet long, a shortening of 0.002 feet because of wear on the brass foot plate being offset by a 0.002-foot lengthening distributed over the entire length due to a slight swelling of the wood during damp weather. Determine the true difference in elevation between the two bench-marks.

14. If, in running levels between two points the top of the rod is held 0.3 foot out of plumb on the average, what error would be introduced per set-up when back-sight readings average 1 foot and foresight readings average 10 feet? A 12-foot rod is used for the work.

15. If the sights average 200 feet in length and the probable error of a single observation is ±0.003 foot, what is the probable error in running a line of levels 15 miles long?

16. Two level parties starting from the same bench A at Elev. 19.760 at the foot of a hill are to determine the elevation of bench B at the top of the hill. One party got 1740.65 ft. for the elevation of B and the other party got 1740.90. The aggregate backsights and foresights were equal and errors due to personal equation were compensating. In order to check the work each party closed the level circuit by running back to A where both checked on the original elevation.

How do you account for the differences in elevation the parties got at the top of the hill?

17. It is desired to set a bench-mark on the roof of a building about 325 feet high. The levels are carried up the stair-well substituting a 100-foot steel tape for the usual leveling rod. A bench-mark (B.M.$_1$) is established on the first floor (elevation = 24.57 feet above mean sea level). The tape was tested and found to have a length of 100.015 feet when under a tension of 10 lbs. and supported throughout, at a temperature of 68° F. The weight of the tape is 2 lbs. It is known that the length of a vertically suspended tape of weight w with a weight W attached to the lower end is equal to the length of the same tape supported horizontally throughout its length and when under a tension of $W + \frac{1}{2}w$. The top of the tape is held suspended by a bracket fixed to the handrail of the stairs. A spring balance is inserted between the bottom of the tape and a second bracket. Tension is applied by means of a turnbuckle until the reading of the spring balance is 9 lbs. Instrument set-ups are established on landings in the stair-well at about every tape length. The work was done at an average tape temperature of 74° F. In the following readings, the numbers in italics are readings on the tape. No correction is necessary for the reading on the level rod.

	B.S.	F.S.	Elev.
B.M.$_1$	3.50 ft.		24.57
Tape 1.	*99.22*	0.57 ft.	
Tape 2.	*93.45*	0.16	
Tape 3.	*95.32*	0.38	
Tape 4.	*43.18*	0.20	
B.M.$_{roof}$		2.76	

Compute the correct elevation of the bench-mark on the roof to 0.01 ft.

18. Show by means of a sketch a target on a Philadelphia rod graduated to .01 ft. with the target set at 4.018. Show only sufficient length of rod to indicate the reading and full length of the vernier. Make sketch to scale 0.01 ft. on rod = $\frac{1}{2}''$.

PART II

SURVEYING METHODS

CHAPTER V

LAND SURVEYING

132. PROPERTY SURVEYS. — Surveys of land are usually made for one or more of the following purposes: — (1) to furnish an exact description of the boundaries, (2) to determine the enclosed area, or (3) to furnish data for making a plan. The instruments and methods used will depend upon the land value and the use to be made of the results of the survey. A *cadastral* survey is the survey of legal boundaries of land.

The usual practice is to begin at any convenient corner on the boundary and measure distances and angles (or distances and bearings) in the order in which they occur. This connected series of lines and angles is known as a *traverse*. Whenever it is practicable to do so surveys of this character should be made in closed loops, that is, the survey should return to the point of beginning so that it will be possible to calculate by trigonometry, or to plot, from the starting point continuously around the figure to the closing point; the computed position of this last point should, theoretically, be coincident with the starting point. Such a figure is spoken of as a " closed traverse." It furnishes one of the best means of checking the accuracy of all of the measurements. Since all the measurements contain errors, large or small, the position of the final point will never agree perfectly with that of the initial point. The distance between these two points is the actual error of closure. It is the algebraic sum of all the (component) errors. If this closure distance is divided by the perimeter of the traverse the result is a fraction which can be used in comparing different surveys, since it expresses the **error per foot of distance.** For convenience this fraction is usually stated with a numerator of unity, giving in the denominator the number of feet of distance corresponding to an error of 1 ft. This is usually termed the " error of closure " of the traverse. For example, an error of closure of one part in 5000 parts is expressed as $\frac{1}{5000}$, called "one in 5000."

133. SURVEYING FOR AREA WITH THE COMPASS. — The compass was formerly used extensively as a direction instrument in land surveying. It has little application today except as an aid in running old lines or for a rough survey of low-priced land. If the compass is used, the direction of each boundary is determined by its magnetic bearing and the length measured with a tape. Where it is the custom of the locality to refer to distances as chains and links these will be used instead of feet because in that case previous surveys in this neighborhood will probably be given in these same units.* A heavy tape marked in chains and links is suitable for such work.

One important matter, which should not be overlooked, is to determine the magnetic declination *at the time and place* of the survey, and record it. When comparing with other surveys the difference in declination must be taken into account. It is desirable to have included in the description of the land the date at which the declination was determined. Much confusion arises from not knowing positively the declination at the time of the survey, as well as from doubt as to whether the date is that of the survey itself or merely the date of copying an old description. A definite statement, such as "Bearings are magnetic; magnetic declination, 1930, was 14° 30′ West" will clarify the record. To be of value this should be incorporated into the deed or recorded on the plan.

When making a survey enclosing an area it is customary to begin at some convenient corner, which can be easily identified and described, and to take bearings and distances in order around the field. As the measurements are made they are recorded immediately in the field note book. It is not really necessary to measure the distances and bearings in the order in which they occur, but since they must be arranged in this order for the purpose of computation it will be convenient to have them so arranged in the original notes. Mistakes are less likely if this is always done.

---

* In many of the older states nearly all of the very old surveys are recorded in rods and links. Sometimes *rood*, *perch* or *pole* are used, all of which equal a rod.

If the length and the bearing of one side are omitted the area is nevertheless completely determined; but since these omitted measurements would furnish a valuable check on the accuracy of all the measurements they should never be omitted if they can be taken. **It is of the utmost importance in every survey that check measurements should be taken.** Even a few rough checks in the field which require only a little extra time often prove to be of great value in detecting mistakes. Both a forward bearing and a reverse (or back) bearing should be taken at each corner; from these two bearings the angle at a corner can be obtained which is free from error of local attraction of the needle.

It is often impossible to set the compass up at the exact corners of the property; to overcome this difficulty lines running parallel to the property lines can be surveyed as described in Art. 135, and the area thereby determined. Sometimes the compass can be set on a property line at an intermediate point and the bearing of the line obtained; but the surveyor must be sure that there is no local attraction of the needle at this point. All points where the compass is set should be marked and described so that they can be found again. If any instrument point is not otherwise defined it may be marked temporarily by a small stake and several reference measurements made from this stake to permanent objects nearby which may be readily identified. From these measurements the position can be

(LEFT-HAND PAGE)   (RIGHT-HAND PAGE)

| Survey of Wood Lot of John Smith, Northboro, Mass. | | | | N. Brown, Surveyor   2 rod chain - Temple Compass
J. Long, Chainman   chain 0.1 link too long.
Oct. 7. 1906 | |
Sta.	Bearing	Reversed Bearing	Distance (chains)		Remarks
A	Due E	N 32¼° W	17.75		Stake and stones cor. J. Smith, B. White and I. Richards
B	N 58½° E	N 89½° W	13.55		Pine Stump
C	N 1½° E	S 58¼° W	32.36		Oak Stump
D	S 83¼° W	S 1½° W	23.75		Cedar Stk. 5' S.E. of large oak.
E	S 23½° W	N 85¾° E	30.94		Stone bound, E. side Pine St.
F	S 32¼° E	N 23½° E	11.16		Stone bound, E. side Pine St.

FIG. 50.   NOTES OF CHAIN AND COMPASS SURVEY.

relocated definitely and positively, if the stake is lost. These measurements are called *ties*.   (Art. 142, p. 121.)

Notes of the traverse are often recorded as shown in Fig. 50.

134. SURVEY OF A FIELD WITH TRANSIT AND TAPE. —
The survey of a field for area can usually be made in one of the
three following ways.

(1) By setting up the transit at the corners of the property
and measuring the angles directly, the distances being measured
directly along the property lines.

(2) When the property lines are so occupied by buildings
or fences that the transit cannot be set up at the corners, but
the distances can still be measured along the property lines, then
the angles at the corners are obtained by measuring the angles
between lines which are made exactly parallel to the property
lines.

(3) If the boundaries of the property are such that it is not
practicable to set the transit up at the corners or to measure
the distance directly on the property lines, a traverse is run
approximately parallel to the property lines and these lines connected with the traverse by means of angles and distances.

135. In case (2) the parallel lines are established in the following manner. Set the transit up at some point E (Fig. 51)

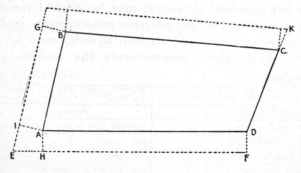

FIG. 51. TRANSIT LINES PARALLEL TO THE SIDES OF FIELD.

preferably within 2 or 3 ft. of the corner A. Establish the line
EF parallel to AD by making $DF = AH$ by trial. Point H
cannot be seen through the telescope, but it is so near the instrument that, by sighting by eye from a position behind the
plumb-line at E toward point F, point H can then be accurately

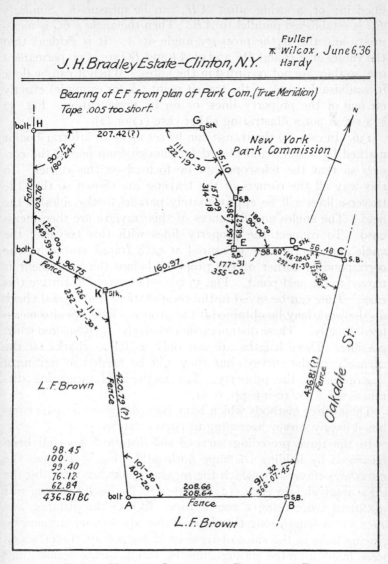

FIG. 52. NOTES OF SURVEY WITH TRANSIT AND TAPE.

lined in; or, a swing offset AH, can be measured. Similarly EG is established parallel to AB. Then the angle FEG is measured; and this is the property angle at A. It is evident that the values of AH and DF and of AI and BG are of no permanent use, so they are not recorded in the notes. When it can be done it is advisable to place the transit point (K for example) exactly on one of the property lines, or on its prolongation. Fig. 52 is a set of notes illustrating either case (1) or (2).

136. In case (3) the transit can be set up at an arbitrary point marked by a stake and placed far enough from one of the corners so that the telescope can be focused on this corner. In this way all the corners of the traverse are chosen so that the traverse lines will be approximately parallel to the sides of the field. The angles and distances of this traverse are then measured. To connect the property lines with this traverse, the angle and distance are measured at each transit station to the corresponding corner of the property before the instrument is moved to the next point. Fig. 53 is a set of notes illustrating this case. Time can be saved in the computations and a good check on the work may be obtained if the property lines are also measured directly. These distances should always be measured when possible. These lengths are not only useful as checks on the accuracy of the survey, but they will be needed in writing a description of the property. For methods of measuring distances see Arts. 10–13, pp. 6–11.

These three methods which have been described may be combined in any survey according to circumstances.

In the three preceding surveys the distances have all been measured by holding the tape horizontal. Fig. 53a shows the notes of a traverse in which the measurements are taken by the slope method (see Arts. 12–13, pp. 9–11). Each distance was measured twice using a 200-ft. tape. Where the distance was over a tape-length long the slope of the tape was maintained by placing nails in the sides of trees or in temporary stakes which were lined in on the proper slope by means of the transit, and measurements taken to the nails. Some of the long lines, where the slope of the ground changed considerably, have been broken into sections (2 to 2A, 2A to 2B, etc.). Under average

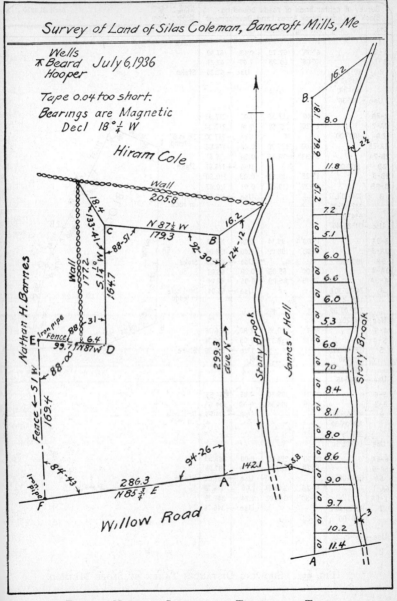

FIG. 53. NOTES OF SURVEY WITH TRANSIT AND TAPE.

Survey of center lines of roads bounding Block 5 – Cedar Brook Acres Land Development					Hunt – Chief White – X McKay – Chain Wood – X	April 21, 1930
Sta.	Hor. Ang.	Vert. Ang.	Slope Dist.	Corr.	Hor. Dist.	Remarks & Sketch
1						Stake
1-2		6°-55'	67.79	0.49	67.30	
2-1		10°-08'	68.38	1.07	67.31	
2	80°-36' L				Use → 67.30	Stake
	161°-12'					
	241°-48'					
Use →	80°-36'					
2-2A		0°-40'	217.35	0.02	217.33	
2A-2		2°-20'	217.52	0.18	217.34	
2A	180°-00'				Use → 217.33	Tk. in 8" Stump
2A-2B		5°-00'	177.30	0.68	176.62	
2B-2A		3°-33'	176.95	0.34	176.61	
2B	180°-00'				Use → 176.61	Stake
2B-3		1°-25'	110.53	0.03	110.50	
3-2B		0°-37'	110.48	0.01	110.47	
3	171°-21'L				Use → 110.48	Drill hole in rock
	342°-41'-30"					
	514°-02'					
Use →	171°-20'-40"					
3-3A		1°-08'	198.14	0.04	198.10	
3A-3		0°-00'	198.09	0.00	198.09	
3A	180°-00'				Use → 198.09	Stake
3A-4		0°-00'	65.05	0.00	65.05	
4-3A		2°-15'	65.09	0.05	65.04	
4	74°-20'-30"L				Use → 65.04	Drill hole in ledge
	148°-41'					
	223°-00'-30"					
Use →	74°-20'-10"					
4-5		8°-25'	259.58	2.80	256.78	
5-4		7°-13'	258.79	2.05	256.74	
5	156°-14'-30"L				Use → 256.76	Stake
	312°-30'					
	468°-45'					
Use →	156°-15'					
5-6		7°-17'	105.50	0.85	104.65	
6-5		4°-19'	104.95	0.30	104.65	
6	112°-02'-30"L				Use → 104.65	Drill hole in rock
	224°-05'-30"					
	336°-08'-30"					
Use →	112°-02'-50"					
6-6A		0°-00'	286.99	0.00	286.99	
6A-6		1°-26'	287.14	0.09	287.05	
6A	180°-00'				Use → 287.02	Stake
6A-1		5°-38'	348.47	1.68	346.79	
1-6A		6°-30'	349.02	2.24	346.78	
1	125°-25'-30"L				Use → 346.78	
	250°-50'					
	376°-16'					
Use →	125°-25'-20"					
2						

FIG. 53a. SHOWING DISTANCES TAKEN BY SLOPE METHOD.

conditions prevailing in the field this method is likely to give better results than horizontal taping.

137. Irregular Curved Boundaries. — When a tract of land is bounded by an irregular curved line, such as a brook, it is customary to run the traverse line near it, sometimes crossing it several times, and to take perpendicular offsets to the brook. If it is a winding brook with no distinct turns in it, offsets at regular intervals are measured from the transit line as in the portion near point A of Fig. 53. Near point B in this figure the portions of the brook between turns are almost straight, in which case the proper measurements to make are the offsets to those points where the course of the brook changes and the distances along the transit line between these offset lines. Since they are usually short the right-angle offset lines are laid off in the field by eye.

138. SURVEY OF A FIELD BY A SINGLE SET-UP OF THE TRANSIT. — When it is necessary to economize time in the field at the expense of accuracy and of the time required to calculate the survey the following method may be used. If possible set up at a point within the field, preferably near the middle, from which all the corners can be seen, and measure the angles and distances to each corner. The field is thus divided into several oblique triangles in each of which two sides and the included angle have been measured; from these the area and the third side (property line) can be computed. As a check on the measured angles their sum should be 360°; there is no check on the property lines unless they are measured directly.

This method of surveying a field may be employed as a check on one of the other methods which have already been described, but it is not recommended as a method to be used by itself except in emergencies. One weak point in it is the low degree of precision with which the angles are usually measured. Here the effect of an error of, say, 30 seconds in an angle may often be much larger than the errors in the measured distances (Art. 387, p. 471). The additional measurement of the property line gives the length of all three sides of the various triangles into which the field is divided. If the area is calculated from the three sides of the triangles, using the measured angles as checks only, an accurate result may be obtained, but at the expense of office work.

139. Survey of a Field with a Tape Only. — Sometimes in an emergency it may be necessary to survey a field when a transit is not at hand. This can be done by dividing the field into several triangles and measuring all their sides. To insure accuracy the triangles should be so chosen that there are no angles in them less than 30° or greater than 150°, because in general, weak intersections cause large errors in the results. Sometimes, however, a small angle may enter in such a way as to do no harm. Lining in by eye is sufficiently accurate for obtaining the length of a line. But if a point is set on line by eye for the purpose of measuring perpendicularly to the line, such as the altitude of a triangle, only approximate results can be expected.

140. Selecting the Corners. — If a corner is marked by a stone bound, an iron rod or a pipe the exact point may be easily found; but where it is described as the intersection of stone walls or fences the surveyor will have to examine all evidence as to its position and use his judgment in deciding where the true corner is located. (Art. 151, p. 133.) When the property is bounded by a public way or a town boundary, data relating to the location of these lines must be obtained from the proper local authorities, usually from the town clerk. After determining the positions of the corner points, the surveyor should use precisely the same points in all distance or angle measurements. If stakes are used the exact point should be marked by a tack or nail driven into the top of the stake.

In deciding upon the location of the boundary lines from an examination of artificial features it should be borne in mind that fences or walls along highways should be built entirely on private property so that the face of the wall or fence is on the side line of the highway. In country districts, however, this is not always the custom.

The rerunning of the road lines of public ways in towns and villages so that they will agree with the recorded description is usually next to impossible. Their description is usually so indefinite and inaccurate that one soon finds that occupancy is the better evidence of the position of these public ways. In defining these ways, it is advisable to adhere to the width of road given in the description and to make the alignment of the road fit the positions of the walls, fences, and other objects which are evidence of occupancy. Then it is advisable to get the town authorities to establish that line by proper municipal ordinance.

In most cities the baseboard of a fence is usually built so that its face is on, or nearly on, the street line, but the location of the fences has no weight when the street line is defined by permanent marks or by city ordinance (Art. 270, p. 324). In large cities street lines are defined by records in the City Engineer's office. These sometimes refer to stone bounds, but a better system, adopted by most city engineering offices, defines these lines by a **record of many swing-offset measurements** taken from **permanent** parts of existing buildings, such as the stone faces of party walls or the masonry underpinning of existing buildings.

Since the boundary line between adjacent owners has no width and since every fence occupies some width of land, a reasonable amount of land may be taken for the fence, one-half from each owner, because each owner must contribute his share of land for the division fence. It is the surveyor's duty to set the fence so that it occupies equal amounts of the abutting owners' land. For boundaries between private lands the legal line is the center of the stone wall or Virginia rail fence; in New England it is customary in the case of a tight board or picket fence to set the back side of the board (the face of the rangers) on the property line. This puts the boards entirely on one property and the rangers and posts which support the boards on the other. Since the posts are 6 to 8 ft. apart and the lower ranger is a foot or so above the ground this practice seems equitable. When the entire area is occupied by buildings as in the business portions of large cities the legal line often is the middle of the party-wall (Arts. 303–311, pp. 357–71). If the deed reads " to thread of stream " the boundary is the line midway between the shores when the stream has its average regimen of flow.

Not infrequently woodland is marked off by blazing the trees on one or both sides of the boundary line, the blazing being done on the side of the tree nearest the boundary line. If a tree comes directly on the line it is blazed on both sides at the points where the line strikes the tree. The blazes are sometimes painted red. A small pile of stones, sometimes with a stake in the center of the pile, is often used to mark the corners of such land. Farmland and woodland corners are sometimes marked by a substantial wooden stake with no stones piled around it. In the New England states round cedar posts from 4 to 6 inches in diameter are often used. In Canada and other parts of the continent corners are marked by heavy squared stakes. The early surveyor used to mark these stakes with his private mark. One surveyor named Morrow always cut a pair of crossed swords with initial " M " between them; another cut a pair of axes, and still another carved his two initials "AL" on every corner stake that he placed. The stakes usually extended 3 or 4 ft. into the ground and from 2 to 4 ft. out of the ground. This personal marking of stakes is of great value for it gives not only a clue to the age of the stakes but also to their reliability, for in the past, as in the present, certain surveyors were reputed for their care and accuracy, and where there is evidence of two different lines (and in woodlands this is a common condition) obviously more reliance will be placed on the line defined by a surveyor who had a reputation for accurate work than on the work of the haphazard surveyor. It is not uncommon to find, in the woods, two or more blazed lines near together. The oldest line takes precedence unless there has been acquiescence in a line of later date for a sufficiently long period to make the law of " adverse possession " determine the line (Art. 151, p. 135). The age of blazed lines can be determined readily by cutting into the tree crosswise of the grain and counting the annular rings from the bark to the face of the old blaze. Usually the scar in the tree made by the old blazing has healed over so that only a faint vertical line on the bark is left to indicate where the tree was originally blazed. Consequently the surveyor is liable to overlook the old blazes unless he is resourceful.

141. METHOD OF PROCEDURE. — In deciding where the traverse shall be run the surveyor should keep in mind both convenience in fieldwork and economy in office work. Frequently a method of procedure which shortens the time spent in the field will increase greatly the amount of labor in the office. Circumstances will determine which method should be used. If there is no special reason why the time in the field should be shortened, the best arrangement of the traverse will be the one that will make the computation simple, and thereby diminish the liability of mistakes. If the lines of the traverse coincide with the

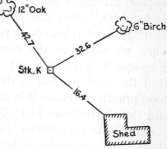

boundary, as in cases (1) and (2) (Art. 134, p. 112), the amount of office work will be the least. If in case (3) the traverse lines are approximately parallel to and near the boundaries of the property this simplifies the computation of the small areas to be added to or subtracted from the area traverse.

142. TIES. — All important points temporarily marked by

FIG. 54. APPROXIMATE TIES.

stakes should be " tied in," i.e., measurements should be taken so that the point may be readily found or replaced in the future.

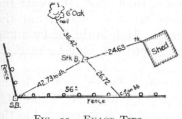

There should be at least three *horizontal* ties which intersect at angles not less than 30°. They should be taken from points which are definite and easily recognized, such as nails driven into trees, drill holes in ledge, stone bounds, fence posts, or buildings. All such measurements should

FIG. 55. EXACT TIES.

be recorded carefully, usually by means of a sketch. Fig. 54 shows a stake located by ties measured to tenths of a foot; these approximate ties are taken simply to aid in finding the stake. It is just as easy and is better practice to take the ties so that the exact point can be replaced. The surveyor should mark carefully by nail the exact points from which measurements (taken to $\frac{1}{100}$ ft.) are made, and record in the notes as shown in Fig. 55. It will assist in finding a tie point if a circle is painted around it. In the woods, especially in winter, bright blue paint is the best color. For further details regarding ties see Art. 275, p. 328.

143. Measurement of the Angles of the Traverse. — There are four common ways of measuring traverse angles; by measuring the *angle to the right*, by measuring the *interior angle*, by measuring the *deflection angle* (equal to the difference between the interior angle and 180°), or by measuring the *azimuth*.

143a. Measurements of Angles to the Right. — In this method all angles are measured to the right (clockwise). After backsighting along the previous line with the horizontal circle reading 0° the telescope is turned *to the right* (clockwise) and the angle measured to the next station (angle point). Then the telescope is inverted and the angle remeasured, "doubled." Half the final reading is the value used for the angle. This is good practice because it is simple to follow, applies to both linear and closed traverses and eliminates most instrumental errors.

143b. Measurement of Interior Angles. — An interior angle is measured by sighting on the previous traverse station with the circle reading 0° and with the telescope direct. The angle is then measured to the traverse point ahead, being sure to measure the arc which represents the *interior* angle of the closed field, even though it is greater than 180°. Leaving the horizontal plate clamped, invert the telescope and repeat the process thereby "doubling" the angle. Half of the final reading is the required angle. Additional repetitions may be made if greater precision is required.

143c. Measurement of Deflection Angle. — This is the angle between the backsight produced by reversing (plunging) the telescope and the forward traverse line; it is recorded in the notes as R or L to indicate whether the telescope was turned to the right (clockwise) or to the left (counterclockwise) in measuring the deflection angle. Evidently a single measurement of this angle would be seriously affected by any error in the adjustment of the line of sight or of the standards; such errors as may exist are doubled by plunging the telescope between the backsight and foresight which process is required. Consequently, it is especially necessary to "double" the deflection angle to eliminate such errors of adjustment (Art. 79, p. 71). Best practice therefore requires making the first backsight with the instrument *direct* so that when the second (latter) foresight is taken the instrument will again be in the *direct* position and hence ready for conveniently carrying on the survey.

144. MEASUREMENT OF AZIMUTHS. — If a backsight is taken with the circle reading 0° and angles are then measured to the line ahead by turning the instrument clockwise (to the right) such angles are *azimuth* angles. The measurement of angles to the right is an application of the azimuth method (Art. 143a). In this case, the traverse station in the rear is always available as a foresight.

Another common use of the term azimuth applies to the measurement of angles clockwise (to the right) from the *true meridian* or from the *magnetic meridian*. In this case it is customary to set the circle to read 0° when sighting toward the south; consequently a sight toward the west would read 90° and one toward the east would read 270°.

If a true meridian line has been established set up the transit at the north end of it, set the " A " vernier at 0°, sight at the south end of the meridian, and then clamp the lower clamp. If the upper clamp is now loosened and the telescope sighted at any point, then vernier " A " will read the true azimuth to that point. The direction of this meridian may then be carried over to other traverse points as will be explained.

If the meridian is not actually marked out, but the true azimuth of some line is known, such as AB (Fig. 56), the transit is set up at station A, the vernier set at the known azimuth of AB (say, 113° 16′) and the upper plate clamped. If the telescope is sighted at B and the lower clamp tightened the circle is oriented. If the upper clamp is now loosened and the telescope sighted at any other point the vernier which was originally set at the azimuth reading will read the true azimuth of that point from station A.

Any line through A may be assumed arbitrarily as the 0° direction and azimuths may be read from this direction. Magnetic south is sometimes used as the 0° azimuth.

Irrespective of the direction that is assumed as the 0° direction, the azimuth is carried ahead to station B as explained in the next paragraph.

The azimuth of BC may be obtained in one of two ways. (1) Invert the telescope and backsight on A, the circles remaining clamped together at the reading of B taken at A; then clamp the lower plate, turn the telescope to its direct position, loosen the upper clamp and sight on *C*. The circle then reads the azimuth of *BC* referred to the same meridian as the azimuth of *AB*. The disadvantage of this method is that the error of collimation enters the azimuth each time. (2) Add 180° to the

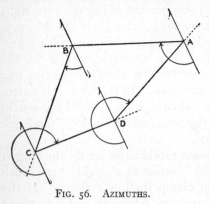

FIG. 56. AZIMUTHS.

azimuth of *AB*, set this off on the circle and vernier, and sight on *A*. The telescope may then be turned directly to *C* (without inverting) and the azimuth of *BC* can be read directly on the circle. The disadvantages of this method as compared with the former are that the error in the angle between opposite verniers (eccentricity and constant angle) enters the result,

that time is consumed in setting the circle at each set-up of the instrument, and that there is an opportunity for mistakes in calculating the angle and in making the setting on the vernier. Therefore if the collimation adjustment is good the first method may be preferred, but if there is doubt about this, then the second method may be safer.

In order to obtain a check on the angles of the traverse occupy station *A* after the angle is measured at *D*, and determine the azimuth of *AB* by backsight on *D*. This new azimuth of *AB* should agree with the original azimuth of *AB*.

145. Checking the Fieldwork. — Reading the horizontal angle to one minute will be suitable for surveys of ordinary precision. "Doubling the angle" is always advisable to prevent mistakes. Referring to Fig. 52, p. 113, it will be seen that the angles were quadrupled where the sides were long, and doubled where they were short. In this instance the angles were repeated to increase the precision as well as to avoid mistakes.

Errors in the angles may be detected by observing the magnetic bearings and calculating the angles from these bearings; or by starting with one observed bearing (assumed to be correct), calculating the other bearings in succession by means of the measured angles, and noting whether the observed bearings agree approximately with the *calculated bearings*.

If a **very short line** enters into a traverse, the errors in angle at either end of this line caused by errors in centering the instrument over the point may be eliminated by first marking a foresight 200 ft. or more distant in the prolongation of this short line and then measuring all angles from this foresight. The angle between the lines on either side of the short line will then have an accuracy consistent with the other angles of the traverse.

The accuracy of the transit work may be tested by adding the measured angles. The sum of the interior angles of the field should equal $(n - 2) \times 180°$, where n is the number of sides in the field. If the deflection angles are used the sum of all the right deflections should differ from the sum of all the left deflections by 360°, or in other words, **the algebraic sum of the deflection angles should be 360°.**

If there is any doubt as regards the correctness of the measurement of a line it should be remeasured, preferably in the **opposite direction,** so that the same mistake will not be repeated. (See line AB in Fig. 52, p. 113; also Art. 136 and Fig. 53a.) If the traverse lines do not coincide with the boundaries, an independent check is obtained by measuring along the boundaries as well as on the traverse lines, as illustrated in Fig. 53, p. 115. This furnishes at once a **rough** check on the distances in the field and a **close** check after the survey has been calculated. It is often advisable to run a line across the traverse, especially when there are many sides to the field, thus dividing the field into two parts, as in Fig. 52, p. 113. If any mistake has been made it is then possible to tell in which portion of the traverse it occurred (Art. 436, p. 526). If the transit is provided with stadia hairs the traverse distances can be checked by stadia readings.

146. ACCURACY REQUIRED. — That the accuracy in the measurement of distances shall be consistent with that of the angles it is necessary that great care should be exercised in holding the tape horizontal, in plumbing, in aligning, and in securing proper tension. On sloping ground inclined distances are measured as explained in Art. 13, p. 11. (See also Fig. 53a.)

If the angles are measured to the nearest minute and the distances to the nearest tenth of a foot, it will be sufficiently accurate to use sighting-rods in " giving line." The error of closure of such a survey should be not greater than $\frac{1}{5000}$, but would seldom be less than $\frac{1}{10000}$ (Art. 132, p. 109).

If the property is very valuable, as in the case of city building lots, it is well to use a transit reading to 30″ or 20″. The angles should be repeated, not only as a check against mistakes, but to increase the precision of the measurement (Art. 59, p. 55). The tape measurements should be made with special care, and should be taken to the nearest hundredth of a foot. In the best work the temperature correction should be applied, a spring balance should be used to give the right pull on the tape, the correction to the standard distance should be determined (Art. 267, p. 319), the alignment given with the transit, and great care taken in plumbing. Sights are given by holding a pencil vertically on top of the tack on the stake or by plumb-line (Art. 65, p. 59). In this work it is important that the property line should be followed, when possible, to insure the most accurate results. In such work an error of closure of $\frac{1}{20000}$ to $\frac{1}{40000}$ can be expected. It is customary on city work to neglect the effect of temperature and to omit the use of the spring balance, the pull being carefully judged. Under these circumstances the closures obtained may be $\frac{1}{20000}$ or higher, but the actual error due to neglecting temperature may be much more than this, since a variation of only 8° F. will introduce an error of about $\frac{1}{20000}$, and a variation of tension of, say, 3 or 4 lb., may introduce a similar error. (See Precise City Surveys, Arts. 303-12, pp. 357-80.)

An analysis of the relative precision of angle and distance measurements can be made in the following manner. Suppose a square lot of land 400 ft. on a side is to be surveyed by using a transit reading to one minute and a tape reading to hundredths of a foot. It may be assumed that the single reading of an angle (in which no mistake has been made) is in error not more than 30″ of angle. The sine of 30″ is 0.00015. Hence the maximum error in the angle will correspond to 0.00015 × 400 = 0.06 ft. in a side of the field. This would correspond to an error of 0.015 ft. per 100-ft. tape length, the error being always in the same direction. A cumulative error of this amount is not likely in good tape work. Therefore it is desirable to double or to treble the angles to secure greater precision, using, say, one third the treble angle for the final angle. This makes the precision of the angle measurements more nearly consistent with the precision of the measurements of distance. The maximum error in the angle thus used is 10″, and this corresponds to a distance of 0.02 ft. in the measurement of a side 400 ft. long, which is a reasonable requirement in measuring this distance.

It is therefore necessary not only to select the proper transit for a given precision but also to determine as suggested above how many repetitions of the angles should be made in order to secure the same precision in angles and distances.

147. ORGANIZATION OF TRANSIT PARTY. — Transit surveys can be carried on readily by a party of three men. The note keeper, who is in charge of the party, directs the entire work; the transit-man, who has the instrument always in his care, sets it up where directed by the note keeper, reads the angles and gives line when it is desired; the tape-man, generally acting as head-tape-man, and the note keeper, as rear-tape-man, measure all distances. There is often economy, however, in having another tape-man so as to leave the note keeper free to keep the notes and to direct the party. Where much clearing of underbrush is required an axeman is also a desirable or even a necessary addition to the party. In cutting out important boundary lines (state, county, or town lines), where a wide cut is required, several axemen may be necessary. The axemen should be trained in the duties of cutting and in marking and driving stakes, preparing for ties, and otherwise assisting in the surveying.

The speed of the party depends upon the way in which the chief of party directs his men. He should plan the work and train his men so that every man realizes his responsibility and anticipates the particular function he is to perform so that there is little necessity for calling off orders. Some surveying parties can perform in a day twice the work of others owing solely to the fact that the chief has trained his men well and insisted upon the kind of discipline that produces accurate results in a short time. The chief of party should check mentally, by estimate, all distances and angles measured, so as to catch a large error the moment the dimension is called off to him. He should be at the spot where important measurements are made, so that he can check the readings himself if he has any doubt of their accuracy.

148. NOTE KEEPING. — All measurements should be recorded in a special note-book **as soon as they are made** and never left to be filled in from memory. When a dimension is called off the note keeper should record it immediately in his note-book. If his sketch is not prepared for that dimension, or if he does not know just where he wants to record it, he should, nevertheless, **write it somewhere in the book at once** and then decide promptly where it should be placed permanently. Even then it is advisable not to erase the original entry. To depend upon carrying a dimension in one's mind even for a few moments is dangerous practice. **The notes should be neat and in clear form so that there will be no doubt as to their meaning.** Great care should be taken that they shall not be susceptible of any interpretation except the right one. They are usually recorded in pencil, but they should always be regarded as permanent records and not as temporary memoranda. As other persons, not familiar with the locality, will probably use the notes and will depend entirely on what is recorded, it is very important that the notes contain all necessary data without any superfluous information. If the note keeper will bear in mind constantly how the survey is to be calculated or plotted it will aid him greatly in judging which measurements must be taken and which ones are unnecessary. Clearness is of utmost importance in note keeping, and to attain it the usual custom is not to attempt to sketch closely to scale; and yet in special surveys where much detail is desired, such as the details of a doorway and steps, it is well to carry out the sketches in the note-book approximately to scale. Care should be taken not to crowd the notes — paper is cheap — and an extra page of the note-book devoted to a survey may save hours of time in the office consumed in trying to interpret a page of crowded notes, and may also avoid mistakes. Too much stress cannot be laid on the importance of being careful not to lose the note-book; not infrequently a note-book contains data which could not possibly be replaced. Such notes should be photostated, and the original book kept in the office vault.

Although sufficient fullness to make the notes clear is always desirable, it is customary to abbreviate the names of the artificial features most commonly met with by the surveyor. To interpret a set of notes properly one must be familiar with these symbols and abbreviations, some of the more common of which are given below.

△	Triangulation Station.	c.	Center.
⊙	Transit Traverse Point.	₵.	Center line.
⊡	Stadia Station.	na.	Nail.
S.B	Stone bound.	tk.	Tack.
Mon.	Monument.	cb.	Curb.
Stk.	Stake.	C.B.	Catch basin.
Spk.	Spike.	M.H.	Manhole.
dh.	Drill-hole.	Tel.	Telephone pole.
B.M.	Bench-mark.	F.S.	Foresight.
T.P.	Turning point.	B.S.	Backsight.
c.f.	Crow-foot (a mark like this ⤡ or ⇓).		
c.c.f.	Cut crow-foot (cut into wood or stone).		
— · — · —	Fence.	b.b.	Base-board of fence.
▭—▭—▭	Fence, showing on which side the posts are.		

 Line of building; the outside line is the base-board, the cross-hatched part is the line of the stone or brick underpinning.

Distances should always be recorded in such a way as to indicate the precision with which they were taken. For example, if they were read to hundredths of a foot and a measurement happened to be just 124 ft. it should be recorded as 124.00, not as 124. The two zeros are of as much consequence as any other two digits which might have come in their places. Angles that have been read to the nearest half-minute, however, are recorded

as follows: 6° 47′ 30″. It will be seen that this is not consistent
with the foregoing. A more proper way of reading and recording
this angle would be 6° 47½′, but this is not common practice.

In addition to the measurements, every set of notes should
contain the following information: the name of the job, the
location and character of the work, the date, and the names of
the field party. It is well also to state the names or numbers of
the instruments used and the error of the tape. Where the
notes of a survey are continued through several pages of a bound
book the date may be placed at the top of every page; other
data need not be repeated, but if loose-leaf notes are used the
sheets should be carefully " paged," and **every leaf headed with
the name of the job.** The underlying fault of the loose-leaf
system is that the note keeper may fail to put the title on each
leaf, with the result that any separate pages of the notes that become misplaced may have no identifying mark on them to indicate the survey to which they belong. Fig. 50, p. 111, Fig. 52,
p. 113, Fig. 53, p. 115 and Fig. 53a, p. 116 are given as illustrations of fieldnotes.

If there are many pages of valuable notes, and especially if
these are being sent back and forth between office and field, it is
advisable to have photostats made as soon as possible. The
originals may then be kept at the office and photostats sent out
to the field party.

On the front cover of every note-book should be plainly lettered the name and address of the surveyor, the fact that the
book is of great value and, if deemed advisable, a note to the
effect that the finder of the book will be rewarded upon its return to the owner.

149. SURVEY OF A FIELD FOR A DEED. — If a description for a deed is to be written, the lengths and bearings of all the
boundaries are desired. The traverse lines should therefore
follow the property lines, if possible. The bearings desired are
not those observed, but are those calculated by means of the
balanced transit angles as explained in Art. 419, p. 502, and
therefore are relatively as accurate as the angles themselves.
If a true meridian is found by astronomical observation (Chapter VIII) the bearings should be referred to this and marked **true**

bearings on the plan, and this information should also be contained in the deed.

A plan which is to accompany a deed should show such features as watercourses, highways, buildings, and adjoining property lines, as well as stone bounds, stakes, fences, walls, or other artificial objects which mark the boundaries of the property.

This plan should contain the following information.

(1) Lengths of all property lines together with their calculated bearings or the angles at the corners.*

(2) Location and description of corner bounds.

(3) Conventional sign or name on walls, fences, etc.

(4) Names of highways, streams or ponds, and names of adjacent property owners.

(5) Scale of drawing and direction of the meridian used (true or magnetic). It is better to refer all bearings to the true meridian when possible, and in such a case the direction of the magnetic needle should be shown also.†

(6) The title should include a simple and complete statement giving the name of owner, place, date, and name and address of surveyor. An explanatory note, such as a statement whether bearings refer to true or to magnetic meridian, may also be necessary. (See Art. 503, p. 578.)

---

* It is customary with many surveyors to omit from the plan certain data such as the angles or bearings, so that, while it may answer the purpose for which it was made, it does not contain all the data and frequently not enough to enable another surveyor to relocate the property. This is done, of course, so that when the tract is to be resurveyed or plotted it will be necessary to employ the same surveyor who has in his possession data for which the owner has paid and which the surveyor should have turned over to him. For a valuable paper on this subject see "The Ownership of Surveys, and what Constitutes a Survey and Map," by Professor William G. Raymond, published in *The Polytechnic*, the student journal of the Rensselaer Polytechnic Institute, Troy, N. Y., January, 1894.

† As magnetic bearings are unreliable (Art. 28, p. 23) true bearings should be used wherever their adoption does not entail too much additional expense. In those parts of the country which have been subdivided by the U. S. General Land Office true meridians can be obtained from the government surveys; in many of the older (Eastern) states true meridians have been established by local authorities. If the survey can be connected with any triangulation system such as that of the United States or the state surveys then, since the true bearings of all of the triangulation lines are known, the bearings of the traverse lines can be obtained.

150. Deed Description. — A deed description should give the bearings (or angles) and distances along each property line and should state whether bounded by a highway, stream, or private property together with the name of the owner. The description should run *to* and *along* lands of adjoining owners to aid in discovering mistakes which may have been made through carelessness of the conveyancer or coypist. The following paragraph is a deed description of the property shown in Fig. 53, p. 115. The magnetic bearing of the traverse line *AB* was assumed correct and from it the bearings of the walls and fences bounding the property were computed. (See Fig. 186, p. 528.)

" Beginning at a point in the northerly line of Willow Road in the town of Bancroft Mills, Maine, at an iron pipe sunk in the ground at the S. E. corner of land now or formerly belonging to Nathan H. Barnes, and running along the said northerly line N 85° 34′ E a distance of two hundred ninety-seven and seven-tenths (297.7) feet to the thread of channel of Stony Brook at land now or formerly belonging to James F. Hall; thence turning and running in a northerly direction, by thread of channel of said Stony Brook and land of said Hall, a distance of about three hundred and eight (308±) feet to a stone wall at land now or formerly belonging to Hiram Cole; thence turning and running along the middle of said stone wall and by land of said Cole N 86° 45′ W a distance of two hundred and five and eight-tenths (205.8) feet to the middle of another stone wall at land of said Barnes; thence turning and running by said latter stone wall and land of said Barnes S 0° 53′ E a distance of one hundred and seventy-seven and two-tenths (177.2) feet to a fence; thence turning and running by said fence and land of said Barnes N 87° 09′ W a distance of ninety-three and three-tenths (93.3) feet to an iron pipe sunk in the ground; thence turning and running by a fence and land of said Barnes S 1° 51′ W a distance of one hundred and sixty-nine and four-tenths (169.4) feet to the point of beginning; all the bearings being magnetic and the parcel containing a calculated area of 79,305 square feet more or less." Careful conveyancers prefer to write the bearings in words as well as in figures.

It is unfortunate that the description of the property in deeds in the vast majority of cases does not define the property in such a manner that it can be plotted from the description. Some descriptions in deeds are so loosely written as to contain nothing but the names of the owners of adjacent property, no bearings or distances being given.

151. LAWS RELATING TO BOUNDARIES.*— The surveyor really has no judicial functions; it is his function to *develop evidence* from his personal examination and measurements of the property and descriptions of it. But to do this intelligently he must obviously have some knowledge of the laws pertaining to property boundaries. All that will be attempted here is to state a few basic rulings to which the surveyor may expect that any court will adhere. It will be his further duty to inform himself as to the practice, professional and legal, prevailing in the particular region of his endeavor and to conform to it, for in this short text it will be impossible to discuss those many legal decisions which vary among the different states.

It is distinctly his duty to **find the position of the original boundaries** of the property and **not attempt to correct the original survey** even though he may be sure that an error exists in it. The surveyor must also fortify himself with the evidence that will convince the judge or jury that he has **actually retraced the old boundaries,** and that he has **followed the tracks of the original surveyor.**

Physical boundaries, provided they are mentioned in the deed,

---

* A more complete statement of the principles mentioned above, particularly with reference to the U. S. Public Land Surveys, will be found in an address on "The Judicial Functions of Surveyors," by Chief-Justice Cooley of the Michigan Supreme Court, read before the Michigan Association of Engineers and Surveyors, and published in the proceedings of the society for 1882, pp. 112-122.

"City Surveying for Title Examination" is a brochure written in 1921 by Edwin P. Clark, Esq., and published by Title Guarantee & Trust Co. of Brooklyn, N. Y., in which the author has contributed a fund of information on the laws and practice of land surveying.

A "Treatise on the Law of Surveying and Boundaries," by Frank Emerson Clark, Esq., published by The Bobbs-Merrill Co., Indianapolis, Ind., in 1922, treats of the usual legal decisions of different states and gives especial emphasis to those lands that come under the U. S. Public Land System.

"Legal Elements of Boundaries and Adjacent Properties" by Ray H. Skelton, published by The Bobbs-Merrill Co., Indianapolis, Ind., treats fully the technical and legal principles of boundary surveying.

have the legal force of monuments and therefore take precedence over courses and distances. These boundaries (or monuments) may be either " natural monuments " such as trees, lakes, boulders, ledges, etc., or " artificial monuments " such as fences, stone walls, posts, stakes, pits, mounds, stone bounds or other physical objects placed by man for boundary marks. Natural boundaries take precedence over those that are artificial because they are more permanent.

Where no physical boundaries can be found after an exhaustive search,* then the testimony of old reliable witnesses may be resorted to. It is important that these witnesses shall have no personal interest in the property and shall have had a good opportunity to observe the lost marks, fences, trees, or corner posts which limited the property. If the witness is personally interested in the land, then to have his testimony valuable it is necessary either that he shall have made the statements depended upon before any controversy has arisen regarding the line or else that his statements are detrimental to his own interest. It is not uncommonly true, after all evidence of persons familiar with the location of the lost lines has been analyzed, that one or more of the physical corner marks can now be found even though careful search had previously been made. Sometimes only a spot of discolored earth at the place pointed out by a witness as the corner will indicate where a corner post or stake, which has long since decayed, was undoubtedly located.

It is to be assumed that the deed was drawn by the grantor with honest intent to convey the property to the grantee. It shall therefore be interpreted if possible so as to make it effectual rather than void. The deed should also be construed in the light of what was known at the time when the title was transferred. In its interpretation it is assumed that it was intended to convey property the boundaries of which will form a closed

---

* It must not be assumed that a boundary is missing because it is not at once visible. Stone bounds are often buried 2 or 3 ft. deep; the top of a stake soon rots off, but evidences of the existence of the stake are often found many years after the top has disappeared, and the supposed location should be carefully examined and then dug over to find traces of the old stake. Care should be taken, however, that the evidence is not destroyed in the process of digging. Traces of the old wood or charcoal may often be found if great care is used.

traverse.   Therefore it is within the jurisdiction of the surveyor to reject any evident mistake in the description when running out the property line, e.g., a bearing that has obviously been recorded in the opposite direction or an entire side or chain-length omitted.   When the area does not agree with the boundaries as described in the deed, then the boundaries control.   All distances unless otherwise specified are to be taken as straight lines; but distances given as so many feet " along a wall " or " by a highway " are supposed to follow these lines even if they are not straight.   When a deed refers to a recorded plan the dimensions on that plan become a part of the deed description of the property.   (See Art. 153.)

Regarding the boundary of ownership of property abutting on highways the state laws are not uniform.   In some states the streets and roads are owned in fee by the state or municipality and when abandoned as highways do not revert to the former owners; in others the fee runs to the middle of the street subject to the public's use of the street; but when abandoned for such use it reverts to the respective private abutters.

The rights of owners of land bordering on streams, lakes, ponds, navigable and nonnavigable streams are different in different states.   The subdivision of lands gained by accretion is also a question as to which there is considerable divergence of opinion and practice.

It not infrequently happens that a land owner A has occupied for many years not only the part within his deed boundaries but also abutting land that formerly belonged to another person B. If such an occupancy by A of B's land has been open, adverse and continuous for 20 years A has become the owner of that part of B's land which he has been so occupying.   This is called obtaining title by " Adverse Possession."   This period of 20 years is the time required in many states of the Union.   In some states A can acquire part of the public highway in 40 years of continuous and notorious use.

It is a general rule that any excess or deficiency found upon subsequent measurement to exist in a line marked by permanent monuments at its ends only, must be distributed among the several subdivisions of the line in proportion to the original measurements. For example, if a city block originally surveyed as 600.00 ft. long and permanently monumented was subdivided into twelve lots of 50.00 ft. frontage, and the block is subsequently found to measure 600.24 ft. between monuments, then each lot should be given a frontage of 50.02 ft. This rule cannot be followed blindly. For example, if the frontage on one of the lots had been omitted from the plan or had been marked 50± ft., then the whole excess of 0.24 ft. should go into that unmarked or approximately marked frontage. This general rule applies also to dimensions of irregular shaped lots and to deficiency or excess in areas, as where the original dimensions appear to leave a strip or to overlap where two lots are intended to abut upon each other and where it is intended to convey the whole tract.

Whenever a plan of a single lot or of a plot in which this lot is contained is mentioned in a deed that plan or plot should also be recorded with the deed unless it has been recorded already.

152. RERUNNING OLD SURVEYS FROM A DEED.— Courses and distances recorded by the original survey are presumed to be correct. They seldom are, because of the change in declination of the needle, stretching of the chain or tape, errors due to poor plumbing, difference in pull of chainmen and even the customs of some of the earlier surveyors to give " full measure." Most distances given in old deeds will be found to be shorter than those obtained in recent surveys.

To follow the old survey is a relatively easy matter when its physical boundaries can be identified. If only one line of an old survey can be found marked by physical boundaries, its length and direction can then be measured and compared with the original survey record. They will doubtless be found to differ from the original, and this difference in course will show the **correction to apply to all of the original courses,** and similarly the difference in distance will give a **correction percentage to apply to all of the original dimensions.** Then with these new values for the courses and distances the old survey can be retraced.

If none of the old lines can be found but one old corner is identified, then the old survey must be rerun by courses and distances. As the old courses are usually magnetic bearings it is first necessary to find the declination of the needle at the date of the original survey as well as at the present time and to change all the bearings accordingly (Art. 29, p. 23). The declination of the needle should appear on the original deed or plan; but unfortunately it seldom does, and the year the survey was made must then be obtained either from the original deed, the old plan, or from witnesses, and the declination of the needle at that time computed. Observations at different places and times have been compiled by the U. S. Coast and Geodetic Survey, and these results may be found in convenient form for calculation in Reports and Special Publications of the Survey.* From these observations the approximate change in declination may be obtained probably as accurately as the original bearings were taken.

When taking magnetic bearings or declinations from a plan the surveyor should be on his guard. Not infrequently a plan is dated years after the bearings were observed, the plan being a copy, or partly a copy, of an older plan, old survey, or old deed description. He should discover additional supporting evidence before relying upon such bearings.

153. How to Look Up a Recorded Deed. — In all the states of the Union the transfer of real property must be recorded in the respective county Registry of Deeds or in the office of the city or town clerk. At the Registry of Deeds is kept an exact copy of the deed, which can be examined by any one. It is frequently necessary for the surveyor to make use of these copies when it is not convenient to obtain the deed from the owner of the property or when it is necessary to look up the deed of adjacent property or previous transfers of any of them.

In every Registry of Deeds is kept an index of deeds, which is divided into two parts, the *grantor* index and the *grantee* index; the grantor being the party who sells the land and the grantee the one who buys it. These indexes are frequently divided by years and for this reason the surveyor should know not only

---

* See U. S. Coast and Geodetic Survey Serial 592, " Magnetic Declination in the United States 1935 " and also Special Publication No. 117 entitled " The Earth's Magnetism." Additional information may be obtained by writing to The Director of U. S. Coast and Geodetic Survey, Washington, D. C.

the name of the party who bought or sold the property (both if it is convenient to get them), but also the approximate date of the transaction. With this information he can find in the proper index the name of the party, opposite which will appear the date of the transaction, the number of the deed book, and the page on which the copy of the deed is recorded. He then finds the deed book, from which he can copy whatever data he desires from the deed; usually the description of the property is all that concerns the surveyor. In the deed book there is usually a reference number in the margin, or in the text of the deed, which refers to the next preceding transfer of the same property or to any attachments, assignments, and the like which may have been made on it. This method of indexing and filing deeds is used in the New England States and in many of the other states; the general principles are the same throughout the country although the details may differ to some extent.

If a plan is referred to in a deed then the plan becomes a part of the description. In this case the filed plan should also be looked up at the Registry.

153a. LAND COURT. — In Massachusetts and in several other states of the Union a Land Registration Act is in force,* by which a Land Court has been established where adjudication of ownership and of boundaries can be had if desired. A decree issued by this Court registering a piece of land virtually makes the State the guarantor of both the validity of the title and the boundaries.

The usual procedure is for the land owner to petition the Court for registration, pay the required registration fees, and have a survey and plan made in accordance with the rules issued by the Court. The Court examines the chain of title to the land and notifies by mail and by public notice all persons that it has reason to believe may have any interest in the land, and a date for hearing is assigned. When the Court sits, the surveyor's plan of the land to be registered is produced and competent evidence as regards ownership and the boundaries shown

---

* In California, Colorado, Illinois, Minnesota, New York, North Carolina, Ohio, Oregon, Washington, Utah, Virginia, North Dakota, South Dakota, Georgia, Hawaii and the Philippine Islands.

by the plan is then heard. In controversial cases an attorney usually represents the petitioner, but in simpler cases the owner or his surveyor may present the evidence before the Court. The Court's decision, except upon matters of law, which may be reviewed by the Supreme Court, is final. Questions of fact may on petition be tried by jury, and if not, are determined by the Land Court.

The surveyor's plan is the basic evidence on which the Land Court starts. It is necessary, therefore, that this plan be prepared carefully and in accordance with the regulations of that Court, some of which regulations are stated in the next paragraph.

The surveyor is expected to indicate to the best of his knowledge the lines of ownership as well as boundary dimensions. His plan must be based upon a closed survey, accompanied by his field notes and computations. The errors of the survey must be balanced so that the boundary angles and distances mathematically and exactly define a polygon. (Art. 422, p. 506.) The accuracy required in the fieldwork is a closure of 1 in 10 000 for valuable city or town land where the boundaries are the middle of partition walls, faces of buildings or fences, etc.; a closure of 1 in 8000 for residential and suburban districts; 1 in 5000 for country estates; and 1 in 3000 for farms and woodlands. Every survey must join two or more permanent bounds, preferably intervisible, from which to relocate the boundaries at any future time. If such bounds do not exist already, then they must be placed by the surveyor. They need not be artificial; they may be drill-holes in ledge or offsets from the masonry underpinning of permanent buildings. Where it is found practicable the survey should be connected with triangulation points of town, city or state survey systems and with municipal boundary lines. Most lands abut on a public or a private way; this necessitates first the rerunning of the side lines of such way. Records of these lines are usually found in the offices of the city or town engineers, county clerks, county commissioners, park, highway, or water commissioners. When re-establishing these lines it should be remembered that stone monuments which have been previously set at angle points or at the beginning or end of curves are sometimes displaced by frost action, or by other causes; these should not be assumed to be in their correct location until verified by accurate survey. Detailed statements of the requirements for land plans are usually issued by the engineer of the Land Court.

THE UNITED STATES SYSTEM OF SURVEYING THE PUBLIC LANDS

154. The System. — The United States System of Surveying the Public Lands, which was inaugurated in 1784, and modified since by various acts of Congress, requires that the public lands "shall be divided by north and south lines run according to the true meridian, and by others crossing them at right angles so as to form townships six miles square," and that the corners of the townships thus surveyed "must be marked with progressive numbers from the beginning." Also, that the townships shall be subdivided into thirty-six sections, each of which shall contain six hundred and forty acres, as nearly as may be, by a system of two sets of parallel lines, one governed by true meridians and the other by parallels of latitude, the latter intersecting the former at right angles, at intervals of a mile.

Since the meridians converge it is evident that the requirement that the lines shall conform to true meridians and that townships shall be six miles square, is mathematically impossible. In order to conform as nearly as practicable to the spirit of the law, and also to make its application both uniform and effective, an elaborate system of subdivision has been worked out. This system will be described in this chapter, first in its general and afterward in its more detailed features; this will then be followed by a discussion of the ways in which the work of present-time county and other local surveyors is related to the Public Lands System.

The work of the Public Lands Surveys is and has been carried on under the direction of the Commissioner of the General Land Office. Usually the area comprised in each State or Territory has been denominated a District, and has been placed in direct charge of a Surveyor General. The functions that the Surveyor General exercises in his District may be likened to those of a division engineer on construction work; he examines the Deputy Surveyors, approves their contracts, and inspects their fieldwork. The maps, field-notes and other records are kept at his office until all the subdivision work in his district is completed, when they are turned over to the State to which they pertain, and the office of the Surveyor General is then discontinued. (See Art. 175, p. 172.)

The actual surveying operations are performed by Deputy Surveyors, who run the lines in the manner specified in the Manual* or as directed in detail by the Surveyor General. This work was formerly done under contract, at stipulated prices per mile for lines of various degrees of importance or difficulty. These prices varied from time to time, with the demand for and supply of deputies, the relative degree of accuracy with which the work was required to be done, and with other conditions.

Higher rates were paid for *standard* lines, which constitute the general framework or control for the subdivision work; the *township* lines in turn were rated higher than the *section* lines. It is the obvious intention, and has been the general practice, to secure a somewhat higher degree of accuracy for the more important lines by awarding them to the more experienced and skilful deputies, while inexperienced or less skilful surveyors were employed on subdivision work. It follows from this that in the relocation of lost corners more weight may properly be given to the more important lines.

In the following named States and Territories the surveying of Public Lands is still in progress.

Alaska	Idaho	Oregon
Arizona	Montana	Utah
California	Nevada	Washington
Colorado	New Mexico	Wyoming

---

* Manual of Surveying Instructions for the Survey of the Public Lands issued by the Commissioner of the General Land Office, Washington, D. C.

TABLE SHOWING RATES FORMERLY PRESCRIBED FOR PAY-
MENT PER LINEAR MILE FOR SURVEYING PUBLIC LANDS

	Standard and Meander Lines	Township Lines	Section Lines
Minimum rates: ordinary favorable conditions	$9	$7	$5
Intermediate rates: lands heavily timbered, or mountainous.........	$13	$11	$7
Maximum rates: exceptionally difficult surveys......................	$18	$15	$12
Special maximum rates: exceptionally difficult surveys in remote districts...........................	$25	$23	$20

NOTE. — Under an act of Congress approved June 25, 1910 (36 stat. 740) it was provided, under " Surveying the Public Lands "; " **The surveys and re-surveys to be made by such competent surveyors as the Secretary of the Interior may select . . .** " This provision of law **brought to a close the contract system,** and payment by the mile for surveys was no longer authorized. In addition to this, the act of Congress approved Mar. 3, 1925 (43 stat. 1144) **abolished the office of Surveyor General** and provided that the duties previously performed by those offices should be transferred to and consolidated with the Field Surveying Service under the jurisdiction of the United States Supervisor of Surveys. There are still maintained twelve surveying districts under the direction of District Cadastral Engineers, one each at Phoenix, Ariz., San Francisco, Cal., Denver, Colo., Boise, Idaho, Helena, Mont., Reno, Nev., Santa Fe, New Mexico, Portland, Oregon, Salt Lake City, Utah, Olympia, Washington and Cheyenne, Wyoming. There is also one at Juneau, Alaska under the direction of the Cadastral Engineer in charge.

155. Process of Subdivision. — It will be convenient to consider the process of subdivision as separated into several distinct operations, to be carried out in sequence. It must be understood, however, that one operation, for instance, the division of the area into 24-mile tracts, is rarely or never completed over the entire area to be covered before the next operation in order is begun; a single surveying camp may be carrying on two or three different operations before removing from the neighborhood, for example, running township exteriors and immediately afterward subdividing the townships into sections.

Briefly stated, the subdivision work is carried on as follows:

FIRST.   The establishment of

(a) An *Initial Point* by astronomical observations.

(b) A *Principal Meridian* conforming to a true meridian of longitude through the Initial Point, and extending both north and south therefrom, and

(c) A *Base-Line* conforming to a true parallel of latitude

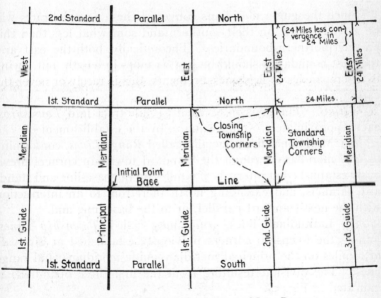

FIG. 57.   SHOWING DIVISION INTO 24-MILE BLOCKS.

through the Initial Point, and extending both east and west therefrom.   This initial operation is indicated in Fig. 57.

Evidently the principal meridian will be marked out on the ground as a straight line, while the base-line will follow the curve of a due east and west line, being at every point at right angles to

the meridian through that point. The field methods prescribed
for running out the principal meridian and the base-line on the
ground are described in detail in Arts. 159–60, pp. 148–53.

SECOND. The division of the area to be surveyed into tracts
approximately 24 miles square (Fig. 57) by the establishment of

(a) *Standard Parallels* conforming to true parallels of latitude
through the 24-mile points previously established on the principal
meridian, and extending both east and west therefrom, and

(b) *Guide Meridians* conforming to true meridians of longitude through the 24-mile points previously established on the
base-line and standard parallels, and extending north therefrom
to an intersection with the next standard parallel or to the base-
line.

Since the guide meridians converge, these 24-mile tracts will
be 24 miles wide on their southern and somewhat less than this
on their northern boundaries. Theoretically, both the east and
the west boundaries should be just 24 miles in length, but, owing
to discrepancies of field measurements, this is rarely or never the
case.

THIRD. The division of each 24-mile tract into *Townships*,
each approximately 6 miles square, by the establishment of

(a) Meridional lines, usually called *Range Lines*, conforming
to true meridians through the standard township corners previously established at intervals of 6 miles on the base-line and standard parallels, and extending north therefrom to an intersection
with the next standard parallel, or to the base-line, and

(b) Latitudinal lines, sometimes called *Township Lines*,
joining the township corners previously established at intervals
of 6 miles on the principal meridian, guide meridians, and range
lines. The division resulting from the first three operations is
indicated in Fig. 58.

It will be apparent that, neglecting the effect of discrepancies
and irregularities in measurement, both the east and the west
boundaries of all townships will be just 6 miles in length, but the
north and south boundaries will vary in length from a maximum
at the standard parallel or base-line forming the southern limit
of the 24-mile tract to a minimum at that forming its northern
limit.

FOURTH. The subdivision of each township into *Sections*, each approximately 1 mile square and containing about 640 acres, by the establishment of *Section Lines*, both meridional and latitudinal, parallel to and at intervals of 1 mile from the eastern and southern boundaries of the township. (See Fig. 63, p. 166.)

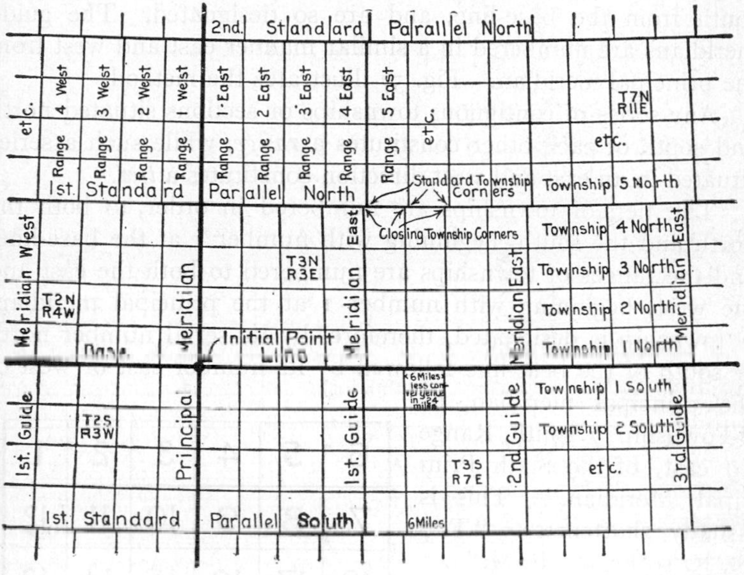

FIG. 58. SHOWING SUBDIVISION OF 24-MILE BLOCKS INTO TOWNSHIPS.

Assuming all fieldwork to be done with mathematical exactness, this subdivision would result in sections exactly 80 chains (1 mile) on each of the four sides,* except the most westerly range of 6 sections in each township, which would be less than 80 chains in width by an amount varying with the distance from the southern boundary of the 24-mile tract. The extent to which this condition is realized in practice is indicated in Art. 167, p. 158, wherein the usual field methods of subdividing a township are described in detail.

---

* These theoretical Sections would not be exactly square, as may be readily perceived, but would be rhomboids.

156. Methods of Designating Lines and Areas. — The various principal meridians and base-lines of the Public Lands Surveys are designated by definite names or by number, as, for example, "The Fifth Principal Meridian and Base-Line," or "The Cimarron Meridian."

The standard parallels are numbered in order both north and south from the base-line, and are so designated. The guide meridians are numbered in a similar manner east and west from the principal meridian. Fig. 57 illustrates the method.

Any series of contiguous townships or sections situated north and south of each other constitutes a *range*, while such a series situated in an east and west direction constitutes a *tier*.

The tiers of townships are numbered in order, to both the north and the south, beginning with number 1 at the base-line; and the ranges of townships are numbered to both the east and the west, beginning with number 1 at the principal meridian. A township is designated, therefore, by its serial number north or south of the base-line followed by its number east or west of the principal meridian, as "Township 7 south, Range 19 east, of the Sixth Principal Meridian." This is usually shortened to "T. 7 S., R. 19 E., 6th P. M."

The sections of a township are numbered commencing with No. 1 at the northeast angle of the township, and proceeding west to No. 6, and then proceeding east to No. 12, and so on, alternately, to No. 36, in the southeast angle as illustrated by Fig. 59. In all cases of surveys of fractional

6	5	4	3	2	1
7	8	9	10	11	12
18	17	16	15	14	13
19	20	21	22	23	24
30	29	28	27	26	25
31	32	33	34	35	36

Fig. 59. Diagram of a Township Illustrating Method of Numbering the Sections.

townships the sections will bear the same numbers they would have if the township were complete.

The regular subdivisions of a Section are indicated by stating briefly the aliquot part of the section intended together with its location in the section, as "the N. $\frac{1}{2}$ of the S.W. $\frac{1}{4}$ of Sec. 27, T. 12 N., R. 5 W."

157. Field Methods. — The work of subdivision of the Public Lands has already been largely completed, and the surveyor of to-day is usually concerned only with the retracing of old lines, the relocation of lost corners, or with the subdivision work that comes with increase in population. For all these, however, a thoroughgoing knowledge of at least the common field processes and methods that have been used in the original surveys is essential. Certain details of field practice have varied somewhat from time to time, but the leading features have remained fairly constant for all those areas that have been surveyed since the system became well established.

In the following pages is given a somewhat detailed description of the methods commonly employed in carrying out the operations briefly indicated in Art. 155. Inasmuch, however, as certain of the east and west lines are required to be established as true parallels of latitude, the two commonly accepted methods of accomplishing this will first be described.

158. TO ESTABLISH A PARALLEL OF LATITUDE. — A parallel of latitude on the surface of a sphere is a curved line. This may be understood from the facts that the meridians converge toward the pole, and that a parallel is at every point at right angles to the meridian at that point. If vertical lines are drawn through every point on a parallel of latitude they will form a conical surface, the apex of the cone being at the center of the sphere. In the case of a straight line all of the verticals would lie in the same plane, and this plane would intersect the sphere in a great circle.

A parallel of latitude may be run out by means of the solar attachment to the transit, since by using this instrument the direction of the meridian may be quickly found whenever the sun is visible (Art. 240, p. 280). A line which at every point is at right angles to the meridian will be a true parallel of latitude. This method, however, is found to give results less accurate than are required, chiefly on account of the errors in the adjustment of the solar attachment.

A better method of establishing a parallel is by taking offsets from a straight line. Two methods of doing this, known as the *Secant Method* and the *Tangent Method*, are used in the Public Lands Surveys.

159. The Secant Method. * — (Fig. 60.) "This method consists of running a connected series of straight lines, each six miles long, on such courses that any one of the lines will intersect the curve of the parallel of latitude in two points, separated by an interval of four miles; and from this line thus established, measuring north or south, as the case may be, to attain other required

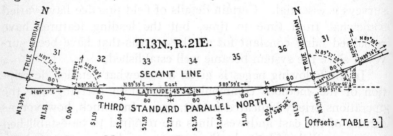

FIG. 60. SECANT METHOD FOR ESTABLISHING A PARALLEL OF LATITUDE.

points on the latitude curve." The o and 6 mile points of a parallel will be north of the secant, and the 2, 3, and 4 mile points will be south of the secant.

The instrument is set up south of the township corner where the survey is to begin, the distance from the corner being found in Table 3 in the column headed "o miles." For example, in latitude 40° the transit would be set 2.79 feet south of the corner. The direction of the first secant at its initial point is found by observing on Polaris (Chapter VIII) to obtain the true meridian and then laying off the azimuth angle found in Table 3 under "o miles." (See Fig. 60.) This angle should be repeated several times to determine accurately the direction of the secant. This direction is then prolonged 6 miles. At each mile and half-mile point an offset is measured to establish a point on the curve, the distance and direction of the offset being shown in Table 3.

* The quotations are from the "Manual of Surveying Instructions for the Survey of the Public Lands of the United States," prepared by the Commissioner of the General Land Office in 1902.

TABLE 3.

Azimuths of the Secant, and Offsets, in Feet, to the Parallel.

Latitude in left-hand column and distance from starting point at top or bottom of the table.

Latitude	Azimuths and offsets at —							Deflection Angle and nat. tan. to Rad. 66 ft.
	o miles.	½ mile.	1 mile.	1½ miles.	2 miles.	2½ miles.	3 miles.	
30	89° 58′.5	89° 58′.7	89° 59′.0	89° 59′.2	89° 59′.5	89° 59′.7	90° (E. or W.)	3′ 00″.2
	1.93 N.	0.87 N.	0.00	0.67 S.	1.15 S.	1.44 S.	1.54 S.	0.69 ins.
31	89° 58′.4	89° 58′.6	89° 58′.9	89° 59′.2	89° 59′.5	89° 59′.7	90° (E. or W.)	3′ 07″.4
	2.01 N.	0.91 N.	0.00	0.70 S.	1.20 S.	1.50 S.	1.60 S.	0.72 ins.
32	89° 58′.4	89° 58′.6	89° 58′.9	89° 59′.2	89° 59′.5	89° 59′.7	90° (E. or W.)	3′ 15″.0
	2.09 N.	0.94 N.	0.00	0.73 S.	1.25 S.	1.56 S.	1.67 S.	0.75 ins.
33	89° 58′.3	89° 58 .5	89° 58′.8	89° 59′.1	89° 59′.4	89° 59′.7	90° (E. or W.)	3′ 22″.6
	2.17 N.	0.97 N.	0.00	0.76 S.	1.30 S.	1.62 S.	1.73 S.	0.78 ins.
34	89° 58′.2	89° 58′.5	89° 58′.8	89° 59′.1	89° 59′.4	89° 59′.7	90° (E. or W.)	3′ 30″.4
	2.25 N.	1.01 N.	0.00	0.79 S.	1.35 S.	1.69 S.	1.80 S.	0.81 ins.
35	89° 58′.2	89° 58′.5	89° 58′.8	89° 59′.1	89° 59′.4	89° 59′.7	90° (E. or W.)	3′ 38″.4
	2.33 N.	1.05 N.	0.00	0.82 S.	1.40 S.	1.75 S.	1.87 S.	0.84 ins.
36	89° 58′.1	89° 58′.4	89° 58′.7	89° 59′.0	89° 59′.4	89° 59′.7	90° (E. or W.)	3′ 46″.4
	2.42 N.	1.09 N.	0.00	0.85 S.	1.46 S.	1.82 S.	1.94 S.	0.87 ins.
37	89° 58′.0	89° 58′.3	89° 58′.6	89° 59′.0	89° 59′.3	89° 59′.7	90° (E. or W.)	3′ 55″.0
	2.51 N.	1.13 N.	0.00	0.88 S.	1.51 S.	1.89 S.	2.01 S	0.90 ins.
38	89° 58′.0	89° 58′.3	89° 58′.6	89° 58′.9	89° 59′.3	89° 59′.7	90° (E. or W.	4′ 03″.6
	2.61 N.	1.17 N.	0.00	0.91 S.	1.56 S.	1.96 S.	2.08 S.	0.93 ins.
39	89° 57′.9	89° 58′.2	89° 58′.6	89° 58′.9	89° 59′.3	89° 59′.7	90° (E. or W.)	4′ 12″.6
	2.70 N.	1.21 N.	0.00	0.94 S.	1.62 S.	2.02 S.	2.16 S.	0.97 ins.
40	89° 57′.8	89° 58′.1	89° 58′.5	89° 58′.9	89° 59′.3	89° 59′.7	90° (E. or W.)	4′ 21″.6
	2.79 N.	1.25 N.	0.00	0.98 S.	1.68 S.	2.10 S.	2.24 S.	1.00 ins.
41	89° 57′.7	89° 58′.0	89° 58′.4	89° 58′.8	89° 59′.2	89° 59′.6	90° (E. or W.)	4′ 31″.2
	2.89 N.	1.30 N.	0.00	1.02 S.	1.74 S.	2.17 S.	2.32 S.	1.04 ins.
42	89° 57′.7	89° 58′.0	89° 58′.4	89° 58′.8	89° 59′.2	89° 59′.6	90° (E. or W.)	4′ 40″.8
	3.00 N.	1.35 N.	0.00	1.05 S.	1.86 S.	2.25 S.	2.40 S.	1.08 ins.
43	89° 57′.6	89° 58′.0	89° 58′.4	89° 58′.8	89° 59′.2	89° 59′.6	90° (E. or W.)	4′ 50″.8
	3.11 N.	1.40 N.	0.00	1.08 S.	1.86 S.	2.33 S.	2.48 S.	1.12 ins.
44	89° 57′.5	89° 57′.9	89° 58′.3	89° 58′.7	89° 59′.2	89° 59′.6	90° (E. or W.)	5′ 01″.0
	3.22 N.	1.45 N.	0.00	1.12 S.	1.93 S.	2.41 S.	2.57 S.	1.16 ins.
45	89° 57′.4	89° 57′.8	89° 58′.3	89° 58′.7	89° 59′.1	89° 59′.5	90° (E. or W.)	5′ 11″.8
	3.33 N.	1.50 N.	0.00	1.16 S.	2.00 S.	2.49 S.	2.66 S	1.20 ins.
46	89° 57′.3	89° 57′.7	89° 58′.2	89° 58′.6	89° 59′.1	89° 59′.5	90° (E. or W.)	5′ 22″.8
	3.44 N.	1.55 N.	0.00	1.21 S.	2.07 S.	2.59 S.	2.76 S.	1.24 ins.
47	89° 57′.2	89° 57′.6	89° 58′.1	89° 58′.6	89° 59′.1	89° 59′.5	90° (E. or W.)	5′ 34″.2
	3.57 N.	1.61 N.	0.00	1.25 S.	2.14 S.	2.67 S.	2.86 S.	1.28 ins.
48	89° 57′.1	89° 57′.5	89° 58′.0	89° 58′.5	89° 59′.0	89° 59′.5	90° (E. or W.)	5′ 46″.2
	3.70 N.	1.66 N.	0.00	1.30 S.	2.22 S.	2.78 S.	2.96 S.	1.33 ins.
49	89° 57′.0	89° 57′.5	89° 58′.0	89° 58′.5	89° 59′.0	89° 59′.5	90° (E. or W.)	5′ 58″.6
	3.82 N.	1.72 N.	0.00	1.34 S.	2.30 S.	2.87 S.	3.06 S.	1.38 ins.
50	89° 56′.9	89° 57′.4	89° 57′.9	89° 58′.4	89° 59′.0	89° 59′.5	90° (E. or W.)	6′ 11″.4
	3.96 N.	1.78 N.	0.00	1.39 S.	2.38 S.	2.97 S.	3.17 S.	1.43 ins.
	6 miles.	5½ miles.	5 miles.	4½ miles.	4 miles.	3½ miles.	3 miles.	Deflection Angle and nat. tan. to Rad. 66 ft.

Latitude.

Azimuths and offsets at—

When the 6-mile point is reached the direction of a new secant is found by turning off to the north the deflection angle given in the right-hand column of Table 3. The offsets are then measured from this line as from the preceding one. The chief advantage of this method is that the offsets are short and hence much cutting is saved in wooded regions.

"With ordinary field instruments, usually reading to single minutes only, fractional parts of the 'least count' are generally estimated by the eye. Greater accuracy may be attained by making use of a linear measure to lay off deflection angles." In the right-hand column of Table 3 are given linear dimensions

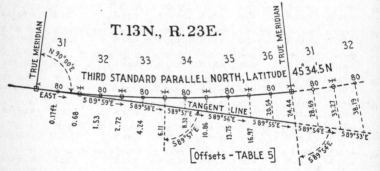

Fig. 61. Tangent Method for Establishing a Parallel of Latitude.

suitable for use in laying off the deflection angles corresponding to the various latitudes noted. In using this extremely valuable method of laying off small angles, a point is first carefully marked, by double centering, at a distance of one chain (66 feet) from the instrument. A scale divided to decimals of an inch is then used to measure off toward the north the appropriate distance taken from the Table, and the vertical cross-wire of the transit is moved through the angle subtended. The reading of the vernier will check the measurement and guard against large errors. The direction thus determined is then prolonged in the usual manner.

160. "The Tangent Method. — This method consists in laying off from a true meridian, established by observations on Polaris at elongation, an angle of 90°, producing the direction thus determined, a distance of 6 miles, in a straight line, and

TABLE 4.

Azimuths of the Tangent to the Parallel.

[The azimuth is the smaller angle the tangent makes with the true meridian and always measured from the north and towards the tangential points.]

Latitude.	1 mile.			2 miles.			3 miles.			4 miles.			5 miles.			6 miles.		
°	°	′	″	°	′	″	°	′	″	°	′	″	°	′	″	°	′	″
30	89	59	30.0	89	58	59.9	89	58	29.9	89	57	59.9	89	57	29.9	89	56	59.8
31	89	59	28.8	89	58	57.5	89	58	26.3	89	57	55.0	89	57	23.8	89	56	52.5
32	89	59	27.5	89	58	55.0	89	58	22.5	89	57	50.0	89	57	17.5	89	56	45.0
33	89	59	26.2	89	58	52.5	89	58	18.7	89	57	44.9	89	57	11.2	89	56	37.4
34	89	59	24.9	89	58	49.9	89	58	14.8	89	57	39.7	89	57	04.6	89	56	29.6
35	89	59	23.6	89	58	47.2	89	58	10.8	89	57	34.4	89	56	58.0	89	56	21.6
36	89	59	22.2	89	58	44.4	89	58	06.8	89	57	28.9	89	56	51.1	89	56	13.4
37	89	59	20.8	89	58	41.6	89	58	02.5	89	57	23.3	89	56	44.1	89	56	05.0
38	89	59	19.4	89	58	38.8	89	57	58.2	89	57	17.5	89	56	36.9	89	55	56.3
39	89	59	17.9	89	58	35.8	89	57	53.7	89	57	11.6	89	56	29.6	89	55	47.5
40	89	59	16.4	89	58	32.8	89	57	49.2	89	57	05.5	89	56	21.9	89	55	38.3
41	89	59	14.8	89	58	29.6	89	57	44.4	89	56	59.3	89	56	14.1	89	55	28.9
42	89	59	13.2	89	58	26.4	89	57	39.6	89	56	52.8	89	56	06.0	89	55	19.2
43	89	59	11.5	89	58	23.1	89	57	34.6	89	56	46.2	89	55	57.7	89	55	09.2
44	89	59	09.8	89	58	19.6	89	57	29.5	89	56	39.3	89	55	49.1	89	54	58.9
45	89	59	08.0	89	58	16.1	89	57	24.1	89	56	32.1	89	55	40.2	89	54	48.2
46	89	59	06.2	89	58	12.4	89	57	18.6	89	56	24.8	89	55	31.0	89	54	37.2
47	89	59	04.3	89	58	08.6	89	57	12.9	89	56	17.1	89	55	21.4	89	54	25.7
48	89	59	02.3	89	58	04.6	89	57	06.9	89	56	09.2	89	55	11.5	89	54	13.8
49	89	59	00.2	89	58	00.5	89	57	00.7	89	56	00.9	89	55	01.2	89	54	01.4
50	89	58	58.1	89	57	56.2	89	56	54.3	89	55	52.6	89	54	50.5	89	53	48.5

Latitude.	7 miles.			8 miles.			9 miles.			10 miles.			11 miles.			12 miles.		
°	°	′	″	°	′	″	°	′	″	°	′	″	°	′	″	°	′	″
30	89	56	29.8	89	55	59.8	89	55	29.8	89	54	59.7	89	54	29.7	89	53	59.7
31	89	56	21.3	89	55	50.0	89	55	18.8	89	54	47.6	89	54	16.3	89	53	45.1
32	89	56	12.5	89	55	40.0	89	55	07.6	89	54	35.1	89	54	02.6	89	53	30.1
33	89	56	03.6	89	55	29.9	89	54	56.1	80	54	22.3	80	53	48.5	80	53	14.8
34	89	55	54.5	89	55	19.4	89	54	44.4	89	54	09.3	89	53	34.2	89	52	59.1
35	89	55	45.2	89	55	08.8	89	54	32.3	89	53	55.9	89	53	19.5	89	52	43.1
36	89	55	35.6	89	54	57.8	89	54	20.0	89	53	42.3	89	53	04.5	89	52	26.7
37	89	55	25.8	89	54	46.6	89	54	07.4	89	53	28.2	89	52	49.1	89	52	09.9
38	89	55	15.7	89	54	35.1	89	53	54.5	89	53	13.9	89	52	33.2	89	51	52.6
39	89	55	05.4	89	54	23.3	89	53	41.2	89	52	59.1	89	52	17.0	89	51	34.9
40	89	54	54.7	89	54	11.1	89	53	27.5	89	52	43.8	89	52	00.2	89	51	16.6
41	89	54	43.7	89	53	58.5	89	53	13.4	89	52	28.2	89	51	43.0	89	50	57.8
42	89	54	32.4	89	53	45.6	89	52	58.8	89	52	12.0	89	51	25.2	89	50	38.4
43	89	54	20.8	89	53	32.3	89	52	43.8	89	51	55.4	89	51	06.9	89	50	18.5
44	89	54	08.7	89	53	18.5	89	52	28.4	89	51	38.2	89	50	48.0	89	49	57.8
45	89	53	56.3	89	53	04.3	89	52	12.3	89	51	20 4	89	50	28.4	89	49	36.4
46	89	53	43.4	89	52	49.5	89	51	55.7	89	51	01.9	89	50	08.1	89	49	14.3
47	89	53	30.0	89	52	34.3	89	51	38.6	89	50	42.9	89	49	47.2	89	48	51.4
48	89	53	16.1	89	52	18.4	89	51	20.7	89	50	23.0	89	49	25.3	89	48	27.6
49	89	53	01.7	89	52	01.9	89	51	02.1	89	50	02.4	89	49	02.6	89	48	02.8
50	89	52	46.6	89	51	44.7	89	50	42.8	89	49	40.9	89	48	39.0	89	47	37.1

TABLE 5.

OFFSETS, IN FEET, FROM TANGENT TO PARALLEL.

Lati-tude.	1 mile	2 miles	3 miles.	4 miles.	5 miles.	6 miles.
30°	0.38	1.54	3.46	6.15	9.61	13.83
31	0.40	1·60	3.60	6.40	10.00	14.40
32	0.42	1.66	3.74	6.65	10.40	14.97
33	0.43	1.73	3.89	6.91	10.80	15.56
34	0.45	1.80	4.04	7.18	11.22	16.16
35	0.47	1.86	4.19	7.45	11.65	16.77
36	0.48	1.93	4.35	7.73	12.09	17.40
37	0.50	2.01	4.51	8.02	12.53	18.05
38	0.52	2.08	4.68	8.32	12.99	18.71
39	0.54	2.15	4.85	8.62	13.47	19.39
40	0.56	2.23	5.02	8.93	13.95	20.09
41	0.58	2.31	5.20	9.25	14.46	20.81
42	0.60	2.40	5.39	9.58	14.97	21.56
43	0.62	2.48	5.58	9.92	15.50	22.33
44	0.64	2.57	5.78	10.28	16.06	23.12
45	0.67	2.66	5.99	10.64	16.62	23.94
46	0.69	2.75	6.20	11.02	17.21	24.79
47	0.71	2.85	6.42	11.41	17.83	25.67
48	0.74	2.95	6.65	11.81	18.46	26.58
49	0.76	3.06	6.88	12.24	19.12	27.53
50	0.79	3.17	7.13	12.68	19.81	28.52

Lati-tude.	7 miles.	8 miles.	9 miles.	10 miles.	11 miles.	12 miles.
30	18.83	24.59	31.13	38.43	46.50	55.33
31	19.59	25.59	32.39	39.99	48.39	57.58
32	20.38	26.61	33.68	41.58	50.32	59.88
33	21.18	27.66	35.00	43.22	52.29	62.23
34	21.99	28.73	36.36	44.88	54.31	64.63
35	22.83	29.82	37.74	46.59	56.38	67.09
36	23.69	30.94	39.16	48.34	58.49	69.61
37	24.57	32.09	40.61	50.13	60.66	72.19
38	25.47	33.27	42.10	51.98	62.89	74.85
39	26.40	34.48	43.63	53.87	65.18	77.57
40	27.35	35.72	45.21	55.82	67.54	80.38
41	28.33	37.01	46.83	57.82	69.96	83.26
42	29.34	38.33	48.51	59.89	72.46	86.24
43	30.39	39.69	50.24	62.02	75.04	89.31
44	31.47	41.10	52.02	64.22	77.71	92.48
45	32.58	42.56	53.86	66.50	80.46	95.76
46	33.74	44.07	55.78	68.86	83.32	99.16
47	34.94	45.63	57.76	71.30	86.28	102.68
48	36.18	47.26	59.81	73.84	89.35	106.33
49	37.48	48.95	61.95	76.48	92.54	110.13
50	38.82	50.71	64.17	79.23	95.87	114.09

measuring north therefrom, at half-mile intervals, distances of correct length, taken from Table 5 (interpolated if necessary), for the given latitude, to attain other points on the latitude curve passing through the tangential or initial points.

" The azimuth or bearing of the tangent at successive mile points will be taken from Table 4 to the nearest whole minute only, and will be inserted in the field notes, no interpolation being required, except when test sights are taken. The true bearing between two points on a standard parallel will be derived from Table 4 by taking it in the column headed with one-half the distance between said points. The offsets at intervals of one mile are inserted in Table 5; to obtain the length of offsets at the half-mile points, take one-fourth of the offset corresponding to twice the distance of the half-mile point from the tangential point.

"This method is suitable for running standard parallels and latitudinal township lines in a level open country, where no intersections with topographical features will be required; but in all cases the secant method will be found most convenient."

" 161. Initial Points. — Initial points from which the lines of the public surveys are to be extended will be established whenever necessary, under such special instructions as may be prescribed in each case by the Commissioner of the General Land Office. The locus of such initial points will be selected with great care and due consideration for their prominence and easy identification, and must be established astronomically.

"An initial point should have a conspicuous location, visible from distant points on lines; it should be perpetuated by an indestructible monument, preferably a copper bolt firmly set in a rock edge; and it should be witnessed by rock bearings, without relying on anything perishable like wood."

162. Base-Line. — From the initial point the base-line is extended both east and west on a true parallel of latitude, one of the methods described in the foregoing paragraphs being used. Great care is taken to secure instrumental accuracy. Two back and two fore sights are taken at each setting of the instrument, the horizontal limb being revolved 180° in azimuth between the observations, in one method, taking the mean of observations. Another method, called double back and fore

sights, is still more exact, and therefore preferable. In this process the vertical cross-wire is fixed upon two transit points at some distance apart, in the rear, and then reversed to set one or two new points in advance. This not only insures a straight line, if the transit is leveled, but also detects the least error of collimation. (See Art. 64, p. 58.)

"Where solar apparatus is used in connection with a transit, the deputy will test the instrument, whenever practicable, by comparing its indications with a meridian determined by Polaris observations; and in all cases where error is discovered he will make the necessary corrections of his line before proceeding with the survey. All operations will be fully described in the field notes.

"In order to detect errors and insure accuracy in measurement, two sets of chainmen will be employed; one to note distances to intermediate points and to locate topographical features, the other to act as a check. Each will measure 40 chains, and in case the difference is inconsiderable, the proper corner will be placed midway between the ending points of the two measurements; but if the discrepancy exceed 8 links on even ground, or 25 links on mountainous surface, the true distance will be found by careful re-chaining by one party or both.

"The deputy will be present when each corner is thus established, and will record in the body of his field notes the distances to the same, according to the measurement by each set of chainmen.

"To obviate collusion between the sets of chainmen, the second set should commence at a point in advance of the beginning corner of the first set, the initial difference in measurement thus obtained being known only to the deputy."

The proper township, section, and quarter-section corners are established at the appropriate intervals, and meander and witness corners (Arts. 171-3, pp. 167-170) are set wherever the line crosses such streams, lakes, bayous, or other objects as may make their use necessary. Stones or posts used to mark the positions of the township or section corners are marked on their north face with the letters SC, for "standard corner," for the purpose of easily distinguishing them from the "closing corners," to be set later.

163. Principal Meridian. — The principal meridian is extended as a true meridian of longitude both north and south from the initial point. The methods used for the determination of directions, and the precautions observed to secure accuracy of measurement, are the same as those described in the preceding article, under the subject of "Base-Line."

Also, as in the case of the base-line, all township, section, quarter-section, and other necessary corners are established in the proper places as the survey proceeds.

164. Standard Parallels. — Standard parallels, which are also sometimes referred to as *correction lines*, are extended both east and west from every fourth township corner previously established on the principal meridian. Sometimes, however, the distance between them is more or less than 24 miles, depending upon the requirements of the particular survey in question. For example, in Kansas the correction lines occur at regular intervals of 30 instead of 24 miles. In all cases deviations from the regular order are made only under the written special instructions of the Surveyor General. The Manual provides further that "where gross irregularities (in previous surveys) require additional standard lines, from which to initiate new, or upon which to close old surveys, an intermediate correction line should be established to which a local name may be given, e.g., 'Cedar Creek Correction Line'; and the same will be run, in all respects, like the regular standard parallels."

Standard parallels are established as true parallels of latitude, and are run in the same manner and with the same precautions for accuracy as in the survey of the base-line.

Appropriate corners are established at the proper intervals, and the township and section corners are marked *SC* on their north face, the same as those on the base-line.

165. Guide Meridians. — Guide meridians are extended north from the base-line, or standard parallels, at intervals of 24 miles east and west from the principal meridian. They are run as true meridians of longitude, and are extended to an intersection with the next correction line north. At the point of intersection of the guide meridian with the correction line a *closing corner* is established, and the stone or post is marked on its south face with the letters *CC*, to distinguish it from the standard corners already in place. Also, the distance of the closing corner from the nearest standard corner is measured and recorded in the field notes. This correction offset will vary with the latitude and with the distance of the corner from the principal meridian. At a distance of 15 or 20 ranges from the principal meridian it may be so great that the closing corner will be nearer to the adjacent quarter-section corner than to the standard township corner. Furthermore, it is obvious that the closing corners will be west of the corresponding standard corners on the east side of the principal meridian, and east of them on the west side.

The mile and half-mile distances on the guide meridians are made full 80 and 40 chains in length until the last half-mile is reached, into which all excess or deficiency due to discrepancies of measurement is thrown.

The general method of running the guide meridians is the same as that used in running the principal meridian, and all the provisions for securing accuracy of alignment and measurement, and for establishing corners, prescribed for the latter apply to the former also.

Provision is made for running guide meridians from north to south where existing local conditions require this departure from the usual practice. In such a case the closing corner is first established on the correction line by calculating the proper correction distance and laying it off from the standard corner; and then the guide meridian is run due south from this point. This method may be used in case the standard corner from which the guide meridian would ordinarily originate is inaccessible, or for other adequate reasons.

The Manual also provides that " where guide meridians have been improperly placed at intervals greatly exceeding the author ized distance of 24 miles, and standard lines are required to limit errors of old, or govern new surveys, a new guide meridian may be run from a standard, or properly established closing corner and a local name may be assigned to the same, e.g., ' Grass Valley

Guide Meridian.' These additional guide meridians will be surveyed in all respects like regular guide meridians."

166. Township Exteriors. — The usual method of subdividing a 24-mile tract into townships is as follows (see Fig. 58).

Beginning at the standard corner at the southeast corner of the southwest township in the tract, the surveyor runs north on a true meridian of longitude a distance of 6 miles, setting all necessary corners by the way. From the township corner thus established he runs due west on a random line (Art. 199, p. 199) to intersect the guide meridian (or the principal meridian, in case he is working in Range 1 East), setting temporary section and quarter-section corners as he goes. When he intersects the meridian, he notes the "falling" * of his random line, and, in case this is within the limit prescribed, he then calculates the course of the true line joining the two township corners and runs back on it, setting permanent corners opposite the temporary ones previously set on the random line. In this way all the deficiency due to the convergence of the meridional boundaries of the township, together with whatever excess or deficiency may arise from inaccuracies in measurement, are thrown into the most westerly half-mile of the latitudinal boundary.

The range line is now continued as a true meridian for another 6 miles, permanent corners being set as before. Then another random line is thrown across to the western boundary of the range of townships, and is corrected back to the true line, in the same manner as that just described. This process is continued until the most northerly township in the 24-mile tract is reached, when the range line is merely continued as a true meridian to an intersection with the correction line, at which point a closing township corner is established. The half-mile intervals on the range line are made full 40 chains for the entire 24 miles, except the most northerly half-mile, into which all excess or deficiency due to irregularities of measurement is thrown.

The two other range lines of the 24-mile block are run in a similar manner, the latitudinal township lines being extended to

---

* That is, the distance of the point at which the random line intersects the meridian from the objective corner.

the westward at the proper intervals and made to connect with the township corners previously established. From the township corners on the last range line, however, random lines are run also to the eastward to meet the guide meridian, and are then corrected back to the westward on a true line between the township corners. This is done in such a way that the excess or deficiency of this line also is thrown into the most westerly half-mile.

"In cases where impassable obstacles occur and the foregoing rules cannot be complied with, township corners will be established as follows:

"In extending the south or north boundaries of a township to the west, where the southwest or northwest corners cannot be established in the regular way by running a north and south line, such boundaries will be run west on a true line, allowing for convergency on the west half-mile; and from the township corner established at the end of such boundary, the west boundary will be run north or south, as the case may be. In extending south or north boundaries of a township to the east, where the southeast or northeast corner cannot be established in the regular way, the same rule will be observed, except that such boundaries will be run east on a true line, and the east boundary run north or south, as the case may be. Allowance for the convergency of meridians will be made whenever necessary."

The Manual provides for a maximum allowable limit for closing the random line upon the township corner, as follows: "If in running a random township exterior, such random exceeds or falls short of its proper length by more than 3 chains, allowing for convergency, or falls more than 3 chains to the right or left of the objective point (or shows a proportionate error for lines of greater or less length than 6 miles), it will be re-run and if found correctly run, so much of the remaining boundaries of the township will be retraced, or resurveyed, as may be found necessary to locate the cause of misclosure." A lateral displacement of 3 chains in a distance of 6 miles is equivalent to an angular deviation of 21 minutes.

167. Subdivision of Townships. — In the subdivision of a township into sections the following routing is followed in the field. The surveyor sets up his instrument at the southeast corner of the township, observes the meridian, and retraces the range line northward for a distance of one mile, and the township line westward for the same distance. This is for the purpose of comparing his own meridian and needle observations and the length of his chain with those of the previous surveyor who laid off the township exteriors.* Then from the southwest corner of Section 36 he runs north on a line parallel with the east boundary of the township, setting a quarter-section corner at 40 chains and a section corner at 80 chains. Then from the section corner just set he runs east on a random line, parallel to the south boundary of the section, setting a temporary quarter-section corner at 40 chains. When he intersects the range line he notes the falling of his random and also the distance it overruns or falls short of the length of the south boundary of the section. If the falling is not more than 50 links (33 feet, representing an angular deviation of 21 minutes), and if the distance overruns or falls short of the length of the southern boundary of Section 36 by not more than the same amount, a return course which will join the two section corners is calculated; this new line is then run toward the west, the permanent quarter-section corner being set at its middle point.

From the section corner just regained the survey is now continued north between Sections 25 and 26, the direction being changed slightly to the east or west according to whether the latitudinal section line just completed exceeded or fell short of the desired length. At 40 and 80 chains on this line the quarter-section and section corners, respectively, are set, and from the section corner a random is run across to the range line, and a return course is calculated and run as before. This process is continued until five of the six sections in the series are inclosed. Then, if the north boundary of the township is not a correction line, from the section corner last established a random is run north to the township boundary, and from the data thus secured a true line is calculated and run from the section corner on the township line back to the initial corner. If the north boundary of the township is a correction line, however, the point at which

---

* See specimen field notes, p. 163.

the random intersects this boundary is established as a **closing corner** and its distance from the nearest **standard corner** is measured and recorded. In either case the permanent quarter-section corner is established at 40 chains north of the initial corner, the excess or deficiency being thrown into the most northerly half-mile.

In a similar manner the succeeding ranges of sections are enclosed, randoms being run across eastward to the section corners previously established and true lines corrected back. From the fifth series of section corners thus established, however, random lines are projected to the westward also, and are closed on the corresponding section corners in the range line forming the western boundary of the township. In correcting these lines back, however, the permanent quarter-section corners are established at points 40 chains from the initial corners of the randoms, thereby throwing all fractional measurements into the most westerly half-miles. Reference to Figs. 62 and 63 will help toward an understanding of this method of subdivision.

Table 6, taken from the Manual, gives (to the nearest whole minute) the angular convergency of meridians from one to five miles apart. The meridional section lines, therefore, by reason of being (theoretically) parallel to the range line on the east boundary of the township, will depart from true meridians by the amounts indicated in the table.

TABLE 6.

CORRECTIONS FOR CONVERGENCY WITHIN A TOWNSHIP.

Latitude.	Correction to be applied to bearing of range lines at a distance of —				
	1 mile.	2 miles.	3 miles.	4 miles.	5 miles.
° °	′	′	′	′	′
30 to 35	1	1	2	2	3
35 to 40	1	1	2	3	3
40 to 45	1	2	2	3	4
45 to 50	1	2	3	4	5
50 to 55	1	2	3	5	6
55 to 60	1	3	4	5	7
60 to 65	2	3	5	7	8
65 to 70	2	4	6	8	10

From a consideration of the foregoing it will be apparent

(1) That interior meridional section lines are 80 chains in length, except those next to the north boundary of the township; and that the south half of these is 40 chains.

(2) That interior latitudinal section lines are within 50 links of the length of the line forming the southern boundary of the range of sections, except those section lines next to the west boundary of the township; and that the east half of these is 40 chains.

(3) That interior section lines, whether meridional or latitudinal, are ordinarily straight for one mile only.

(4) That except in those section lines next to the north and west boundaries of the township, the quarter-section corners are placed equidistant from the two section corners on either side.

(5) That meridional section lines are intended to be parallel to the range line forming the eastern boundary of the township; and similarly, that latitudinal section lines are intended to be parallel to the township line forming its southern boundary.

(6) That the cumulative deficiency in latitudinal lines due to the convergence of the meridians is thrown into the most westerly half-mile of the township.

(7) That no quarter-section closing corners are established on correction lines for the use of the sections south of these lines.

168. Fractional Sections. — In sections made fractional by rivers, lakes, or other bodies of water, lots are formed bordering on the body of water, and numbered consecutively through the section. The boundaries of these lots usually follow the quarter lines of the section, and contain, as nearly as may be, forty acres each. Fig. **62** indicates the method. Also, the quarter quarter sections along the north and west boundaries of a township, into which the discrepancies of measurements or the deficiencies due to the convergence of the range lines are to be carried when the sections are subdivided, are usually numbered and sold as lots. (See Art. 177, p. **176**.) These lot lines are not actually run in the field, but, like the quarter-section lines, are merely indicated on the plates, and the areas by which the lots are sold are computed in the office.

Field notes taken in connection with the survey of public lands are required to be returned to the General Land Office in the narrative form. A sample page of notes, somewhat condensed from those given in the Manual, is herewith presented

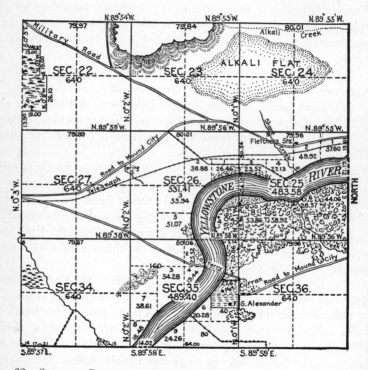

Fig. 62. Showing Part of a Typical Township; also Showing Method of Forming Lots in Fractional Sections.

for its value not only as an illustration of a section line survey but also as an instructive example of this very valuable method of note keeping.

Fig. 62, taken from the Manual, shows the nine sections in the southeastern part of a typical township, and illustrates the specimen notes given on the following page.

Specimen of Field Notes.

Subdivision of T. 15 N., R. 20 E.

Chains.	
	From the Tp. cor. already described,* I run
	North, on the 5th Guide Meridian and E. bdy. of sec. 36; and, at 40.01 chs., intersect the ¼ sec. cor.; and, at 79.98 chs., fall 1 lk. W. of the cor. of secs. 25, 30, 31, and 36; therefore, the line bears north.
	From the Tp. cor. I run N. 89° 57′ W., on the S. bdy. of sec. 36; at 39.99 chs., fall 0½ lk. N. of the ¼ sec. cor.; and at 80.01 chs. fall 1 lk. S. of the cor. of secs. 1, 2, 35, and 36, on S. bdy. of the Tp.; consequently, the S. bdy. of the sec. 36 bears N. 89° 57′ W.
	Therefore, the bearings are as stated by the surveyor general, and my chaining practically agrees with the field notes of the original survey.
	I commence at the cor. of secs. 1, 2, 35, and 36, on the S. bdy. of the Tp., which is a sandstone, 6 × 8 × 5 ins. above ground, firmly set, and marked and witnessed as described by the surveyor general.
	Thence I run
	N. 0° 01′ W., bet. secs. 35 and 36.
	Over level bottom land.
4.50	Wire fence, bears E. and W.
20.00	Enter scattering cottonwood timber, bears E. and W. F. G. Alexander's house bears N. 28° W.
29.30	Leave scattering cottonwoods, bearing E. and W.; enter road, bears N.
30.00	SE. cor. of F. G. Alexander's field; thence along west side of road.
39.50	To crossroads, bears E. to Mound City; N. to Lake City. F. G. Alexander's house bears S. 40° W. The ¼ sec. cor. point will fall in road; therefore
	Set a cedar post, 3 ft. long, 3 ins. sq., with quart of charcoal, 24 ins. in the ground, for witness cor. to ¼ sec. cor., marked W C ¼ S 35 on W. and 36 on E. face; dig pits, 18 × 18 × 12 ins. N. and S. of post, 3 ft. dist.; and raise a mound of earth 3½ ft. base, 1½ ft. high, W. of cor.
40.00	Point for ¼ sec. cor. in road.
	Deposit a marked stone, 24 ins. in the ground, for ¼ sec. cor.
	The SE. cor. of Pat. Curran's field bears W., 5 lks. dist.
40.50	Set a limestone, 15 × 8 × 6 ins. 10 ins. in the ground, for witness cor. to ¼ sec. cor., marked W C ¼ S on W. face; dig pits, 18 × 18 × 12 ins. N. and S. of stone, 3 ft. dist.; and raise a mound of earth, 3½ ft. base, 1½ ft. high, W. of cor.
	Thence along E. side of field.
50.50	NE. cor. of Pat. Curran's field, bears W. 4 lks. dist.
51.50	Leave road; which turns to N. 70° W., leads to ferry on Yellowstone River; thence to Lake City.
57.50	Enter dense cottonwood and willow undergrowth, bears N. 54° E. and S. 54° W.
72.50	Leave undergrowth, enter scattering timber, bears N. 60° E. and S. 60° W.
80.00	Set a locust post, 3 ft. long, 4 ins. sq., 24 ins. in the ground, for cor. of secs. 25, 26, 35 and 36, marked
	T 15 N S 25 on NE.,
	R 20 E S 36 on SE.,
	S 35 on SW., and
	S 26 on NW. face; with 1 notch on S. and E. faces; from which
	An ash, 13 ins. diam., bears N. 22° E., 26 lks. dist., marked T 15 N R 20 E S 25 B T.
	A sycamore, 23 ins. diam., bears S. 71¼° E., 37 lks. dist., marked T 15 N R 20 E S 36 B T.
	A walnut, 17 ins. diam., bears S. 64° W., 41 lks. dist., marked T 15 N R 20 E S 35 B T.
	A cottonwood, 13 ins. diam., bears N. 21¼° W., 36 lks. dist., marked T 15 N R 20 E S 26 B T.

---

* Description omitted. A description of the determination of a true meridian by both solar and Polaris observations is also omitted.

169. "**Summary of objects and data intersected by the line or in its vicinity, to be noted.** — 1. The precise course and length of every line run, noting all necessary offsets therefrom, with the reason for making them, and method employed.

"2. The kind and diameter of all bearing trees, with the course and distance of the same from their respective corners; and the precise relative position of witness corners to the true corners.

"3. The kind of materials of which corners are constructed.

"4. Trees on line. The name, diameter, and distance on line to all trees which it intersects.

"5. Intersections by line of land objects. The distance at which the line intersects the boundary lines of every reservation, town site, donation claim, Indian allotment, settler's claim, improvement, or rancho; prairie, bottom land, swamp, marsh, grove, and windfall, with the course of the same at all points of intersection; also, the distances at which the line begins to ascend, arrives at the top, begins to descend, and reaches the foot of all remarkable hills and ridges, with their courses, and estimated height in feet, above the level land of the surrounding country, or above the bottom lands, ravines, or waters near which they are situated. Also, distance to and across large ravines, their depth and course.

"6. Intersections by line of water objects. All rivers, creeks, and smaller streams of water which the line crosses; the distances measured on the true line to the bank first arrived at, the course down stream at points of intersection, and their widths on line. In cases of navigable streams, their width will be ascertained between the meander corners, as set forth under the proper head.

"7. The land's surface — whether level, rolling, broken, hilly, or mountainous.

"8. The soil — whether rocky, stony, sandy, clay, etc., and also whether first, second, third, or fourth rate.

"9. Timber — the several kinds of timber and undergrowth, in the order in which they predominate.

"10. Bottom lands — to be described as wet or dry, and if subject to inundation, state to what depth.

"11. Springs of water — whether fresh, saline, or mineral, with the course of the streams flowing from them.

"12. Lakes and ponds — describing their banks and giving their height, and whether it be pure or stagnant, deep or shallow.

"13. Improvements. Towns and villages; houses or cabins, fields, or other improvements with owners' names; mill sites, forges, and factories, U. S. mineral monuments, and all corners not belonging to the system of rectangular surveying; will be located by bearing and distance, or by intersecting bearings from given points.

"14. Coal banks or beds; peat or turf grounds; minerals and ores; with particular description of the same as to quality and extent, and all diggings therefor; also salt springs and licks. All reliable information that can be obtained respecting these objects, whether they be on the line or not, will appear in the general description.

"15. Roads and trails, with their directions, whence and whither.

"16. Rapids, cataracts, cascades, or falls of water, with the estimated height of their fall in feet.

"17. Precipices, caves, sink holes, ravines, remarkable crags, stone quarries, ledges of rocks, with the kind of stone they afford.

"18. Natural curiosities, interesting fossils, petrifactions, organic remains, etc.; also all ancient works of art, such as mounds, fortifications, embankments, ditches or objects of like nature.

"19. The magnetic declination will be incidentally noted at all points of the lines being surveyed, where any material change in the same indicates the probable presence of iron ores; and the position of such points will be perfectly identified in the field notes."

170. MARKING CORNERS. — Corners are marked on the ground by various kinds of monuments, depending upon the character and importance of the corner to be perpetuated, the soil, the materials available, and upon other local and special conditions. In places where stone is plentiful monuments of this material are usually set. In timbered districts where suitable stones are difficult to obtain, posts are driven to mark the points. In prairie regions where neither stones nor timber are available a mound of earth may be raised over the corner, a small marked stone, a charred stake, a quart of charcoal, or some other permanent and distinguishable mark being deposited beneath it. Occasionally in the timber the corner falls on a spot occupied by a tree, in which case the tree itself may stand as the monument.

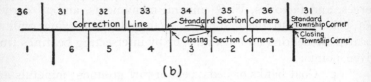

(b)

(a)

FIG. 63. SHOWING THE SUBDIVISION OF A TOWNSHIP INTO SECTIONS AND THE METHOD COMMONLY USED FOR MARKING TOWNSHIP AND SECTION CORNERS.

In case stones or posts are set they are marked with notches as shown in Figs. 63 and 64, in order to indicate their respective positions in the township. Section corners on range lines, including under this term principal and guide meridians, are marked with notches on their north and south faces, the number of notches being equal to the number of miles to the next adjacent township corner north or south. In a similar manner the section corners on the township lines, including base-lines and standard parallels, are notched on their east and west faces. Township corners, being located on both range and township lines, are marked with six notches on each of the four sides. In addition to being notched as just indicated, corners on correction lines are marked *SC* on their northern or *CC* on their southern faces,

FIG. 64. SKETCH OF STONE MONU-
MENT, SHOWING NOTCHES.

depending upon whether they are standard or closing corners. Section corners in the interior of a township are given notches on their east and south faces corresponding to the number of miles to the east and south boundaries of the township. Thus, the corner common to sections 20, 21, 28, and 29 would have two notches on the south and four on the east face, as sketched in Fig. 64. Quarter-section corners are marked with the fraction "$\frac{1}{4}$", those on meridional lines on their west and those on latitudinal lines on their north faces.

171. Witnessing Corners. — Wherever possible the monument set at a corner is witnessed by several nearby objects, which may be easily found by anyone looking for the corner itself, which are not readily moved or obliterated, and which are comparatively permanent. In timbered country the stone or post is usually witnessed by "bearing trees" located near the corner. The process of establishing a witness tree is to take its bearing and distance from the corner, then to blaze off the bark from a short section of the trunk on the side facing the corner and to cut into the wood with scribing tools certain letters and numerals indicative of the section in which the tree is located. For example, the tree northeast from the corner shown in Fig. 64 might be marked

$$
\begin{array}{ccc}
T & 7 & S \\
R & 15 & E \\
S & 21 & \\
& B\ T.
\end{array}
$$

the letters and figures being abbreviations of "Township 7 south, Range 15 east, Section 21, Bearing Tree." Usually one tree is marked in each of the sections to which the corner refers, provided suitable trees can be found within a reasonable distance of the corner.

In prairie regions small rectangular pits are dug near to the corner, the earth taken from them being used to form a mound. These pits are placed either on the section lines leading from the corner or at angles of 45 degrees with these lines, depending on the kind of corner witnessed; and the mound may be either alongside the monument or, in case the monument is merely a deposit beneath the surface of the ground, may be placed immediately over it. Fig. 65, adapted from illustrations given in the Manual, indicates the manner of using this method of witnessing corners of the several classes. Marks of this kind are of much greater value than might at first be supposed, for, although the sharp outlines are quickly worn away, the grass sod soon covers the mound and grows down into the pits and preserves them from entire obliteration. In many places on the plains four slight depressions in the prairie sod with a little mound between have perpetuated the location of the section corner for a generation or more, until the country has been settled up and the fence lines strung. Under other prevailing conditions corners have been witnessed by mounds of stone, by prominent boulders, and by various other suitable objects.

172. Witness Corners. — In case a regular corner falls in a creek, pond, or in any other place where it is impracticable to set or maintain a monument, *witness corners* are set on all the lines leading to this corner. These are marked with the letters *WC* in addition to the markings that would be appropriate to the corner of which they are witnesses. Witness corners are, in turn, referenced by bearing trees, pits and mounds, and other objects, the same as true corners.

173. Meander Corners. — Where a surveyed line intersects the bank of a stream whose width is more than three chains, or of a lake, bayou or other body of water having considerable extent, a *meander corner* is established. The distance from the nearest section or quarter-section corner is measured and recorded

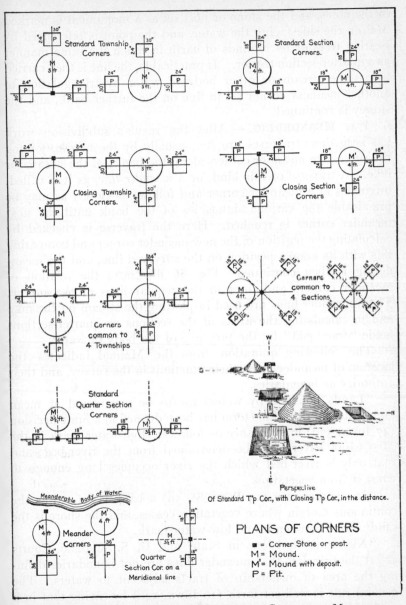

FIG. 65. SHOWING SCHEME FOR DESIGNATING CORNERS BY MEANS OF MOUNDS AND PITS.

in the notes, and the stone or post set as a monument is marked *MC* on the side facing the water, and the point is referenced by bearing trees or by mounds of earth in much the same manner as a quarter-section corner. If practicable, the line is then carried across the stream or other body of water by triangulation to another meander corner set in line on the further bank, and the survey is continued.

174. MEANDERING. — After the regular subdivision work has been done traverses are run, usually by the needle, joining the successive meander corners along the banks of the streams or lake. A traverse of this kind, or a *meander line*, as it is called, originates at a meander corner and follows as closely as may be practicable the various sinuosities of the bank until the next meander corner is reached. Here the traverse is checked by calculating the position of the new meander corner and comparing this with its known position on the surveyed line, and the meandering is then continued. Fig. 66 illustrates the relation of meander corners and lines to the regular lines of the survey. These meander lines are used in plotting the stream on the map and in calculating the areas of the sections or quarter-sections made "fractional" by the presence of the body of water.

The following quotation from the Manual indicates the location of meander lines, their functions in the survey, and their authority as boundaries.

"Lands bounded by waters are to be meandered at mean high-water mark. This term has been defined in a State decision (47 Iowa, 370) in substance as follows: High-water mark in the Mississippi River is to be determined from the river-bed; and that only is river-bed which the river occupies long enough to wrest it from vegetation.

"In another case (14 Penn. St. 59) a bank is defined as the continuous margin where vegetation ceases, and the shore is the sandy space between it and low-water mark.

"Numerous decisions in State and U. S. Supreme Courts assert the principle that meander lines are not boundaries defining the area of ownership of tracts adjacent to waters. The general rule is well set forth (10 Iowa, 549) by saying that in a navigable stream, as the Des Moines River in Iowa, high-water mark is the boundary line. When by action of the water the river bed changes, high-water mark changes and ownership of adjoining land changes with it. The location of meander lines does not affect the question.

"Inasmuch as it is not practicable in public land surveys to meander in such a way as to follow and reproduce all the minute

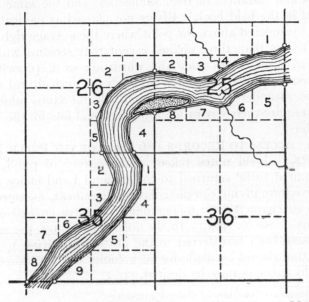

FIG. 66. SHOWING THE RELATION OF MEANDER CORNERS AND MEANDER LINES TO THE SECTION LINES.

windings of the high-water line, the U. S. Supreme Court has given the principles governing the use and purpose of meandering shores, in its decision in a noted case (R. R. Co. v. Schurmeier, 7 Wallace, 286–7) as follows:

"In cases where the deputy finds it impossible to carry his meander line along mean high-water mark, his notes should state the distance therefrom, and the obstacles which justify the deviation.

"Proceeding down stream, the bank on the left hand is termed the left bank and that on the right hand the right bank. These terms will be universally used to distinguish the two banks of a river or stream.

"Navigable rivers, as well as all rivers not embraced in the class denominated 'navigable,' the right-angle width of which is three chains and upwards, will be meandered on both banks, at the ordinary mean high-water mark, by taking the general courses and distances of their sinuosities, and the same will be entered in the field book. Rivers not classed as navigable will not be meandered above the point where the average right-angle width is less than three chains, except that streams which are less than three chains wide and which are so deep, swift, and dangerous as to be impassable through the agricultural season, may be meandered, where good agricultural lands along the shores require their separation into fractional lots for the benefit of settlers."

175. ACCESS TO RECORDS AND MAPS OF THE PUBLIC LANDS SURVEYS. — Field notes taken in the survey of public lands are required to be returned to the General Land Office and in narrative form giving complete data of alignment, measurement, and of all characteristic topographical features crossed or near the lines. (See p. 163.) In the following States the original notes have been transferred to the State authorities, to whom application should be made for such copies of the original plats and field notes as may be desired, viz.:

Alabama: Secretary of State, Montgomery.
Arkansas: Commissioner of State Lands, Little Rock.
Florida: Commissioner of Agriculture, Tallahassee.
Illinois: Auditor of State, Springfield.
Indiana: Auditor of State, Indianapolis.
Iowa: Secretary of State, Des Moines.
Kansas: Auditor of State and Register of State Lands, Topeka.
Louisiana: Register of State Lands, Baton Rouge.
Michigan: Commissioner of State Land Office, Lansing.
Minnesota: Secretary of State, St. Paul.
Mississippi: Commissioner of State Lands, Jackson.
Missouri: Secretary of State, Jefferson City.
Nebraska: Commissioner of Public Lands and Buildings, Lincoln.
North Dakota: State Engineer, Bismarck.
Ohio: Auditor of State, Columbus.
Oklahoma: Commissioner of General Land Office, Washington, D. C.
Wisconsin: Commissioners of Public Lands, Madison.

In many if not all these States named either the original records or copies of the same have been distributed among the various Counties of the State, and are kept for reference and inspection in the office of the County Register of Deeds, County Surveyor, or other official.

Photolithographic copies of township plats and field notes of surveys of the area covered by the Public Land Surveys in the above states may also be obtained from the General Land Office at Washington, at nominal prices. In other public land states copies of the records can be procured on application to the Surveyors General located at the Capitols, except in California and Oregon, whose Surveyors General are at San Francisco and Portland respectively.

Township maps of much of the area covered by the Public Lands Surveys may be obtained from the General Land Office at Washington, at nominal prices.

176. RELOCATING LOST CORNERS. — It has been the common experience that many of the monuments and marks originally established on the lines of the Public Lands Surveys become lost or obliterated by the time the country has been settled for a generation or two. Witness and line trees * are cut down when the land is cleared, the pits and mounds marking the corners on the prairie are quickly destroyed when the sod is broken up, posts rot away, and no one takes the trouble to see that new and more durable marks are set to perpetuate the location of the points. Largely owing to the fact that in the areas covered by the Public Lands Surveys the public roads are usually located along the section lines, even substantial stone monuments oftentimes are carelessly knocked out of place and eventually are thrown into the ditch or the fence corner.

An act of Congress, approved February 11, 1805, specifically provides that corners actually located in the field shall be established as the proper corners of the sections or quarter-sections which they were intended to designate, **irrespective of whether they were properly located in the first place or not.** A further

---

* "Line trees" are those directly on a line of the survey. They are blazed on opposite sides, the blazes facing backward and forward along the line. Trees near the line are scored with two blazes "quartering" toward the line; the further the trees are from the line the nearer together the two blazes are placed, and vice versa. These blazed trees are of great service in marking the approximate position of the line through the timber.

provision is that "the boundary lines actually run and marked" (in the field) "shall be established as the proper boundary lines of the sections, or subdivisions, for which they were intended, and the length of such lines as returned by . . . the surveyors aforesaid shall be held and considered as the true length thereof." These are the principles upon which is based the present practice in the relocation of the corners of the original survey.*

The General Land Office distinguishes between an **obliterated** and a **lost** corner, as follows:

"An **obliterated** corner is one where no visible evidence remains of the work of the original surveyor in establishing it. Its location may, however, have been preserved beyond all question by acts of landowners, and by the memory of those who knew and recollect the true situs of the original monument. In such cases it is not a **lost** corner.

"A **lost** corner is one whose position cannot be determined beyond reasonable doubt, either from original marks or reliable external evidence."

In the case of a corner that is merely obliterated the method of procedure, obviously, is to establish a new monument in the same location as the old one, this location being determined by the evidence presented, which should be adequate for the purpose. Instances of this kind occur when old witness trees, or their stumps, or the depressions left in the forest floor by their decay, may be identified; or when the point is marked by the intersection of hedge or stone or other permanent fences which admittedly were constructed on line when the monument was still in place; or when the "true situs of the monument" is testified to by other competent witnesses. (See Art. 151, p. 133.)

In the case of lost corners the true location must ordinarily be determined from data obtained by actually rerunning the old lines, as nearly as may be. But here, in accordance with the principle first stated above, the aim should be to relocate the

---

* The General Land Office publishes a Circular on the Restoration of Lost or Obliterated Corners and Subdivision of Sections, which states these principles and suggests methods of procedure in conformity therewith. Many of the methods referred to in the following paragraphs are condensed from this Circular.

corner at the exact point at which it was originally established, irrespective of whether it was properly located in the first place or not. As a help toward this end the following suggestions are offered, taken mainly from the Circular of the General Land Office to which reference was made in the earlier part of this Article.

A lost corner on a principal or guide meridian or range line will be located by proportional measurements from the nearest original corners in place north and south of the lost corner. It will be located on the straight line joining these original corners, irrespective of whether the measurements to corners east or west of the lost corner correspond with the original field notes or not.

A lost standard corner on a base-line or standard parallel or other correction line will be located by proportional measurements to the nearest original corners east and west of the lost corner, and will be located on the true line joining them, irrespective of whether the required distances to corners north or south would tend to pull it off this line or not. In like manner, a lost corner on an interior latitudinal township line will be recovered by proportional measurements to corners in place east and west of it.

In other words, **a lost corner is to be relocated by proportional measurements from corners which were established at the same time and with the same degree of care as the lost corner.** It sometimes happens that errors are discovered which throw a doubt upon the accuracy of the field notes of the line upon which the corner in question was located, in which case the lateral measurements might prevail and the corner be located in accordance with them; but ordinarily the rule as stated is the one to be observed.

A lost section corner in the interior of a township is to be located by proportional measurements from the corners nearest to it in all four directions. It is sometimes found, however, that the meridional section lines have been run with greater care than the latitudinal lines, owing to the operation of certain routine methods in use on some surveys. In case this is found to be true, the measurements on the meridional section lines may be given a certain precedence over those on the latitudinal lines.

A lost closing corner on a correction line should be located at the intersection of the correction line with the meridional line closing upon it, even though the distance called for would place the corner north or south of the correction line. It is even held true of a closing corner actually in place, if it happens to be a little off the correction line, that such corner is to be construed as establishing merely the **direction** and not the **termination** of the meridional line upon which it is located. This is one of the very few cases in which the statutory provision quoted in the early part of this Article is not rigidly adhered to.

A lost quarter-section corner is always to be established at the middle point of the section line upon which it was originally located, except those next to the west and north boundaries of the township. On correction lines the quarter-section corners referring to the sections south of the line* are to be located midway between the adjacent closing section corners, except that in the north boundary of Section 6, which is to be placed forty chains west from the east boundary of the section.

177. Subdivision of Sections. — When the Public Lands were parceled out to settlers the quarter-section was usually the unit area granted as a "homestead." To locate the lines of a "quarter," however, obviously required the establishment of the quarter-section corner at the center of the section. Also, the subsequent division of the original "quarters" into "eighties," "forties," or other minor subdivisions has necessitated the location of numerous corners in addition to those originally established by the Government. Much of the routine work of the present day surveyor is in connection with subdivisions of this kind. In the following paragraphs a number of typical examples will be given, illustrating common practice in the location of subdivisional corners. It will be noted that the methods given are based upon those employed in the original surveys of the sections.

The interior quarter-section corner of a section is always to be located at the intersection of straight lines joining the quarter corners on opposite sides of the section. This method holds wherever the section may be located within the township; that is,

---

* It will be remembered that these corners were not established on the original survey.

it applies to those in the north and west tiers as well as to the other sections of the township. For example, the center of Section 19, in Fig. 67, would be properly located at the intersection of *ab* and *ef*. This rule would still hold even though, through some error in the original fieldwork, the corner *f*, for instance, had been set too far east by one chain-length. If the corner is still in the place at which it was actually set by the Deputy Surveyor, this location is established for all time as the proper corner for the northern quarters of the section, and the line from *e* will be run to it.

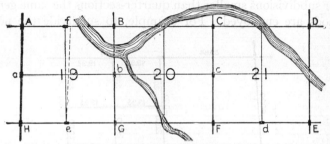

FIG. 67. ILLUSTRATING METHODS OF LOCATING INTERIOR QUARTER-SECTION CORNERS.

In case one or more of the exterior quarter-section corners are not accessible, lines are run through the interior of the section from whatever quarter corners are in place, having as nearly as possible the same directions as they would have were all the exterior corners actually in place, and the interior quarter-section corner is located at their intersection. For example, in Fig. 67 the corner at the center of Section 21 would be located by the intersection of a line run north from *d* in a direction which is a mean between that of *ED* and that of *FC*, with a line run east from *c* having a direction which is a mean between those of *CD* and *FE*. In case only one of the interior lines can be run, the corner may be established by proportionate measurements along that line. For example, the center of Section 20 would be located by measuring out from *c* on the line *cb* a distance equal to half the mean length of *CB* and *FG*. A modification of this method is required in the west and north tiers of sections in a township. In the case of sections lying in the west tier the meridional line run from the quarter corner on the north or south boundary of the section is run parallel to the east line of the section; and similarly, in the case of sections lying in the north tier the latitudinal interior line initiated at the quarter corner on the east or west boundary is run parallel to the south line of the section. The reasons for this method of procedure in these special cases are easily apparent from a consideration of the methods previously described for the establishment of the original quarter-section corners in these sections.

For subdivisions smaller than quarter-sections the same general methods are employed. For example, to subdivide the north-

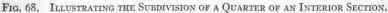

FIG. 68. ILLUSTRATING THE SUBDIVISION OF A QUARTER OF AN INTERIOR SECTION.

NOTE. — Figures on the outside lines of the illustration are those of the original survey. (Lengths of subdivisional lines are to be determined from these by proportionate measurement.)

east quarter of Section 10 (Fig. 68) into quarter-quarters or " forties," straight lines are run connecting the middle points of the opposite sides of the quarter. In case one or more of these starting corners are inaccessible, the quarter will be subdivided by the application of methods similar to those just outlined for the location of the quarter-section corner at the center of a section.

In the subdivision of quarter-sections adjacent to the west or north boundaries of the township the excesses or deficiencies* originally thrown into these quarters are not divided up between the different subdivisions, but are carried forward into the western or northern tiers of forty-acre lots.   Fig. 69 illustrates this point

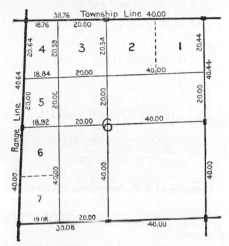

FIG. 69.   SHOWING THE SUBDIVISION OF THE NORTHWEST QUARTER OF SECTION 6.

NOTE. — Figures on the outside lines of the illustration are those of the original survey.   (Lengths of subdivisional lines are to be determined from these by proportionate measurement.)

by showing an ideal subdivision of the northwest quarter of Section 6, in a township not immediately south of a correction line.   In order to make them apparent in the figure, the original excesses and deficiencies are shown on an exaggerated scale. The tract marked 4 might be properly described as " the northwest quarter of the northwest quarter of Section 6," or simply as " Lot 4, of Section 6," of the appropriate township and range.

178. CONVERGENCE OF THE MERIDIANS. — The angular convergence of the meridians, given in Table 6, may be computed as follows.   In Fig. 70 AB is an arc of a parallel of latitude and EQ the arc of the equator intercepted by the meridians

---

* This refers to the excess or deficiency found by the original surveyor, not to that found during a re-survey.

through A and B. AT and BT are lines tangent to the meridians at A and B, meeting the earth's axis, prolonged, at T. It will be seen that the angle BTO equals the angle BOQ, which is the latitude of points A and B. The angle $AO'B$ is the difference in longitude of points A and B. The angle between the meridians at A and B is the angle ATB.

In the sector $AO'B$ (Fig. 70),

$$\frac{AB}{BO'} = \text{angle } AO'B$$

In the sector ATB,

$$\frac{AB}{BT} = \text{angle } ATB \text{ (approximately)}$$

But

$$BT = \frac{BO'}{\sin BTO'} = \frac{BO'}{\sin BOQ}$$

$$\therefore \text{angle } ATB = \frac{AB}{BO'} \sin BOQ$$

$$= \text{angle } AO'B \sin BOQ,$$

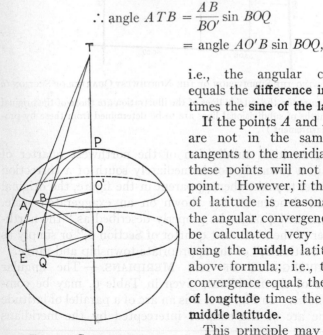

FIG. 70. CONVERGENCE OF MERIDIANS.

i.e., the angular convergence equals the **difference in longitude** times the **sine of the latitude**.

If the points A and B (Fig. 70) are not in the same latitude, tangents to the meridians through these points will not meet at a point. However, if the difference of latitude is reasonably small, the angular convergence may still be calculated very closely by using the **middle** latitude in the above formula; i.e., the angular convergence equals the **difference of longitude** times the **sine of the middle latitude**.

This principle may be applied to a township where 6 miles is

TABLE 7

LENGTH OF A DEGREE OF LONGITUDE.

Lat.	Degree of Longitude. Statute Miles.	Lat.	Degree of Longitude. Statute Miles.	Lat.	Degree of Longitude. Statute Miles.
0	69.172	30	59.956	60	34.674
1	9.162	31	9.345	61	33.623
2	9.130	32	58.716	62	32.560
3	9.078	33	8.071	63	31.488
4	69.005	34	57.407	64	30.406
5	68.911	35	56.725	65	29.315
6	8.795	36	6.027	66	28.215
7	8.660	37	55.311	67	27.106
8	8.504	38	54.579	68	25.988
9	8.326	39	53.829	69	24.862
10	68.129	40	53.063	70	23.729
11	67.910	41	52.281	71	22.589
12	7.678	42	51.483	72	21.441
13	7.410	43	50.669	73	20.287
14	7.131	44	49.840	74	19.127
15	66.830	45	48.995	75	17.960
16	6.510	46	8.136	76	16.788
17	6.169	47	47.261	77	15.611
18	65.808	48	46.372	78	14.428
19	5.427	49	45.469	79	13.242
20	65.026	50	44.552	80	12.051
21	64.606	51	43.621	81	10.857
22	4.166	52	42.676	82	9.659
23	63.706	53	41.719	83	8.458
24	3.228	54	40.749	84	7.255
25	62.729	55	39.766	85	6.049
26	2.212	56	38.771	86	4.842
27	61.676	57	37.764	87	3.632
28	1.122	58	36.745	88	2.422
29	60.548	59	35.716	89	1.211

the distance between the meridians through A and B along the southern boundary and 6 miles the distance between the parallels forming the northern and southern boundaries of the township. If the latitude of the southern boundary is 37° 00′ N, then the northern boundary is 6 × 5280 feet further north. There are approximately 6080 feet in one minute of latitude along a meridian on the earth's surface, so that 5280 × 6 ft. equals 5.2 minutes of latitude, and the latitude of the northern boundary is 37° 05′.2 N and that of the middle parallel of the township is 37° 02′.6 N. From Table 7 the length of 1° of longitude in the middle latitude (37° 02′.6 N) is 55.28 miles.

$$\text{Angular convergence} = \frac{6}{55.28} \times \sin 37° 02′.6 \times 60 = 3′.92.$$

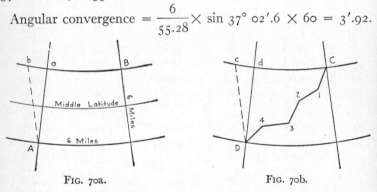

FIG. 70a.   FIG. 70b.

The linear convergence or the amount by which the northern boundary is shorter than the southern boundary is shown by ab in Fig. 70a. The full lines in Fig. 70a represent the meridians and parallels through A and B; the line ab is a line drawn through A parallel to the eastern meridian through B. The triangle Aba may be considered as a plane triangle with a right angle at a. The angle aAb is equal to the angular convergence just computed. Therefore in the triangle Aba

$$ab = 6 \times 5280 \times \sin 0° 3′.92 = 36.1 \text{ feet.}$$

Whenever traverses of considerable extent are being run, it is very desirable to check the bearings along the traverse by astronomical observations or by tying into triangulation stations (Art. 318, p. 386) and checking the bearings against an azimuth from such stations. The convergence of the meridians must

be taken into account when the distance east or west of the starting point is large in order to obtain a check on the angular measurements. The same formulae employed above may be used,
but it will probably be more convenient to make use of Table 7A.
The total east or west distance between the points C and D
(Fig. 70b) may be found from the difference in the coördinates
of these points as explained in Art. 429, p. 519. In the column
containing the number of thousands of feet of this east or west
distance and on a line with the mean latitude will be found the
angular convergence of the meridians. The convergence for
numbers not in the table may be found by combining those that
are given. For instance, that for 66,500 feet, in mean latitude
40°, may be found by adding together 10 times the value for 6000,
the value for 6000, and one-tenth the angle for 5000. The result
is 550″, which is the correction to apply to the second observed
azimuth to refer the line to the first meridian.

EXAMPLE. — In Fig. 70b assume that at station C the azimuth
of the line C to 1 is 28° 42′ 40″ and that the survey proceeds in
a southwesterly direction to point D where the azimuth of line
D to 4 is found by observation to be 226° 17′ 20″. The calculation of the survey shows that D is 3100 feet south and 15,690
feet west of C. The mean latitude of the traverse is 40° N.

From Table 7A the convergence for 15,690 feet by parts is
83 + 41 + 5 + 1 = 130″ or 2′ 10″. This is the correction that
must be added to the observed azimuth of D–4 to make it refer
to the meridian through C. The azimuth at D referred to the
meridian at C is, therefore, 226° 19′ 30″ and the difference in
the directions of lines C–1 and 4–D is 226° 19′ 30″ − 180° − 28°
42′ 40″ equals 17° 36′ 50″ which should agree with the algebraic
sum of the deflection angles of the traverse C to D, within the
range of the precision expected.

Note that in the above computations 180° was subtracted
from the azimuth of D–4 to change its direction from D–4 to
4–D so that the azimuth of C–1 and of 4–D would be taken in
the same order.

TABLE 7A

Convergence of the Meridian in Seconds for each 1000 Feet on the Parallel

Latitude	Distance East or West (in feet)								
	1000	2000	3000	4000	5000	6000	7000	8000	9000
°	″	″	″	″	″	″	″	″	″
20	3.5	7.0	10.5	14.0	17.5	21.0	24.5	28.0	31.5
25	4.6	9.2	13.8	18.4	23.0	27.6	32.2	36.8	41.3
30	5.7	11.4	17.1	22.7	28.4	34.1	39.8	45.5	51.2
35	6.9	13.8	20.7	27.6	34.5	41.4	48.3	55.2	62.1
40	8.3	16.5	24.8	33.0	41.3	49.6	57.8	66.1	74.3
45	9.8	19.7	29.5	39.4	49.2	59.0	68.9	78.7	88.6
50	11.7	23.5	35.2	46.9	58.6	70.3	82.1	93.8	105.5

PROBLEMS

1. At sta. 1 the meridian is established by an observation on the pole-star. (Art. 232b, p. 261b.) A traverse is run northerly and westerly to sta. 120. The total difference in latitude is 2400 ft. N and the total departure is 61,000 ft. W. The latitude of sta. 1 is 43° 10′ N. At sta. 120 an observation is made on the sun for azimuth of line 120–121. (Art. 238, p. 271.) What correction should be applied to the azimuth of 120–121 to refer it to the meridian of sta. 1? (One minute of latitude equals about 6080 ft.)

2. Test the angles of the traverses shown in Probs. 8, 9, 10, and 11, Chapter XIV.

3. What is the difference in the lengths of the northern and southern boundaries of a Township (Art. 155), the latitude of the southern boundary being 43° 00′ N? (One minute of latitude equals 6080 ft., nearly.)

4. A field that is approximately square is surveyed by setting the transit up in its approximate center and measuring the four angles between lines running to its corners. Angles are correct to the nearest minute and diagonal distances from the transit to the corners are measured to the nearest 0.01 ft. Assuming that diagonal distances to the two ends of line AB are 842.17 and 837.86 and that there is not over 0.03 ft. error in either of these measurements, what is the maximum possible error in the computed length of line AB?

5. From a base line 250.00 ft. long (on a street line monumented at both ends), the back corners of a rectangular lot 400.00 ft. deep are to be set with transit and tape. Assume that the probable error of measuring a 100-ft. tape-length is ±0.01 ft. and the probable error of turning the right angles after repetitions with a one-minute instrument is ±15 seconds of arc.

(a) What is the probable linear error in setting a back corner because of error in measuring with tape?

(b) What is the probable linear error in setting a back corner because of error in turning the angle?

(c)   What is the probable linear error in setting a back corner from these combined causes?

(d)   What is the maximum error in the back length of the lot from these probable errors?

(e)   Assuming the worst possible case, what is the error in the area?

6.   The angles of a five-sided traverse are being measured by the deflection angle method.   All the deflection angles are to the right and the probable error of measuring each deflection angle is ± 10 seconds.   What is the probable sum of the deflection angles?

7.   A transit point X was referenced by means of three tie measurements radiating at angles of about $120°$ from X. $AX = 43.26$, $BX = 42.98$, $CX = 39.21$. The measurements were carelessly made; the tape was 1 ft. higher at A than at X, 2 ft. lower at B than at X, and 6 in. higher at C than at X.   Later the point X was lost and had to be reproduced by means of ties AX and BX.   The point C was also lost so that CX could not be used.   In reproducing the point care was taken to hold the tape horizontal as it should be held.   How far was the second determination of X away from the original position?

8.   Angle AOB is to be determined by tape measurements.   Along OA and OB a point is placed exactly 200 ft. from O at C and D. CD measures 80.66 ft.

(a)   Compute the angle AOB to the nearest $\frac{1}{2}$ minute.

(b)   Assume that in measuring CD an error of 0.2 ft. was made and it was actually 80.86 ft.   What error did this mistake introduce in the angle AOB?

9.   Referring to Fig. 51, p. 112, a line EF is to be established parallel to AD. As a first trial the instrument is set up at E and sighted on a swing offset $FD = 4.00$ ft.   The distance AH is measured and found to be 3.08 ft.   How far should points H and F be moved to the left or right in order to establish line EF truly parallel to AD?

Give results to nearest half-hundredth.   The distance $EA = 6.55$ ft., $AD = 268.72$ ft.

10.   The boundaries of a triangular lot of land are: $AB = 400.00$ ft., $BC = 300.00$ ft., $CA = 500.00$ ft.

(a)   What is the angle at A?

(b)   If the point B is set by laying off the angle CAB and measuring out 400.00 ft. from A, what discrepancy may be expected in the length of BC if the angle is laid out to the nearest minute only?   Assume AC is exactly 500.00 ft.

(c)   How closely should the angle at A be laid off so that no error greater than .01 ft. will be introduced in line BC due to this cause?

(d)   Explain how you would obtain this precision in laying out the angle.

11.   Compute the azimuths of all the lines in the traverse shown in Fig. 53a, assuming line 1–6 is due South.   Show check on last azimuth.

CHAPTER VI

TRAVERSE LINES — LOCATION OF BUILDINGS — MISCELLANEOUS SURVEYING PROBLEMS

TRAVERSE LINES

179. TRAVERSES WHICH DO NOT FORM CLOSED FIGURES.—
A great many surveys, such, for example, as the preliminary surveys for railroads, highways, or pipe lines, call for traverses which do not return to the starting point. In this work the line is usually measured continuously from one end to the other, and the form of notes is commonly as follows. The starting point of the traverse is called " station o," the next station 100 ft. away is " station 1," the next " station 2," etc. Every 100-ft. length is a *full station* and any fractional distance is called the *plus*. The distance from station o to any point, **measured along the traverse line,** is the station of that point and is recorded always by the number of the last station with the plus station in addition, e.g., the station of a point at 872.4 ft. from station o is 8 + 72.4.

At the angle points it is customary to measure the **deflection angles** rather than the interior angles because the former are usually less than 90°. **These should be checked in the field by** " **doubling** " **the angles.** (See Arts. 143–5, pp. 122–5.)

The notes are kept so as to read **up the page.** The left-hand page is for the traverse notes and the right-hand page for the sketch, the stations in the sketch being opposite the same station in the notes. Fig. 71 is a set of notes illustrating this kind of traverse. Frequently no notes are kept in tabular form, all of the data being recorded on the sketch. Figs. 80, p. 196; 96, p. 232; and 147, p. 409 illustrate this style of notes.

180. CHECKING BY ASTRONOMICAL METHODS. — The angles of any traverse may be checked by determining the azimuths of the first and last lines by astronomical methods. On long traverses requiring many days for their completion it is advisable to make such observations daily. The two most useful methods are (1) direct solar observations, which interrupt the regular work only a few minutes, and (2) observations of Polaris, which are simple and accurate but usually necessitate a special night trip to the place of observation. For details of these methods

(LEFT-HAND PAGE) (RIGHT-HAND PAGE)

Preliminary Survey for X and Y. R.R., Knowlton, N.D. — Redman, Lyons ⊼, Noyes h.c., Rolf r.c., Grover l.f., Baird r.f. — Oct. 17, 1936

Sta.	Point	Defl. Angle	Observed Bearing	Calculated Bearing
10				
9			N 13°E	N. 13°06'E
	⊙ +84.2	43°17'L		
8				
+94.5				
+46.5				
7			N 30°W	N30°11'W
	⊙ +70.2	18°43'L		
6				
+17.2				
5			N 11½°W	N 11°28'W
	⊙ +62.1	16°17'R		
4				
3				
+42				
2				
1			N 27¾°W	N 27°45'W
0	⊙			

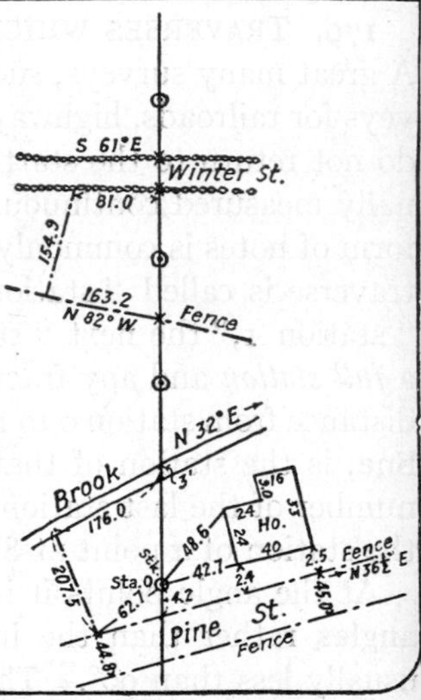

FIG. 71. TRAVERSE NOTES.

see Chapter VIII. Since the meridians converge toward the pole it is necessary to make proper allowance for this convergence when comparing the azimuths; the amount of the correction can be obtained from Table 6, p. 160, or Table 7A, p. 182.

181. Checking by Cut-Off Lines. — The angles may be checked occasionally by cutting across from one point on the traverse to another at a considerable distance ahead, and measuring the angles from the traverse line at each end of this cut-off line, thereby obtaining all the angles of a closed traverse in which the length of one side only (the cut-off line) is missing. Some-

times the angle at only one end of the cut-off line can be measured, but the calculations for checking the angles are not so
simple as when all the angles are known. When both angles have
been measured the check consists in simply obtaining the algebraic sum of the deflection angles, whereas the traverse must be
computed as explained in Arts. 439–42, pp. 529–30, if an angle
and a side are missing.

182. Checking by Angles to a Distant Object. — A practical
and useful method of checking the azimuth of any line of the
traverse is as follows. At intervals along the line, measure carefully the angle from the traverse line to some well-defined distant
object, such as a distinct tree on a hill or the steeple of a church.
If the survey is plotted and it is found by laying off the angles
taken to the distant object that these lines do not meet at one
point on the plan there is a mistake in the angles, and a study of
the plot will show the approximate location of the mistake. If
convenient, an angle to the distant object should be taken at
every transit point. When plotted, if these lines meet at the
same point in one section of the traverse and in another section
meet at another point, then there is a mistake in the line which
connects these two parts of the traverse. Plotting, however,
may not be sufficiently accurate for the purpose and, if the point
is so far away that it falls outside the limits of the plan, it will
not be practicable. It is always possible, however, to make the
check by calculating the coördinates of the point, as explained in
Art. 447, p. 533.

183. Checking by Connecting with Triangulation Points. —
An accurate and practical method of checking both the angles
and distances of a traverse is to connect the traverse with reliable *triangulation points* that can be identified. (See Art. 314,
p. 382.) The latitude and longitude of these triangulation
points and the distances between them can be obtained from
the proper sources. (Federal, State, or Municipal departments.)
Sometimes the distances between them are not known but can
be computed. (See Vol. II, Chap. I, Art. 53.) Then by connecting the traverse lines with these triangulation points by
angles and distances a closed traverse is obtained, which serves
as a good check. (See Vol. II, Art. 55, p. 85.)

Many surveyors fail to appreciate the value of this method of checking and do not realize how many such points are available. The information concerning such triangulation points can be obtained from The U. S. Coast and Geodetic Survey, The U. S. Geological Survey, State surveys, and frequently from City or Town surveys.

LOCATION OF BUILDINGS FROM TRANSIT LINE

184. METHODS OF LOCATING BUILDINGS. — When locating any objects, such as buildings, from the survey line the measurements should be such as will permit of accurate and rapid plotting. In city plans, for instance, accurate location is of great importance and should be made the first consideration whereas in some topographic maps rough locations will suffice, and accuracy may be sacrificed to speed. In the following pages the examples are limited to locations of buildings because these illustrate all the necessary principles involved in any location. Locations by (3) (angle and distance) are not discussed because the method is evident.

185. GEOMETRIC PRINCIPLES. — Whether the locations are accurate or only rough, the principles involved are the same. In order to make clear the various methods used in the location of buildings it will be well, before giving particular cases occurring in practice, to enumerate the geometric principles to be used.

A **point** may be located from a traverse: —

    (1) By rectangular coördinates, i.e., by its station and perpendicular offset.

    (2) By two ties from known points.

    (3) By an angle and a distance from a known point (polar coördinates).

    (4) By an angle at each of two known points.

    (5) By a (perpendicular) swing offset from a known line and a tie from a known point.

    (6) By (perpendicular) swing offsets from two known lines which are not nearly parallel.

    (7) By an angle from one point and a distance from another point.

A **line** may be located:

    (1) By locating two points on the line.
    (2) By locating one point on the line and the direction
        of the line. (Angle or Range.)

186. TIES, OFFSETS, SWING OFFSETS, AND RANGE LINES. —
In the preceding list, the word *tie* is used as meaning a direct
horizontal measurement between two points.

An *offset* is the **horizontal** distance from a line, usually at right
angles.

A *swing offset* is the **perpendicular** distance to a line and is
found by trial. The zero end of the tape is held at the point to
be located and the tape is swung in a short arc about this point
as a center, the tape being **pulled taut and kept horizontal.**
The tape is read from the transit in various positions; the shortest
reading obtainable is the perpendicular distance desired.

A *range line* is a line produced to intersect the transit line or
some other line.

187. GENERAL SUGGESTIONS. — By whatever method the
buildings are located the following suggestions should be carried
out.

    (1) All the sides of the building should be measured and
checked by comparing the lengths of opposite sides.

    (2) Other things being equal, a long side of a building should
be located in preference to a short side.

    (3) Two ties or two directions should intersect at an angle as
near 90° as practicable, and never less than 30°. If method (7)
is used, however, the tie and the sight line should make as small
an angle as possible.

    (4) One or more *check measurements* should be taken in the
location of each building.

    (5) In order to secure the best location the surveyor should
**keep constantly in mind how the building, or other object which
is being located, is to be plotted.**

In most work of this character it is customary to record the
measurements to tenths of a foot. How precisely the measurements should be taken, however, depends upon the scale to
which they are to be plotted.

188. TYPICAL CASES. — Although each case will have to be dealt with according to circumstances there are certain typical cases which will serve as guides. These are illustrated by the following examples.

189. Example I. Building Near Transit Line and Nearly Parallel to it. — As will be seen in Fig. 72 swing offsets are taken at the two front corners; these ties, together with the tie from A to station 1 and the length of the front of the building locate points A and B. The general dimensions of the building furnish sufficient data for plotting and checking the remaining sides. It is assumed that the corners of the building are square unless it is obvious that they are not. (In city buildings this assumption may not be a safe one to make.) The tie from C to station 2 is a check against an error in the other measurements.

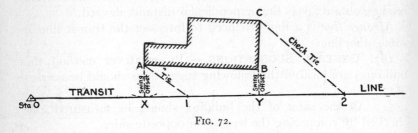

FIG. 72.

PLOTTING. — This building would be plotted thus: — lay off the distance AX perpendicular (estimated) to the transit line (say $A'X'$) and draw a line through A', with triangles, parallel to the transit line; then scale $A1$ from station 1 to this parallel line. Point A is where the tie $A1$ cuts the parallel line. Point B is located in the same way, AB being used as the tie from A. Then by means of triangles and scale the building is completed and the distance $C2$ scaled and compared with the notes. Another way to plot point A would be to set on the compass the distance $1A$ and swing an arc about 1 as a center; then, keeping the scale perpendicular to the transit line, find where the distance XA will cut this arc, thus locating point A. Point B can be similarly located after A has been plotted. For the same degree of accuracy distances can be measured more rapidly with a scale than they can be laid off with a compass, therefore the former method is usually preferable.

This building might have been located by four ties AO, $A1$, $B1$, and $B2$. The plotting in this case would be slow because at least two of the ties must be swung by use of a compass, and inaccurate because the intersections would be bad.

190. Example II. Building Near Transit Line and Making a Slight Angle with it. — Fig. 73 illustrates two ways of locating a building in such a position that the intersection of the transit line by the long side (produced) can be readily obtained.

The left-hand building is located by the method of Example I. The tie $B1$ could have been taken instead of $B2$. It would have given a better intersection at B, but since it is a longer tie than $B2$ the fieldwork necessary is slightly greater. If $B2$ is taken $B1$ might be measured as a check tie although $A1$ would make a better check tie since it will also check the measurement of the side AB.

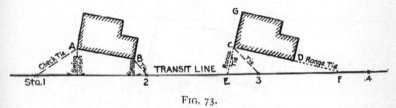

FIG. 73.

The right-hand figure illustrates another method of locating such a building. The front and side of the building are ranged out by eye, a method which is practicable and sufficiently precise for all ordinary purposes, and the plus stations of points E and F are measured. The range lines CE and DF are also measured and the check tie $C3$. $C2$ could have been taken as a check tie; it would have given a better intersection at C than the tie $C3$, but it is much longer.

PLOTTING. — The left-hand building is plotted as described in Example I. In plotting the right-hand building the plus stations on the transit line are first scaled. Then with the compass set at the distance EC an arc is swung from E as a center. From F the distance FC is scaled to intersect the arc, which locates point C and at the same time the direction of the side CD. The building is then plotted with triangles and scale. The check tie $C3$ should scale to agree with the notes and the line GC produced should strike point E.

There is little difference between these two methods in the amount of fieldwork, there being only one more measurement in the right-hand than in the left-hand figures, but one extra check is thereby obtained. In plotting, the method used in the right-hand figure is shorter.

191. Example III. Building Located Entirely by Direct Ties. — Any building can be located and checked by four ties as in Fig. 74 provided the pairs of ties intersect at favorable angles (say not less than 60° nor over 120°). This method has the advantage of being very simple and direct, especially in the field, but the plotting of the building calls for the use of the compass in two of the ties and hence is less rapid and accurate than where swing offsets or ranges can be used.

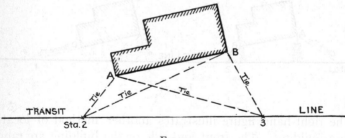

FIG. 74.

PLOTTING. — The plotting of this building is done by swinging the tie from one station to a corner of the building and scaling from the other station the tie to the same corner. Then the other corner is plotted in the same way or by using the side of the building as one of the ties if it gives a better intersection.

192. Example IV. Building Located at a Considerable Skew to the Transit Line. — A building which is at a considerable skew to the transit line can be located best by range ties as illustrated in Fig. 75. The range ties through A are sufficient to locate the building, provided AE and AF are not too short in comparison with the sides of the building. If these ranges are long enough, then B_3 is a check tie; but if the ranges are short, B_3 must be depended upon to determine the position of point B and in this event one of the range ties becomes a check. But if A is within two or three feet of the transit line it will be well to omit one of the ranges and take the additional tie $2C$ or the range tie DC produced.

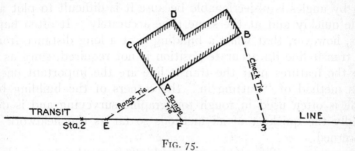

FIG. 75.

PLOTTING. — If the ranges are of fair length the building is plotted as explained for the right-hand building in Art. 190, but if the range ties are short point B is located either by swinging the arc with radius EB and scaling B_3 or by arc $3B$ and scaling EB. The direction of AB is now determined and the building can be plotted. CA produced should strike at F, and AF should scale the measured distance.

193. **Example V. Buildings at a Long Distance from the Transit Line.** — It is evident that here (Fig. 76) the tape is

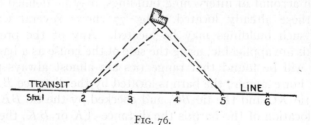

FIG. 76.

not long enough to allow the use of swing offsets. Range ties may be used provided the building is not so far away that the eye cannot judge the range line with reasonable accuracy.

Sometimes the only methods available are long ties or angles or a combination of the two. In any specific case there may be some objections to any of these methods, and the surveyor will have to decide according to circumstances which method he will use. For example, where there are obstacles to the measurement of ties, the corners of the building may have to be located entirely by angles from two points on the transit line. Location by angles is objectionable because it is difficult to plot an angle quickly and at the same time accurately. It often happens, however, that when a building is at a long distance from the transit line its accurate position is not required, since as a rule the features near the transit line are the important ones. This method of " cutting in " the corners of the building by angle is often used in rough topographic surveying and is decidedly the quickest of all methods so far as the fieldwork is concerned.

PLOTTING. — The angles are laid off from the transit line with a protractor and the proper intersections determine the corners of the buildings. If the building is measured, the side between the corners located will serve as a check tie.

In some cases, e.g., in making a topographic map on a small scale, the buildings are not measured at all, their corners being simply " cut in " by several angles from different transit points, and the shape of the building sketched in the notes.

194. Example VI. Buildings Located from Other Buildings.— Buildings which cannot be located conveniently from the transit line, on account of intervening buildings, may be defined by ties from those already located. Fig. 77 shows several ways in which such buildings may be located. Any of the preceding methods are applicable, using the side of the house as a base-line, but it will be found that range ties are almost always preferable. For example, the barn is located by the distance BK, the range tie KC and the tie BC, and checked by the tie BE. Another location of the barn is the distance AK or BK, the range tie KC, and the two range ties AJ and CJ. By this latter method the directions of both sides of the barn are checked. Still another location of the point C would be to substitute in the place of the range tie CK a swing offset from C to the house. The shed is located by the range ties AF and FG and by the tie AG. The check tie HD checks in general the location of both the barn and the shed. If the side HL is ranged out instead of

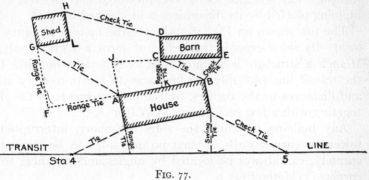

FIG. 77.

the opposite side it will be seen that the tie AL will give a poorer intersection at L. If convenient a tie from L to 4 or the range GF continued to the transit line may be measured as a check.

195. Example VII. Buildings of Irregular Shape. — Not infrequently a building of irregular shape has to be located. For example, the shop in Fig. 78 is located on the front by ties and

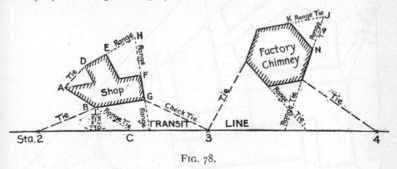

FIG. 78.

swing offsets like Example I; then the direction of AB is determined by the range tie BC. The back corner E is determined by the ranges FH and EH, and by the dimensions of the building; FA is assumed parallel to GB. If the angle F is a right angle the tie EF may be taken instead of the range ties FH and

EH, but even when F is a right angle it will be well if time will permit to take these range distances as they give valuable checks on the other measurements which the single tie EF does not furnish. ED is scaled along HE produced and the rest of the building plotted by its dimensions and checked by AD.

The ties shown on Fig. 78 to locate the factory chimney will locate its sides even if these do not form a regular polygon. If such a structure is situated at a considerable distance from the transit line probably the best way to locate it is by angles and distances to the corners, by the measurements of the sides, together with a few such ranges as NJ or KJ.

Any building in which the sides are short, interrupted by towers or curved walls, so that no one side can be located accurately, can always be located by angles and distances to the corners. (Method (3).)

196. Example VIII. Large City Buildings. — Fig. 79 illustrates the location of several buildings in a city block where

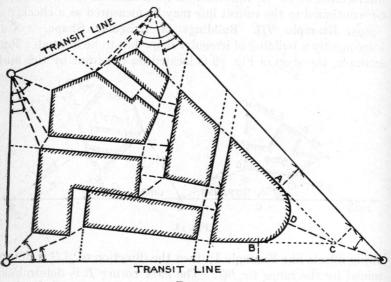

TRANSIT LINE

Fig. 79.

the transit line runs around the block. The fronts of the buildings are located from the transit line and the rear corners are tied together. The range ties are shown by dotted lines and other ties by dashes. The angles measured are marked by arcs. At the curve AB, the side lines of the building are ranged out to point C, which is located from the transit line by an angle and distance, and checked by a swing offset; CD is also measured to locate point D on the curve.

Many large buildings have their walls reinforced by pilasters, and care should be taken when locating corners not to confuse the neat line of the wall with the line of the pilasters.

197. Example IX. Location of Buildings by Angles and Distances. — It will be seen from Figs. 79 and 80 that some of the buildings have been located by angles and distances from transit points. Any of the buildings in the preceding examples could be located by this method, and on account of the rapidity with which the work can be done in the field many surveyors prefer to use it almost exclusively.

198. Location of Buildings and Fences from Transit Line. — Fig. 80 is a sample page from a note book illustrating the above principles. It will be noticed that in the field-notes the letter R appears where the lines are ranges.

198a. DEFECTIVE LOCATIONS. — In Fig. 80a are shown six locations which are weak or defective, given for the purpose of showing that some locations that appear at first glance to be complete may give trouble when an attempt is made to plot them. In No. 1 the arc defined by the tie nearly coincides with the line defined by the angle. The position of the corner of the building is therefore indefinite. A tie from $11 + 00$ would have been better, but not so good as one from a point still nearer the transit. A range on the left side would fix the direction. In No. 2 the building is really located, but it cannot be plotted until calculations or geometric constructions have been made to determine another tie. That is, no one corner has been located directly from the transit line. For example, a tie from $+ 20$ to the corner where the swing offset is taken would make it possible to plot that corner directly. A range on the front side would be still better. In No. 3 the offsets were presumably estimated to be at right angles to the line. Upon this assumption the building can be plotted, but its location along the line is rather weak. If the

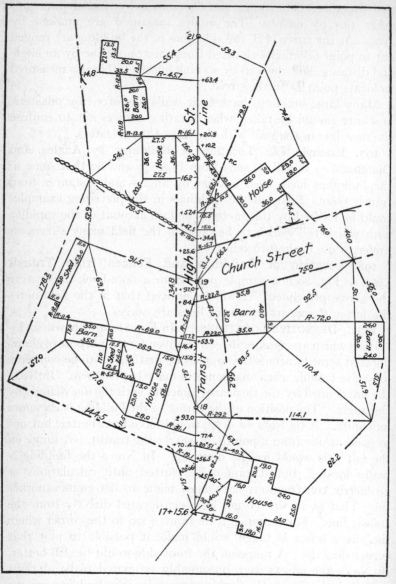

Fig. 80.

offsets are not at right angles the location is indeterminate. One diagonal tie would make the location a strong one, although not checked. In No. 4 no one corner can be plotted directly until

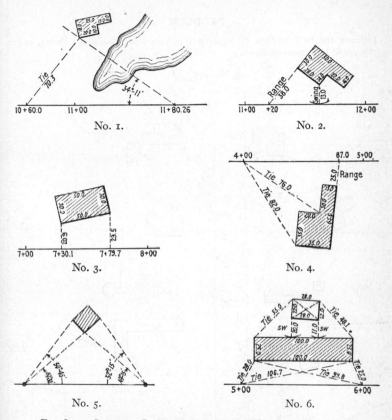

FIG. 80a. SHOWING LOCATIONS THAT ARE WEAK OR DEFECTIVE.

another distance has been calculated or found by construction. Additional measurements should be made. In No. 5 the building can be rotated a little about the front corner and yet the sight lines to the outer corners will pass through their respective corners. Only one corner of the building is really fixed. In the last figure (No. 6) the building in the rear cannot be plotted directly. A range on one side of the building instead of a swing, or, a tie to one of the nearer corners to intersect the swing, would remedy this defect.

PROBLEM

Indicate the best method of locating the fences and buildings shown below, by means of tape measurements.

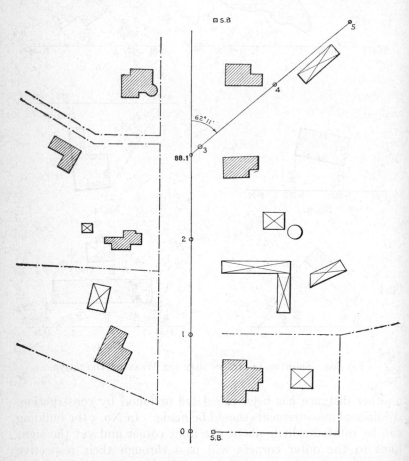

MISCELLANEOUS SURVEYING PROBLEMS

199. RANDOM LINE. — Not infrequently in attempting to run a straight line between two points A and B (Fig. 81) it is found impossible to see one point from the other or even to see both A and B from an intermediate set-up on a straight line between them. When this condition exists it is necessary to start at one point, e.g., A, and run what is called a trial, or *random*, line AC by the method explained in Art. 64, p. 58, in the direction of the other end of the line as nearly as this can be judged.

Where the random line passes the point B the perpendicular offset YB is measured and also the distance to point Y along AC. Unless the random line is very close, say, within about two feet of the line AB, the point Y where a perpendicular to AC will pass through B cannot be accurately chosen by eye. The method resorted to is one which has general application in all kinds of surveying work, and is as follows.

With the transit at A point X is set carefully on the line AC and as nearly opposite point B as possible. Then the instrument is set up at X and 90° turned off in the direction XZ. If this line does not strike B (and it seldom will exactly) the distance BZ is carefully measured by a swing offset as described in Art. 186, p. 187. The distance BZ is equal to the distance XY which, added to AX, gives the length of the long leg AY of the right triangle AYB. The distance YB is then measured, and AB and angle YAB are easily calculated.

Angle DAY has been measured from the previous course, AD; the addition of the angle YAB together with the known distance AB makes the traverse complete to the point B without any further fieldwork. If the transit is now moved to B with a view to carrying on the survey it will be found that, since A cannot be seen from B, there is no point on the line BA to use as a backsight. But any point such as E can be set on the line AB by making the offset $ME = BY \dfrac{AM}{AY}$. Another point can be set similarly on AB as a check on this backsight.

This random-line method is sometimes employed when AB is a boundary which is covered with shrubs. Although the view from A to B may not be obstructed, it may be so difficult to **measure** the line AB that its length can be more easily obtained by the use of the random line while the **angle** DAB may be measured directly at A. If it is desired to mark the line AB by several intermediate points these may be established by means of perpendicular offsets calculated as described above.

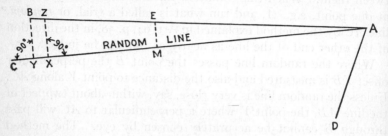

FIG. 81.

The random line is not necessarily a single straight line — it may be a traverse consisting of several lines, as shown in Fig. 81a. If the last point (3) is in such a position that a good closing

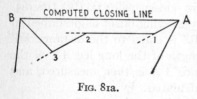

FIG. 81a.

can be made on B (that is, accurate angles) then the distance and bearing of AB may be computed as described in Art. 434; but if the line 2–3 passes so close to B that it is not desirable to make 3–B a line of the traverse, then the connection may be made as shown in Fig. 81.

200. OBSTACLES ON LINE. — When an obstacle, such as a building or a small pond, lies on the transit line various methods are resorted to for prolonging the line through such obstructions; the most useful of these methods will be explained.

201. Offsetting Transit Line. — This method is illustrated by Fig. 82. It is desired to produce the line AB beyond the house. Point B is set on line and as near as is practicable to the house. The instrument is then set up at B and a right angle ABF laid off with the transit. BF is made any convenient distance which will bring the auxiliary line beyond the building. Similarly point E is set opposite point A, and sometimes a second point E' opposite A', points A and A' being **exactly** on the transit line. These points E and E' need not be set by means of a transit set up at A and at A' unless AE is quite long.

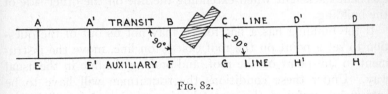

FIG. 82.

The instrument is then set up at F and backsighted on E, the sight is checked on E', the telescope inverted, and points G, H', and H set on line. Leaving the telescope inverted, another backsight is taken on E, and the process repeated as described in Art. 64, p. 58. Then the transit is moved to point G, and a right angle turned off, and point C set on the right angle line, the distance GC being made equal to BF.

Then by setting up at C and sighting ahead on D ($DH = GC$), and checking on point D' ($D'H' = GC$), the transit line is again run forward in its original location. The distance FG is measured carefully and is used as the length for BC. Thus it is apparent why it is so necessary that the lines BF and GC shall be laid off at right angles by means of the transit. The other offsets AE, $A'E'$, DH, and $D'H'$ are not in any way connected with the measurement along the line; they simply define the direction of the line. So it is only necessary to show these distances as swing offsets for the transitman to sight on. It will be seen that offsets $A'E'$ and $D'H'$ are not absolutely necessary, but they serve as desirable checks on the work and in first-class surveying they should not be omitted. For obvious reasons the offsets AE and DH should be taken as far back from the obstacle as is practicable.

Should the house be in a hollow so that it is possible to see over it with the instrument at A, the point D, or a foresight of some sort (Art. 64, p. 58) should be set on line beyond the house to be used as a foresight when the transit is set up again on the original line. The distance may be obtained by an offset line around the house or by slope measurements to the ridgepole. Sometimes it is possible to place exactly on line on the ridgepole of the house a nail or a larger wooden sight which gives an excellent backsight when extending the line on the other side of the building.

If the building has a flat roof it may not be out of the question to set a point on the roof exactly on line, move the instrument to this point on the roof, and prolong the line in the usual way. Under these conditions the transitman will have to be extremely careful in the use of his instrument as it will be set up on an insecure foundation. If he walks around the transit he will find that it affects the level bubbles and the position of the line of sight; it is therefore well for him to stand if possible in the same tracks while he backsights and foresights. Sometimes two men, one in front and one behind the transit, can carry on the work more accurately and conveniently. This method insures an accurate prolongation of the line, but the distance through the building must be measured by an offset method, unless it can be done by plumbing from the edge of the flat roof or by taking an inclined measurement and the vertical angle.

202. SHORT TRANSIT SIGHTS. — Sometimes the offset BF (Fig. 82) does not need to be more than 2 or 3 feet. The shorter this offset line can be made, and still clear the building, the better. But to lay off the short line BF will require a method somewhat different from any that has been explained heretofore. As the ordinary transit instrument cannot be focused on a point much less than about 5 ft. distant it is impossible to set point F directly. The method employed is to set a temporary point, by means of the transit, say 10 ft. distant, on which the transit can be focused, and on a line making 90° 00′ with the original transit line. From the transit point B to this auxiliary point a piece of string may be stretched and the point F set at the required distance from B and directly under the string.

203. Bisection Method. — A method which is economical in fieldwork but not very accurate is the following. In Fig. 83 the instrument is set up at A, backsighted on the transit line, and equal angles turned off on each side of the transit line pro-

duced. Points B' and C' are carefully set on one of these lines
and at convenient distances from A, and on the other line points
B'' and C'' are set at the same distances from A.   Then point B
is placed midway between B' and B'', and similarly point C is

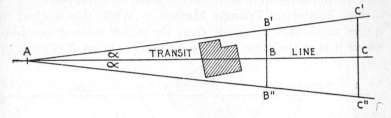

FIG. 83.

set midway between C' and C''.   The line BC is the prolongation of the transit line.   Of course the distance $B'C'$ should be
made as long as practicable.   The two angles should be tested
by the method of repetition and corrected if necessary.   (Art.
61, p. 57.)

The distance AB can be computed from the formula

$$AB' - AB = \frac{\overline{BB'}^2}{2AB} \text{ (approximately).   (See foot-note, p. 14.)}$$

204. Measuring Around a Small Obstacle.   In Fig. 84 the
line AB runs through a tree, and points A, D, and B have been set

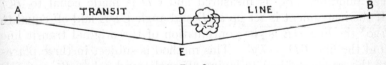

FIG. 84.

on line. DE is made some convenient short distance judged by
eye to be at right angles to the transit line.   Then AE and
EB are measured.   The distance

$$AB = AE - \frac{\overline{DE}^2}{2AE} + EB - \frac{\overline{DE}^2}{2EB}. \text{   (See foot-note, p. 14.)}$$

When *DE* is taken as some whole number of feet the computation of the above is extremely simple.

This method of measuring around a small obstacle might be applied much more generally than it is at present if its accuracy and its simplicity were more fully realized by surveyors.

205. Equilateral Triangle Method. — While this method requires much less fieldwork than the offset method described above it is at the same time less accurate.   Point *B* (Fig. 85) is

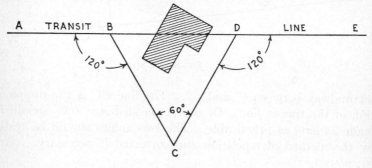

FIG. 85.

set on the transit line as near the building as practicable but so that a line *BC* at 60° with the transit line can be run out.   The instrument is set up at *B*, backsighted on *A*, and an angle of 120° laid off; the line *BC* is made long enough so that when the instrument is set up at *C* and 60° is laid off from it, *CD* will fall ouside the building.   *BC* is measured and *CD* is made equal to *BC*. If the instrument is set up at *D* and angle *CDE* laid off equal to 120° the line *DE* is the continuation of the original transit line and the line *BD* = *BC*.   This method is subject in three places to the errors incident to laying off angles and, when *BC* and *CD* are small, it has in two of its intermediate steps the disadvantages due to producing a short line.   The results may be made more accurate by (1) repeating the angles, and (2) by applying the principle explained at the end of Art. 145, p. 125.

The triangle need not be exactly equilateral, although the latter is simpler to use.   If the angle at *B* must be made a little greater or smaller than 120° on account of obstructions, the angles at C and D and the sides of the triangle may be made such that D is on AB prolonged and the length BD may be calculated. The triangle BCD must be solved by the formulas for oblique triangles, or as two right triangles by means of a perpendicular.

206. INACCESSIBLE DISTANCES. — If the obstruction is a pond, points on the farther side of it can be set and these should be used in producing the transit line. When the line can be produced across the obstacles the following methods may be used.

207. Inaccessible Distance by Right Triangle Method. — In Fig. 86 the line AB is made any convenient length and inclined at any convenient angle to the transit line. The line BC is laid off at 90° to BA (and verified by repetition); it is intersected with the transit line at C and the distance BC measured. AC is calculated from AB and cos A and checked by BC and sin A. Also the angle ACB can be measured; this will check the transit work.

208. INTERSECTING TWO TRANSIT LINES. — In many kinds of surveying work it is necessary to put in points at the intersection of two transit lines as at C, Fig. 86. It would be an easy matter to set the point if two transits could be used, one on each line,

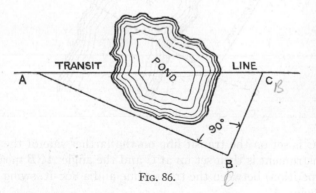

FIG. 86.

and the sight given simultaneously by the transitmen. As it is seldom practicable to use more than one transit in a surveying party the following method is much used.

An estimate is made by eye where the lines will cross each other and two temporary points not more than 10 ft. apart are set on one of the transit lines by means of the instrument, making sure that the second line will cross somewhere between the two temporary points. A string is then used to connect these two temporary points; the transit is set up on the other transit line and the point where the second line cuts the string is the intersection point. When the two transit lines cross at a very small angle, it is impossible to judge by eye within several feet where the lines will intersect, so a number of points must be set on the first line, because in practice the stretching line is seldom applicable for distances much over 15 ft. For short distances the plumb-line can be used as a stretching line.

209. Inaccessible Distance by Swing Offset Method. — If the distance across a pond or a river is not great the following method may be used. It has the advantage of requiring the minimum amount of fieldwork. With the instrument at A (Fig. 87)

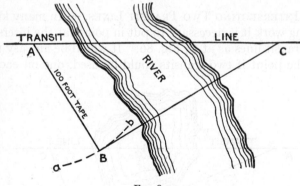

Fig. 87.

point C is set on the transit line on the farther side of the river. The instrument is then set up at C and the angle ACB measured (by repetition) between the transit line and a 100-ft. swing offset from point A.

A pencil is held vertically at the 100-ft. mark of the tape and while the zero-point is held firmly at A the tape, which is constantly kept **horizontal** and **taut,** is swung **slowly** in an arc ab. The transitman, using the tangent screw, can follow the pencil with the vertical cross-hair of the transit, stopping the cross-hair when the pencil is in its farthest position from A. Then as the tape is swung the second time he can check his setting; when this is determined the angle ACB is read. The distance AC then is easily calculated. It should be noted, however, that if AC is several times as long as AB the resulting error in AC may be so great as to prohibit the use of this method where very precise results are required. There is no reason why the swing offset could not be made at C while the instrument is set up at A if this is more convenient.

210. Inaccessible Distance by Tangent Offset Method. — In the method previously described the distance across the pond may be so great that 100 ft. will be too short a base to use, or point A may be situated on ground sloping upward towards B so that a swing offset cannot be made. In such cases the line AB (Fig. 88)

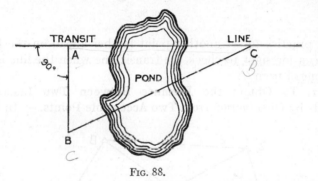

Fig. 88.

can be laid off **exactly** at right angles to the transit line and of any convenient length. Then the angle ACB is measured (by repetition) and the line AC computed. By another set-up of the instrument the angle B can be measured as a check, and if the line BC does not cut across the pond its length can also be measured as a further check.

211. Inaccessible Distance by Oblique Triangle Method. — Often the shores of a stream are covered with trees so that none of the above methods is applicable. It may be possible, however, to measure a base-line AB (Fig. 89) along the shore, to set the point C in line on the opposite side, and to measure the angles at

A and at *C*. The distance *AC* can then be computed. It will be well also to set up at *B* and measure the angle *B* as a check on the work. At the time when point *C* is set it is also

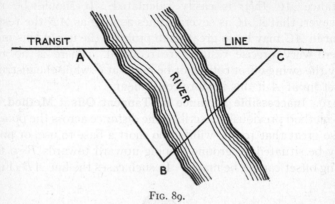

FIG. 89.

good practice to set another point farther ahead on the line, to use as a foresight to check the transit line when the line is being prolonged from *C*.

212. To Obtain the Distance Between Two Inaccessible Points by Observation from Two Accessible Points. — In Fig. 90

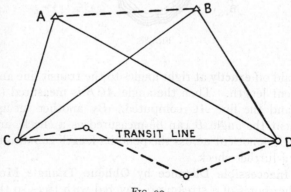

FIG. 90.

the points *A* and *B* are inaccessible and it is desired to obtain the distance *AB* and the angle that *AB* makes with the transit line

From the point D the distance DC and the angles BDA and ADC are measured; similarly at C the angles ACB and BCD are measured. AB can then be calculated as follows: — in the triangle CBD compute CB; in triangle ACD compute AC; and in the triangle ACB calculate AB, the inaccessible distance. In the triangle ACB, angle ABC can be computed; this, together with the measured angle BCD, will give the difference in direction between AB and CD. It is not necessary that DC should have been measured as one straight line in the traverse; the traverse might have run as indicated by the dotted lines. If so, the distance CD and the necessary angles could be computed; the remainder of the computation would be the same as before.

This problem occurs when the distance between two triangulation stations, A and B, and the azimuth of AB are desired and when it is inconvenient or impossible to measure the line AB or to occupy the points with the transit.

213. To Obtain the Inaccessible Distance Between Two Accessible Points by Observations on Two Inaccessible Points of Known Distance Apart. — In this problem (Fig. 90) A and B are the two accessible points and C and D are the two inaccessible points but the distance DC is known; the distance AB is required. With the transit at A, the angles CAD and DAB are measured; at B the angle CBD and ABC are measured. While it is easy to obtain CD in terms of AB, it is not easy to determine AB directly in terms of CD; it will be well therefore to use an indirect method. Assume AB as unity. Then by the same process as described in the preceding problem the length of CD can be found. This establishes a ratio between the lengths of the lines AB and CD, and since the actual length of CD is known the distance AB can be computed.

A problem of this sort would occur under the following circumstances. If the distance CD between two church spires were accurately known (from a triangulation system) and it is desired to use this line CD as a base-line for a survey, two points A and B could be assumed, and the distance between them and the azimuth of AB could be found by this method.

PROBLEMS

1. In the quadrilateral in Fig. 90, angle $ACD = 73°\ 01'$, $ACB = 37°\ 30'$, $BDC = 58°\ 20'$, and $BDA = 31°\ 00'$. No distance is known. Find the angle BAD.

2. In Fig. 85 suppose angle $ABC = 121°\ 52'$, $BC = 91.27$ ft., angle $C = 59°\ 30'$; what will be the required distance CD to place D on AB prolonged? What will be the angle to lay off at D to place E on ABD prolonged? What is the length of BD?

3. In Fig. 81 $AX = 391.24$ ft.; swing offset $BZ = 2.04$ ft.; $YB = 8.91$ ft. What will be the offset ME if $AM = 190.10$ ft.?

4. In Fig. 80a indicate complete and accurate location for each building shown.

5. The horizontal tape distance from the center of the base of an inclined pole to the transit set at A is 214.72 ft. When the telescope is horizontal the line of sight cuts the pole at a point 5.14 ft. above its base. A vertical angle of $21°\ 16'$ is measured to the top of the pole, and as this is done it is found that the pole lines up with the vertical cross-hair (i.e., it appears vertical in that direction). The transit is then set up at a point B on a line running from the base of the pole at right angles to the first line. This time the horizontal tape distance from center of pole to transit is 210.16 ft., and when the transit telescope is horizontal the line of sight cuts the pole 5.32 ft. above base of pole. The pole is not vertical when viewed from point B through the transit; it is straight but it inclines to the left toward A. A sight is then taken bisecting the top of the pole, the telescope lowered and an offset taken horizontally from the center of the pole at its base to this transit line. It measures 4.66 ft.

(a) What is the actual length of the pole (to 0.01 ft.) if the 100-ft. tape used was 0.015 ft. too long?

(b) What should the vertical angle at B read to the top of the pole?

(c) Suppose the vertical angle at B to top of pole read $21°\ 43'$, what would this indicate to you?

6. Two church steeples, A and B, have been located by triangulation; they are approximately in latitude 40° North. The distance between them is 9347.9 feet. The bearing of A from B is N 2° 53' W. It is desired to use this known distance and bearing for surveys in the vicinity. The steeples are visible from two intervisible points, C and D, on the ground. The line CD lies to the eastward of AB, point C being to the northward of D. Angles are measured as follows: $DCB = 27°\ 54'$; $ADC = 32°\ 47'$; $BDA = 68°\ 21'$; $ACB = 57°\ 38'$. Compute the distance CD and the bearing of C from D.

7. Referring to Fig. 86, the computed value of AC is 1000.00 ft. The angle A is $30°\ 00'$, and the angle B is $90°\ 00'$. Now, suppose angle A was measured only to the nearest minute but angle B is exactly 90°. What is the maximum error in the line AC due to the precision adopted for angle A?

8. Plot the buildings in Fig. 80, p. 196, to scale: 1 in. = 50 ft.

9. A church steeple is over the center of a square masonry base. The south, east and west faces of the base measure 32.00 ft.; the north side is inaccessible but can be assumed to be 32.00 ft. The east side is ranged out for a distance of 100.00 ft. to A at which the transit is set up and vertical angle measured to top of steeple is $40°\ 34'$. The telescope of the transit is leveled; it cuts the steeple base 4.72 ft. above the base.

(a) Are there sufficient data to compute to 0.01 ft. the height of top of steeple above the base course? If not, what additional data are required?

(b) If there are sufficient data, what is the height of the top of steeple above the base?

(c) Had the vertical angle been 30 seconds more, how much greater would the vertical distance be?

10. Indicate on a sketch drawn to scale how you would lay out with transit and tape the front corners (E and F) of the proposed building $EFGH$ (Fig. 90a) so that they will be exactly on line with the front corners (A and B) of the existing building $ABCD$; also E must be precisely 8.00 ft. from B. The front of building $ABCD$ is slightly irregular so that EF cannot be ranged out from AB.

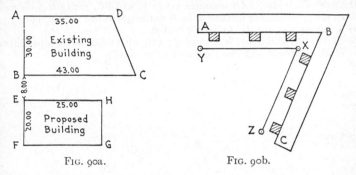

FIG. 90a.   FIG. 90b.

11. Referring to Fig. 90b, explain explicitly with the help of a sketch how you would establish lines XY and XZ precisely parallel to lines AB and BC respectively, for the purpose of measuring the angle $YXZ = ABC$. The lines AB and BC are straight between corners of the building; the building is faced with pilasters as shown in Fig. 90b.

12. From a corner post at A a random line was run in a westerly direction towards another corner B. The perpendicular offset to B in a northerly direction from the random line at X was 2.64 ft. The distance AX on the random line was 1052.40 ft. Another random line was run southerly from A towards another corner C. The perpendicular offset to C in an easterly direction from a point Y on the random line was 1.98 ft. and the distance AY was 1292.50 ft. The angle at A between random lines was 87° 49′ 20″.

(a) Find the angle between the property lines AB and AC.

(b) Find the length of the property lines AB and AC.

13. If, in Fig. 83, the angles $B'AB$ and $B''AB$ were laid off to the nearest minute only, what maximum displacement may occur in the position of point B from its correct position on the prolongation of the line, and what maximum angular divergence from the true line may occur in line BC? Distances $AB' = AB'' = B'C' = B''C'' = 200.00$ ft.

14. The following measurements were taken to check the perpendicularity of a tapering factory chimney of circular cross-section. Point A was established on the ground about 150 ft. from the base of the chimney and the shortest dimension to the base measured carefully and found to be 150.32 ft. The instrument was set up at A and sighted so as to bisect the top of the chimney; the telescope was then lowered and a point B set on the circumference at the base, which was level with the telescope. The instrument was reversed and the sighting repeated, and, the instrument being in adjustment, the line of sight again fell at B. With the transit at A an angle was measured from B to a line tangent to the right side of the chimney at the base and found by repetition to be 2° 12′ 20″. Similarly an angle

was measured from AB to the extreme left side of the chimney and found to be 2° 58′ 40″.

(a) How much is the chimney out of plumb at the top in a direction at right angles to AB?

(b) What is the radius of the chimney at the base to 0.01 ft.?

15. A line is being measured along the side of a straight highway pavement. Between transit points A and C a river intervenes, and a point B is chosen off line on the floor of a bridge. AB measures 538.21 ft. and BC, 762.18 ft. By means of a rod, the perpendicular distance from B to the transit line AC measures 7.5 ft.

(a) Compute distance AC to nearest 0.01 ft.

(b) If the offset at B were 1 ft. instead of 7.5 ft., what would be the tape distances AB and BC consistent with the computed value of AC?

CHAPTER VII

THE STADIA METHOD* — THE PLANE-TABLE METHOD

This chapter includes the theory of stadia measurements and the application of the method to various kinds of surveys. It also includes a brief treatment of the Plane-Table Method. These subjects are continued in Chapters IV and V, Vol. II, where the application of these methods to topographical surveys is fully treated.

214. Stadia Method of Measuring Distances. — The stadia method of locating points is one in which distances are measured by observing through the telescope of a transit the space, on a graduated rod, included between two horizontal hairs called *stadia hairs*. If the rod is held at different distances from the telescope different intervals on the rod are included between the stadia hairs, these intercepted spaces on the rod depending upon the distances from the rod to the instrument, so that the intercepted space is a **measure** of the distance to the rod.

Owing to the fact that in making a stadia measurement the intervening country does not have to be traversed, as is necessary when making a tape measurement, distances can be taken across ravines and water surfaces, and over rough as readily as over smooth ground. This gives the stadia a great advantage over the tape in point of speed. Another advantage of this method over that of tape measurements is that the chief errors of stadia measurements are compensating while those of tape measurements are mostly accumulative. (Art. 23, p. 16.) Furthermore, the accuracy of the stadia measurements is not diminished in rough country, so that the results obtained by this method are, under some conditions, as accurate as tape measurements. While surveys of property boundaries ordinarily demand the use of transit and tape, still the stadia method is well adapted

---

* The word *telemeter* is sometimes used instead of *stadia*.

to the survey of cheap land, such as marsh or timber land. In many instances the boundaries of such properties are so uncertain that the latter method is amply accurate. In highway or railroad surveys preliminary plans must often be prepared in a short time; for this purpose the stadia method is well adapted. Furthermore, where an accurate tape and transit survey is being made it is often desirable to locate also certain physical features whose precise location is not required; these may properly be located by stadia measurements, and the use of stadia for locating such details is common. As a means of obtaining a rough check upon steel tape measurements the stadia is of especial value. The lengths of all lines may be read quickly by stadia, and mistakes of a foot or more readily detected. It is also useful for taking sights across a traverse, or " cut-off lines," for the purpose of dividing the traverse into parts which may be checked independently. The stadia method is also especially adapted to topographical surveying.

215. Instruments. — The only equipment needed for this work in addition to the ordinary engineer's transit is a set of stadia hairs in the telescope, and some form of graduated rod on which distances may be read from the instrument. The two stadia hairs are usually placed on the cross-hair diaphragm parallel to and equidistant from the horizontal cross-hair. In some instruments they are so arranged that the distance between them is adjustable. For accurate work the fixed hairs are to be preferred as they do not get out of adjustment; the instrument maker can set them at the desired distance apart with sufficient accuracy. Sometimes the stadia hairs and the ordinary cross-hairs are placed on separate diaphragms or in different planes, so that when the eyepiece is focused on the ordinary cross-hairs the stadia hairs are invisible, and *vice versa*; these are called *disappearing* stadia hairs.

The telescope of a transit intended for stadia work should have a magnifying power of from 20 to 30 diameters, and should give a clear, well-defined image. It is desirable, although not necessary, that the instrument should be provided with a compass needle. Stadia instruments should have a vertical arc reading to the nearest minute. Since vertical angles are often required in stadia work it will prove to be a great saving in time to have the vernier and a spirit level mounted on a separate arm (Fig. 91), so that the index correction can be made zero each time a vertical angle is read. (See Art. 67, p. 62, and Fig. 97, p. 243.)

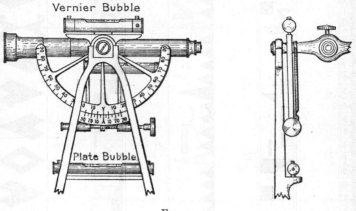

FIG. 91.

216. Stadia Rods. — There are many kinds of stadia rods, differing both as to the construction of the rod itself and the style of diagram used to mark the graduations. The diagrams for ordinary work should be simple, so that long distances may be read quickly. Complicated diagrams are to be avoided except where all of the sights are short and where greater precision is desired than is usually required in stadia work. In the rods shown in Fig. 92 the diagrams are made so that the 0.05-ft. or 0.10-ft. spaces can be distinguished easily and the hundredths of a foot estimated.

The rods on which these graduations are painted consist of wooden strips from 3 to 5 inches wide and 10 to 15 ft. in length. For convenience in carrying the rods they are usually made in two sections joined by hinges, but sometimes the two parts are separate and are clamped together when in use

In Fig. 92 the rods marked (*a*) and (*b*) are particularly useful for reading distances up to about 500 ft. Rod (*c*) is useful up to

about 1000 ft. and rod (e) is particularly applicable to distant
readings.   Rod (d) is useful both for short and medium distances.   Other styles of stadia rods and different types of hinges
and clamps used on them are shown in Fig. 47, p. 201, Vol. II.

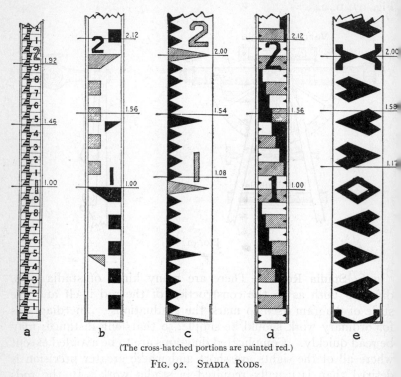

(The cross-hatched portions are painted red.)

FIG. 92.   STADIA RODS.

The ordinary Philadelphia leveling rod graduated to hun
dredths is suitable for short sights, say up to 300 ft.

217. Principle of the Stadia. — The fundamental principl
upon which the stadia method depends is the simple geometri
proposition that in two similar triangles homologous sides ar
proportional.   In Fig. 92a, suppose that the telescope is leve
and is sighted on a vertical rod, then with the stadia hairs fixed,

$$D : D_1 = s : s_1$$

It will be demonstrated that for the *ordinary transit* the dis tance (in feet) from the plumb-line of the transit to the vertical rod is **100 × (interval on rod intercepted between upper and lower stadia hairs) + 1.** If then the stadia rod interval is 1.12 (as in Rod b, Fig. 92) then the distance from center of transit to the rod is 113 ft. In all stadia work the rod **must be absolutely vertical** when the reading is taken.

While this simple proportion in Fig. 92a illustrates the stadia principle it is not quite exact, because the distance from the objective to the stadia hairs changes as the telescope is focused

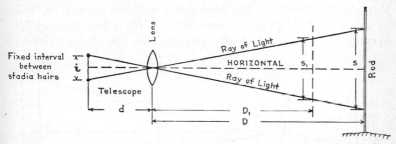

FIG. 92a. DIAGRAMMATIC REPRESENTATION OF PRINCIPLE OF THE STADIA.

for different distances. Following is a more rigorous treatment of the general case.

In Fig. 93 let L be the optical center* of the objective, a and b the stadia hairs, and A and B the points on the rod where the stadia hairs appear to cut it. AB is then the intercepted space when the rod is at the distance LX. If the rod were moved to the position Y, where the distance is one-half LX, then the intercepted space $A''B''$ would be one-half AB. That is, **the space on the rod is proportional to the distance.** Let $Lp = f_1$ and $LX = f_2$ (these distances being known as conjugate foci) and also let $AB = s$, and $ab = i$.

---

* Strictly speaking the lines representing the rays of light should not be drawn straight through the optical center as in the figure but should be bent at the surfaces of the lens. As a result the vertices of the two triangles ALB and aLb do not fall at L but at two points L' and L'' inside the lens (Nodal Points). The same ratio will be seen to exist between the sides of these triangles ($AL'B$ and $aL''b$) as exists in the triangles discussed in the text. The error introduced by neglecting the distance $L'L''$ is entirely inappreciable in stadia measurements.

Then from the similar triangles,

$$f_2 : f_1 = s : i \qquad [1]$$

When the rod is moved from X to Y, however, it becomes necessary to alter the focus of the objective, i.e., the distance between the objective and the cross-hairs must be increased. In some telescopes this is accomplished by moving the tube containing the eyepiece and the cross-hairs, and in others by moving the objective. In Fig. 93 let L remain fixed and suppose the cross-hairs to move to the position $a'b'$. If the rod is now viewed through the telescope the cross-hairs will not appear to strike at A'' and B'' but at A' and B'. $A'B'$ is less than $A''B''$ because the distance from the objective to the stadia hairs had

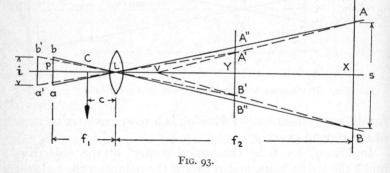

FIG. 93.

to be increased when focusing on the shorter distance LY, and since the stadia interval $i = ab = a'b'$ is fixed, the angle of divergence of the rays of light is decreased from ALB to $A'LB'$.

In determining the position of point V it is necessary to make use of the "Law of Lenses," namely,

$$\frac{1}{f_1} + \frac{1}{f_2} = \frac{1}{F} \qquad [2]$$

in which F is the *focal length* of the objective, i.e., the distance from the optical center to the cross-hairs when the telescope is focused on a distant object. (Art. 46, p. 39.) Solving equations [1] and [2] simultaneously, we have

$$f_2 = \frac{F}{i} s + F \qquad [3]$$

i.e., the distance LX is made up of two parts, — the variable distance VX, or $\frac{F}{i} s$, and the constant LV, or F. Since equation [3] was derived from a general case, LV is a constant for all stadia readings made with the same instrument, and the distance VX is a variable depending upon the rod interval. Hence all stadia distances (from the objective) are obtained by multiplying the space on the rod by a constant $\frac{F}{i}$, and adding to this result the focal length, F. The distance desired, however, is from the center of the instrument to the rod. This is found by adding to the above result the distance CL from the objective to the center of the instrument, which will be called c. The complete expression for the **distance from the center of transit to the rod** is then

$$\text{Distance} = f_2 + c = \frac{F}{i} s + (F + c) \qquad [4]$$

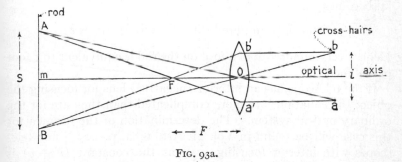

Fig. 93a.

217a. The formula just derived may also be found (by Gauss's method) as follows: Let the stadia hairs be a and b (Fig. 93a) placed a fixed distance apart ($= i$). Let $FO = F$, the focal length of the objective. A ray from A (on the rod) through the principal focal point F emerges from the lens in a line parallel to the optical axis. A second ray from A straight through the optical center* O intersects the first ray at a, the image of A.

---

* See Art. 46, p. 39 and note on p. 215 for remarks on Nodal Points.

From the similar triangles it is clear that

$$\frac{Fm}{AB} = \frac{F}{a'b'}, \quad \text{that is}$$

$$Fm = \frac{sF}{i}$$

Therefore the distance

$$Om = \frac{sF}{i} + F$$

The distance from the center of the transit to the rod is therefore

$$\frac{F}{i} s + (F + c) \qquad [4]$$

Since the ratio $\frac{F}{i}$ should be 100 in all instruments having fixed stadia hairs (most instruments have fixed hairs) then equation [4] becomes

Distance from plumb-line $= 100 s + (F + c)$

Hence every hundredth of a foot on the rod is equivalent to 1 foot of distance.

If the telescope has an interior (negative) lens for focusing the object the equations are more complicated than they are for the ordinary optical system. The determination of the formula for this case will be found in Vol. II, Art. 148a, p. 205. For telescopes with interior focusing systems the constant $(F + c)$ is about 0.3 ft.

218. Stadia Constants. — The quantity $(F + c)$ is virtually a constant for any given instrument. F is strictly a constant, and c is constant when the telescope is focused by moving the eyepiece; if the focusing is done by moving the objective, c will vary only about a hundredth of a foot in ordinary stadia sights, a negligible quantity in stadia measurements. Since in practice it is customary to read the rod interval to the nearest hundredth of a foot only, the distances are obtained to the nearest foot. If the stadia hairs are not set at exactly the correct interval the error may be determined by measuring a base-line with a steel tape and taking several readings on a rod held at two different distances, say 100 ft. and 600 ft. In order to obtain these rod intervals accurately it is advisable to use a leveling rod with two targets, the lower hair being set on the lower target and the upper target being set opposite the upper hair or *vice versa*. When the rod intervals have been determined carefully at both of the distances, the constant may be found by substituting these values and the measured distances in equation [4], thus forming two equations of the same form in which $\frac{F}{i}$ and $(F + c)$ are the only unknowns. Solving these two equations simultaneously will give an accurate value for the constant $\frac{F}{i}$. Suppose $\frac{F}{i}$ is found to be 99.2 instead of 100; then the rod intercept should be multiplied by 99.2.

This, however, is not a satisfactory method for determining the constant $(F + c)$, since errors in the readings cause a comparatively large error in the result. The constant F is the distance from the objective to the cross-hairs when the telescope is focused for a distant object, and c is the distance from the objective to the center of the instrument when focused for an average length of sight, both of which distances may be measured directly on the transit (instrument) with the tape or a 2-ft. rule.

The constant $(F + c)$ varies from about 0.75 to about 1.35 in different American transits, but it is customary and sufficiently accurate to regard it as 1 ft., since the distances are usually read to the nearest foot only.

The simple form that equation [4] now assumes for the ordinary transit is

$$\text{Distance from plumb-line} = 100\,s + 1$$

219. Formulas for Inclined Sights. — In practice it is customary to hold the rod **plumb** rather than perpendicular to the line of sight, because the former position can be judged easily and accurately, whereas it is not easy to determine when the rod is perpendicular to the line of sight and often is difficult to maintain it in that position. On inclined sights, when the rod is plumb, the vertical and horizontal distances evidently cannot be found simply by solving a right triangle. In Fig. 94 let AB be the intercept on the rod when it is held vertical, $A'B'$ the intercept when the rod is perpendicular to the line of sight, i.e., $A'B'$ is perpendicular to CO. *In the triangle AOA', $\angle O = \angle \alpha$, the measured vertical angle; $\angle A' = 90° + m$; and $\angle A = 90° - (\alpha + m)$, m being half the angle between

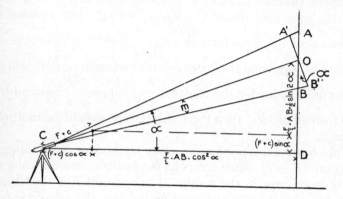

FIG. 94.

the stadia hairs. In the triangle BOB', $\angle O = \angle \alpha$; $\angle B' = 90° - m$; and $\angle B = 90° - (\alpha - m)$.

Then
$$\frac{AO}{A'O} = \frac{\sin (90° + m)}{\sin \{90° - (\alpha + m)\}}$$

and
$$\frac{BO}{B'O} = \frac{\sin (90° - m)}{\sin \{90° - (\alpha - m)\}}$$

$$AO + OB = AB = \tfrac{1}{2} A'B' \left\{ \frac{\cos m}{\cos (\alpha + m)} + \frac{\cos m}{\cos (\alpha - m)} \right\}$$

from which may be obtained

$$A'B' = AB \cos \alpha - AB \frac{\sin^2 \alpha}{\cos \alpha} \tan^2 m$$

---

* This demonstration is nearly the same as that given by Mr. George J. Specht in "Topographical Surveying," published by Van Nostrand Company, New York.

The value of the second term is very small; for $AB = 15.00$ ft., $\alpha = 45°$, and $m = \tan^{-1} 0.005$, this term is only 0.0002 ft., and hence it may always be neglected. In other words it is sufficiently accurate to regard the angles A' and B' as right angles.

$$\therefore A'B' = AB \cos \alpha$$

The difference in elevation between the center of the instrument and the point O on the rod is derived as follows:

$$DO = CO \sin \alpha$$
$$= \left\{ \frac{F}{i} A'B' + (F + c) \right\} \sin \alpha$$
$$= \frac{F}{i} AB \sin \alpha \cos \alpha + (F + c) \sin \alpha$$
$$= \frac{F}{i} AB \cdot \tfrac{1}{2} \sin 2\alpha + (F + c) \sin \alpha \qquad [5]$$

For the horizontal distance from the transit point to the rod we have

$$CD = CO \cos \alpha$$
$$= \left\{ \frac{F}{i} A'B' + (F + c) \right\} \cos \alpha$$
$$= \frac{F}{i} AB \cos^2 \alpha + (F + c) \cos \alpha \qquad [6]$$

220. Most of the stadia tables, diagrams, and stadia slide rules in common use are based upon these two formulas [5] and [6]. Table VIII, p. 674, gives values for the first term only of equation [5], based on $AB = 1.00$ ft. and on $\frac{F}{i} = 100$ (the usual stadia hair interval). The difference in elevation between the axis of the telescope and the point on the rod where the middle hair cuts it is called the *vertical height*, and is obtained by multiplying the rod interval by the number in Table VIII. But that gives only the first term of equation [5]. The vertical height represented by the second term is obtained as follows:

The value $(F + c)$ is obtained directly from the instrument;

it may be 0.75 ft., it may be 1.25 ft. or any value between these two. The error in DO is almost negligible if $(F + c)$ is first added to $100 \times AB$ which is equivalent to adding 0.01 ft. to the rod interval, and then obtaining the vertical height from the table as before. Hence the process of finding the vertical height, DO, involves merely adding 0.01 ft. to the rod interval and multiplying the result by the tabular amount (Table VIII).

Table VIII, p. 674, also gives the amount the horizontal distance is less than $100 \times AB$. This is not equation [6]; it is the value of $100\, AB \sin^2\alpha$. To allow for the constant $(F + c)$ its amount (1 ft.) is added to $100 \times AB$ and from this sum the horizontal correction is subtracted in obtaining the true horizontal distance.

Strictly, the way in which the second factor in equations [5] and [6] have been used is not precise, but wholly in keeping with the fact that the rod interval is not read closer than 0.01 ft. corresponding to 1 ft. in horizontal distance.

221. For small vertical angles, say under 3°, the horizontal correction may be omitted and if in this case the constant $(F + c)$ is also omitted, it will be observed that since one of these is positive and the other negative the resulting error will be smaller than either of these corrections. It will be seen in Table VIII that the horizontal correction to be subtracted from 400 ft. for an angle of 3° is 1.1 ft. (equivalent to the value of $(F + c)$ to be added). For a 1000-ft. distance, the amount to be subtracted is 2.7 ft., and when $(F + c)$ is added, the net amount to be deducted is 1.7 ft. It is difficult to read the rod interval to nearer than 0.02 ft. at 1000-ft. distances. Hence to disregard the horizontal correction for angles of less than 3° is consistent. Care should be taken, however, that the constant $(F + c)$ is not omitted when computing or plotting a traverse, for in this case the error tends to accumulate and may seriously affect the accuracy of the map. In very rough work, however, or on small-scale maps where 1 or 2 ft. cannot be plotted, the constant $(F + c)$ may then be omitted.

221a. A study of Table VIII will show that when the vertical angle is about 0° 35′ the corresponding vertical height is 1% of the distance; when the vertical angle is 2° 52′ the corresponding vertical height is 5% of the distance; when the vertical angle is 5° 46′ the corresponding height is 10% of the distance, and when 8° 44′ it is 15% of the distance. It is an easy matter to remember these four angles, 0° 35′, 2° 52′, 5° 46′ and 8° 44′. Roughly they are $\frac{1}{2}$°, 3°, 5$\frac{3}{4}$° and 8$\frac{3}{4}$°; corresponding to 1%, 5%, 10% and 15% of the stadia distance. With these in mind a rough value of the vertical height can be computed mentally as a check against computed values obtained through the use of tables, diagrams or slide rules. The surveyor should always apply this mental calculation as a guard against large mistakes.

Suppose, for example, that the rod interval reading was 4.36 and vertical angle 6° 10′, then the vertical angle can be considered to be 5$\frac{3}{4}$° + $\frac{1}{2}$°, and the vertical height is about 11% of the distance, i.e., 48 ft. Actually it is 4.37 × 10.68 = 46.7.

222. Fieldwork. — In surveying by the stadia method points are located by means of (1) the azimuth, (2) the angle of elevation or depression, and (3) the distance. When the survey does not involve the determination of elevations the vertical angles are merely read close enough for computing the horizontal correction to the distances read. But when a topographical survey is made, the determination of elevations becomes necessary and all vertical angles must be read closer, usually to the nearest minute. The azimuths and distances are read in both kinds of surveys with a precision that is consistent with the accuracy required in the final result. The azimuths are usually referred to 0° on any traverse line running through the set-up point, which must be recorded in the field notes as on p. 232.

Traverse lines which form the control of the survey are run out either by means of the transit and tape or by stadia, according to the accuracy demanded. Where a number of transit points are to be distributed over a large area, a system of triangulation may be employed in which a base and a few additional lines are measured with the tape, the horizontal angles are measured by repetition with the transit, and the lengths of all the lines are computed; the additional measured lines will serve as checks on the accuracy of the work. Where the survey is controlled by such a triangulation or by tape traverses the stadia work is confined to filling in details. Where no great precision is required the main traverses may be measured by stadia alone; but the distances should be read on both forward and backsights.

From the traverse line as a control, points taken for the purpose of locating details are determined by angles and stadia distances. These observations are commonly called " side shots." The precision with which these measurements are taken need not be so great as that of the traverse measurements, because any error in the measurements will affect but a single point, whereas an error in the traverse line will be carried through the remainder of the traverse. The side shots are usually numbered consecutively in the note-book. When taking side shots it is customary not to clamp the horizontal plates because the angles are read only to the nearest 5', which is close enough for plotting.

In locating points as described above the readings are taken most conveniently in the following order. The vertical hair is set on the rod and the upper plate clamped; the distance is read by setting one stadia hair on a whole foot-mark and reading the position of the other stadia hair (Fig. 92); finally the middle horizontal hair is set on that point on the rod to which the vertical angle is to be taken. After making this setting the transit-man signals the rodman to proceed to the next point; in the meantime he reads the azimuth and the vertical angle.

223. Azimuths. — Azimuths are sometimes counted from the south point through the west up to 360° in accordance with geodetic practice. If the true azimuth of any line is known, all the azimuths of the survey may be referred to the true meridian. If the direction of the true meridian is not known an initial azimuth may be taken from the magnetic bearing of some line and all azimuths referred to the magnetic meridian. The latter method has the advantage that all azimuths may be checked directly by reading the magnetic bearings. If the magnetic meridian cannot be used, any direction may be arbitrarily assumed as a meridian and all azimuths referred to this direction. If a transit and tape traverse has been run previously it is convenient to assume one of the transit lines as the 0° line of azimuths, a new traverse line being taken as a reference line for the azimuths at each set-up if desired.

The stadia method often is used to supplement the data obtained by transit and tape, and for this purpose it is not considered important to orient the circle on the true meridian at each set-up of the instrument. At each set-up the horizontal circle is set at 0°, the telescope is sighted at the preceding station, and all azimuths are read (clockwise) from this backsight.

If azimuths are measured from the meridian the direction of the meridian must be carried forward from one transit point to the next; there are two methods in common use, each of which has its advantages. Suppose that the work at point A has been completed, all of the azimuth angles about A having been referred to the meridian which was chosen as the 0° direction, and that the transit is to be moved to a new station B. Before leaving A the transit point B is located from A by its distance and azimuth. The transit is then set up at B and the azimuth of any line (BC) is determined in either of the following ways.

(1) Backsight on A with the telescope inverted, the horizontal vernier remaining at the same reading it had at A (the azimuth of line AB); clamp the lower plate, turn the telescope into its direct position, and, loosening the upper plate, turn toward C. The vernier will then read the azimuth of BC referred to the same meridian as the azimuth of AB. It is evident that this method does not eliminate any error that may exist in the line of collimation, so that the error in the azimuth will tend to accumulate on a long traverse. The advantage of this method is the rapidity with which the instrument can be oriented.

(2) Add 180 degrees to the azimuth of AB, set this off on the plate, and sight on A with the telescope in the direct position. Clamp the lower clamp, loosen the upper clamp and sight the telescope toward C; the angle read will be the azimuth of BC. The disadvantages of this method as compared with the former are that time is consumed in setting the circle at each new set-up of the instrument, and that there is an opportunity for mistakes in calculating and in making the setting on the vernier.

224. Vertical Angles. — When vertical angles are to be taken the middle horizontal cross-hair is sighted at a point on the rod whose distance above the foot of the rod is equal to the distance from the center of the transit to the ground (or the stake) be-

neath.   This distance is known as the *height of instrument* (H.I.);
it is not the same as the H.I. used in ordinary leveling;   the
latter is the height of the instrument above the datum plane.
If the cross-hair is sighted at this H.I. point on the rod, it is
evident that the line of sight is parallel to the line from the transit point to the foot of the rod, and also that the difference in
elevation between the center of the instrument and the H.I.
point on the rod is the same as the difference in elevation between
the point under the transit and the foot of rod.   It is common
practice to fasten a wide, heavy rubber band or a strip of red
cloth on the rod so that it can be set on the new H.I. point at
each set-up.

225. Distances. — The distance is read by setting one of the
stadia hairs on a whole foot-mark and counting the feet and
tenths between the stadia hairs, the hundredths of a foot being
estimated.   If a Philadelphia leveling rod is used and the distances are short, the hundredths of a foot may be read directly.
**Great care should be taken not to mistake the middle horizontal
cross-hair for one of the stadia hairs.**   This mistake is liable to
occur when the telescope is of high power, because the stadia
hairs appear to be far apart in the field of view and consequently
the eye does not see all three hairs at once.   In counting the
number of feet in the rod interval between the stadia hairs great
care should be taken to obtain this interval correctly.   It can
be checked by reading the interval between the middle hair and a
stadia hair and observing if this is nearly one half of the whole
interval.   (Fig. 92, p. 214.)

In reading the distance it is customary to set the lower stadia
hair on that foot-mark which will bring the middle cross-hair in
the vicinity of the H.I.   In finding the horizontal correction to
apply to the distance read it is customary to use the vertical
angle that was read when the middle cross-hair was on the H.I.
Theoretically a slight error is thus introduced, because when the
distance is read with a stadia hair on a whole foot-mark the inclination of the line of sight is not the same as the vertical angle
read when the middle cross-hair is set on the H.I. point.   The
distance and the angle introduced into the formula do not correspond.   The middle hair, however, need never be more than

half a foot above or below the H.I. when the distance is read, and it is easy to show that the consequent error in horizontal distance is negligible.

Whenever a portion of the rod is obscured, by leaves for instance, or when the distance is so great that the two stadia hairs do not fall on the rod at the same time, an approximate value of the distance may be obtained by reading first the interval between the upper and middle hairs and then the interval between the middle and lower hairs, and taking the sum of the two readings. If the two spaces are found to be exactly equal it will be sufficient thereafter to take one reading and double it, but it should never be assumed that the two are equal until they are found to be so by test.

It is of great importance that the rod be held plumb when the distance is being read, as any inclination of the rod evidently will introduce an error into the observed distance. This error becomes greater as the inclination of the line of sight increases. For example, if a 10-ft. stadia rod is held so that the top is 0.5 ft. farther from the transit than when it is vertical (inclination of 2° 52′) then for a distance of 700 ft. and vertical angle of 5° the resulting error will be 0.04 ft. on the rod or 4 ft. of distance. For 15° the error is 0.11 ft. on the rod or 11 ft. of distance. To hold a 10-ft. rod more nearly vertical than this requires great care. In some classes of stadia work it is desirable and even necessary to plumb the rod by means of a rod level whenever highly inclined sights are taken. (Art. 109, p. 88.)

226. STADIA TRAVERSES. — In a stadia traverse the instrument is set at the first station and the telescope set on the meridian (or reference line) with the vernier reading 0°. The position of the second station is located by reading the distance, azimuth, and vertical angle. In determining the azimuth of the line it is well for the rodman to show the narrow edge of his rod as a foresight, so that the transitman can make a more exact setting of the vertical cross-hair. The transit is then moved to the second station and placed in position by backsighting on the first point as explained in Art. 223; at the same time the vertical angle and the distance are again read, thus checking the distance between the two points and also the difference in elevation if stadia levels are also being taken. In reading the distances both ways there is also an opportunity to guard against an inaccurate reading due to poor illumination of the rod. By sighting both directions with the telescope erect the index error of the vertical circle is eliminated; this process is similar in principle to the peg method of testing a level. (See Art. 128, p. 99.)

227. Checks on the Traverse. — In running a closed stadia traverse the azimuths may be checked by redetermining the azimuth of the first line from the last and noting whether this value checks the azimuth of the first line as determined at the beginning of the traverse. If these differ by less than 5 minutes of angle the result will be sufficiently accurate for most topographical purposes. The azimuths may be checked roughly at any point by reading the magnetic bearings of the lines. Where there are triangulation points connected with the survey the known azimuths of these triangle sides will furnish a complete check.

In running stadia traverses for several miles where no other check on the azimuths can be obtained it is advisable to make observations on the sun for true azimuth. (Art. 238, p. 271.) Such observations can be taken quickly and if made in the morning or afternoon, when the sun is not very near the meridian, will give the azimuth within about one minute of arc, which is as accurate as is required for this purpose. The convergence of the meridians, if appreciable, should be allowed for. (See Art. 178 and Table 7A, p. 182.)

228. Stadia Notes. — To the beginner the taking of good stadia notes presents great difficulties. The general instructions with regard to transit notes apply equally well to notes for stadia surveys. (Art. 148, p. 128.) A large amount of sketching or description of details is required in order to convey sufficient information to enable the draftsman, who may not be familiar with the locality, to plot the results. Furthermore it is necessary to locate a large number of points in order to be sure of sufficient data to sketch the details correctly. If the map can be plotted soon after the fieldwork is done and by the person who made the survey, and especially if the map can be taken afterward into the field and the sketching completed there, then much greater accuracy in regard to details can be secured; this field sketching on the map is important and should be done whenever it is practicable.

The notes for the survey of a lot of land are shown in Fig. 95. The notes given at the top in tabular form show in the first column the station at which the instrument was set up; the second column indicates the station to which it was sighted; the distances read are in the third column. The azimuths are read to the nearest minute because they are to be used for purposes of calculation; the observed bearings are taken as a check upon the azimuths. The vertical angles are taken only on those lines where the horizontal correction would change the distances as much as a foot, and they are read only to the nearest quarter degree or half degree, because for the distances and the vertical angles in these notes this will give the horizontal correction to the nearest half-foot. Evidently there is no necessity for indicating whether the angles were plus or minus. The traverse was measured in a right-hand direction around the field beginning at A, and finally the instrument was set up at A again, backsighted on E, and the azimuth of the line AB redetermined from the backsight on E. The notes indicate that an error of one minute was found in the azimuths. The notes also show that two shots, Nos. 1 and 2, were taken to the corners of a barn merely for the purpose of obtaining data for plotting it on the map. The figure in the lower part of the page is a sketch of the property, on which are lettered the names of the abutting owners, and the physical features which define the boundaries.

It will be observed that the distances on the traverse were measured both forward and backward, two independent readings being taken. Before computing the area of this field the average of these two readings should be taken as the correct distance and to this distance should be added the constant of the instrument (1 ft.). The horizontal correction should be applied to all inclined distances if the correction amounts to more than half a foot.

Fig. 96 is a double page of stadia notes of a survey in which elevations were required. The survey was made for the purpose of obtaining a preliminary map of a grade crossing. The traverse

Stadia Survey of Pasture Land of L. K. Miller   King △ Stone
Jan. 15, 1935

△ at	Sta.	Dist.*	Az. L 0° on Mag. S	Obs. Bearing	Vert. L	Remarks
A	E	717			− 2° 15′	
	B	642	211° 21′	N. 31° 15′ E.	——	
B	A	642			——	
	C	786	272° 47′	S. 87° 15′ E	——	
C	B	784				
	D	971	359° 03′	S. 1° 00′ E	+ 4° 40′	Cedar Post
D	C	973			− 4° 30′	
	E	897	76° 05′	S. 77° 00′ W	——	Stake and Stones
E	D	895			——	
	A	718	157° 34′	N. 22° 15′ W.	+ 2° 00′	Stake and Stones
A			211° 20′ check			
A	1	467	199° 00′			
A	2	491	199° 50′			

* F + c = 1.2 ft.
(Not included)

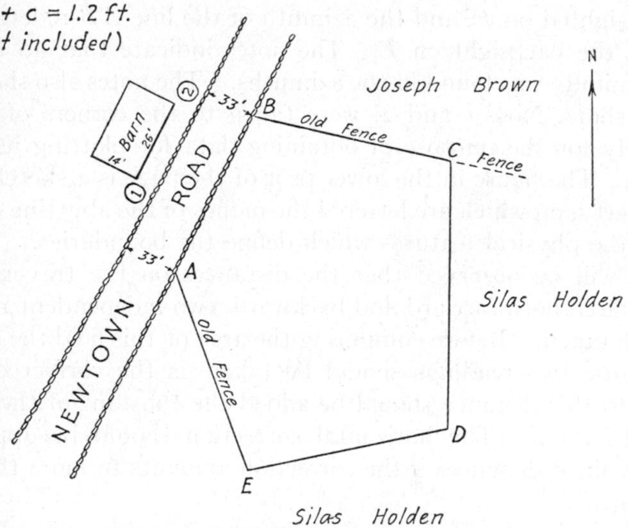

FIG. 95. STADIA SURVEY OF PASTURE LOT.

was run by transit and tape along the center line of the straight track and, at curves, running to the point of intersection of the tangents or else cutting across on long chords. The points occupied by the instrument are numbered and are designated by a ⊡, the usual symbol for a stadia station. The side shots are numbered consecutively either throughout the survey or through each day's work; the vertical angles are designated + or − to indicate whether they are above or below the horizontal line. If the middle cross-hair is sighted at any point other than the H.I. the point on which it is sighted should be noted directly under the vertical angle, as was done on side shot 41. The first five columns only are entered in the field; most of the values in the last two columns are computed in the office; those which are recorded with inclined figures were computed in the field for the purpose of checking elevations and for establishing station elevations to be used later in the same day's fieldwork. The erect figures were computed in the office.

Referring to the notes on the left-hand page of Fig. 96 it will be seen that the elevation of ⊡ 6, where the transit was set up first, was obtained by means of a level reading of 5.26 taken on the B.M. The elevation of ⊡ 6 equals $57.62 + 5.26 − 4.6 = 58.3$. A rectangle is drawn about this figure 58.3 because it is used for all computations of elevation of points that were sighted when the instrument was at ⊡ 6. After all necessary side shots were taken at ⊡ 6 the elevation of ⊡ A was determined by the stadia method as 95.3. The azimuths were checked by sighting again on sta. $1 + 62.47$. The instrument was then moved to ⊡ A and a backsight taken on ⊡ 6. The elevation of ⊡ 6 was determined as 58.3 by direct leveling from the bench-mark. It is therefore recorded below opposite station ⊡ 6 as 58.3, and by means of the difference in elevation 36.7 the new elevation of ⊡ A is $58.3 + 36.7 = 95.0$. Its elevation, however, was determined above from ⊡ 6 as 95.3 so there has been entered in these notes in the last column opposite " Instrument at ⊡ A " the figure 95.1, which is the mean (to the nearest tenth) of 95.0 and 95.3.

The side shots at ⊡ A are next taken and then sta. $12 + 14.37$ has its elevation established by stadia as 65.3. Before picking up the instrument, ⊡ 6 was sighted to check the azimuth. If

Sta.	Dist.	Az. Ang.	Bear.	Vert. Ang.	Diff. El.	Elev.
⚲ at ⊡6,		0° on 1+62.47,			H.I. = 4.6	58.3
B.M.		Top S. B. at P.T.	3+24.94	0° 00' on 5·26		57·62
1	298 -1	221° 20'		+3° 27'	+18.0	76.3
2	238 -1	217° 15'		+2° 44'	+11.4	69.7
3	183	205° 10'		+1° 37'	+ 5.2	63.5
4	165	180° 00'		+0° 31'	+ 1.5	59.8
5	167	115° 40'		-0° 16'	- 0.8	57.5
6	177	142° 25'		-0° 42'	- 2.2	56·1
7	212	111° 00'		-1° 22'	- 5.1	53·2
8	323	80° 15'		-1° 57'	-11.0	47.3
9	426	70° 05'		-1° 47'	-13.3	45·0
10	409 -2	67° 30'		-3° 36'	-25.7	32·6
Etc.						
⊡ A	825 -2	221° 23'		+2° 34'	+37.0	95.3
1+62.47	437	0° 00'				
⚲ at ⊡A,		0° on ⊡6,			H.I. = 4.7	95.1
⊡ 6	823 -2		S. 7°15'E.	- 2° 33'	-36.7	58.3
39	312	357° 10'		-1° 25'	- 7.7	87.4
40	133 -1	17° 35'		-3° 46'	- 8.8	86·3
41	156	22° 05'		-2° 46' on 6.7	- 9.6	85.5
42	274 -1	3° 20'		-2° 24'	-11.5	83.6
Etc.						
⊡ 12+14.37	547 -2	48° 02'	S. 41°00'W.	-3° 07'	-29.8	65.3
⊡ 6		0° 01'				
⚲ at ⊡12+14.37,		0° on ⊡6,			H.I. = 4.8	65.2
⊡ 6		0° 00'		0° 00' on 11.7	- 6.9	58.3
⊡ A	546 -2	269° 25'		+3° 08'	+29.9	95.1
52	640 -3	56° 25'		-3° 40'	-40.9	24.3

The table is titled: Survey for Elimination of Grade Crossing at Westwood, A.&B.R.R.

FIG. 96. STADIA SURVEY REQUIRING ELEVATIONS

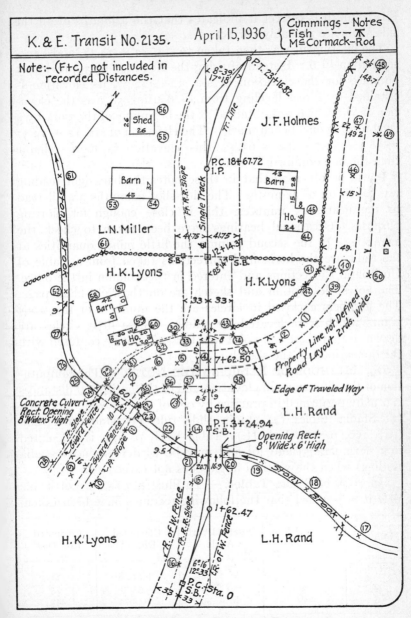

FIG. 96. STADIA SURVEY REQUIRING ELEVATIONS.

this azimuth is correct it indicates that the azimuths of all the side shots are probably correct.

The instrument was then taken to sta. 12 + 14.37, and back-sighted on ⊡ 6. Instead of using the elevation 65.3, previously obtained for the elevation of sta. 12 + 14.37, its elevation is obtained by direct leveling from ⊡ 6 using 58.3 as the eleva-tion of ⊡ 6 which was obtained at the beginning of the work by a level reading on a bench-mark. The elevation of sta. 12 + 14.37 = 58.3 + 11.7 − 4.8 = 65.2; this elevation is more reliable than the one obtained by stadia.

It will be observed that in these notes the backsight reading was taken on 0° azimuth. The side-shot azimuths are all read to the nearest 5 minutes, this is close enough for plotting purposes. Occasional bearings have been taken to check the azimuths. In the second column the little minus quantities at the right are the horizontal corrections taken from a Table of Horizontal Corrections and entered in this column in the office. The notes, description and sketch are on the right-hand page. The numbers enclosed in circles are the numbers of the (rod) points which were located by stadia. These little circles are drawn so that these rod-point numbers will not be confused with the dimensions on the sketch.

229. Methods of Reducing the Notes. — The computa-tion of the differences in elevation and of the horizontal distances is usually performed in practice by one of the following methods: (1) Stadia tables (2) stadia slide rule (3) stadia diagram. (Art. 160, p. 224, Vol. II.) Table VIII, p. 674, is calculated from formulas [5] and [6] and may be used to reduced stadia readings when the vertical angle does not exceed 40°.

230. Use of Stadia Tables. — To illustrate the use of Table VIII it is assumed that the following readings have been taken.

Station	Observed Rod Intervals	Observed Vert. Angle	Computed Diff. El.	Computed Hor. Dist.
1	311	+ 3° 54′	+ 21.18	311
2	91	− 25° 28′	− 35.71	75
3	240	+ 0° 39′	+ 2.74	241

$(F + c)$ = 1.12 foot (say 1 foot).

The rod intervals are recorded here as distances (100 × rod interval), in accordance with common practice, rather than as actual rod intervals. The constant $(F + c)$ has not been included in the recorded distances in the above notes.

To obtain the difference in elevation for station 1 from the Table of Vertical Heights (Table VIII), we look in the column headed 3 degrees and on the line opposite 54 minutes, where 6.79 ft. is found as the difference in elevation for a 1-ft. rod interval, i.e., a 100-ft. distance. By adding $(F + c)$ to the distance 311 the corrected distance 312 is obtained. Then 6.79 ft. (the difference for 100 ft.) multiplied by 3.12 gives 21.18 ft. as the difference in elevation between the center of the instrument and the point on the rod where the middle cross-hair was sighted when taking the vertical angle. This multiplication may be performed with an ordinary slide rule. Beneath the Table of Vertical Heights is given the Table of Horizontal Corrections. The horizontal correction for 311 ft. and 3 degrees 54 minutes is found by interpolating between 3 degrees and 4 degrees and also between 300 ft. and 400 ft., the result being 1.4 feet. The horizontal distance, to the nearest foot, is then $311 + 1 - 1 = 311$.

At station 2 the difference in elevation is 0.92 × 38.82 = 35.71. The horizontal distance is $91 + 1 - 17 = 75$ ft. At station 3 the vertical height for 0 degrees 39 minutes and for 100 ft. is taken from the 0 degree column by interpolation between 38 and 40 minutes and is 1.14, the difference in elevation for the rod interval 2.40 being 2.74 ft. The horizontal correction is only 0.1 and is therefore neglected. Suppose that at station 3 the vertical angle + 0° 39′ had been taken at a point on the rod 4 ft. **below** the H.I., the difference in elevation would then be $+2.74 + 4.00 = 6.74$. Had the sight been taken on the rod 4 ft. **above** the H.I. the difference in elevation would be $+ 2.74 - 4.00 = -1.26$.

Stadia Diagrams. — Where stadia notes are reduced in the office it is sometimes convenient to determine the difference in elevation and the horizontal distance by means of a diagram, from which the results can be taken by inspection. There are several possible arrangements, but they all depend upon formulas [5] and [6]. Fig. 96a shows a simple form which can be made in the office on ordinary coördinate paper. The accuracy of printed coördinate paper is not always sufficient, however; for an accurate diagram it is better to construct the coördinate lines on heavy drawing paper. Only the degree lines are shown

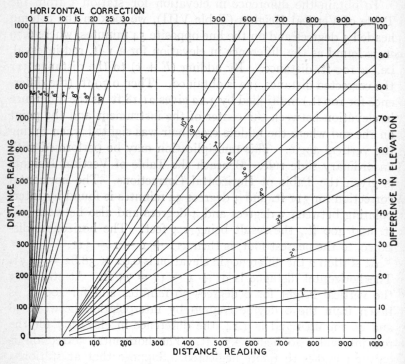

FIG. 96a.   DIAGRAM FOR REDUCING STADIA READINGS.
(INCLUDE $(F + c)$ IN DISTANCE READING.)

in Fig. 96a, but the subdivision may be carried to 10′, or to 5′ of vertical angle, sometimes closer, by plotting additional points.

In using this diagram the inclined line corresponding to the vertical angle is intersected with the vertical line corresponding to the distance reading; the difference in elevation for this point is read from the scale on the right, by interpolating between the horizontal lines. The horizontal correction to the distance is taken from the left-hand part of the diagram in exactly the same manner.

Stadia Arcs. — Some instruments have graduated on the vertical arc, or on an auxiliary arc, a series of lines corresponding to those vertical angles for which the difference in elevation is a simple multiple of the rod interval. Such angles would be 0° 34′ +, 1° 08′ +, 1° 43′ +, etc. If these angles are looked up in Table VIII they will be seen to correspond to the multiples 1.00, 2.00, 3.00, etc. To use such an arc for computing the difference in elevation the telescope must be inclined until the index mark is exactly opposite some line on the stadia arc. This changes the position of the horizontal hair on the rod, so the new reading of the middle hair must be taken. In order that the vertical angle shall be the true one, free from index error, it is important that the telescope be leveled and the stadia index set at 0 before the sight is taken.

As an illustration suppose that the elevation of the transit point is 203.4 ft., the height of instrument is 4.0 ft., the rod interval (stadia) is 2.50 ft., and that the stadia index line is near the −13 line. When the −13 line is made to coincide exactly with the index line the middle hair is found to read 7.8 ft. on the rod. The elevation of the foot of the rod is therefore 203.4 + 4.0 − 13 × 2.50 − 7.8 = 167.1 ft. In this manner elevation may be computed rapidly in the field.

Various forms of stadia arc are manufactured. The original one was that designed by W. M. Beaman of the U. S. Geological Survey. On this arc the −13 would be marked as 37, the 50 mark being the zero, as shown in Fig. 96b. From another set of graduations on the same piece of metal, the horizontal corrections (for a 1-ft. intercept) can be read off at the same time. In the setting shown in Fig. 96b this is between 1 and 2.

231. METHODS OF PLOTTING STADIA NOTES. — Stadia notes are usually plotted by means of a circular protractor and a scale. If the main traverse is a transit and tape survey, or if the scale of the map is such that a protractor would not be sufficiently accurate, the traverse may be plotted by some more accurate method and the side shots put in afterward by the protractor and scale. In general, however, any measurement taken by stadia may be plotted with sufficient accuracy by means of a protractor. (See Chap. XVI for methods of plotting traverses.)

In setting the protractor in position for plotting it should be centered with care and turned to the proper azimuth as defined by a o° line drawn through the point and extending each way beyond the circumference of the protractor. It is not safe to depend upon a line extending only one way, because the center of a protractor is usually marked in such a way that it is difficult

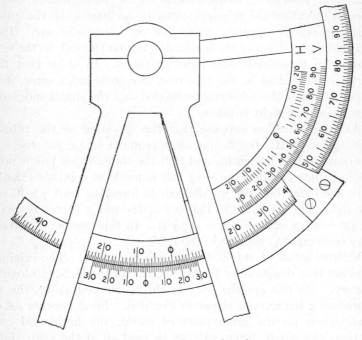

FIG. 96b. THE BEAMAN STADIA ARC ATTACHMENT.

to place it exactly over the transit point on the plan. Many protractors which are accurately graduated have the center point carelessly marked. The most accurate way to use a protractor is to draw two lines at right angles to each other, one of them being the meridian or reference line. These lines may be drawn at right angles as explained in Art. 486, p. 564. The protractor is then **oriented,** i.e., turned in the proper direction by making the cardinal points on the circumference line up with lines drawn at right angles, without regard to the position of the center mark on the protractor.

The usual process is to place the protractor in position and plot all of the azimuths first, marking each by a light dot or a short radial line in the proper azimuth and writing opposite the mark the number of the shot. This work can be done conveniently by two persons, one reading the azimuths and the numbers while the other plots the angles. When all of the azimuths have been plotted the protractor is removed and the distances are scaled off, the proper elevation being written opposite each point. Sometimes the plotted position of the point is indicated by a dot enclosed by a small circle, the height being written at one side. Another way, which is convenient when the plotted points are close together, is to write the whole number of feet of the elevation to the left of the point and the tenths to the right, the plotted point itself serving as the decimal point.

If much plotting is to be done it will be found convenient to use a large paper protractor from which the central portion has been removed, leaving the graduations close to the inner edge of the remaining paper. This enables the draftsman to set the zero of his scale on the station and the edge of the scale on the azimuth and to plot the points directly without the necessity for drawing lines or moving the protractor. Such a protractor can be made in the office. (Fig. 96c.)

231a. Locating Contours. — If contours are to be located by stadia there are two general methods which may be used. First, if the scale is comparatively large and the contours are to be located accurately it may be advisable to obtain points which are exactly on the contours. This process is slower but more accurate than the other. In obtaining these elevations the transit is used as a leveling instrument. The rod is first held on a benchmark and a backsight is taken to determine the H.I. The notes may be kept on a separate page in the form of ordinary level notes. The proper foresight to give a point on a contour is next found by subtracting the contour elevation from the H.I. Suppose, for instance, that the H.I. is 117.23 ft. and that the 110 contour is to be located. A rod reading of 7.23 will be obtained when the rod is held exactly on the 110 contour. It would be sufficient

to read this as 7.2 when locating contours.   The instrument man
directs the rodman to move up the slope or down the slope until
the foresight reading is 7.2.   When this point is found it is
located by azimuth and stadia distance in the usual manner.
This, however, requires changing the inclination of the telescope
in order to read the stadia distance, or else it requires making

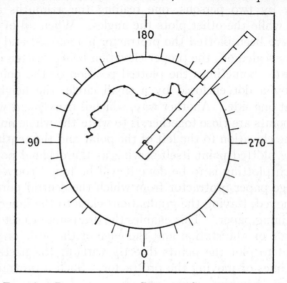

FIG. 96c.   PROTRACTOR FOR PLOTTING STADIA SIDE SHOTS.

two readings and subtracting them.   It is not therefore a rapid
method.

Second, if the scale to be used is small, or if the required accuracy is not great, the rod may be held on such points as determine the various slopes of the ground, and these points may be
located by distance, azimuth and vertical angle to the H.I. point
on the rod.   The points which will naturally be selected are those
situated along the ridge lines and the valley lines, and especially
those points where the slope changes.   If all such points are
located then it may be assumed that the slopes are uniform between rod points.   There should be, however, enough points
located so that errors may be detected.   If the elevation of a
single point is in error it will affect the contours over a wide

area unless there are additional elevations to check it. It is better to have an excess of points and avoid such mistakes, than to have so few that the mistakes pass unnoticed. After these points are plotted the contours are found by interpolating between the elevations of the rod points.

Sketching Contours. — One of the weaknesses of the stadia method is that the plotting is usually done in the office. Very complete notes are necessary to give the draftsman a correct idea of the ground he is depicting, and complete notes are the exception, not the rule. Even if the draftsman did all the field-work himself he may not be able to remember all the details. It is not easy to foresee all the needs of the draftsman. The sketching done in the office, apart from that which is purely mechanical, is liable, therefore, to be in error.

An excellent way of supplementing the sketch is to take the map into the field, mounted on a drawing board, and to complete the details of the sketch while the ground is in sight. Many little details of the contours may now be sketched which would probably be omitted in the notes, or which, if recorded, would require that a large number of points be determined. By this procedure the stadia method can be made to give almost as good results as the plane table. It is possible also to supplement the field-work further by using the hand level and the pocket compass in connection with this sketching. It is perfectly feasible to have this plotting and sketching carried on simultaneously with the fieldwork if the size and importance of the job warrant it.

231b. Stadia Leveling. — Lines of levels may be run by means of the transit and stadia, but it requires careful work to obtain good results. These elevations depend upon the measured vertical angles, and these angles are, as a rule, the least accurate measurements given by the transit. For rapid work when the closest results are not required the distances and vertical angles may be read but once, the transit being set up in between rod stations. For more careful work the transit stations and the rod stations should be the same points. The distances between stations should be read both forward and backward. The illumination of the rod often will be quite different on these two sights, so that one will give a good determination, while the other is at best only an approximate check on it. It is especially important to read the vertical angles both forward and backward. Careful attention should be given to leveling the plates and determining the index error. The adjustment should, of course, be kept as close as possible at all times. This statement applies particularly to the adjustments of the horizontal hair, the long level on the telescope, and the vernier of the vertical arc. Large vertical angles should be avoided if possible, because the effect of errors in the vertical angle is usually greater for steep angles. The constant $(F + c)$ cannot be neglected in leveling, because the resulting error tends to accumulate.

231c. Traversing with Magnetic Needle. — Rough surveys can be made very rapidly by using the compass needle on the transit for obtaining directions and by measuring the distances by stadia. If the instrument and the rod are placed at alternate stations the amount of work is greatly reduced and ground can be covered rapidly. In this method there is no check on the accuracy. The transit is set up at station 2, and a distance and a compass bearing taken (backsight) to station 1. The rod is then taken to station 3 and a distance and bearing taken (ahead) to this point. The transit is then removed to station 4, and the process repeated. Side shots can be taken, when needed, by taking needle readings instead of azimuths. The notes must show clearly just what the different stations are and care must be exercised to read the needle correctly, and not to reverse a bearing. It must be remembered, however, that in using this method in a region where there is **local attraction** the results obtained may be **almost worthless.**

THE PLANE TABLE

231d. The Plane Table. — The plane table consists of a drawing board mounted on a tripod in such a manner that it can be leveled and oriented, like a transit. This arrangement enables the operator to fasten his map to the drawing board and work directly on the map in the field.

The alidade is an instrument used on the plane table for taking sights and drawing lines when locating points on the map. It consists of a telescope, or else open sights, mounted on a metal straight-edge, with spirit levels for making the telescope axis and its rotation axis truly horizontal.

Among the various plane-table equipments obtainable we may distinguish three types. First, the most elaborate, in which the leveling of the table is done by means of a leveling head like that of the transit and the orienting is controlled by means of

FIG. 97. PLANE TABLE.

a clamp and a tangent screw. The alidade in this outfit has a high-power telescope equipped with stadia hairs, and three straight-edges, one directly beneath the center of the instrument and two on the outer edges of the metal blade. The telescope has a vertical arc (or circle) and a vernier carrying a level. Most alidades are provided also with a striding level. On some instruments there is a stadia arc. (Fig. 97.)

The second design of table is one in which the leveling and orienting is done by means of a compact arrangement of spherical surfaces. (Fig. 97a.) This table is fully described in Vol. II, Art. 172, p. 249. With this table may be used either the alidade previously described, or, if preferred, a somewhat lighter one, according to requirements. One compact form of telescopic alidade, designed to save weight and space, is the explorer's alidade. It is set very low and has a more limited range of vertical motion. It carries a prism on the eyepiece so that the operator looks down into it, in the same general direction as the sketch upon which he is working. This compact alidade can be slipped into a small leather carrying case and slung on the shoulder.

The third kind, which is the lightest outfit, is the sketching board, about 15 inches square. It has no leveling arrangement,

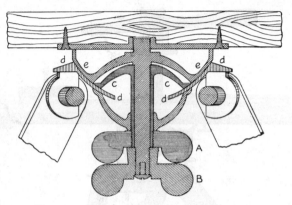

FIG. 97a.   JOHNSON PLANE-TABLE MOVEMENT.

but simply a clamp at the center. A magnetic needle is set into one side of the board, to be used for orienting the table. The alidade usually consists of a narrow straight-edge with two vertical sights. This outfit is especially adapted for traversing and sketching, usually on comparatively small scales. (Fig. 97b.)

231e. Accessories. — The stadia rods, used when points are located by stadia distance and direction, are of the same patterns as those used in transit and stadia surveying. (See Fig. 92, p. 214.) Plane tables intended for use on very large-scale maps, such as those required in landscape architect's work, are sometimes provided with an apparatus for plumbing a point on the map exactly over a station mark on the ground. This is needed only when using such scales as are capable of showing a fraction of a foot. Most plane tables are provided with a magnetic needle, or *declinatoire*. This may be fastened to the base of the alidade or it may be entirely separate.

231f. Advantages and Disadvantages of the Plane Table. — The advantages of the plane table over the transit and stadia method are, 1. That all the sketching is done while the topographer can see the ground that he is representing, and he can therefore sketch more accurately. Also, he requires a smaller number of points to obtain the contours. He can decide what to include and what to omit. If any lines are sketched wrongly, or any points wrongly located, he is almost certain to observe this when in the field, but is not so likely to notice it if he is

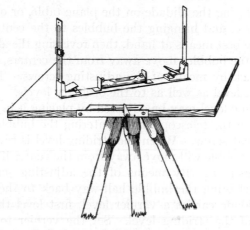

FIG. 97b.

plotting it in the office. 2. The plane table can be set up at any assumed position and the corresponding plotted position of the station found quickly by resection; the position does not have to be found from the preceding station. This is not true of the transit, for the transit point must either be found from the preceding station or else from a trigonometric solution of the three-point problem. 3. It is much easier when using the plane table to determine at once whether the entire ground has been covered, than it is when making the survey with the transit.

The disadvantages of the plane table are, 1. That in rainy or in windy weather it may not be practicable to continue the field-work. 2. A longer time is usually required to complete the fieldwork than when a transit is used, although this is not always true. 3. Many surveyors' offices are not equipped with a plane-table outfit, while all are equipped with transits. 4. The plane-table outfit is bulkier and heavier to transport than the stadia outfit.

231g. Adjustments of the Alidade. — The adjustments of the alidade are simple and easy to make. But the adjustments are not easily disturbed; so, as a matter of fact, they are not often required.

The levels attached to the base of the instrument may be tested by placing the alidade on the plane table, or on any horizontal surface, and bringing the bubbles to the centers of their tubes by the best means at hand, then reversing the alidade, end-for-end; if the bubbles move away from the centers, bring them half-way back by means of the adjusting screws. This applies to a circular level as well as to the ordinary levels.

The striding level may be adjusted by placing it in position on the collars on the telescope, and centering the bubble by means of the tangent screw. When the striding level is reversed, end-for-end, the bubble will move away from the center if the adjustment is imperfect. By means of the adjusting screw on the striding level bring the bubble half-way back to the center.

If the alidade carries a vernier level, first level the telescope by means of the striding level. Set the vernier to read zero. Then center the vernier bubble by means of the adjusting screw on this level. If there is no striding level the adjustment must be made by means of the " peg " method (See Art. 128, p. 99). After the line of sight has been made horizontal the vernier is set at zero and the vernier bubble centered by means of its adjusting screw.

In some alidades the telescope is so mounted that it can be turned 180° in a sleeve. The point of intersection of the cross-hairs may be centered in the tube by sighting a point, turning 180°, and then bringing the cross-hairs half-way back by means of the capstan head screws on the diaphragm. This is similar to the test of the wye level. (See Art. 121, p. 95.)

231h. Locating Points. — In order to begin a survey with the plane table there must be at least two points on the ground whose positions are represented to some scale (known or unknown) on the map. If these points are the ends of a measured (or calculated) base-line and the table can be set at one or both of these stations, then the other points may be located at once by means of lines drawn along the straight edge of the alidade.

231i. Intersection. — Suppose that *a* and *b* on the sheet represent *A* and *B* on the ground. (Fig. 97c.) To find point *c*

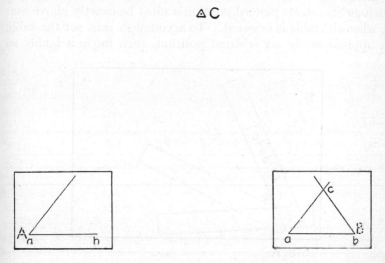

FIG. 97c. LOCATING POINT BY INTERSECTION.

representing *C* on the ground, place the plane table so that *a* is vertically above *A* as nearly as the scale permits, the table being level. Then *orient* the table by pointing *ab* toward *B*. This is done by placing the straight edge along *ab*, turning the table until the vertical cross-hair is on the signal at *B*, and then clamping the table. If the alidade is centered on *a* and turned until *C* is sighted, then the line along the straight edge from *a* is directed to *C*. Therefore *c* is somewhere on this indefinite line. Next move the table to station *B*, level it and center point *b* over *B*. Direct *ba* toward *A*, and clamp the table. Then draw a line from *b* toward *C* by means of the alidade. These two indefinite lines intersect at the point *c*, which represents *C* to

the scale of the map.   This method of plotting is very accurate,
and is the method chiefly used in locating the control points.
As a check on this location the table may now be taken to
station C, set up, leveled, and oriented by sighting ca toward A.
If cb is found to be in the direction of B the work is checked.
Locating points by this method is spoken of as "plane-table
triangulation," or "graphical triangulation."

When centering the plane table over a point on the ground
such as Sta. A, its plotted position a must be exactly above Sta.
A when the table is oriented.   To accomplish this, set the table
in approximately an oriented position, then move it bodily so

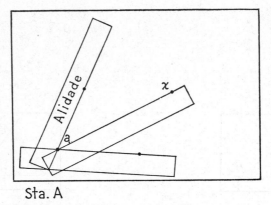

Sta. A

FIG. 97d.   LOCATING POINTS BY "RADIATION."

that a is vertically over A; then level the table and proceed with
the work.   This is sufficient for small-scale maps.   For large-
scale maps it may be found that, after the process just described,
when the table is actually oriented by means of the alidade, it will
have to be moved to one side or the other to get a exactly over A.

231j. Direction and Distance. — Another method of locating
points is that which is sometimes called "radiation."   The
alidade is centered on the point representing the plane-table
station.   Then any point, say X, Fig. 97d, is located by sighting
it with the alidade, drawing a line in this direction along the
straight edge, and then determining the distance, either by stadia
or by tape measurement.   This distance is plotted to scale or

the line at x. This method is used in locating details, after the principal stations have been located and checked. The radiating lines are not actually drawn, as a matter of fact, except in some special cases; for ordinary points the scale is laid down close to the straight edge and the point is plotted directly. This avoids covering the sheet with useless lines.

231k. Resection. — If both ends of a base cannot be occupied with the table a new point can be located as readily as by inter-

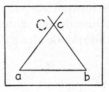

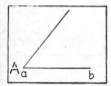

FIG. 97e.   LOCATING POINT BY RESECTION.

section, provided one end of the base can be occupied. In Fig. 97e, either point B cannot be occupied or else it is desired to avoid going to B. The table is set at A and oriented on B as before, and a line is drawn toward C. Then the table is taken to C, set up and oriented on A by means of the indefinite line ac. Then with the alidade on b, and pointing at B, a line is drawn **backwards** from b until it intersects the line from a. This locates c by *resection*. There is not the same opportunity to check in this case as there was when locating by intersection.

2311. Three-point Problem. — If the table is set up at any unknown point D (Fig. 97f) in the field its position d on the plane table sheet may be located provided three stations A, B and C whose positions are plotted on the sheet (at a, b and c), can be seen. Set up the table at D and roughly orient it by eye so that a, b and c appear to point toward A, B and C. Then mark a point on the plane table sheet to indicate where the planetabler thinks his position d is. If any topography has already been sketched on the sheet it will aid in locating the position of d. When d has been thus located the edge of the alidade is placed along da, and a short line drawn along the edge of the alidade through d. Leaving the alidade along da the table is then rotated

$\triangle$ A $\triangle$ C

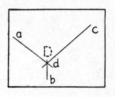

$\triangle$ B

FIG. 97f. THREE-POINT PROBLEM.

about its vertical axis, until A is bisected by the vertical hair, and then clamped. Lines are then drawn by resecting from B and C; i.e., Bb and Cc are extended by drawing short lines along the edge of the alidade near point d. If these two resection lines intersect at d (representing D in Fig. 97f) the point d is in the correct position and table is correctly oriented by the first guess. If the table had not been correctly oriented the three short lines would not have met at a common point but would have formed a triangle.

There is one case where the above method of orientation will not apply; this is when a circumference passing through ABC also passes through D.

In Fig. 97g is shown an example in which the first orientation was in error. This is indicated by the "triangle of error" formed by the resection lines from a, b, and c. As soon as the triangle of error is drawn we are able to determine at once the approximate position of d, the point representing D. A circle through a, b, and the vertex of the triangle of error which corresponds to the lines from a and b will also pass through the true point. Similarly a circle through b and c and the vertex formed by the lines from b and c will pass through the true point. The true point is therefore at their intersection. A circle through the

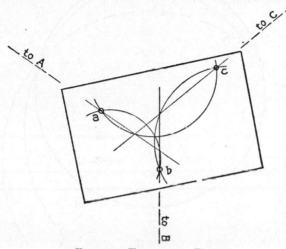

FIG. 97g.   TRIANGLE OF ERROR.

points c and a and the corresponding vertex should also pass through the true point. (See also Figs. 97h and 97i.)

Instead of constructing these circles carefully it is usually quicker to estimate a new position for d, correct the orientation by setting the straight edge on d and, say, c, and turning the table until C is sighted. A new triangle of error is then found as before. This time the size of the triangle of error should be much smaller. After two or three trials the triangle will be reduced to a point. This is the true point sought and the table is then correctly oriented.

If the table happens to be on the circle through A, B, and C, the three resection lines will pass through a common point at the first trial, no matter whether the orientation is correct or not. Whenever the table is on this circle the location of the table is

indeterminate. If, therefore, the triangle of error is a mere point at the first trial the relative positions of the signals and the table should be examined at once to see if the table is on the circle. If so this solution fails. The only way out of this difficulty is to

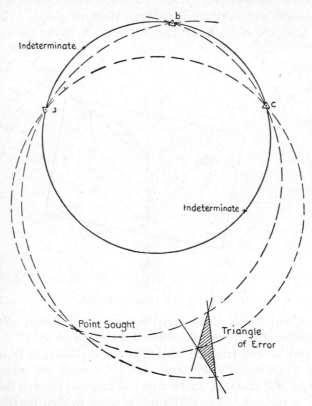

FIG. 97h. UNFAVORABLE POSITION OF SIGNALS.

choose another group of stations such that the circle through the three signals does not pass near to the table.

Whenever it is found that the three circles cut each other at small angles the position of the table will not be accurately determined, and it is better to abandon this solution and try another. When the plane-table station is inside the large triangle the true point is inside the triangle of error and the de termination is usually accurate. If the plane table is on one side of the triangle, that is, " in range," the solution is accurate.

There are other solutions of the three-point problem, such as the " inscribed quadrilateral," and the " similar triangles." The former is described in Art. 191, p. 264, Vol. II; the latter is seldom used. A trigonometric solution will be found in Art. 50, Chap. I, Vol. II.

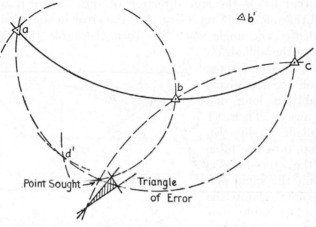

FIG. 97i. FAVORABLE POSITION OF SIGNALS.

231m. Two-point Problem. — If neither end of the base can be occupied with the table it is still possible to locate other points from this base, although the process is indirect, and the checks are insufficient. The solution consists essentially in assuming another base-line, unknown in length and position. The table is oriented by guess or by magnetic needle. From this second base-line the first base-line is located by triangulation. The difference in direction of the located position and the original plotted position of this base is the error in the original orientation of the table. The table is then turned through this angle so as to correct the orientation. The true position of the table can now be found by resecting from the ends of the original base.

One method of carrying out this solution is indicated in Fig. 97j. Points a and b are the plotted positions of stations A and B. The table is set up at any point D; d, a preliminary point, is found by resecting from A and B. The alidade is centered on d, another point C, is sighted, and an indefinite line dc is drawn. The table is next carried to station C, leveled, and oriented by sighting cd toward D. By resecting from B with the alidade centered on b, the position of c is found. Line dc is the plotted base DC. Next draw from c a line toward A. This gives a' as the plotted position of A from the new (assumed) base. This shows that ba' is the true direction of AB. Since it was intended that ab should represent AB, the error in the orientation is evidently the angle aba'. To turn the table through this

angle, set the alidade on line ba', and find some point on the cross-hair, preferably a long distance away. Then set the alidade on line ba, unclamp, turn the table until the cross-hair is again on the same distant point; clamp the table. The table now is oriented correctly. Points d, c, a', are no longer needed, and may be erased. New resec-

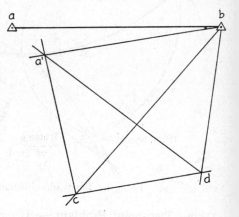

Fig. 97j. Two-Point Problem.

tions from A and B will give the true position of c. If the position of d is desired it may be found by the method of resection. (See Art. 231k.) There is no check on this result except such as may be obtained later from new points.

231n. Traversing. — The plane table may be used for running traverses, although the results are not usually accurate, unless checked by triangulation. A rough check may be obtained by using the magnetic needle. The table is set at A, represented by a (Fig. 97k), and a line drawn to B. This distance is determined by stadia, or other means, and ab is plotted. The table is next set at B, oriented by sighting ba toward A, and clamped. The alidade is then turned toward C, and bc is plotted in a similar manner. By this method the angles are plotted as accurately as the centering of the table permits, and the distances are as good as the scale permits. The method is inaccurate because the errors accumulate and there is not a sufficient check; nevertheless the method is often extremely useful. For rough work the table may be oriented by means of the magnetic needle, only alternate stations being occupied with the table, as described under the stadia method. (See Art. 231c.) In Fig. 97k, for instance, the table would be placed at *b* and *d*, and the rod held at *a*, and *c*, *e*. Distances may be paced, or even estimated, in some kinds of work.

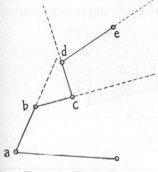

FIG. 97k. PLANE-TABLE TRAVERSE.

231 o. Elevation of Table. — The elevation of the instrument or of the plane-table station may be found (1) by direct levels to the station (2) by stadia and vertical angle to a B.M. near the station, or (3) by a vertical angle to a triangulation point of known position and elevation.

If the second method is employed the vertical angle will usually be taken to the H.I. point on the rod, so that the elevation of the plane-table station is the elevation of the B.M. plus or minus the calculated difference in elevation. If the third method is used the (horizontal) distance must be found by scaling it from the map. If the distance is greater than about half a mile it will be necessary also to allow for the effect of the curvature of the earth and of the refraction of the air. Suppose, for example, that the vertical angle to the top of a signal is $+2° 39'$, the scaled distance to the point being 7440 ft., and the elevation of the signal being 1070.3 ft. The true difference in elevation $= 7440 \times \tan 2° 39' +$ correction for curvature and refraction.* The correction for a distance of 1000 ft. is nearly 0.02 ft. Therefore the correction for 7440 $= (7440)^2/(1000)^2 \times$ 0.02 ft. $= 1.1$ ft. The difference in elevation $= 344.3 + 1.1 =$

---

* See Art. 118, p. 93.

345.4 ft., and the elevation of the alidade is 1070.3 − 345.4 = 724.9 ft. The alidade is 4.2 ft. above the station point; the elevation of the station point is therefore 720.7 ft. (Fig. 971.) If the vertical angle is negative the correction is subtracted from the difference in elevation.

231p. Fieldwork. — When making a map on a comparatively large scale (as, 20 ft. to the inch, or 40 ft. to the inch) it is important that the plotted plane-table point be plumbed carefully over the station, that the straight edge which is vertically beneath the telescope be used for plotting all important points,

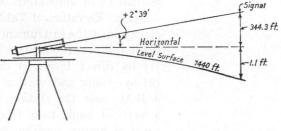

FIG. 971.

and that the distances be determined with an accuracy consistent with the scale. This often will mean that the distances to corners of buildings, large trees, boundary posts, or plane-table points, must be measured with the tape. The stadia may be sufficient for locating contour points. When the plane table is set carefully over a station it must be nearly oriented before centering the point, otherwise the point will be thrown out of position when the table is turned in orienting.

If the scale is smaller, say 100 ft. or 200 ft. to the inch, the plane-table point need not be centered over the station with the same accuracy, the side straight edge of the alidade may be used for all sights, and stadia measurements may be used much more freely. The errors of all of these approximations will fall within the limits of a pencil dot.

The control of such a plane-table map should consist of a transit and tape traverse, or triangulation, to locate the main plane-table stations accurately, and direct levels to furnish bench marks wherever needed. Only instrument stations of minor importance should be located with the table itself. The traverse points should be plotted by rectangular coördinates and the plotting carefully checked. The elevations of the B.M.'s should also be checked.

In locating contours on a large-scale map it may be advisable to place the rod exactly on the contour for each point located, thus tracing out the contour in a direct manner, as was described in the section on the stadia method.* If less accuracy is required in any particular survey, the contours may be obtained by interpolating between elevations of points located by stadia and vertical angles, as is usual on small-scale maps.

While the plane table is preëminently an instrument for contour mapping, it may be used profitably for filling in details of other kinds of surveys. The control lines of the survey may be measured with a tape and plotted on the plane-table sheet by means of the alidade and scale. This gives a traverse which is sufficiently accurate from which to locate all details and does not require a long time to prepare. The topographic details are put in by setting the plane table at the established stations and locating points by the usual methods of intersection and radiation. (See Arts. 231i–j, pp. 247–8.) These details are plotted as the survey progresses and are checked by sights taken from different stations. As much or as little tape work may be introduced as is required. All sorts of checks such as ties, ranges, etc., may be applied. By the use of this method the survey takes little longer, perhaps no longer, in the field than it would if made by the transit and tape method and the party returns to the office with an accurate pencil plan of the' site, which then merely requires to be inked in by the draftsman.

Preliminary plans for the study of a highway location, or the elimination of a grade crossing, the survey of a cemetery, a map of the site of an accident, or a survey for the reconstruction of an existing bridge, are examples of plans which may be made economically by the plane-table method.

---

* See Art. 231a, p. 239.

PROBLEMS

1. COMPUTE THE HORIZONTAL DISTANCES AND THE ELEVATIONS IN THE FOLLOWING STADIA SURVEY (F + c = 1, not included).

Pt.	Dist.	Azimuth	Observed Bearing	Vert. Angle	Diff. El.	Eleva.
		Instr. at ⊡ 4		H.I. = 4.29		133.1
81	61	168° 20′		− 13° 40′		
82	90	84° 30′		− 5° 45′		
83	140	218° 10′		− 5° 40′		
84	101	343° 10′		− 2° 16′ on 9.3		
85	185	310° 05′		− 4° 56′ on 5.3		
86	276	301° 25′		− 5° 26′ on 2.3		
87	373	277° 05′		− 4° 05′		
88	280	261° 45′		− 4° 44′		
89	210	233° 15′		− 5° 13′		
90	220	216° 50′		− 3° 55′		
91	201	202° 30′		− 3° 25′		
⊡ 5	255	202° 19′	N 22° E	− 3° 08′		
		Instr. at ⊡ 5		H.I. = 5.01		
92	88	85° 30′		− 1° 55′		
93	157	113° 20′		− 2° 55′		
94	183	169° 10′		− 1° 36′		
95	90	205° 20′		+ 0° 09′		
96	193	194° 25′		− 0° 06′		
97	218	222° 15′		+ 2° 06′		
98	115	228° 40′		+ 2° 30′		
99	39	230°		+ 2° 56′		
100	90	283° 40′		+ 1° 32′		
101	122	255° 20′		+ 3° 18′		
102	185	279° 00′		+ 2° 10′		
103	213	261° 30′		+ 3° 14′		
104	308	272° 00′		+ 0° 55′		
105	353	279° 10′		+ 0° 05′		
106	225	284° 50′		+ 0° 46′		
107	288	290° 30′		− 0° 20′		

2. A plane table is located by the three-point method and the elevation of the alidade found by measuring vertical angles to the following three stations.

STA.	VERTICAL ANGLE	SCALED HORIZONTAL DISTANCE	ELEVATION OF POINT SIGHTED
A	+ 3° 52′	1530 ft.	510.6 ft.
B	− 2° 33′	4340 ft.	212.0 ft.
C	− 1° 23′	7420 ft.	227.9 ft.

Compute the elevation of the alidade.   The ground is 3.6 ft. lower.

3. In running a stadia traverse 6000 ft. long the transit points were taken at about every 300 ft., care was exerted in holding the rod vertical, the vertical angles were closely read, and the rod interval was read to the nearest 0.01 ft. on both the backsight and foresight.   The probable error of reading a distance between transit points is ±0.5 ft.

(a) What error in the distance would be caused by neglecting the constant of the instrument ($F + c = 1$ ft.)?

(b) What is the probable error in the distance of the entire traverse due to the probable error of reading a distance between transit points?

4. Stadia levels are being run up an approximately constant grade from station A to station K. The average stadia distance ($F + c$ included) is 250 ft. and the average vertical angle is $+3°$ (read to the nearest 05'). If the levels are run for a distance of 2500 ft., what maximum error may be expected in the difference of elevation between A and K? What probable error may be expected in the difference of elevation between A and K?

5. In a closed stadia traverse approximately 1200 ft. long, and with 6 nearly equal sides, the elevation of each station was obtained by stadia distances and vertical angles read to the nearest minute and taken backward and forward from each point. The forward angles from A to D were from $+1°$ to $+1°$ 30' and from D to A were from $-1°$ to $-1°$ 30'.

(a) How close would you expect the elevation of A obtained by going around the traverse to agree with the elevation originally used?

(b) If instead the elevations had been obtained by using the transit as a level and the same points occupied as in (a), how close would you expect the first and last elevations to agree? Rod-readings were taken to nearest .01 ft. and the instrument was free from errors of adjustment.

6. The alidade on a plane table is sighted on the top of the mast of a signal 3500 ft. away and a vertical angle of $-2°$ 58' measured to nearest minute. The height of the mast is 18.5 ft. and the height of the alidade above the point over which it is set is 3.7 ft. The elevation of base of signal is 356.79 ft.

(a) Compute the elevation of point under alidade.

(b) What is probable error in the elevation determined in (a) introduced by measuring the vertical angle to the nearest minute?

7. Compute the Horizontal Distances and the Elevations in the following stadia survey ($F + c = 1$, not included below).

Pt.	Dist.	Azimuth	Observed Bearing	Vert. Angle	Diff. El.	Eleva.
Instr. at ⊡ A		B.S. 0° on ⊡ X		H.I. = 4.34		
B.M.				0°00' on 2.73		82.68
1	254	36° 25'		$-2°$ 29'		
2	125	72° 20'		$-4°$ 43'		
3	311	112° 10'		$+1°$ 42'		
4	262	226° 05'		$+5°$32' on 6.5		
5	74	278° 55'		$+3°$ 21'		
⊡ B	421	178° 26'	N 16° $\frac{1}{4}$ W	$+2°$ 58'		
Instr. at ⊡ B		B.S. 0° on ⊡ A		H.I. = 4.12		
⊡ A	420			$-2°$ 57'		
6	56	24° 50'		$-1°$ 23'		
7	178	78° 40'		$-0°$ 20'		
8	212	234° 45'		$+3°$ 17'		
9	317	178° 15'		$+5°$14' on 2.00		
⊡ C	389	156° 24'		$+4°$ 37'		

CHAPTER VIII

OBSERVATIONS FOR MERIDIAN AND LATITUDE*

OBSERVATIONS FOR MERIDIAN

232. THE CELESTIAL SPHERE. — When making observations on the sun, stars or other celestial objects with an engineer's transit and when calculating the results from such observations, it is convenient to assume that these celestial objects are situated on the surface of an imaginary sphere, called the celestial sphere, whose center is at the center of the earth and whose radius is infinite. This is perfectly consistent with what is actually seen by an observer on the earth because all celestial objects are so far away that they appear to the eye to be at the same distance and on the inside surface of a great sphere. The reason for adopting the celestial sphere is that all problems involving angular distances between points and angles between planes at the center of the sphere may readily be solved by spherical trigonometry.

Fig. 98 shows a celestial sphere with a transit set up at point C on the earth's surface. The earth is so small compared with the celestial sphere that, in astronomical calculations, vertical angles measured to celestial objects are practically the same whether measured at the surface or at the center of the earth, therefore the point C may be assumed as at the center of the sphere. Where this assumption would cause an appreciable error, the angle measured on the surface can be corrected to give the corresponding angle at the center. (See Art. 232a.)

The points where the axis of the earth produced intersects the sphere are the *celestial poles*. The great circle $EQWQ'$ is the *celestial equator*. It is the trace on the celestial sphere where the plane of the earth's equator if extended would intersect the sphere. It is everywhere 90° from the celestial poles. The point Z where the plumb-line of the transit prolonged upward

---

* See also Chapter II, Volume II.

intersects the celestial sphere is called the *zenith*. If prolonged downward it pierces the sphere at N', the *nadir*. The great circle $NESW$ midway between and everywhere 90° from the zenith and nadir is called the *horizon*. It is obvious that every observer has a different zenith and hence a different horizon. No matter what horizontal direction a telescope of a transit is pointing, if it is rotated about the horizontal axis until it points vertically,

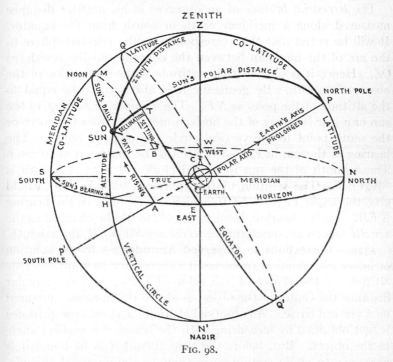

FIG. 98.

it will point to the zenith and will have traced on the sphere a great circle called a *vertical circle*. The vertical angle to any celestial object, called the *altitude*, is the angular distance the object is above the horizon, as HO. The great circle $SZPN$ is the observer's *meridian*; it is also a vertical circle. It should be noted that the observer's meridian passes through the pole and his zenith. The small circle AMB, parallel to the equator, is a *parallel of declination*; the apparent daily path of a star or the sun (approximately) is a parallel of declination. The *declination* of the sun or a star is its angular distance north or south of the equator, as OT. The declination is considered positive when north, negative when south. Values of the declination of celestial bodies are given in the American Ephemeris and Nautical Almanac. The polar distance of the sun or a star is 90° plus or minus the declination, as OP.

The *terrestrial latitude* of an observer is his angular distance measured along a meridian north or south from the equator. It will be noted that this corresponds on the celestial sphere to the arc of the meridian between the equator and the zenith, as QZ. Hence it is seen that the latitude is the declination of the observer's zenith. By geometry it is also seen to be equal to the altitude of the pole, as NP. The *azimuth*, or *bearing*, of the sun or a star is an arc of the horizon measured from the north or the south point to the vertical circle through the object. The bearing of the sun in Fig. 98 is SH (in the southeast quadrant). The azimuth of the sun measured clockwise from the south is $SWNEH$. The solution of the spherical triangle PZO would give the angle $PZO = NCH$, which corresponds to the bearing NEH. Such a bearing, being over 90°, would be changed to the arc SH (southeast quadrant) or to the arc $SWNEH$, the azimuth.

232a. Corrections to Observed Altitudes. — In the solution of many astronomical problems it is necessary to know the true altitude of the center of the celestial body; i.e., the angular distance the center of the object is above the horizon, measured on a vertical circle. An observed altitude (approx. true altitude) is first obtained by measuring with the transit the vertical angle to the object. But, before the true altitude can be found it is necessary to apply certain corrections to the observed altitude.

INDEX CORRECTION. — The first correction to the recorded vertical angle is the *index correction*. It is determined and applied as explained in Art. 67, p. 62.

REFRACTION CORRECTION. — Light rays passing through the air are refracted, and cause celestial objects to appear always at a greater altitude than they really are; for this reason the refraction correction is **always subtracted.** Values of this correction are given in Table 11, p. 274.

SEMI-DIAMETER. — When the celestial object has an appreciable diameter such as the sun and moon it is customary to obtain the altitude by measuring the vertical angle to either the upper or lower limb (edge). As the required altitude is to the center of the object, the semi-diameter (angular distance from the limb to the center) is added to or subtracted from the observed altitude corresponding to the limb that has been observed. Values of the semi-diameter of the sun and moon are given in the American Ephemeris and Nautical Almanac and the smaller publication, the Nautical Almanac (see footnote, page 275). Stars are so far away that they appear in the telescope as small points and are bisected when the altitude is being observed.

PARALLAX. — Parallax is the difference in direction of a celestial object as seen from the surface and from the center of the earth. Altitudes of celestial objects are necessarily measured from the earth's surface. The coördinates given in the Ephemeris and the Nautical Almanac are referred to the earth's center. Hence the observed altitude must be reduced to the earth's center. In order to do this a correction called the parallax correction is applied to the altitude. It is **always added.** No parallax correction is necessary when stars are observed. They are so far away that the parallax correction is inappreciable. In the case of the sun the maximum correction is only 9 seconds and for the moon about one degree. For observations made with ordinary surveying instruments, values of the parallax correction are found in various publications. Table 12, page 291, is a table in which the refraction and parallax corrections are combined. This table can be used only for observations made on the sun. Corrections should be applied in the order given.

232b. TO ESTABLISH A TRUE MERIDIAN LINE BY OBSERVATION ON POLARIS (THE POLE-STAR). — Since the celestial pole is not visible it is necessary to make use of the celestial objects for establishing meridians. One of the simplest and at the same time the most accurate method for this purpose is to observe the Pole-star (*Polaris*). On account of the earth's daily rotation on its axis all heavenly bodies appear to revolve once a day around the earth. Stars which are near the equator appear to revolve in large circles parallel to the equator. As we look farther north the apparent size of the circles grows smaller.

The Pole-star (*Polaris*) revolves about the celestial pole in a small circle whose radius (polar-distance) is about one degree. (Fig. 98a.)

When the star is directly above the pole it is in the plane of the meridian (bearing true north) and is said to be at *upper culmination*. About 12 hours later it will be directly below the pole (bearing true north) at *lower culmination*. About half-way between these two positions the star reaches its greatest east or west bearing, and at such times is said to be at its *greatest elonga-*

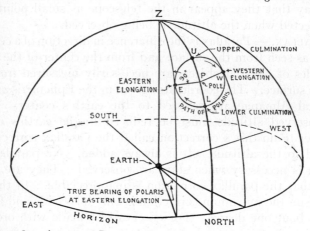

FIG. 98a. APPARENT PATH OF POLARIS AS SEEN FROM THE EARTH.

tion. At either eastern or western elongation the star's bearing is not changing because the star is moving vertically at that instant. The instant of elongation is therefore the most favorable time for an accurate observation for meridian. At culmination the star is changing its bearing at the maximum rate, so this is not so good a time to make an accurate observation. Polaris moves so slowly, however, that even at culmination its bearing can be obtained with fair accuracy.

This star can be found easily by means of two conspicuous constellations near it, *Cassiopeia* and *Ursa Major*. The seven bright stars in the latter constellation form what is commonly known as the "Great Dipper" (Fig. 98b). The two stars forming the part of the bowl of the Dipper farthest from the handle are called the "pointers," because a line through them points almost directly at the Pole-star. On the opposite side of Polaris is *Cassiopeia*, shaped like a letter W. A line drawn from δ *Cassiopeiæ*,* the lower left-hand star of the W, to ζ *Ursæ Majoris*, the middle star of the dipper handle, passes very close to Polaris and also to the pole itself.

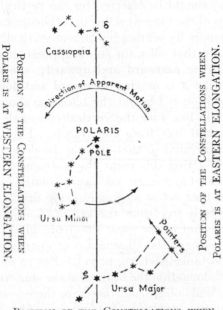

FIG. 98b. RELATIVE POSITION OF THE CONSTELLATIONS NEAR THE NORTH POLE.

233. OBSERVATION FOR MERIDIAN ON POLARIS AT ELONGATION. — When the Dipper is on the right and Cassiopeia on the left, Polaris is near its **western elongation;** when the Dipper is on the **left** Polaris is near **eastern elongation.** When the constellations are approaching one of these positions the transit

---

* The Greek Alphabet will be found on p. 687.

should be set over a stake and leveled, and the telescope focused upon the star.* Unless the observation occurs at about sunrise or sunset it will be necessary to use an artificial light to make the cross-hairs visible. If the transit is not provided with a special reflector for throwing light down the tube a good substitute may be made by cutting a small hole in a piece of tracing cloth or oiled paper and then fastening it over the end of the telescope tube with a rubber band. If a light is then held in front and a little to one side of the telescope the cross-hairs can be plainly seen. The star should be bisected by the vertical hair and followed by means of the tangent screw in its horizontal motion until it no longer changes its bearing but moves vertically. (It will be seen from Fig. 98a that when the star is approaching eastern elongation it is moving **eastward** and **upward**; when approaching western elongation it is moving **westward** and **downward**.) As soon as this position is reached the telescope should be lowered and a point set in line with the vertical cross-hair at a distance of several hundred feet from the transit. Everything should be arranged beforehand so that this can be done quickly. Immediately after setting this point the instrument should be reversed, **re-leveled** if necessary, and again pointed on the star. A second point is then set at one side of the first. The mean of these two points is free from the errors of adjustment of the transit. On account of the great difference in altitude between the star and the mark the elimination of instrumental errors is of unusual importance (Art. 79, p. 71). For 10 minutes of time on either side of elongation the bearing of the star does not change more than 5 seconds of arc and therefore there is sufficient time to make these two pointings accurately. The times of the elongations may be obtained from Tables 9 and 9A, p. 268.

After the direction of the star at elongation has been found, the meridian may be established by laying off an angle equal to the azimuth, or true bearing of the star. Since this angle to be laid off is the **horizontal** angle between the star and the pole, it

---

* It is difficult to find a star in the field of view unless the telescope is focused for a very distant object. The surveyor will find it a convenience if he marks on the telescope tube the position of the objective tube when it is focused for a distant object.

is not equal to the polar distance itself, but may be found from the equation: —

$$\text{Sin Star's True Bearing} = \frac{\text{Sin Polar Distance of Star *}}{\text{Cos Latitude}}$$

The mean polar distances for the year 1937 to 1948 may be found in Table 8. The latitude may be obtained from a reliable map or by observation (Arts. 242–3, pp. 286–7).

TABLE 8

MEAN POLAR DISTANCE OF POLARIS†

Year	Mean Polar Dist.	Year	Mean Polar Dist.
	° ′ ″		° ′ ″
1937	1 02 10	1943	1 00 22
1938	1 01 52	1944	1 00 04
1939	1 01 34	1945	0 59 46
1940	1 01 16	1946	0 59 28
1941	1 00 58	1947	0 59 10
1942	1 00 40	1948	0 58 52

* This equation may be derived as follows: In Fig. 98a, compute triangle PZE by spherical trigonometry,

$$\frac{\sin PZE}{\sin ZEP} = \frac{\sin PE}{\sin ZP}$$

But PZE is the angle between the two vertical circles and equals the bearing. $ZEP = 90°$; ZE is tangent to the circle $UWLE$, which represents the path of Polaris. PE is the polar distance and ZP is $90° -$ latitude.

Hence, $$\sin PZE = \frac{\sin PE}{\cos \text{lat}}$$

† The above table was derived from data furnished by the Director of Nautical Almanac, Washington, D. C. The Mean Polar Distance is the polar distance the star would have at the beginning of the year, if unaffected by small periodic variations.

In taking the polar distance from the table for the purpose of looking up its sine the student should keep in mind the degree of precision desired in the computed

When the transit is set up at the south end of the line the angle thus computed must be laid off to the **right** if the elongation is **west,** to the **left** if the elongation is **east.** A convenient and accurate way of laying off the angle is by measuring the distance between the two stakes A and B (Fig. 99), and calculating the perpendicular distance BC which must be laid off at the north stake B to give a meridian AC.

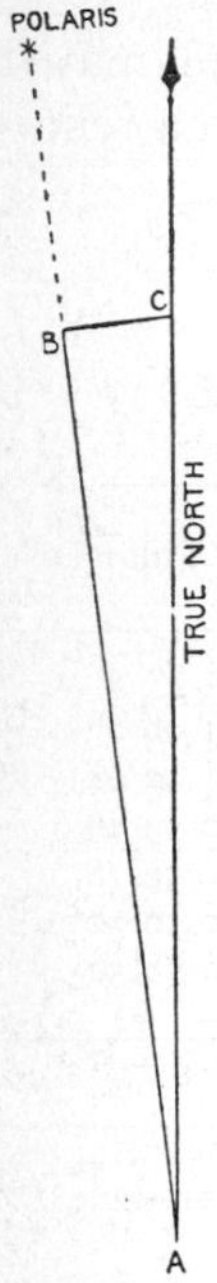

234. OBSERVATION FOR MERIDIAN ON POLARIS AT CULMINATION. — The direction of the meridian may be determined by observing with a transit the instant when Polaris and some other star are in the same vertical plane and then waiting a certain interval of time (depending upon the date and the star observed) until Polaris will be in the meridian. At this instant Polaris is sighted and its direction is then marked on the ground by means of a stake. The line thus determined is a meridian. The star sighted should be near the hour circle through Polaris (i.e., the great circle through Polaris and the true pole). Referring to Fig. 98b it will be noted that at the present time the stars δ *Cassiopeiæ* and ζ *Ursæ Majoris* satisfy this condition. At the instant when Polaris is above the pole (upper culmination) the star ζ *Ursæ Majoris* will be almost exactly underneath Polaris. When Polaris is below the pole (lower culmination) δ *Cassiopeix* will be almost directly below Polaris. In order to know when Polaris is exactly on the meridian, it is necessary first to observe the instant when one of these two stars is vertically below

FIG. 99

azimuth. If the azimuth is to be within about one minute of the true value the polar distance need be taken only to the nearest minute, but if the azimuth is to be correct within a few seconds the polar distance should be taken more precisely. It should be noted, however, that since the values given in the table take no account of the variations during the year, there will in general be an error of a few seconds due to neglecting the variation of the polar distance during the year. The accurate value for every day in the year may be found in the "American Ephemeris and Nautical Almanac," published by the Nautical Almanac Office, U. S. Naval Observatory. (Sold by the Superintendent of Documents, Washington, D. C.)

Polaris. From this instant the time interval when Polaris will be on the meridian may be obtained from tables and the time of culmination may be computed. Accurate values of these intervals for every 10 days will be found in American Ephemeris and Nautical Almanac, Table VI.

The observation to determine when the two stars are in the same vertical plane is at best only approximate, since the instrument must be pointed first at one star and then at the other; but since Polaris changes its azimuth only about one minute of angle in two minutes of time, there is no difficulty in getting fair results by this method. The vertical hair should be set first on Polaris, then the telescope is lowered to the approximate altitude of the other star to be used. As soon as this star comes into the field the vertical hair is set again carefully on Polaris. As it will take the other star about two minutes to reach the center of the field there will be ample time for this pointing. Then the telescope is lowered and at the instant when the star passes the vertical hair the time is noted on a watch. This will be the time desired, with an error of only a few seconds. The time of culmination should then be computed as described above and the vertical hair set on Polaris when this computed time arrives. The telescope is then in the meridian, and this may be marked on the ground.

In this method the actual error of the watch has no effect on the result since it is used only for measuring the **interval** of a few minutes. The error in the meridian obtained by this method will seldom exceed one minute of angle.

235. To Find the Standard Time of Culmination and Elongation. — The approximate times of culmination of Polaris may be found in Table 9. The times of elongation may be found by means of Table 9A.

Eastern elongation precedes and western elongation follows upper culmination by the time interval given in Table 9A. Lower culmination precedes or follows upper culmination by $11^h58.0^m$. It should be noted that there are two upper culminations on one day in October (17th in 1937) and two lower culminations in April (17th in 1937). There are also two western elongations on one day in January and two eastern elongations on one day in July.

TABLE 9

Local Civil Time of Upper Culmination of Polaris in the Year 1937
(Computed for 90°, or 6 hours west of Greenwich)

Date, 1937	Civil Time of Upper Culmination			Variation per Day		Date, 1937	Civil Time of Upper Culmination			Variation per Day	
	h	m	s	m	s		h	m	s	m	s
Jan. 1.........	18	56	26	−3	57	July 10.....	6	29	15	−3	55
Jan. 11.......	18	16	56	−3	57	July 20.....	5	50	09	−3	55
Jan. 21.......	17	37	25	−3	57	July 30.....	5	11	01	−3	55
Jan. 31.......	16	57	54	−3	57	Aug. 9......	4	31	55	−3	55
Feb. 10.......	16	18	24	−3	57	Aug. 19.....	3	52	46	−3	55
Feb. 20.......	15	38	55	−3	57	Aug. 29.....	3	13	37	−3	55
Mar. 2........	14	59	26	−3	57	Sept. 8......	2	34	27	−3	55
Mar 12.......	14	19	59	−3	57	Sept. 18.....	1	55	17	−3	55
Mar. 22.......	13	40	36	−3	56	Sept. 28.....	1	16	05	−3	55
Apr. 1........	13	01	14	−3	56	Oct. 8......	0	36	50	−3	56
Apr. 11.......	12	21	53	−3	56	Oct. 17.....	23	57	33	−3	56
Apr. 21.......	11	42	35	−3	56	Oct. 27.....	23	18	16	−3	56
May 1........	11	03	21	−3	56	Nov. 6......	22	38	57	−3	56
May 11.......	10	24	07	−3	55	Nov. 16.....	21	59	34	−3	56
May 21.......	9	44	55	−3	55	Nov. 26.....	21	20	10	−3	56
May 31.......	9	05	45	−3	55	Dec. 6......	20	40	45	−3	57
June 10.......	8	26	36	−3	55	Dec. 16.....	20	01	18	−3	57
June 20.......	7	47	28	−3	55	Dec. 26.....	19	21	49	−3	57
June 30.......	7	08	21	−3	55	Jan. 5, 1938..	18	42	20	−3	57

TABLE 9A

Mean Time Interval Between Upper Culmination and Elongation

Latitude	Time Interval		Latitude	Time Interval		Latitude	Time Interval		Latitude	Time Interval	
°	h	m	°	h	m	°	h	m	°	h	m
10......	5	58.3	35.....	5	56.1	48.....	5	54.5	58.....	5	52.5
15......	5	57.9	40.....	5	55.6	50.....	5	54.1	60.....	5	51.9
20......	5	57.5	42.....	5	55.3	52.....	5	53.8	62.....	5	51.3
25......	5	57.1	44.....	5	55.1	54.....	5	53.4	64.....	5	50.6
30......	5	56.6	46.....	5	54.8	56.....	5	52.9	66.....	5	49.8

(a) To refer the times in Table 9 to other years —

For Year	m	For Year	m
1938.................add	1.7	1942.................add	3.9
1939.................add	3.3	1943.................add	5.3
1940, up to Mar. 1.......add	4.9	1944, up to Mar. 1........add	6.7
1940, on and after Mar. 1..add	0.9	1944, on and after Mar. 1...add	2.7
1941.................add	2.4	1945.................add	4.1

Tables 9, 9A and (a) are from data furnished by the Director of the Nautical Almanac.

(b) *To refer to other than the tabular days.* — Subtract from the time for the preceding tabular day the product of the variation per day and the days elapsed, as given in Table 10.

TABLE 10

Days Elapsed	Variation per Day			Days Elapsed	Variation per Day		
	$3^m\ 57^s$	$3^m\ 56^s$	$3^m\ 55^s$		$3^m\ 57^s$	$3^m\ 56^s$	$3^m\ 55^s$
	m s	m s	m s		m s	m s	m s
1.........	3 57	3 56	3 55	6.........	23 42	23 36	23 30
2.........	7 54	7 52	7 50	7.........	27 39	27 32	27 25
3.........	11 51	11 48	11 45	8.........	31 36	31 28	31 20
4.........	15 48	15 44	15 40	9.........	35 33	35 24	35 15
5.........	19 45	19 40	19 35				

(c) *To refer to any other than the tabular longitude* (90°). — Add 0.1^{m} for each 10° east of the ninetieth meridian or subtract 0.1^{m} for each 10° west of the ninetieth meridian.

(d) *To refer to standard time.* — Add to the quantities in Table 9 four minutes for every degree of longitude the place of observation is west of the standard meridian (60°, 75°, 90°, etc.). Subtract when the place is east of the standard meridian.

236. Meridian Observation on Polaris at a Known Instant of Time. — This observation consists in measuring the horizontal angle, by repetition, from a reference mark to Polaris, the watch time of each pointing and the altitude of the star both being noted.

It is assumed that the average of all the azimuths is the same as the azimuth corresponding to the average of the watch readings. The average watch reading is therefore corrected for any known error in the timepiece and the resulting time taken as the Standard time of the observation. This Standard time is then converted into Local Civil Time by means of the longitude of the place, as explained on p. 275. Next it is necessary to find the " hour angle " of Polaris at this instant. This is obtained by taking the difference between the local time just found and the time of the nearest Upper Culmination as given in Table 9. This difference, increased by 10^s for each hour in the interval, is the hour angle of Polaris, which should now be converted into degrees and minutes.   (1° = 4 min.)

The azimuth of Polaris is computed by the formula

$$Z = p \sin P \sec h$$

in which p is the polar distance in seconds (or minutes), P is the hour angle, and h is the altitude; Z is the azimuth in the same units as p.* If the observed time is earlier than the time of upper culmination the star is east of north (unless the hour angle is greater than 12 hours); if the observed time is later than the time of upper culmination, the star is west of north (unless the hour angle is over 12^h). This azimuth combined with the measured horizontal angle gives the azimuth of the reference mark.

EXAMPLE

Observations on Polaris for Azimuth Oct. 20, 1940, by three repetitions between reference mark and star.   Latitude, 42° 32′ N; Longitude, 71° 07′.5 W.

	Watch (10^s fast of E. S. T.)	Horizontal Angle (to the right)	Altitude
Mark		0° 00′	
Polaris	6^h 59^m 30^s P.M.	261° 37′	42° 55′
"	7 03 10	(163 15)	42 56
"	7 05 30	64° 52′	42 57
Mark		0° 00′	
Mean	7 02 43	261° 37′.3	42° 56′
Watch fast	− 10		refr. − 1′
E. S. T.	7 02 33		$h = 42° 55′$
Dif. Long.	15 30 (= 3° 52′.5)		
Loc. Time	7 18 03 P.M.		
	12		
Loc. Civ. Time	19^h 18^m 03^s		

* Table IV in the Ephemeris gives azimuth of Polaris for all hour angles and for all latitudes from 10° to 70°.

$p = 1° 01'.0 = 61'.0$

$\log p'$	$= 1.78533$
$\log \sin P$	$= 9.96526$
$\log \sec h$	$= 0.13528$
$\log Z'$	$= 1.88587$
Z'	$= 76'.9$
	$= N\ 1° 16'.9\ E$

Horiz. Angle = 261 37.3
Mark to N = 260° 20'.4
N to mark = 99 39.6
Azimuth = 279 39.6
Bearing = S 80° 20'.4 E

Table 9, Oct. 17, 1937, U. C.	$23^h\ 57^m\ 33^s$
Correction for 3 days	$-11\ \ 48$
Oct. 20	23 45 45
Corr. for 1940	$+\ \ \ \ 54$
Oct. 20, 1940, U. C.	23 46 39
Corr. for Long.	$+12$
Loc. Civ. T., U. C.	23 46 51
" " ", obs'n.	19 18 03
Diff. in time	4 28 48
$4^h.5 \times 10^8$	$+45$
Hour Angle = P	4 29 33
P	$67° 23'.25$ east

237. SOLAR OBSERVATIONS. — Where great accuracy is not required many surveyors prefer solar observations because they can be made without much additional work, while star observations have to be made at night and require special arrangements for illuminating the field of view and the mark. If it is sufficient for the purpose in view to obtain the azimuth within $\frac{1}{2}$ minute of angle solar observations will answer. In making these observations with the ordinary transit it is necessary to have some means of cutting down the sun's light so that it will not be too bright for the eye while making pointings. This is usually effected by placing a dark glass over the eyepiece. A dark glass in front of the objective will introduce error into the pointings unless the faces of this glass have been made plane and exactly parallel. If the instrument is not provided with a dark glass the observation may be made by holding a white card back of the eyepiece while the telescope is pointing at the sun. If the eyepiece tube is drawn out the sun's disc and the cross-hairs can both be focused sharply on the card. By this means pointings can be made almost as well as by direct observation.

238. OBSERVATION FOR MERIDIAN BY A SINGLE ALTITUDE OF THE SUN. — The most convenient method of obtaining the azimuth of a line is by measuring an altitude of the sun and computing the sun's azimuth by spherical trigonometry. This observation may be made in a few minutes time while the survey is in progress and is therefore preferred by many surveyors to the observation on Polaris, which consumes more time and usually requires a special trip to the point of observation.

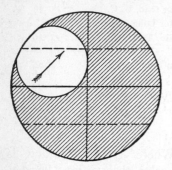

Fig. 100a.   Sun's Disc before Observation.

(A.M. Observations.)

Northern Hemisphere.

To make this observation set up the transit at one end of the line whose azimuth is to be determined and set the plate vernier to read 0°. Sight the vertical cross-hair on the point marking the other end of the line, using the lower clamp and tangent screw.   Place the colored shade glass over the eyepiece, loosen the upper clamp and point the telescope toward the sun.   Before attempting to make the pointings focus carefully so that the edge of the sun is distinct, and then examine the field to be certain which is the middle horizontal hair.   The three horizontal hairs cannot all be seen at once through the colored screen and there is danger of using one of the stadia hairs by mistake.

When making observations in the forenoon in the northern hemisphere it is best to observe first the right-hand and lower edges of the sun's disc, and then the left-hand and upper edges as shown in Fig. 100a. In the afternoon the positions would be as shown in Fig. 100b.* In order to avoid the necessity of setting on both edges at the same instant the forenoon observations may be made as follows.   Set the horizontal hair so that it cuts a small segment from the lower edge of the disc,

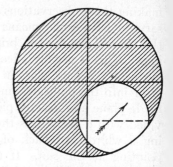

Fig. 100a.   Sun's Disc before Observation.

(A.M. Observations.)

Northern Hemisphere.

---

* In the diagram only a portion of the sun's disc is visible on account of the small angular diameter of the field of the telescope.   In a telescope having a very large field the whole disc may be seen.

and the vertical hair tangent to the right edge.* Since the sun is now rising and moving to the right it is only necessary to keep the vertical hair tangent to the right edge with the upper

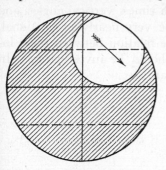

FIG. 100b. SUN'S DISC BEFORE OBSERVATION.

(P.M. Observations.)

Northern Hemisphere.

plate tangent screw; the apparent motion of the sun itself will set the horizontal hair after a lapse of a few seconds. At the instant both hairs are tangent to the disc stop following the sun's motion and note the time by the watch. Read the vertical and horizontal circles, and record all three readings. The second observation is made in a similar manner except that the vertical hair is set a little way in from the left edge of the sun and the horizontal hair is kept tangent to the upper edge by means of the tangent screw on the standard. If it is desired to increase the precision several such observations may be made in each position, being careful to take the same number of pointings in each. If the transit has a full vertical circle the telescope should be inverted between the two observations, thus eliminating errors of adjustment of the cross-hairs and the horizontal axis. Before the plate is unclamped the index correction should be determined and recorded. After the pointings on the sun are completed the telescope should be sighted again along the line whose azimuth is being determined and the

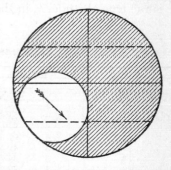

FIG. 100b. SUN'S DISC BEFORE OBSERVATION.

(P.M. Observations.)

Northern Hemisphere.

---

* It should be kept in mind that if the telescope has an inverting eyepiece the direction of the sun's apparent motion is reversed. If a reflecting prism is attached to the eyepiece, the upper and lower edges of the sun are apparently interchanged, but the right and left edges are not affected.

vernier read to be certain that the plate has not moved during the observations.

Before attempting to calculate the azimuth examine the intervals between the successive watch times, vertical angles, and horizontal angles. These should be very nearly proportional. If there is any sudden change in the relation between these intervals it indicates a mistake and should be investigated. In the example on p. 278 the intervals are:

Horizontal	Vertical	Time
32′	19′	157^s
25′	13′	120^s

indicating that no large mistake has been made, since the lower interval is in all three cases about three-quarters of the upper one.

The mean of all the vertical circle readings, corrected for index error, is the apparent altitude. This altitude decreased by the correction for atmospheric refraction (Table 11 or where greater precision in solar observations is desired, Table 12) is the true altitude, h, in the formula given on p. 276.

TABLE 11
Refraction Correction.

Altitude.	Refraction.		Altitude.	Refraction.	
10°	5′	19″	20°	2′	39″
11	4	51	25	2	04
12	4	27	30	1	41
13	4	07	35	1	23
14	3	49	40	1	09
15	3	34	45	0	58
16	3	20	50	0	49
17	3	08	60	0	34
18	2	57	70	0	21
19	2	48	80	0	10

In order to compute the azimuth it is necessary to know the latitude of the place. The latitude may be obtained from a reliable map; or, if this is likely to be in error a half minute or more, it may be observed as described in Arts. 242–3, pp. 286–7.

It is also necessary to know the declination of the sun at the instant of observation.

The sun's declination required in this observation may be taken from the " American Ephemeris and Nautical Almanac,"* Ephemeris of the sun, under the heading " apparent declination." The value of the declination given is that for the instant of 0^h (or midnight) each day at Greenwich. The tabulated difference for 24^h is given in the next column to the right. In order to find the declination for any instant of local or of Standard Time it is necessary first to find the corresponding instant of Greenwich Civil Time. In the United States, where Standard Time is in general use, the relation to Greenwich Time is simple. In the *Eastern* time belt the Standard Time is exactly 5^h earlier than at Greenwich; in the *Central* belt it is 6^h earlier; in the *Mountain* belt it is 7^h earlier; and in the *Pacific* belt it is 8^h earlier.† If the declination is desired for 7^h A.M. Eastern Time we must compute it for 12^h of Greenwich Time; if we wish the declination for 3^h P.M. Central Time we must compute it for 9^h P.M. or 21^h of Greenwich Civil Time. If any instant of *local* time is to be converted into Greenwich Time this may be done by changing the west longitude of the place into hours, minutes and seconds, and adding it to the given local time.

For converting degrees into hours or hours into degrees the following table is convenient.

$$15° = 1 \text{ hour}$$
$$15' = 1 \text{ minute}$$
$$15'' = 1 \text{ second}$$
also
$$1° = 4 \text{ minutes}$$
$$1' = 4 \text{ seconds.}$$

It is important that the watch used should be nearly correct,

---

* Published annually by the Nautical Almanac Office, Navy Dept., and sold by the Superintendent of Documents. There is also the small "Nautical Almanac" which gives the declination of the sun. Various instrument makers publish a "Solar Ephemeris" containing this information.

† Daylight Saving Time is one hour later than Standard Time. If this kind of time is in use first subtract one hour and then proceed as described above.

at any rate within 2^m or 3^m. The correct Eastern Standard Time may be obtained by radio.

The declination for any hour of Greenwich Time is the value at 0^h increased (algebraically) by the "tabulated difference for 24^h" times the hours of Greenwich Civil Time divided by 24. That is, if the declination at 0^h is $-4°\,44'\,26''.8$, the tabulated difference for 24^h is $+1407''.5$, and the declination is desired for 10^h Greenwich Time, then the corrected declination equals $-4°\,44'\,26''.8 + (+1407''.5) \times 10 \div 24 = -4°\,34'\,40''.3$. North declinations are marked $+$ and South declinations are marked $-$. An examination of the values for successive days will also show which way to apply the correction.

The azimuth of the sun's center may be computed by either of the formulas

$$\cos Z_n = \frac{\sin D - \sin L \sin h}{\cos L \cos h}$$

or,

$$\cos Z_n = \frac{\sin D}{\cos L \cos h} - \tan L \tan h$$

in which L is the latitude of the place, h the true altitude of the sun's center, and D the sun's declination, $+$ if North, $-$ if South; Z_n is the azimuth of the sun east or west of the North point.

In making this computation five place logarithms will be found sufficiently precise. Five-place tables define the angle within $5''$ to $10''$, which is a greater degree of precision than can be expected from such an observation. After the angle Z has been computed it is combined with the readings of the horizontal circle to obtain the azimuth of the line.

In order to determine the azimuth as accurately as possible by this method the observation should be made when the sun is nearly due east or due west, because the trigonometric conditions are then most favorable. Observations made near to noon are not reliable because small errors in the observed altitude and latitude cause large errors in the computed azimuth. Observations should also be avoided when the sun is less than $10°$ above the horizon, even though the sun is nearly east or west, because the correction for atmospheric refraction is uncertain. Table 11 gives values of the correction for an average temperature and pressure of the air; any deviation from these average conditions will produce changes in the correction, especially near the horizon. Table 12, p. 291, contains the corrections for refraction and parallax for different air temperatures. (The parallax is never greater than 9″.)

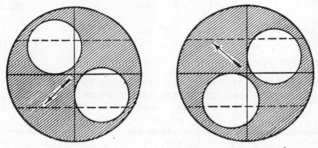

P.M. Observation   **A.M. Observation**

POSITION OF SUN'S DISC A FEW SECONDS BEFORE OBSERVATION. (Southern Hemisphere – Looking North)

Fig. 100c.

239. Southern Hemisphere. — If the point of observation is in the southern hemisphere the following changes will be necessary: first, the pointings will be those indicated in Fig. 100c (provided the latitude is greater than the sun's declination); second, the formula must be modified suitably. This may be accomplished in either of two ways. The first would consist in treating the latitude L as negative and using the formula as in Example 1 on p. 278. (See also p. 276.) The second method would be to consider L as positive and to reverse the sign of D. If this is done the azimuth Z will be that counted from the elevated (S) pole, either to the east or to the west. But if the sign of the right-hand side is changed then Z is counted from the north. (See Example 2.)

EXAMPLE 1

Observation on Sun for Azimuth

(Northern Hemisphere)

Latitude 42° 21′ N   Longitude $4^h44^m18^s$ W

Date, Nov. 28, 1925, A.M.

	Horizontal Circle			Vertical Circle	Watch
	Vernier A	B	Mean		(E. S. T.)
Mark	0° 00′	00′	00′		
Sun, R. and L. limbs	73 34	34.5	34.2	14° 41′	8^h 39^m 42^s A.M.
" " "	74 06	06	06	15 00	8 42 19

Instrument reversed

Sun, L. and U. limbs	74 13	12.5	12.8	15 55	8 45 34
" " "	74 38	37.5	37.8	16 08	8 47 34
Mark	0 00	00	00		Mean = 8^h 43^m 47^s A.M.

Mean horizontal angle 74° 07′.7   Mean alt. 15° 26′

$$\begin{array}{r} 5^h \\ \hline 13^h\ 43^m\ 47^s \end{array}$$

refr. $\dfrac{-3.5}{}$

h = true alt.   15′.5   = Gr. Civ. T.

h = true alt.   15° 22′.5

nat. sin D = −.36300

log sin L =

log sin h =   9.82844

nat. sin L sin h = $\dfrac{.17865}{}$ log = 9.25200

numerator   = −.54165

$\qquad$ 9.42356

Decl. at 0^h, G. C. T. = −21° 10′ 58″.8

tab. diff.   = −639″.3

$-\dfrac{639″.3}{24} \times 13^h.73 = -6′05″.7$

Corrected Decl   = −21° 17′ 04″.5

log numerator = 9.73372 n

log sec L = 0.13133

log sec h = 0.01584

log cos Z_n = 9.88089 n

$\quad Z_n$ = 139° 28′.5 (from N toward E)

hor. angle   = 74° 07′.7

N 65° 20′.8 E = bearing of mark.

EXAMPLE 2

Observation on Sun for Azimuth
(Southern Hemisphere)

At a place in Latitude, 33° $01'$ S; Longitude, 71° $39'$ W, an observation is made on the sun Aug. 5, 1929, to determine the azimuth of $A-B$, as follows:

Instrument at Station A

	Vernier A	Vertical arc	Watch (local time) P.M.
Sta. B.	0° $00'$		
$\frac{\mid}{\mid\bigcirc}$	75° $15'$	24° $22'$	3^h 00^m 10^s
$\frac{\bigcirc\mid}{\mid}$	74 52	23 03	3 05 12
Mean	75° $03'.5$	23° $42'.5$	3^h 02^m 41^s
Refr. and Par., Table III		$-2'.0$	12
	$h =$	23° $40'.5$	15^h 02^m 41^s

Longitude 71° $39'$ $= 4^h$ 46^m 36^s
Local Civil Time $= 15$ 02 41

Greenwich Civil Time $= 19^h$ 49^m 17^s
$= 24^h - 4^h$ 10^m 43^s
$= 24^h - 4^h.18$

Decl. at 0^h Aug. 6 $= +16^\circ$ $54'$ $37''$

$\dfrac{971''.0}{24} \times 4^h.18 = 2'$ $49''$

$$D = +16^\circ\ 57'\ 26''$$

The formula is:

$$\cos Z_n = \tan h \tan L - \frac{\sin D}{\cos h \cos L}$$

log tan h	9.64192	log sin $D =$	9.46487 n
log tan L	9.81279	log sec $h =$	0.03818
	9.45471	log sec $L =$	0.07649
	.28491		9.57954 n
	$-.37979$		$-.37979$

nat cos Z_n $=$ .66470
Z_n $=$ 48° $20'.5$ northwest
Hor. Angle $=$ 75° $03'.5$
N 123° $24'.0$ W

Bearing,
A to B = S 56° $36'.0$ W

If desired the time may be computed from the same data, the formula for the sun's hour angle being

$$\cos t = \frac{\sin h - \sin L \sin D}{\cos L \cos D}$$

Using the data of Example 1, p. 278, we find $t = 42° 15'.5$. This is the angle east of the meridian. Its equivalent in hours is $2^h 49^m 02^s$, and it represents the time that will elapse before noon. The local *apparent* time is therefore $9^h 10^m 58^s$. Subtracting from this the *equation of time*,* $+12^m 03^s$, given in the Nautical Almanac, we have $8^h 58^m 55^s$ for the Local Civil Time. Subtracting $15^m 42^s$, the difference between the longitude of the place and that of the Eastern Standard Meridian ($75°$ W), we have $8^h 43^m 13^s$ for the Standard Time. Since the watch read $8^h 43^m 47^s$, it is 34^s fast.

240. OBSERVATION FOR MERIDIAN BY MEANS OF THE SOLAR ATTACHMENT. — One of the auxiliaries to the engineer's transit, formerly in common use, is the *solar attachment*, one make of which is illustrated in Fig. 100d. This consists of a small instrument having motions about two axes at right angles to each other, like the transit itself, and which is attached to the transit; by means of this attachment a true meridian line can be found by an observation on the sun. This instrument seldom gives as great precision as direct solar observations but has the advantage that less calculation is required than with direct observations. In the form shown in Fig. 100d, which is a modification of the Saegmuller pattern, the principal parts are the *polar axis*, which is attached to the telescope tube and is adjusted perpendicular to the line of sight and also the horizontal axis, and the *solar telescope*, which is mounted on the polar axis. The solar telescope is provided with clamps and tangent screws and can be revolved about the polar axis and can also be inclined to it at any desired angle.

---

* *Apparent* noon occurs when the sun is on the meridian. *Mean* noon is the instant when the sun would be on the meridian if it moved at a uniform rate along the equator. The difference between the two is known as the *Equation of time* and may be found in the Nautical Almanac. For example, on November 1st, the sun passes the meridian $16^m 18^s$ before *mean* noon, i.e., when it is $12^h 00^m 00^s$ *apparent* time it is $11^h 43^m 42^s$ *mean* time. See Arts. 68–70, Chap. II, Vol. II, for definition of *apparent* and *mean* times.

FIG. 100d.   SOLAR ATTACHMENT TO TRANSIT.

(The authors are indebted to C. L. Berger & Sons for the photograph from which this cut was made.)

Attached to the solar telescope is a level tube, the axis of which is supposed to be parallel to the line of sight of the solar telescope. This is used when setting off the sun's declination by means of the vertical circle of the transit. At the base of the polar axis are four adjusting screws for making this axis perpendicular to the line of sight and to the horizontal axis of the main telescope. The solar telescope is provided with four additional cross-hairs which form a square whose angular diameter is equal to that of the sun. The eyepiece is covered with a colored glass to protect the eye while observing.

In another form, known as Burt's solar attachment, the telescope is replaced by a small bi-convex lens and a metallic screen carrying ruled lines in place of cross-hairs. The sun's image is thrown on the screen and viewed with a magnifying glass; this device is really the equivalent of a telescope of low power. The sun's image is centered in the square formed by the ruled lines. The instrument is provided with a *declination arc* for setting off the declination of the sun when determining the direction of the meridian. To avoid the necessity of having a declination arc extending both ways from 0° the instrument has two sets of solar lenses and screens pointing in opposite directions; one is used for north and one for south declinations.

The Smith solar attachment is mounted on the side of one of the standards of the transit. The solar telescope serves as the polar axis. In front of the objective of the solar telescope is a mirror attached to a movable arm to which is attached the vernier of the declination arc. On the solar telescope is a special *latitude arc*, the vernier for which is at the top of the standard. The solar telescope may be rotated about its own axis. This instrument has the advantage that all of the settings may be made and allowed to remain without interfering with the use of the transit telescope for other purposes.

241. OBSERVATION ON THE SUN WITH SOLAR ATTACHMENT — FIELDWORK. — If the polar axis is pointed to the celestial pole, made parallel to the earth's axis, then the small telescope can be made to follow the sun in its daily path by giving it an inclination to the polar axis equal to the sun's polar distance and revolving it about the polar axis.

(1) To find the true meridian by an observation on the sun first make the angle between the polar axis and the solar telescope equal to the sun's polar distance at the time of the observation. This is done by turning the solar telescope into the same plane as the main telescope by sighting both on some distant object, and then making the angle between the two telescopes equal to the sun's declination. Some instruments are provided with a *declination arc* upon which the declination angle can be laid off directly. Others have a small spirit level attached to the small telescope, the vertical circle of the transit being used for laying off the declination angle. Incline the main telescope until the vertical circle reading equals the declination, and clamp; then level the solar telescope by means of the attached level. The angle between the polar axis and the solar telescope is then 90° plus or minus the reading of the vertical circle.

(2) By means of the vertical circle of the transit incline the polar axis to the vertical by an angle equal to the **co-latitude of the place,** that is, 90° minus the latitude. The polar axis now has the same angle of elevation as the celestial pole. (For a method of finding the latitude by observation see Art. 243.)

(3) If the observation is in the forenoon, place the solar telescope on the left of the main telescope (on the right if in the afternoon); then, by moving the whole instrument about the vertical axis and the solar telescope about the polar axis, point the solar telescope at the sun. The sun's image is brought to the center of the square formed by four cross-hairs, or ruled lines, in the solar telescope. The final setting is made by the tangent screw controlling the horizontal motion of the transit and that controlling the motion of the solar telescope about the polar axis. **Only one position can be found where the solar telescope will point to the sun.** In this position the vertical axis points to the zenith, the polar axis to the pole, and the solar telescope to the sun. The instrument has thus solved mechanically the spherical triangle ZPO (Fig. 100e). The horizontal angle between the two telescopes is equal to the sun's true bearing. Since the solar telescope is pointing to the sun the main telescope must be in the plane of the meridian. If all of the work has been done correctly the sun's image will remain between the cross-

hairs which are parallel to the equator, and therefore the sun can
be followed in its apparent path by a motion of the solar telescope alone.   If it is necessary to move the instrument about the
vertical axis in order to point the solar telescope again at the
sun this shows that the main telescope was not truly in the
meridian.

After the meridian has been determined the main telescope
may then be lowered and a point set which will be due north or
due south of the instrument.

The declination of the sun for the time of the observation is
computed as explained in Art. 238, p. 276.   After the correct

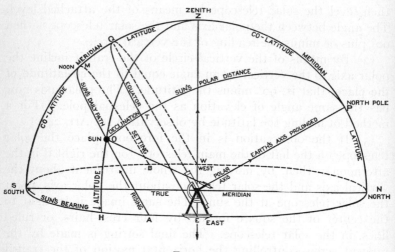

Fig. 100e.

declination is found it has still to be corrected for refraction of
the atmosphere.   The effect of refraction is to make the sun
appear higher in the sky than it actually is.   In the northern
hemisphere, when the declination is north, the correction must
be added numerically; when south, subtracted.   Algebraically
it is always added.   The correction may be taken from Table
IX, p. 678 (**not**, in this case, from Table 11 or 12), the declination being given at the top of the column and the number
of hours from local noon either way at the left of the page.

EXAMPLE

Latitude 40° N.
Declination at Greenwich 0^h =
$\quad -22°\ 03'\ 53''\ .6$

Longitude 71° 15' = $4^h\ 45^m$ W.
Date, Jan. 10, 1925

Tab. diff. for 24^h = $+532''\ .1$

Required the declination settings for 2^h, 3^h and 4^h P.M., Eastern Standard Time.

2^h P.M. E. S. T. = 7^h P.M. Gr. Time = 19^h Gr. Civ. Time

$+ \dfrac{532''\ .1}{24} \times 19^h = + 7'\ 01''\ .2$

Decl. at 2^h P.M. E. S. T. = $- 22°\ 03'\ 53''\ .6 + 7'\ 01''\ .2$
$\qquad\qquad\qquad\qquad = - 21°\ 56'\ 52''\ .4$

The values for 3^h and 4^h are obtained by subtracting $\dfrac{532''\ .1}{24} = 22''.17$ for each hour. The declination, refraction corrections and final settings are as follows:

TIME. E. S. T.	DECLINATION.	REFR CORR.	SETTING.
2^h P.M.	$- 21°\ 56'\ 52''.4$	$1'\ 57''$	$- 21°\ 54'\ 55''$
3^h	$- 21\ 56\ 39\ .2$	$2\ 36$	$- 21\ 53\ 54$
4^h	$- 21\ 56\ 08\ .0$	$4\ 59$	$- 21\ 51\ 09$

Observation for meridian should not be made when the sun's altitude is less than about 10°, because the refraction correction will be unreliable. Observations near noon are to be avoided because a slight error in altitude produces a large error in the resulting meridian. For good results therefore the observation should be made neither within an hour of noon nor near sunrise or sunset.

MISTAKES IN USING THE SOLAR ATTACHMENT. —

1. Solar on wrong side of main telescope.
2. Refraction correction applied wrong way.
3. Declination set off in wrong direction.

ADJUSTMENTS OF THE SOLAR ATTACHMENT

241a. ADJUSTMENT OF POLAR AXIS. — To make the Polar Axis Perpendicular to the Plane of the Line of Sight and the Horizontal Axis. Level the transit and the main telescope. Bring the bubble of the solar telescope to the center of its tube while it is parallel to a pair of opposite adjusting screws which are at the foot of the polar axis. Reverse the solar telescope 180° about the polar axis. If the bubble moves from the central position, bring it half-way back by means of the adjusting screws just mentioned and the other half by means of the tangent screw controlling the vertical motion of the solar. This should be done over each pair of opposite adjusting screws and repeated until the bubble remains central in all positions.

ADJUSTMENT OF THE CROSS-HAIRS. — To make the Vertical Cross-Hair truly Vertical. Sight on some distant point with all the clamps tightened and, by means of the tangent screw controlling the vertical motion of the solar, revolve the solar telescope about its horizontal axis to see if the vertical cross-hair remains on the point. If not, adjust it by rotating the cross-hair ring, as described in Art. 71, p. 66.

ADJUSTMENT OF TELESCOPE BUBBLE. — To make the Axis of the Bubble Parallel to the Line of Sight. Level the main telescope and mark a point about 200 ft. from the instrument in line with the horizontal cross-hair. Measure the distance between the two telescopes and lay this off above the first point; this will give a point on a level with the center of the solar telescope. Sight the solar at this point and clamp. Bring the bubble to the center by means of the adjusting screws on the bubble tube.

OBSERVATIONS FOR LATITUDE

242. (1) **BY THE ALTITUDE OF POLARIS AT UPPER OR LOWER CULMINATION.** — When Polaris is approaching either upper or lower culmination (see Art. 232b, p. 261B, and Fig. 98a) set up the transit and point the horizontal hair on the star. Keep the cross-hair pointed on the star until the culmination is reached. Read the vertical arc and determine the index correction. The observed altitude is to be corrected for refraction by Table 11, p. 274. This gives the true altitude. If Polaris is at upper culmination subtract from the true altitude the polar distance of the star at the date of the observation (Table 8, p. 265). If the star is at lower culmination the polar distance is to be added. The result is the latitude of the place of observation.

243. (2) **BY THE ALTITUDE OF THE SUN AT NOON.** — The observation consists in finding the maximum altitude of the sun's lower limb. This will occur (very nearly) when the sun is on the meridian. Begin the observation a little before *apparent* noon, remembering that this differs sometimes more than 16^m from *mean* noon. Furthermore it should be remembered that standard time may differ as much as half an hour from *mean* time. When the maximum altitude is found the following corrections are to be made: first, the refraction correction is to be subtracted (Table 11, p. 274); second, the sun's semi-diameter (found in the American Ephemeris and Nautical Almanac)* is to be added; third, the sun's declination is to be subtracted if plus or added if minus. The result, subtracted from 90°, is the latitude of the place.

EXAMPLE

Observed maximum altitude of the sun's lower limb on Jan. 15, 1925, = 26° 15' (sun south of zenith); index correction = +1'; longitude = 71° 06' W; sun's declination Jan. 15 at 0^h Greenwich Civil Time = −21° 15' 19''; Tab. diff. for 24^h = +657''.5; equation of time = −9^m 17^s; semi-diameter = 16' 18''.

Observed altitude =	26° 15'		Local App. Time	−	12^h
Index Correction =	+ 1'		Longitude	=	4 44 24
	26° 16'		Gr. App. Time	=	16^h 44^m 24^s
Refraction	1' 58''		Equa. of Time	=	9 17†
	26° 14' 02''		Gr. Civil Time	=	16^h 53^m 41^s
Semi-diameter	+ 16' 18''				
	26° 30' 20''		† Sign reversed		
Declination =	−21° 07' 36''				
Co-latitude =	47° 37' 56''		Decl. at 0^h	= − 21° 15' 19''	
Latitude =	42° 22' 04''		$+ \dfrac{657''.5}{24} \times 16^h.90 =$	+7' 43''	
			Declination	− 21° 07' 36''	

243a. **MERIDIAN BY EQUAL ALTITUDES OF THE SUN.** — This observation consists in measuring in the forenoon the horizontal

---

* Or in " Ephemeris of the Sun and Polaris," published by the General Land Office, price 5 cents.

† The equation of time is explained in footnote on p. 280.

angle between the sun and some reference mark at the instant when the sun has a certain altitude, and again measuring the angle when the sun has an **equal** altitude in the afternoon. If the distance of the sun from the equator were the same for the two observations the horizontal angles between the sun and the meridian would be the same in both observations, hence the mean of the two readings of the horizontal circle would be the reading for the meridian. But since the sun is changing its distance from the equator the measured angles must be corrected accordingly. The correction to the mean is computed by the equation

$$X = \frac{d}{\cos L \sin t}$$

in which X = the correction to the mean vernier reading, d = the hourly change in declination of the sun taken from Table 11A and multiplied by **half** the number of hours between the two observations, L = the latitude, and t = half the elapsed time converted into degrees, minutes, and seconds. Since the hourly change for any given day is nearly the same, year after year, an almanac is not necessary but the following table is sufficient.

TABLE 11A

HOURLY CHANGE IN THE SUN'S DECLINATION

	1st.	10th.	20th.	30th.
January.........	+ 12″	+ 22″	+ 32″	+ 41″
February......	+ 43	+ 49	+ 54	....
March.........	+ 57	+ 59	+ 59	+ 58
April..........	+ 58	+ 55	+ 51	+ 46
May..........	+ 45	+ 39	+ 31	+ 23
June..........	+ 21	+ 12	+ 01	− 09
July..........	− 10	− 19	− 28	− 36
August........	− 38	− 44	− 49	− 54
September....	− 54	− 57	− 58	− 59
October........	− 58	− 57	− 54	− 49
November.....	− 48	− 42	− 34	− 25
December......	− 23	− 14	− 02	+ 10

The observation is made as follows: *At some time in the forenoon, preferably not later than 9 o'clock, the instrument is

---

* The nearer the sun is due East or due West, the better the result.

set up at one end of the line the azimuth of which is to be found, and one vernier is set at 0°. The vertical cross-hair is then sighted at the other end of the line and the lower plate clamped. The upper clamp is loosened and the telescope turned until the sun can be seen in the field of view. The horizontal cross-hair is to be set on the **lower** edge of the sun and the vertical cross-hair on the **right** edge (northern hemisphere). Since the sun is rising and also changing its bearing it is difficult to set both of the cross-hairs at once and it will be found easier to set the horizontal hair so that it will cut across the sun's disc, leaving it clamped in

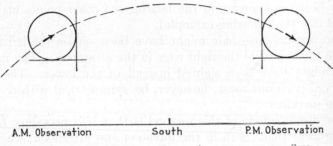

A.M. Observation   South   P.M. Observation

FIG. 100f. MERIDIAN BY EQUAL ALTITUDES OF THE SUN.

this position while the vertical hair is kept tangent to the right edge of the sun by means of the upper tangent screw. When the sun has risen until the lower edge is on the horizontal hair the instrument is in the desired position and after this position is reached the upper tangent screw should not be moved. As soon as this position is reached the time is noted. Both the vertical and the horizontal circles should now be read and the angles recorded.

In the afternoon, when the sun is found to be nearly at the same altitude as at the forenoon observation, the instrument should be set up at the same point and again sighted on the mark. The observation described above is repeated, the pointings now being made on the **lower** and **left** edges of the disc. The telescope is inclined until the vernier of the vertical circle reads the same as it did at the forenoon observation. When the sun comes into the field the vertical hair is set on the left edge and kept there until the lower edge is in contact with the horizontal hair. The time is again noted and the verniers are read. If desired, the accuracy may be increased by taking several pairs of observations. The mean of the two circle readings (supposing the graduations to be numbered from 0° to 360° in a clockwise direction) is now to be corrected for the sun's change in declination. The correction as obtained by the formula given on p. 288 is to be added to the mean vernier reading if d is minus, and subtracted if d is plus, i.e., if the sun is going south the mean vernier reading is east of the south point, and *vice versa.* When the circle reading of the south point is known the true bearing of the mark becomes known and the bearings of other points may be found (see the following example).

The vertical cross-hair might have been set on the left edge in the forenoon and the right edge in the afternoon. The upper edge might have been sighted instead of the lower. The two observed positions must, however, be symmetrical with respect to the meridian.

The disadvantage of this method is that it is necessary to be at the same place both in the forenoon and afternoon, whereas in many cases the surveyor might in the afternoon be a long distance from where he was working in the forenoon.

EXAMPLE

Latitude 42° 18′ N.   April 19, 1940.

A. M. Observation.

Reading on Mark, 0° 00′ 00″
Pointings on Upper and Left Limbs.
Vertical Arc, 24° 58′
Horizontal Circle, 357° 14′ 15″
Time 7^h 19^m 30^s
½ elapsed time = 4^h 27^m 12^s
        = 66° 48′ 00″
log sin t 9.96338
log cos L 9.86902
              —————
                9.83240
log 227″ .0   2.35603
              —————
                2.52363
correction = 333″ .9 = 5′ 33″ .9

P. M. Observation.

Reading on Mark, 0° 00′ 00″
Pointings on Upper and Right Limbs.
Vertical Arc, 24° 58′
Horizontal Circle, 163° 15′ 45″
Time 4^h 13^m 54^s
Increase in declination in 4^h 27^m 12^s =
        51″ × 4.45 = 227″ .0

Mean circle reading = 80° 15′ 00″
                        5 34
                      —————
                    S 80° 09′ 36″ E

Azimuth of mark = 279° 50′ 34″

TABLE 12*

CORRECTION TO OBSERVED ALTITUDE OF THE SUN FOR REFRACTION AND PARALLAX

APP'T ALT.	-10° C. -14° F.	- 5° C. +23° F.	0° C. +32° F.	+ 5° C. +41° F.	+10° C. +50° F.	+15° C. +59° F.	+20° C. +68° F.	+25° C. +77° F.	+30° C. +86° F.	+35° C. +95° F.	APP'T ALT.
°	,	,	,	,	,	,	,	,	,	,	°
10	5.52	5.42	5.30	5.20	5.10	5.00	4.92	4.83	4.75	4.67	10
11	5.02	4.92	4.82	4.73	4.63	4.55	4.47	4.38	4.32	4.23	11
12	4.60	4.50	4.42	4.33	4.25	4.17	4.10	4.03	3.97	3.88	12
13	4.23	4.15	4.07	4.00	3.92	3.85	3.78	3.72	3.65	3.58	13
14	3.92	3.83	3.77	3.70	3.62	3.55	3.50	3.45	3.37	3.32	14
15	3.65	3.58	3.50	3.43	3.37	3.32	3.25	3.20	3.13	3.08	15
16	3.43	3.35	3.30	3.23	3.17	3.12	3.07	3.00	2.95	2.90	16
17	3.22	3.15	3.10	3.03	2.98	2.92	2.88	2.82	2.77	2.72	17
18	3.02	2.95	2.90	2.85	2.80	2.75	2.70	2.65	2.60	2.55	18
19	2.83	2.78	2.73	2.68	2.63	2.58	2.53	2.48	2.43	2.40	19
20	2.68	2.63	2.58	2.53	2.48	2.43	2.38	2.33	2.30	2.27	20
21	2.53	2.48	2.43	2.38	2.35	2.30	2.27	2.22	2.17	2.13	21
22	2.38	2.35	2.30	2.25	2.22	2.18	2.13	2.08	2.05	2.02	22
23	2.28	2.25	2.20	2.15	2.12	2.08	2.03	1.98	1.95	1.93	23
24	2.17	2.13	2.08	2.05	2.02	1.98	1.93	1.88	1.87	1.83	24
25	2.07	2.03	1.98	1.95	1.92	1.88	1.83	1.80	1.77	1.75	25
26	1.99	1.95	1.90	1.87	1.83	1.80	1.75	1.72	1.70	1.67	26
27	1.88	1.85	1.82	1.78	1.75	1.72	1.68	1.63	1.62	1.60	27
28	1.80	1.77	1.72	1.70	1.67	1.63	1.60	1.57	1.53	1.52	28
29	1.72	1.68	1.65	1.63	1.60	1.57	1.53	1.50	1.47	1.46	29
30	1.65	1.62	1.58	1.57	1.53	1.50	1.47	1.45	1.42	1.40	30
32	1.53	1.50	1.47	1.45	1.42	1.38	1.35	1.33	1.30	1.28	32
34	1.41	1.37	1.35	1.33	1.30	1.27	1 25	1.23	1.20	1.18	34
36	1.30	1.27	1.25	1.22	1.20	1.18	1.15	1.13	1.10	1.08	36
38	1.20	1.18	1.15	1.13	1.12	1.10	1.07	1.05	1.02	1.02	38
40	1.11	1.10	1.07	1.05	1.03	1.02	0.98	0.97	0.95	0.93	40
42	1.03	1.00	0.98	0.97	0.95	0.93	0.90	0.88	0.87	0.87	42
44	0.96	0.93	0.92	0.90	0.88	0.87	0.85	0.83	0.82	0.80	44
46	0.89	0.88	0.87	0.85	0.83	0.82	0.80	0.78	0.77	0.75	46
48	0.83	0.82	0.80	0.78	0.77	0.75	0.73	0.72	0.70	0.68	48
50	0.77	0.75	0.73	0.72	0.70	0.68	0.67	0.67	0.65	0.63	50
55	0.63	0.62	0.60	0.60	0.58	0.57	0.57	0.55	0.53	0.52	55
60	0.52	0.52	0.50	0.50	0.48	0.47	0.47	0 45	0.45	0.43	60
65	0.42	0.40	0.40	0.40	0.38	0.38	0.37	0.37	0.35	0.38	65
70	0.32	0.32	0.32	0.30	0.30	0.30	0.28	0.28	0.28	0.27	70
75	0.23	0.23	0.23	0.22	0.22	0.22	0.20	0.20	0.20	0.18	75
80	0.15	0.15	0.13	0.13	0.13	0 13	0.13	0.12	0.12	0.12	80
85	0.07	0.07	0.07	0.07	0.07	0 07	0.07	0.05	0.05	0.05	85
90	0.00	0.00	0.00	0.00	0.00	0.00	0.00	0.00	0.00	0.00	90

* From *Principal Facts of Earth's Magnetism, Coast and Geodetic Survey.*

PROBLEMS

1. (a) What was the azimuth of Polaris at its greatest western elongation at Boston when the polar distance of the star was $1° 14' 12''$? The latitude of Boston is $42° 21'$ N.

(b) In making an observation for meridian two stakes were set 329 ft. apart, marking the direction of the star at elongation. Compute the length of the perpendicular offset to be laid off at one end of the line to obtain the true meridian.

2. What is the approximate Eastern Standard Time of the eastern elongation of Polaris on August 10, 1940 at a place in longitude $72° 56'$ West and latitude $40°$ North?

3. Compute the azimuth of the mark from the following observations on the sun May 25, 1925.

	VERNIER A	ALTITUDE	WATCH (E.S.T.)
Mark	$0° 00'$		
Left and	$71° 16'*$	$40° 33'$	$3^h 14^m 50^s$ P.M.
Lower Limbs	$71° 28'$	$40° 22'$	$3^h 15^m 50^s$
Telescope reversed			
Upper and	$72° 21'$	$40° 42'$	$3^h 16^m 50^s$
Right Limbs	$72° 32'$	$40° 32'$	$3^h 17^m 48^s$
Mark	$0° 00'$		

Latitude = $42° 29'.5$ N; longitude = $71° 07'.5$ W; I. C. = $0''$.

Declination at 0^h Greenwich Civil Time = $+20° 48' 55''.8$ (North); tabular difference for 24^h = $+651''.6$ (sun going north); Equation of time = $+3^m 19^s.5$.

4. Observation for latitude. The observed altitude of Polaris at upper culmination was $43° 27'$. The polar distance of the star was $1° 12'$. What was the latitude of the place?

5. Observed maximum altitude of the sun's lower limb April 27, 1925 = $61° 28'$ (bearing south). Index Correction = $+30''$. Eastern Standard Time is $11^h 42^m$ A.M. Sun's declination April 27 at 0^h Gr. Civ. Time = $+13° 35' 51''$; tabular difference for 24^h = $+1149''.7$; semi-diameter = $15' 55''$. Compute the latitude.

6. A mark was set roughly in the meridian (to the north of the transit) and 3 repetitions taken from Polaris to the mark (mark east of star), the third reading being $4° 51' 00''$. The observed watch readings were $6^h 28^m 30^s$, $6^h 31^m 20^s$, and $6^h 34^m 20^s$. The watch was 15^s slow of Eastern Standard Time. Observed altitude of Polaris, $42° 18'$; date, April 6, 1940; latitude, $42° 21'$; longitude, $71° 05'$ W. Compute the true bearing of the mark. Watch readings are P.M.

7. With the transit at station 12 on June 7, 1937, in latitude $42° 29'.5$ N, longitude $71° 07'.5$ W, a sun observation is made to obtain the bearing 12–13. The corrected altitude is $42° 03'$, the corrected declination is $+22° 46'.5$, the mean horizontal angle from 13, clockwise, to the sun is $156° 22'$, and the mean watch reading is $3^h 15^m 54^s.7$ P.M., E. S. T. The deflection angle at station 13 is $5° 26'$ R; at 14 it is $7° 36'$ L; at 15 it is $2° 09'$ R. At station 15 an observation is taken on Polaris; $0°$ on station 16; first angle, at $7^h 02^m 05^s$ P.M., E. S. T., $252° 44'$ (clockwise); second repetition, at $7^h 04^m 25^s$, $145° 29'$; third repetition, at $7^h 06^m 40^s$, $38° 14'$. The corrected mean altitude is $41° 29'.5$. Station 15 is 2800 feet east of station 12. Assuming no error in the observations, compute the error in the traverse angles.

---

* Angle to the right.

CHAPTER IX

LEVELING

244. DEFINITIONS. — Leveling consists in ascertaining differences in elevation; there are two methods in common use, *Direct Leveling*, and *Trigonometric Leveling*. The former alone will be considered in this book. For a description of trigonometric leveling see Vol. II, Chap. III, Art. 122.

Wherever extensive leveling operations are to be carried on it is necessary to have a system of reference points called *bench marks* (B.Ms.), the relative heights of which are known accurately. These heights are usually referred to some definite surface such, for instance, as *mean sea-level* or *mean low water*, and the height of a point above this surface is called its *elevation*. This surface is known as the *datum*, or " datum plane." (See Art. 263, p. 309, and Art. 272, p. 326.) Strictly speaking it is not a plane but a level surface, i.e., it is at every point perpendicular to the direction of gravity. If mean sea-level has not been established a datum can be assumed arbitrarily.

245. LEVELING TO ESTABLISH BENCH MARKS. — When it is necessary to run a line of levels to establish new bench marks the rod is first held on some bench mark the elevation of which is accurately known, and a *backsight* taken (Art. 116, p. 91). If this backsight is added to the known elevation of the bench mark it gives the *height of the instrument* (H.I.) above the datum. A *turning point* is then selected ahead on the route to be traversed, and a *foresight* taken on it. (See Art. 250, p. 298.) If the foresight is subtracted from the height of the instrument the elevation of the turning point is obtained. This process is continued until the line or circuit is completed.

The terms *backsight* and *foresight* as used in leveling bear no relation whatever to the backward or forward direction along the traverse line. A **backsight** is a rod-reading on a point the elevation of which is **known;** it is **added** to the elevation to obtain

293

the H.I. A **foresight** is the rod-reading on a point the elevation of which **is not known**; it is **subtracted** from the H.I. to obtain the elevation.

When a bench mark is being established it should be **used as a turning point.** The elevation of this bench mark could be obtained by taking a foresight upon it and not using it as a turning point, but by making the bench mark also a turning point it becomes a part of the line of levels and if the level circuit checks, the elevation of the bench mark is also checked. Each bench mark should be recorded by a description or a sketch, or both. The elevations of the turning points are as accurate as those of the bench marks themselves. Consequently it is advisable to describe those turning points that can be identified readily so that they may be used later when an established bench mark is not available.

In leveling uphill the backsights are long and the foresights are short; in leveling downhill the reverse is true. To obtain the minimum number of set-ups of the level the long rod-readings should be near the top of the extended rod and the short rod-readings should be near the foot of the rod. The levelman must use good judgment in selecting the positions for his level and the rodman must apply good judgment in selecting the turning points, else much time will be lost. For example, in leveling downhill set up the level roughly (without pressing the tripod legs into the ground), turn the telescope toward the rod and then level it, approximately, in that direction. By sighting along the outside of the telescope, the approximate place where the line of sight will strike the rod can be noted and the distance the instrument should be moved up or down the slope can be estimated. Then move to the new position, level up carefully, and proceed to take the backsight. The rodman then proceeds downhill and selects a suitable point for a new turning point and one which he estimates will give a reading near the top of the rod. The levelman should be alert and, if the line of sight cuts above the top of the rod he should immediately indicate this fact to the rodman and tell him (or signal to him) the approximate amount the top of the rod is below the line of sight so that the next point selected will be at about the right height. In carrying a line of levels uphill the same general procedure should be followed, but now the levelman stops the rodman when his ankles are on the line of sight, and the rodman should then select a turning point at the level of the ground on which he is standing.

246. In this work it is very important to eliminate as far as possible errors of adjustment in the instrument. If at every set-up of the level the foresight and the backsight are taken at points which are equally distant from the instrument such errors will be eliminated. If the level is not in perfect adjustment the resulting error in any reading is proportional to the distance. At equal distances from the instrument the errors are equal, and, since it is the difference of the rod-readings that gives the difference in elevation, the error is eliminated from the final result by this method. By making the length of foresights and backsights equal on turning points it is possible to eliminate not only the error due to non-adjustment of the bubble but also any error due to non-adjustment of the objective tube, since this will occupy the same position in the telescope in each sight. The distance to the backsight is determined by the place where the instrument is set up, and the rodman, as he passes from one turning point to the next, can by pacing make the foresight distance approximately equal to that of the backsight. Where the shape of the ground may be so irregular that backsight distances cannot be made about equal to foresight distances and at the same time adhere to the suggestion above of making the long rod-readings near the top of the rod and the short rod-readings near the foot of the rod, the high and short rod-readings should be sacrificed to make the distance from the level to the rod approximately equal on backsights and foresights. This will, of course, entail more set-ups of the instrument. In running a line of levels from one B.M. to another some distance away, if the sum of the backsight distances is approximately equal to the sum of the foresight distances, even though each pair of backsights and foresights may not be taken on points equally distant from the level, the instrumental errors referred to above will be eliminated. The line of levels should be " closed " by continuing the leveling until the original bench mark, or some other bench mark whose elevation is well established, is reached.

247. The notes for this work may consist of five columns, as shown in Fig. 101. The height of instrument is obtained by adding the backsight rod-reading to the elevation of the point on which it is taken. The elevation of any point is found by subtracting the foresight rod-reading for that point from the corresponding height of the instrument. Notice that the calculations may be checked by adding the column of foresights and

(LEFT-HAND PAGE)　　　　　　(RIGHT-HAND PAGE)

Point	B.S.	H.I.	F.S.	Elev.	Remarks.
					B.M. Leveling for Eastern Intercepting Sewer.
					B. Jones ⚲ M. Brown Oct. 30, 1935
B.M.$_1$	4.122	93.139		89.017	Top S.E. cor. granite foundation S.E. cor. City Hall.
T.P.$_1$	3.661	90.611	6.189	86.950	Curb
T.P.$_2$	4.029	89.630	5.010	85.601	N.E. bolt top hydrant opp. #42 Main. St.
B.M.$_2$	3.901	86.161	7.370	82.260	S.W. cor. S.B. on N.W. cor. Main and Broad Sts.
B.M.$_3$	3.512	83.056	6.617	79.544	N.W. cor. lower stone step #62 Broad St.
T.P.$_3$	6.007	80.348	8.715	74.341	Cobble stone
B.M.$_4$			9.070	71.278	Chisel cut N.W. cor. C.B. curb S.W. cor. Broad and State Sts.
	25.232		42.971		True elev. B.M. = 71.274 Book 27, P.36.
			25.232	89.017	
			17.739	17.739	"Check"

FIG. 101. BENCH MARK LEVEL NOTES.

the column of backsights. The difference between these sums should be the same as the difference in elevation between the first and last points. This **check is important** and **should not be omitted.** (See Fig. 101.) The notes should be computed in the field to catch errors when they occur and then and there eliminate them. Also the note-keeper should compute mentally and not on a scratch pad or in the back of the book.

248. Double-Rodded Lines. — A good check on the line of levels may be secured by running a double line of turning points. Instead of taking a foresight on a single turning point, foresights may be taken on two different points near together, from the same set-up of the instrument. When the level is set up again a backsight is taken on each turning point and two independent

values of the new height of instrument are obtained. In ordinary
bench-mark leveling these two values should not differ by more
than 0.002 or 0.003 ft. from the previous difference, i.e., if the
two heights of instrument differed by 0.013 at a certain set-up
they should not differ by more than 0.016 nor less than 0.010 at
the next set-up. The two turning points of a pair should be
so chosen that their difference in elevation is more than a foot

(LEFT-HAND PAGE)   (RIGHT-HAND PAGE)

Sta.	B.S.	H.I.	F.S.	Elev.	Description
— B.M. Levels – Bridge #67 to Mile Post- #45 A&B. R.R.					April 17, 1936 {Smith / Lowe ☓ / Rich
B.M.₁₆	4.691	50.965		46.274	N.E. cor. W. Bridge seat bridge #67 A.&D.RR.
T.P.₁ L.	6.040	49.721	7.284	43.681	
T.P.₁ H.	4.441	49.719	5.687	45.278	
T.P.₂ L.	10.641	53.621	6.741	42.980	
T.P.₂ H.	7.902	53.617	4.004	45.715	
B.M.₁₇ L.	4.805	54.748	3.678	49.943	S.E. cor. Stone step S. side Jameston Sts.
T.P.₃ H.	2.972	54.747	1.842	51.775	
T.P.₄ L.	4.959	55.027	4.680	50.068	
B.M.₁₈ H.	3.489	55.029	3.207	51.540	d.h. S.W. cor. first step W. wing N. abut. bridge #70 A.&B.R.R.
B.M.₁₉			2.709	52.318	
				52.320	52.319 Top Mile post #45.

FIG. 102 BENCH MARK LEVEL NOTES, DOUBLE-RODDED LINE.

so that any mistake of a foot in the computations or in reading
the rod will not occur.

In this way, by little additional work, mistakes in the levels
may be eliminated as the work progresses. This method is
particularly useful in running long lines of levels where no established bench marks are available for checking and where the line
of levels cannot return to the first bench mark to close the circuit.
This method does not eliminate errors in adjustment of the
instrument, but making backsights and foresights equal will do so.

249. A set of notes illustrating double turning points is
shown in Fig. 102. It will be noticed that the higher and lower
turning points of a pair are arranged in a systematic order. Here
the readings have been taken on the lower turning point first
at each set-up. It is very important that some such definite

system shall be followed so that the two lines of levels will not be confused. Great care must be taken in reading the first B.S. and the last F.S. for this system gives no check on these two readings.

It should be observed, however, that the above process does not furnish a complete check on the resulting elevations because any inclination of the line of sight, such as that due to non-adjustment of the level affects the two nearby T.Ps. by almost exactly the same amount. The close check of the two H.Is. is no indication that such errors have been eliminated. The only check against such errors is that obtained by the closed circuit, and by equalization of fore- and backsights.

250. Bench Marks and Turning Points. — Both the bench marks and the turning points should be such that their elevations will not change during the time they are needed. The only difference between the two is that turning points may be of use for only a few minutes while bench marks may be needed for many years. Bench marks should be described, very carefully and accurately, and their heights should be checked before being accepted as correct. They are frequently taken on such points as these: stone bounds, tops of boulders, spikes in trees, and on sills, stone steps, or underpinning of buildings. Curb stones or tops of hydrants are also used but are not so permanent. As it is often impossible in a new country to find existing points where bench marks can be established, it is usual to set stone monuments or iron rods and to determine their elevation carefully. The U. S. Geological Survey, and the U. S. Coast and Geodetic Survey use metal tablets set into concrete piers, into rock, or into the stone foundations of buildings. Some of the older bench marks of the Coast Survey and of the Missouri River Commission consist of stones the tops of which are buried 3 or 4 ft. under ground. The exact bench is the top of a spherical headed bolt set in the top of the stone. This is reached by lowering the rod through an iron pipe which extends from the surface of the ground to the top of the stone.

Bench marks should be established at frequent intervals for convenience in subsequent work. Some surveyors consider it advisable to have two bench marks in the same locality to serve as checks on each other. In choosing a bench or a turning point it is best to select a point which is slightly raised so that the rod will always rest on exactly the same point. A rounded surface is better than a sharp point, especially when it is on a rock, as the rod may chip off a small piece and alter the elevation. If a turning point is taken on a flat surface it is difficult to get the rod at exactly the same height each time. Bench marks are, however, sometimes established on flat level surfaces such as the coping stone of a masonry structure, because permanence is of more importance than great precision. Bench marks are not only described in the notes, but are themselves marked by paint, chisel marks, or drill-holes.

251. LEVELING FOR PROFILE. — Profile leveling is for the purpose of determining the changes in elevation of the surface of the ground along some definite line like the center line of a highway. The line is first " stationed," i.e., marked at every hundred feet or such other interval as is desired. The level is set up and a backsight taken on a bench mark to determine the height of the instrument. Foresights are then read on as many full station points on the line as can be taken conveniently from the position of the instrument. Intermediate sights are taken at any points where there are marked changes of slope, and the plus stations of these intermediate points are recorded with the rod-readings. It will be remembered that the terms foresight and backsight do not refer to the **forward** and **backward** direction. **A backsight is a reading taken on a point of known elevation for the purpose of obtaining the height of the instrument. A foresight is a reading taken on a new point to determine its elevation.** Backsights are frequently called *plus sights* $(+ S)$ because they are added to an elevation to obtain the H.I., and foresights are called *minus sights* $(- S)$ because they are subtracted from the H.I. to obtain elevation. When it is necessary to move the level to a new position in order to take readings on stations ahead, a turning point is selected and its elevation is determined. The level is then taken forward and the new height of instrument determined by taking a backsight on the turning point. This general process is continued until the end of the line is reached.

A line of levels should be checked by connecting with some

reliable bench mark if possible. If there are any bench marks along the line of levels they should be used as turning points if convenient, or at least check readings should be taken on them in order to detect mistakes. When reading on such points it is evident that the reading taken on the bench mark is really a fore-

(Left-Hand Page)　　　　　　　　　　(Right-Hand Page)

Sta.	+S	H.I.	−S	Elev.	B.M.& T.P. Elev.	Description
						Profile of Meadow Park Road. Sept.16,1940 {Rowe Harkins 兀 Jacobs
B.M₃	12.23	34.98			22.748	d.h. in wall near Sta.0
0			9.8	25.2		
1			6.6	28.4		
2			3.0	32.0		
T.P₁	11.18	44.73	1.43		33.55	Stump
3			6.1	38.6		
+65			2.7	42.0		
4			3.7	41.0		
+20.7			5.2	39.5		
5			6.7	38.0		
6			11.2	33.5		
T.P₂	3.48	42.59	5.62		39.11	Nail in stump 80'W. Sta. 6+80.
7			10.2	32.4		
8			8.6	34.0		
9			7.6	35.0		
+62.4			4.0	38.6		
10			2.4	40.2		
+43			1.1	41.5		
11			2.6	40.0		
12			8.0	34.6		
T.P₃	0.42	31.89	11.12		31.47	Boulder
13			2.8	29.1		
14			8.7	23.2		
+23.8			11.2	20.7		
B.M₄	0.63	27.79	4.73		27.16	Elev. = 27.14 (Book 12, p 26) Highest point large isolated boulder 200'E. Sta 16.
15			6.8	21.0		
16			7.2	20.6		
17			8.1	19.7		
18			9.0	18.8		
+54			9.2	18.6		

Fig. 103. Profile Level Notes.

sight since its elevation is being found anew from the height of instrument. Readings on bench marks and turning points should be taken to thousandths or to hundredths of a foot, according to the accuracy desired. If the elevations of the profile are desired to the nearest hundredth of a foot, as, for example, on a railroad track, the turning points should be taken to thousandths of a foot. Elevations on the surface of the ground will not usually be needed closer than to tenths, so the T.Ps. are

taken only to hundredths. In calculating the elevations the results **should not be carried to more decimal places than the rod-
readings themselves,** otherwise the results will appear to be more
precisely determined than they really are.

252. Profile notes are kept as shown in Fig. 103. In these
notes also the computation of the heights of instrument and of
the elevations of turning points may be checked by means of the

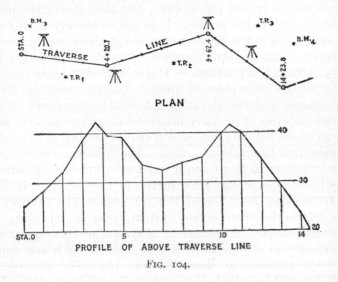

PLAN

PROFILE OF ABOVE TRAVERSE LINE

FIG. 104.

sums of the foresights and backsights, provided that only the
sights on turning points and the initial and final benches are
included. If it seems desirable the computation of the elevations
of stations may be checked by means of differences in foresights.
The difference between the elevations of any two points that
are obtained at the same set-up of the instrument is equal to
the difference between the foresights taken on these points. In
these notes the elevations of B.Ms. and T.Ps. are put in a different column from the surface elevations simply for the sake of
clearness, but many prefer to put all the elevations in the same
column. Another arrangement of columns which, if adopted, will
be found convenient when plotting the notes, is to place the
station column immediately to the right of the elevation column.

If two foresight ($-$) columns are carrried, one for T.Ps. and one for surface points, the verification of the B.M. elevations is more easily made.

Fig. 104 represents a rough plan and profile of the line of levels shown by the notes in Fig. 103. Angle points in the transit line are shown in the plan, but they do not appear in the profile of the line. It will be noticed that the T.Ps. and B.Ms. are not on the transit line in plan, and that they consequently do not appear on the profile. It is not customary to introduce any sketches into the profile notes except those used in describing bench marks or turning points. (See Art. 498, p. 573.)

253. CROSS-SECTIONING. — If it is desired to know the shape of the surface of a piece of ground, the area may be divided into squares and the elevation taken at each corner of these squares and also at as many intermediate points as seem necessary to determine the changes of slope. These surface elevations are measured to tenths of a foot. The squares, which may be anywhere from 10 ft. to 100 ft. on a side, are laid out with the transit and tape, stakes being driven at the corners. It is well to choose some long line of the traverse as the primary line from which the cross-section system is to be laid out. The points are usually designated by a system of rectangular coördinates, one set of parallel lines being marked by letters and the other by numbers, as shown in Fig. 105. For example, the point p would be called $(C, 7)$; the point s $(D, 5)$; the point r, which may be a hollow or a knoll which does not happen to fall on the grid lines, would be designated as $(B + 80, 4 + 35)$. The notes are kept as in profile leveling except as to designation of points. (See Art. 331, p. 399.)

254. Use of the Tape Rod in Cross-Section Work. — In this work, where there are many elevations to be calculated, it will save much time to use a tape rod (Art. 106, p. 85), which is so arranged that little figuring is required. In this rod the numbers increased from the top toward the bottom, the opposite way from ordinary rods. The level is set up at a convenient point and the rod held on a bench mark. The tape, or band, on the rod is then moved up or down as directed by the levelman until he reads the feet, tenths, and hundredths which are the same as those of the elevation of the bench mark, e.g., if the elevation of the B.M. is 195.62, the tape will be moved until he reads 5.62. The tape is then clamped firmly to the rod. If the rod is then held on a point 1.61 ft. lower than the bench, the rod-reading will be 4.01, since with this rod the readings decrease as the rod is lowered. The elevation of that point is therefore 194.01 ft. or, sufficiently precise for topographic work, 194.0 ft. In this way the elevations are read directly on the rod to feet and decimals of feet, the tens and hundreds of feet being supplied mentally. Obviously the only notes kept are the columns of stations and elevations.

(LEFT-HAND PAGE)   (RIGHT-HAND PAGE)

Cross-Sections for Grading the A.M.Cole Estate, Westfield.					March 10, 1936	Hatch Allen ⚲ Rolfe
Sta.	+S.	H.I.	−S	Elev.		
B.M.	3.02	124.92		121.90	100 f. Squares.	
A 4			1.2	123.7		
A 5			1.7	123.2		
A 6			2.4	122.5		
B 6			2.9	122.0		
B.5+40			2.8	122.1		
B 5			2.0	122.9		
B 4			1.8	123.1		
B+60,4			1.8	123.1		
C 4			3.0	121.9		
B+80, 4+35			0.8	124.1		
C 5			5.0	119.9		
C 6			7.2	117.7		
D 6			8.9	116.0		

FIG. 105. CROSS-SECTION LEVEL NOTES.

255. CROSS-SECTIONING FOR EARTHWORK. — Whenever it is desired to ascertain the quantity of earthwork in an excavation or an embankment, it is necessary to take levels to determine the vertical dimensions, and to obtain the horizontal dimensions by means of the transit and tape. The three general cases where the quantity of earthwork is to be estimated by the engineer are: (1) an excavation or embankment having a known base and side slopes as in the construction of a railroad or a highway (2) an irregular excavation from a bank of earth called a *borrow-pit* (3) a trench excavation such as is used for sewer construction.

256. Road Cross-Sections. — Cross-sections for estimating the earthwork in roads, dams or canals are usually taken at full station points (sometimes oftener) and at right angles to the center line of the construction project.* By this method a section of the general shape shown in Figs. 106 and 107 is obtained. These cross-sections are taken in the field before the construction begins so that a proper record of the surface heights can be obtained before the ground is disturbed.

From the plan of the proposed road its alignment is staked out and a profile is taken along the center line; this profile is subsequently plotted (Art. 251, p. 299). On this profile is drawn the *grade line* which corresponds to the finished surface of the road. Roads are usually first finished to *subgrade*, which is below the

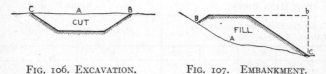

FIG. 106. EXCAVATION.   FIG. 107. EMBANKMENT.

completed surface by an amount equal, in a highway, to the thickness of the pavement, or in a railroad to the thickness of ballast, ties and rails. The width of the base of the road and the inclination of the side slopes are known. For ordinary gravel the slope is usually $1\frac{1}{2}$ ft. horizontal to 1 ft. vertical, called " a slope of $1\frac{1}{2}$ to 1 " or, " a slope of 1 on $1\frac{1}{2}$."

For construction work the engineer sets grade stakes at every full station or oftener on the center line and at both sides where the finished slope intersects the surface of the ground, e.g., at points A, B and C on Figs. 106 and 107. All of these stakes are marked, giving the amount of " cut " or " fill " to be made at these points. The cut or fill marked on the stakes at B and C is the vertical distance from the base of the road to the surface of the ground at these points, e.g., the distance bC.

These cuts and fills are determined in the field by the following method. The level is set up and the height of instrument obtained from some convenient bench mark. Then, the elevation of the subgrade being known (from the profile prepared

* For a more complete treatment of this subject see "Railroad Curves and Earthwork," by Professor C. F. Allen, published by McGraw-Hill Book Company, New York.

in the office), the difference between the height of instrument and the elevation of the finished subgrade gives what is called the *rod-reading for grade*, i.e., the rod-reading which would be obtained if the foot of the rod could be held on the finished subgrade of the road. Then the rod is held on the surface of the ground at the center stake and a reading is taken (to the nearest tenth of a foot), and the difference between the rod-reading for grade and the rod-reading on the surface will give the cut or fill at that point, and this is marked on the center grade stake thus, $C_{5.2}$ if a cut, or $F_{4.7}$ if a fill.

There is one case, in fill only, when the rod-reading for grade must be added to the surface rod-reading to give the depth of fill. This occurs when the finished embankment is higher than the Height of Instrument (H.I.)

257. Setting Slope Stakes.— The points where the side slopes intersect the surface of the ground are found by trial as follows. Hold the rod at a point where it is estimated that the side slope will cut the surface, and take a rod-reading. The difference between this rod-reading and the rod-reading for grade will give the cut or fill at this point; from this the distance out from the center of the section to the point on the side slope having this cut can be computed. This distance out equals ($\frac{1}{2}$ *base* + *cut* × *slope*). Then the distance is measured from the center stake to the rod, and if the measured distance equals the computed distance the rod was held at the right place and the stake should be driven and marked with the cut or fill at that point (distance bC, Fig. 107). If the measured distance does not agree with the calculated distance a second trial must be made by holding the rod at another point and repeating the operation. The difference between the measured and calculated distances is an aid in judging where the rod should be held at the second trial. After a little practice it will be possible to set the slope stake at the second or third trial.

258. Earthwork Notes for Road Cross-Sections. — The notes for this work will contain the cut or fill at the center, the cut or fill at either side, and the corresponding distances out. A cut is usually written in the notes as a plus (+) height and a fill as a minus (−) height; but the stakes are marked C or F

rather than + or −. If the surface is irregular levels are taken at intermediate points and are recorded as shown opposite station 11 + 50, and station 12 in the notes, Fig. 108. Where the surface of the ground is parallel to the base of the road, as in station 10, the section is called a *Level Section*. Where the surface of the ground is not parallel to the base and where three cuts or fills only are recorded, as at station 11, the section is called a *Three-Level Section*. If, besides the three readings which are

Sta.	Surface Elev.	Grade Elev.	Cross-Sections.–Base 40.'– Slope 1½ to 1				
12	99.5	96.50	$\frac{29.0}{+6.0}$	$\frac{12.0}{+4.5}$	+3.0	$\frac{15.0}{+4.0}$	$\frac{22.4}{+1.6}$
+50	98.7	96.25	$\frac{27.2}{+4.8}$	$\frac{20.0}{+4.0}$	+2.4	$\frac{20.0}{+3.0}$	$\frac{24.8}{+3.2}$
11	97.6	96.00	$\frac{26.0}{+4.0}$		+1.6		$\frac{25.4}{+3.6}$
10	97.5	95.50	$\frac{23.0}{+2.0}$		+2.0		$\frac{23.0}{+2.0}$

Cross-Section for Jamestown Road
Aug. 17. 1936

Hatch
Wood
Appleton

FIG. 108.   CROSS-SECTION NOTES FOR A ROAD.

taken for a three-level section, two more intermediate readings are taken, one directly over each end of the base, as at station 11 + 50, the section is called a *Five-Level Section*. If intermediate readings (one or more of them) are taken anywhere except over the ends of the base, as in station 12, the section is called an *Irregular Section*. For methods of computing the amount of earthwork see Chapter XIII.

It will be noticed that in the column of the notes headed " Cross-Sections " the distances out appear above and the corresponding cuts below the lines. Besides this set of notes there is kept also a simple set of level notes similar to Fig. 101, p. 296, from which the height of instrument is determined. This is conveniently kept in another part of the note-book, often at the back of the book.

When a highway or railroad runs along the side slope of a hill, there often is little or no cut or fill at the center line whereas there may be considerable out at the side slope stake. The cross-section may then have a slope like those in Fig. 108a (a) being the case of no cut or fill at the center stake and (b) the case of a small fill at the center. Again special sections occur when passing out of a cut into a fill. The excavation gradually becomes less and finally ends on the up-hill side of the cross-section, but the

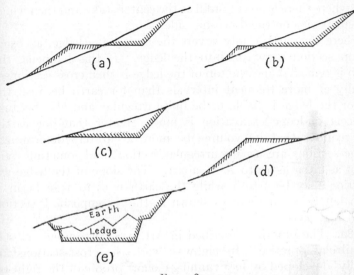

FIG. 108a.

embankment has begun on the down-hill side before the cut has run out on the up-hill side. The first section in passing from cut to fill is usually taken where the cut ends on the down-hill side; this is at the station where the rod-reading for grade is the same as the rod-reading on the surface when the rod is held on the down-hill side line of the base, i.e., half the width of the cut base out from the center line. Such a section is shown in (c) Fig. 108a. The next cross-section is taken where the rod-reading for grade is the same as the surface rod-reading on the center line, as in (a) Fig. 108a. The third and last cross-section is taken

where the rod-reading for grade is the same as the rod-reading or
the surface when the rod is held on the up-hill side line of the base
i.e., half the width of the fill base out from the center stake, as
(d) in Fig. 108a. At (c) the cut ends on the down-hill side,
at (a) there is cut on the up-hill and fill on the down-hill side
at (d) the fill has just begun out on the up-hill side and from there
on the sections will all be fill sections until the line passes again
into a cut, when the corresponding three sections will be taken
as explained above, first where the fill ends on the up-hill side,
next where there is no cut or fill at the center stake and then where
the cut begins on the down-hill side.

Where the earth thinly covers the underlying ledge, an excavation section may run into the ledge. If this happens, the
earth is removed and the top of the ledge is then cross-sectioned,
usually at more frequent intervals than for earth because the
top of the ledge is liable to be quite irregular and also because
the cost of ledge excavation is much greater than for earth,
this requires that its volume be more accurately determined.
Ledge sections are usually irregular sections and sometimes are
taken as often as 10 to 20 ft. apart. The slope of the ledge excavation may be $\frac{1}{2}$ to 1 while the earth is $1\frac{1}{2}$ to 1; a berm is
often left between them as shown in the " composite " section
in (e) Fig. 108a.

258a. The practice described in Art. 258 corresponds closely
to railroad practice. In highway work the cross-sections are
usually developed by first running a short profile of the right-of
way at right angles to the line at each full station. No attempt
is made in the first survey to determine the embankment o
excavation slope intersections in the field. The width of base
and slope of the cross-sections are frequently changed. The
standard section is seldom a simple level or three-level section
even for grading purposes. The practice is to plot the ground
sections in the office station by station, and to superimpose the
section adopted for that particular place upon these ground
sections. As the line of the highway is shifted sidewise the sec
tions will be correspondingly shifted. When the alignment is
determined finally on the plan, and the construction work is
about to start, then the surveyor goes back into the field and sets

the slope stakes according to the approved plans. There are four usual forms for keeping the field notes in taking cross profiles for cross-section purposes as follows.

SAMPLE FORMS OF CROSS-SECTION NOTES

Left			L		Right	

(a) Numerator is distance "out." Denominator is actual ground elevation.

$\dfrac{33}{114.8}$	$\dfrac{20}{113.7}$	$\dfrac{10}{119.4}$	117.2	$\dfrac{17}{121.3}$	$\dfrac{25}{120.0}$	$\dfrac{33}{124.6}$

(b) Numerator is distance "out." Denominator is rod-reading on ground.
Height of Instrument (H.I.) = 125.2

$\dfrac{33}{10.4}$	$\dfrac{20}{11.5}$	$\dfrac{10}{5.8}$	8.0	$\dfrac{17}{3.9}$	$\dfrac{25}{5.2}$	$\dfrac{33}{0.6}$

(c) Combination of (a) and (b). "Rod-readings" being recorded in field, and "elevations" computed either in field or in office.

$\dfrac{33}{10.4}$	$\dfrac{20}{11.5}$	$\dfrac{10}{5.8}$	8.0	$\dfrac{17}{3.9}$	$\dfrac{25}{5.2}$	$\dfrac{33}{0.6}$
(114.8)	(113.7)	(119 4)	(117.2)	(121.3)	(120.0)	(124.6)

(d) Elevations referred to elevation of ground at center line as zero. Points above this are (+); points below are (−).

$\dfrac{33}{-2.4}$	$\dfrac{20}{-3.5}$	$\dfrac{10}{+2.2}$	0.0	$\dfrac{17}{+4.1}$	$\dfrac{25}{+2.8}$	$\dfrac{33}{+7.4}$

Methods (a), (b) and (c) are applicable where engineer's level, or occasionally Locke (hand) level, is used. Method (d) is applicable where a "level board" is used. A "level board" is a long straight board about 10 ft. long with a spirit level set in it, similar to a carpenter's level. When the ground slopes away from the center stake, one end of the board is placed on the ground at the center stake and the board held in a level position. Then distances from the board to the ground are measured with the rod and distances out from the center stake to the rod are read from a scale marked on the board. If the ground is higher than the center stake, then the board is supported on the ground and leveled, and rod-readings and distances out measured as before. In the first case the points determined on the cross-section are referred to the elevation of the center stake; in the second case they are referred to the elevation of the ground on which the "level board" rests and must be corrected so that they refer to the center stake.

Notes represent the "lay of the ground" best when they are recorded up the page. If, however, cross-section notes are kept on the same pages as the "level notes" of B.S., H.I. and F.S., the notes usually read down the page. In any case points on the left of the center line must be recorded on the left-hand side of the page in the notebook.

259. Cross-Sections for Borrow-Pits. — The ground is first staked out in squares or rectangles and the elevation at each corner and at every change in slope is determined as explained in Art. 253, p. 302. The base-line from which the system is laid out should be outside the area to be excavated so that the marks will not be obliterated. The bench mark should also be outside this area. Then the work of excavating is carried on, and when it is desired to determine the amount that has been excavated, the same system of cross-sections is again run out and the new elevations at the corners and at the necessary intermediate points are determined. In borrow-pits, there is usually a steep face of bank left after the material has been removed. Some of the lines of the grid that was laid out before excavation was started will, when reproduced after the pit excavation has been completed, cross the face of the steep slope. It is necessary, therefore, to take a rod-reading at every point where the foot of slope or top of slope crosses a grid line and to record these, as well as readings at all grid corners, in the notes. Fig. 173, p. 489, illustrates a borrow-pit of this sort.

The notes are kept as shown in Fig. 105, p. 303. For methods of computing the earthwork in borrow-pits see Art. 408, p. 489.

260. Cross-Sections for Trench Excavation. — The surface elevations are determined by making a profile of the center line. The grade of the bottom of the trench is obtained either from the plan or by direct leveling. The width of the trench is measured wherever it changes and the stations of these places noted.

261. LEVELING TO ESTABLISH A GRADE LINE. — The level may be used for setting points at desired elevations as, for example, in establishing the grade line of street or sewer not yet constructed. To set any point at a desired elevation, set up the level and take a backsight on a bench mark, thus determining the height of instrument. Subtract the desired elevation from the height of instrument and the result is the rod-reading for grade. Raise or lower the rod until the horizontal cross-hair indicates this reading. The foot of the rod is then at grade. This is usually set for construction work to hundredths of a foot; for some purposes tenths of a foot will be sufficiently exact. If a target rod is used the target is set at the proper reading, and the bottom of the rod is at grade when the cross-hair bisects the target. A mark is then made at the bottom of the rod on a stake or a batter board. If the grade line such as for a sewer comes beneath the surface of the ground and cannot be reached, a point may be set on a stake or on a batter board where the point is at a convenient whole number of feet above grade and the depth marked; or it may be set a whole number of feet below if the grade line comes far above the surface. Setting grade stakes for a curbstone or for resurfacing a street are treated in Art. 297–9, pp. 348–50.

262. " Shooting in " a Grade Line. — To save time and to diminish the liability of mistakes, grades are often set by a method known as " shooting in " the grade. First set a mark at the grade elevation at each end of the straight grade line. The instrument (usually a transit with a telescope level) is set up 6 or 8 inches to one side of the first point, and the distance from that mark to the axis of the telescope is measured with the tape or rod.* Then the rod, which is set at this reading, is carried to the last point on the straight grade line, and, while it is held vertical on the grade mark at that place, the instrument man inclines the telescope until the horizontal cross-hair is on the target, clamping the instrument in this position. If a level is used the horizontal cross-hair is set on the target by means of the leveling screws; but if the transit is used the cross-hair is set by means of the clamp and tangent screw of the vertical motion. The inclined line of sight is then parallel to the grade line. All intermediate points on the grade line are set by raising or lowering the rod until the target coincides with the horizontal cross-hair.

263. To Establish a Datum Plane by Means of Tidal Observations. — Whenever it is necessary to establish a datum from tidal observations it may be determined as follows. Set up a vertical staff, graduated to feet and tenths, in such a manner that both the high and low water can be read for all ranges likely to occur. Read the positions of high and low water for each day

---

* Where the grade is flat some surveyors prefer to set the instrument just behind the point instead of to one side of it.

for as long a period as practicable. The mean value obtained from an **equal** number of high and low water observations will give the approximate value of mean sea-level.

The datum obtained in this manner is also called the *half-tide level* and must be carefully distinguished from *mean sea-level*. The former is the plane exactly midway between the planes of *mean high water* and *mean low water*. Mean sea-level is a datum plane so placed that the area between this plane and the curve of high waters is exactly equal to the area between this same datum plane and the curve of low waters. This plane is the datum used by the U. S. Coast and Geodetic Survey, Geological Survey, U. S. Engineers and other governmental organizations when establishing control levels. For a single lunar month, the two data may differ by as much as one foot. If the observations extend over just one lunar month the result will be fairly good, whereas in less than one month a close result cannot be obtained; to determine this accurately will require observations extending over a year or more.

Other common datum planes based upon the tides are *mean high water*, *mean low water*, *lower low water*, and *higher high water* (terms used by U. S. Coast and Geodetic Survey). These data are of great engineering importance in interpreting charts and in the design of waterfront developments. For example, if the depths on nautical charts are referred to extreme low water, there is no danger that mariners will run aground through misinterpretation; whereas the extreme high water elevations are essential in the selection of height for piers and wharves.

The place chosen for the gauge should be near the open sea where local conditions will not influence the tide. It should be sheltered against heavy seas.

At the beginning of the series of observations the zero of the staff and some permanent bench mark should be connected by a line of levels. The elevation of some point close to the gauge, such as a spike driven in a pile to which the gauge is fastened, should be determined at the same time, so that the gauge can be readily replaced if it should become dislodged. Such a point is called a *Reference Point*, or R.P. These should be tested occasionally to see if the staff has moved.

After the reading of the staff for mean sea-level is found the elevation of the bench mark can be computed.

264. The Staff Gauge. — This is a form of gauge (Fig. 109) which can be easily constructed, and which is sufficient where only a short series of observations is to be made. If made in sections not over 3 ft. long, as described below, it can be packed in a small box for transportation. Each section consists of two strips of wood about $1\frac{1}{2}$ inches square, and 3 ft. long, fastened together at the ends by strips of brass, leaving a space between them of about 1 inch. In this space is placed a glass tube of about $\frac{3}{4}$ inch diameter and held in place by brass hooks. On one side of the tube a red stripe is blown into the glass. When the gauge is set up for observations the sections are screwed to a long vertical piece of joist. The ends of the tube are nearly closed by corks, into which small glass tubes of approximately 1 mm. (inside) diameter have been inserted. When the water rises in the main tube, the red stripe appears to be much wider than it really is on account of the refraction of light by the water. Above the water surface the stripe appears its true width. By observing the position of the wide stripe the height of the water surface can be read within a hundredth of a foot. The heights are read on a scale of feet and tenths painted on the wooden strips. If the size of the small glass tube is properly chosen, the fluctuations of the water surface outside will not disturb the water in the tube, so that the reading is a fair average of the water surface. A gauge of this sort may be read to hundredths from a distant point by means of a transit telescope or a field glass.

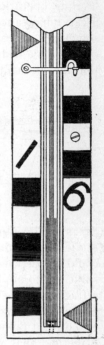

FIG. 109.
STAFF GAUGE.

When a long series of observations is to be made, particularly if it is important to obtain a record of every tide, an automatic tide gauge should be used. A description of such a gauge may be found in an article entitled " Instructions for Tide Observations," by G. T. Rude, in Special Publication No. 139 of the U. S. Coast and Geodetic Survey. (See also Volume II, Art. 338.)

265. LEVELING ACROSS A RIVER. — While the effect of curvature and refraction (Art. 118, p. 93) is usually negligible in leveling operations, it may in certain special cases become of great importance to eliminate this error. For example, it is sometimes necessary to carry a line of levels across a river of considerable width, say, half a mile. In this distance the correction for curvature and refraction amounts to about 0.143 ft. un-

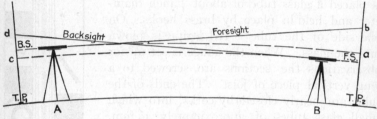

FIG. 110. LEVELING ACROSS A RIVER.

der normal conditions, which in a line of bench levels is too large a quantity to neglect. If the correction derived from formulas could be depended upon under all circumstances it would be sufficient to apply it to the rod-reading; but the amount of the refraction correction is variable because of atmospheric changes.

If it is desired to obtain the difference in elevation between two distant points with great accuracy it will be necessary to use a method that will **eliminate** the effects of curvature and refraction no matter what their actual amount may be. In Fig. 110 suppose a backsight were taken on T.P.$_1$ with the instrument at A and then a foresight taken on T.P.$_2$ The elevation of T.P.$_2$ as computed from T.P.$_1$ will be too low by the amount ab, since the foresight on T.P.$_2$ is too great by this amount. If the difference in elevation is determined by the instrument at B the backsight on T.P.$_1$ is too large by the amount cd. Hence the H.I. of the instrument at B is too great, and consequently the elevation of T.P.$_2$ too great by the amount cd. The mean of the two determinations would give the true elevation of T.P.$_2$

if $ab = cd$, but this occurs only when the two sights are taken under the same atmospheric conditions. Therefore it will be seen that the two sights must be taken **simultaneously.** In order to eliminate the errors of adjustment* in the instrument it is necessary to use the same instrument at both ends of the line. To accomplish both of these results at once it is necessary to take simultaneous readings with two instruments and then to repeat the operation with the instruments interchanged. The magnifying powers of the two telescopes and the sensitiveness of the two spirit levels should be about equal in order to give the best results. It will be noticed that this process is similar to that of the peg adjustment (Art. 128, p. 99).

265a. Water Levels. — Lines of levels often can be checked satisfactorily by means of a water surface if the line is close to a lake or a pond so that this forms a connecting link between any two benches. The difference between the elevation of a bench mark and the elevation of the water should be determined carefully for the two bench marks selected. Then the water surface elevation is assumed to be the same in both places, and thus furnishes a connecting link between the two benches. The water levels should be taken when there is little or no wind blowing. Or, if this cannot be done, the effect of waves can be partly eliminated by constructing stilling boxes, which admit water slowly through small holes, but check the wave action almost entirely.

265b. Distributing the Error in a Level Circuit. — Whenever a line of levels is closed upon itself or upon any bench of known elevation some error of closure is sure to be found. In the first instance the error noted is the algebraic sum of the various errors entering into the circuit. When closing on the work of another party the error is composed of the errors of both parties.

A complete discussion of the methods of adjusting level circuits would take us beyond the scope of this book, but a few simple cases will be illustrated. It is always satisfactory to distribute such errors and to know that the elevations are consistent among themselves; this at least avoids having several values for

---

* Errors due to non-adjustment are of unusual importance because the sight is much longer than that used in adjusting the instrument.

the same bench mark and the uncertainty of not knowing which one to use.

If the leveling is continuously performed as described in Art. 246, p. 295, then the remaining errors of leveling are chiefly of the class that tend to balance each other, and hence do not increase directly with the distance run, but only as the square root of this distance. The distance itself is not really the measure of the number of set-ups, but it is sufficiently close to it for the purpose of distributing a small error over long lines.

If a line is run in duplicate, forward and back, the difference in elevation is obviously the mean of the two results.

If two bench marks are joined by three routes, all of different lengths, say, 2 miles, 3 miles, and 4 miles, respectively, the best determination should be that from the two-mile line, other things being equal; and the least accurate should be that from the four-mile line. The result obtained from the two-mile line should therefore have the greatest weight in computing the mean, that of the three-mile line should have the next, and the four-mile line should have the least weight. The assignment of weights is made most conveniently by dividing some number (say 12 in this example) by each of the distances in succession. The results are the weights to be used. Dividing 12 by 2, 3, and 4 we obtain the weights 6, 4, and 3. The " weighted mean " is obtained by multiplying each difference in elevation by its weight, adding the results, and dividing by the sum of the weights.

Suppose that three results for a difference in elevation are 41.16 ft., 41.20 ft., and 41.12 ft., then the weighted mean and probable error are computed as follows (see Art. 23b, p. 18 for explanation of this method).

Line	M	(Weight) w	$w \times M$	v	$w \times v$	$w \times v^2$
1	41.16	6	246.96	0.00	0.00	0.0000
2	41.20	4	164.80	−0.04	−0.16	0.0064
3	41.12	3	123.36	+0.04	+0.12	0.0048
		$\Sigma w = 13$	$\Sigma w \times M = 535.12$		$\Sigma w \times v = -0.04$	$\Sigma w \times v^2 = 0.0112$

$$\text{Weighted Mean } M_0 = \frac{\Sigma w \times M}{\Sigma w} = \frac{535.12}{13} = 41.16 \text{ ft.}$$

$$\text{Probable error of weighted mean} = \pm 0.6745 \sqrt{\frac{.0112}{13(2)}} = \pm 0.6745(.02) = \pm 0.01 \text{ ft.}$$

This computation can be shortened by omitting the whole number of feet since these are all the same, or by omitting 40 ft. If we omit 41 ft. the calculation becomes

$$\frac{6 \times 0.16 + 4 \times 0.20 + 3 \times 0.12}{6 + 4 + 3} = 0.163$$

Elev. $= 41 + 0.163 = 41.16$ ft.

Another convenient way to do this is to deal with the correction instead of with the elevation itself. If we take the first elevation as being a close value, to be used as a first approximation, then its preliminary correction is 0.00; that of the second value is $41.20 - 41.16 = +0.04$. That of the third value is $41.12 - 41.16 = -0.04$. If we multiply each correction by the corresponding weight we have the results shown in the following table:

Line	wt.	corr.	product
1	6	0.00	0.00
2	4	+0.04	+0.16
3	3	−0.04	−0.12
	13		13)+0.04
			+0.003

The final value for the elevation is therefore

$$41.16 + 0.003 = 41.16, \text{ as before.}$$

When there are intermediate bench marks along these routes their adjusted elevations are usually computed by proportioning the error directly as the distance. That is, if a point is half-way from the start to the second bench, it receives half the error.

When the circuits are entangled the method becomes more complicated. The exact solution of this problem is one that must be made by the method of least squares. An approximate method used by the U. S. Geological Survey is given in the Appendix to Vol. II.

For general treatment for errors in measurements see Art. 23–23c, pp. 16–18d.

PROBLEMS

1. Compute the following set of level notes and show check.

Sta.	+ S	H. I.	− S	Elev.
B. M._1	4.702			16.427
B. M._2	11.846		6.727	
T. P._1	7.276		9.689	
B. M._3	8.760		4.726	
T. P._2	0.687		11.000	
B. M._4			8.496	

2. Compute the following set of level notes and show check.

Sta.	B. S.	H. I.	F. S.	Elev.
B. M._12	6.427			62.473
20			6.2	
21			7.4	
+ 42			5.2	
22			4.7	
T. P._27	4.724		9.976	
23			11.2	
+ 63			10.4	
B. M._22	0.409		7.482	
24			11.2	

3. Compute the following set of level notes and show check.

Sta.	+ S	H. I.	− S	Elev.
B. M._24	6.214			84.238
T. P._1 L.	3.515		9.280	
T. P._1 H.	2.152		7.919	
T. P._2 L.	2.971		8.263	
B. M._25 H.	2.338		7.629	
T. P._3 L.	4.278		7.529	
T. P_3 H.	2.646		5.894	
B. M._26 L.	5.721		6.072	
T. P._4 H.	4.837		5.187	
B. M._27			5.817	

4. Make up a set of cross-section notes for road construction which shall be consistent with the following data: width of road, 50 ft., slopes $1\frac{1}{2}$ to 1; grade elevation of Sta. 0 = 107.20; grade, + 1.4. Show complete notes from Sta. 0 to Sta. 3 inclusive as follows: Sta. 0, a level section; Sta. 1, a three-level section; Sta. 2, a five-level section; Sta. 3, an irregular section.

5. Compute the following set of level notes and show check.

Sta.	+ S	H. I.	− S	Elev.
B. M.₁	8.21			47.19
T. P.	11.01		3.07	
T. P.	9.61		4.19	
0			9.0	
+ 50			8.1	
1			6.0	
+ 50			4.5	
2			1.0	
T. P.	12.00		0.17	
+ 50			11.0	
3			8.8	
B. M.₂			7.91	

6. Compute the following set of level notes and show check.

Sta.	+ S	H. I.	− S	Elev.
B. M.₆	8.21			207.33
0			4.0	
1			8.1	
2			11.2	
+ 50			11.9	
T. P.	4.01		12.19	
3			6.9	
+ 10.90			1.0	
4			2.6	
5			2.9	
B. M.			5.27	

7. Compute the following set of level notes and show check.

Sta.	+ S	H. I.	− S	Elev.
B. M.₂₁	0.27			1164.20
T. P.	1.16		12.41	
T. P.	1.01		10.91	
T. P.	2.16		7.99	
T. P.	0.79		11.32	
B. M.₂₂	4.71		4.90	
T. P.	3.02		8.00	
T. P.	0.64		9.69	
T. P.	2.26		11.49	
B. M.₂₃			10.20	

8. The elevation of B.M.$_1$ is 20.96 ft. By route 1, B.M.$_A$ is 60.17 above B.M.$_1$. B.M.$_2$ is 101.10 above B.M.$_A$. By route 2, B.M.$_2$ is 161.40 above B.M.$_1$. By route 3, B.M.$_2$ is 161.10 above B.M.$_1$. Route 1 is 6 miles long and B.M.$_A$ is 3 miles from B.M.$_1$. Route 2 is 4 miles long. Route 3 is 8 miles long. Compute the ajusted elevation of B.M.$_2$ and of B.M.$_A$. Compute the probable error in difference in elevation between B.M.$_1$ and B.M.$_2$.

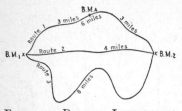

FIG. 110a. DIAGRAM ILLUSTRATING PROBLEM 8.

9. By route 1 (3 miles long) point B is 111.20 ft. higher than point A. By route 2 (4 miles long) B is 110.97 ft. above A. By route 3 (6 miles long) B is 111.26 ft. above A. Compute the adjusted elevation of B above A. Compute the probable error in difference in elevation between A and B.

10. The accepted elevation of B.M. 572 is 1928.73 feet. A fifteen-mile level circuit was run, closing back on B.M. 572 with an elevation, as determined from the notes, of 1928.58 feet. The observed elevations of other bench marks which were established during the run, and their approximate distances from the initial bench, are given below. Adjust the elevations of the intermediate bench marks.

Bench Mark	Dist. from B.M. 572 (Miles)	Observed Elevation
B.M. 573	1.2	1983.21
B.M. 574	2.5	2091.76
B.M. 575	3.8	2243.19
B.M. 576	5.3	2339.70
B.M. 577	7.1	2302.95
B.M. 578	9.4	2441.62
B.M. 579	11.3	2117.37
B.M. 580	13.8	2003.49

11. Level notes taken in a tunnel read as follows.

Sta.	B.S.	H.I.	F.S.	Elev	
B.M. 16	4.57			162.72	Top of bolt in floor of shaft 16th level
Sta. 161	−3.24		−2.35		In Roof of Tunnel
Sta. 162	−2.19		−3.62		" " " "
Sta. 163	4.07		3.33		" Floor " "
Sta. 164	5.12		4.01		" " " "
Sta. 165	−0.85		−1.12		" Roof " "
Sta. 166			5.16		" Floor " "

In the above set of level notes compute the elevations of stations 161 to 166 inclusive.

Note: Sights marked − (minus) indicate that the point on which the rod was held is above the H.I. The rod-reading on these points was obtained by inverting the rod.

CHAPTER X

CITY SURVEYING*

LINES AND GRADES FOR CONSTRUCTION — SURVEY OF CITY LOTS, BUILDINGS AND PARTY WALLS

266. INSTRUMENTS USED. — Owing to the value of city land a relatively high precision is demanded in city surveys. Furthermore, much of the work of a city engineering department or of the city surveyor in private practice is the establishing of lines and grades for construction work. These classes of surveying work require the use of transits, levels, tapes and rods capable of yielding a high degree of precision. For less exact work, such as the location of contours and physical objects, a plane-table outfit may be economically employed; it should be used much more than it is at present. Steel tapes graduated to hundredths of a foot are required for most work; steel or metallic tapes reading to tenths of a foot are employed in taking measurements used for estimates of construction. For precise measurements invar tapes are coming into more common use.

267. Tapes and Tape Measurements. — The tape most commonly employed is the light 100-ft. steel ribbon, graduated to hundredths of a foot, described in Art. 7, p. 2. Ordinary measurements are taken in the usual manner, the pull and the horizontal position of the tape being judged by the men making the measurements. But frequently it is necessary to obtain results with a greater degree of precision than is afforded by this method. For example, in measuring the base-line for triangulation work or in the survey of the more valuable portions of large cities, there is demand for an exactness of measurements which can be obtained only by using the utmost care and sometimes by using special methods. Care must be taken to insure the proper pull on the **supported** tape so as to make it of standard length when the measurement is made; either to give the proper

---

* See " Technical Procedure for City Surveys," Am. Soc. C. E., Jan. 15, 1934, p. 65.

pull to the **suspended** tape so as to stretch it until its end marks are the standard distance apart, or else to determine the shortening due to sag and then to correct the recorded distances; and also to adopt some means by which the temperature of the tape may be measured and a correction for its effect applied to the measured distances. (Arts. 19–22, pp. 13–16.)

Most tapes are of standard length at 68° F. (20° C.) under a tension of 10 lbs. and **supported** throughout their length, but since tapes vary in cross-section and material some manufacturers etch on the tape itself the number of pounds pull at which that particular tape is of standard length. If the temperature of an ordinary 100-ft. tape happens to be, say, 30° F. it is shorter by about 0.02 ft. than it is at 68° F. and if, beginning at 10 lbs., increasingly greater pull is exerted the tape will be stretched; thus, within certain limits, temperature effects can be eliminated in the field, provided the surveyor knows the amount of extra pull it is necessary to exert on that particular tape for any given drop in temperature below 68° F. A table giving the length under different tensions can be prepared for any tape, as suggested in Art. 19, p. 13. This method will not apply for any considerable **increase** in temperature, for the pull might have to be slackened so much as to make the measurements unreliable. For this reason, and to simplify the matter of temperature correction when a full tape-length is used, some tapes are provided with a " temperature scale " at the 100-ft. end, where the tape is marked in degrees (not feet); the temperature mark represents a point exactly 100 ft. from the zero end of the supported tape when it is given a pull equal to that which was given to produce the standard length of 100 ft. at 68° F.

Sag tends to shorten the tape; increase of pull, to lengthen it. Hence if the tape is unsupported (except at its ends) it can be lengthened by giving it that amount of additional pull which will stretch it by the same amount the sag has shortened it, as indicated in Art. 22, p. 15. To make this correction simple for a full tape-length some manufacturers etch on the tape the number of pounds of pull necessary to make it of standard length; this holds good only when the temperature is 68° F. and the tape is **supported only at the ends.**

Tapes should be compared frequently with the City Standard of Length (Art. 269, p. 322), for the distance between their end marks and at all intermediate points that may be marked on the Standard. The temperature and the pull should be determined carefully and recorded. From this information all of the field measurements can be reduced to agree with the City Standard and exact and consistent results may thus be obtained.

If there is no City Standard available, then one or more " certified " tapes should be kept in the office for test purposes; they should never be used in the field except for comparison. The service tapes should be compared with these certified tapes, both when new and after being mended. Any good tape may, for a nominal charge, be compared with the U. S. Standard and a certificate furnished by the U. S. Bureau of Standards at Washington. This Bureau will test any tape offered and will return a " report " upon it, but it will not furnish a " certificate " for one that does not conform to certain requirements. If the tape does come within that class, and most tapes do, then the Bureau will place on this tape a number, will test the tape and return it with a certificate that gives the error of the supported tape at 68° F. The Bureau will (for an additional charge) test the tape at any intermediate points along its length as requested. On page 323 is a copy of such a certificate.

When the ground is not level and there is necessity for frequent plumbing it is impossible to obtain precise results unless the plumbing is carefully done by experienced tapemen. Plumbing can sometimes be eliminated by measuring directly on the surface (on a uniform slope) from point to point; the difference in elevation is obtained by leveling, and the horizontal projection of each sloping distance computed, or the inclination of a line parallel to the tape and passing through the axis of the telescope may be measured, as in stadia leveling, and this vertical angle used to reduce the slope measurement to horizontal. A more common method is to measure the inclined distance from the telescope axis of a transit set up at alternate points which are a little less than a tape-length apart, obtain the inclination of the tape by measuring the vertical angle to the adjacent points and then compute the horizontal distances by the method explained in Arts.

12–13, pp. 9–11, and Art. 136, p. 114. When plumbing is necessary, or when a slope distance is measured directly from the telescope axis, the effect of sag is present and allowance must be made for it.

268. Transits and Levels. — The transits usually employed in city work read to 30″ or to 20″. With these instruments angles to the nearest 5″ can be obtained by repeating the angles as explained in Art. 59, p. 55. If much of this precise work is required it will be of advantage to use an instrument reading to 10″. It is well also to have transits equipped with stadia hairs for use on certain classes of surveys.

Much of the city work, such as the staking out of new streets, paving, sewers, or curbs, requires the establishment of both lines and grades. This class of work does not as a rule call for a precision in distances and elevations closer than .01 ft.; the measurements and rod-readings are usually taken to hundredths of a foot. It is not convenient, for the ordinary surveying party of three men, to carry both a transit and a level instrument in addition to the ordinary equipment of sighting-rods, level-rod, stakes, tape, etc., so the engineer's transit, with a level attached to the telescope, is extensively used in setting grades as well as in establishing lines. The degree of precision possible with an engineer's transit is entirely satisfactory for all ordinary leveling.

Where leveling work alone is to be done the ordinary wye or dumpy level instrument is used together with target or self-reading rods. For bench leveling it is customary, in large cities at least, to use a *precise level* or *geodetic level*, an instrument which is similar in principle to the ordinary level but which has a more delicate bubble and a telescope of higher power, and is therefore capable of yielding more accurate results. (See Art. 100, p. 79, and Chap. III, Vol. II.)

269. CITY STANDARD OF LENGTH.* — It is customary in some cities to maintain a standard of length, usually 100 ft. long, established in some convenient place, often near the office of the City Engineer. It sometimes consists of a long steel rod supported on rollers on the side of a wall or building in such a way that the rod can expand or contract freely. The end-points

---

* See footnote at bottom of p. 323.

DEPARTMENT OF COMMERCE

LVJ:HER
II-1

Bureau of Standards

Certificate

Bureau File Reference:
II-I, Test No. Twl 68191

FOR

100-Foot Steel Tape
B. S. No. 3119

Maker's Identification Mark: Lufkin

SUBMITTED BY

Massachusetts Institute of Technology,
Department of Civil & Sanitary Engineering,
Cambridge A. Mass.

This tape has been compared with the standards of the United States. It complies with the specifications for a standard tape and the intervals indicated have the following lengths at 68° Fahrenheit (20° centigrade) under the conditions given below:

Supported on a Horizontal Flat Surface:

Tension	Interval	Length
10 pounds	(0 to 100 feet)	100.005 feet
15 "	(0 to 100 ")	100.011 "
20 "	(0 to 100 ")	100.018 "

Supported at the 0 and 100-foot Points:

Tension	Interval	Length
10 pounds	(0 to 100 feet)	99.976 feet
15 "	(0 to 100 ")	99.997 "
20 "	(0 to 100 ")	100.010 "
16 "	(0 to 100 ")	100.000 "

Note: See note 3(b) on the reverse side of this certificate.

L J BRIGGS

Date of test: October 21, 1932

Lyman J. Briggs, Acting Director

Washington, D. C.,

The comparisons of this tape with the United States Bench Standard were made at a temperature of 82° Fahrenheit and in reducing to 68° Fahrenheit (20° centigrade), the coefficient of expansion of the tape is assumed to be 0.00000645 per degree Fahrenheit (0.0000116 per degree centigrade). 11–8242

TAPE CERTIFICATE
Form **579**
U.S. GOVERNMENT PRINTING OFFICE 1928

* See a paper entitled " The 100-foot Standard of Length of the Boston Water Works at Chestnut Hill Reservoir," by Charles W. Sherman, published in the Jour. Assoc. Eng. Soc., Vol. XVIII, No. 4, April, 1897. See also description of standard presented to City of Chicago by Western Soc. C. E., see Journal of Western Society of Engineers, Sept. 1914; also Eng. News, Vol. 72, p. 748, Oct. 8, 1914.

See also " Constructing 100-ft. Standard for Checking Steel Tapes," by J. E. Earl, City Engineer, Passaic, N. J. — Eng. News-Record, Dec. 22, 1927, p. 1015.

and sometimes the 25-ft., 50-ft. and 75-ft. points are so marked that they can be used conveniently for testing tapes.

A city standard is often established by carefully transferring the length of some other standard, by means of different tapes and under different weather conditions; or it can be established by means of tapes which have been certified by the U. S. Bureau of Standards (Art. 267, p. 319). The City Standard is generally placed where it will not be exposed to the direct rays of the sun, consequently it is usually covered with a wooden box.

When a tape is tested it should be stretched out at full length beside the standard and left there so that it may acquire the same temperature as the standard before the comparison is made; from 15 to 30 minutes will be sufficient.

ESTABLISHING AND STAKING OUT CITY LINES AND GRADES

270. Establishing Street Lines. — It has not been uncommon for the streets in new districts to be accepted by city officials as part of the city's street system without intelligent study of their value or adaptability to the existing street system. Plans of streets presented for adoption should be modified to fit the general scheme of the City Planning Board, if there is one, or to meet the judgment of the City Engineer, before being passed, as he is, or should be, the best qualified official to judge of the merits of such matters.

The plan of proposed streets should show clearly and accurately the mathematical relation of these new street lines to existing monuments on the old streets with which the new ones connect.

When a private way is widened to make it a suitable public way or when it becomes advisable to establish new lines, the correct procedure is to make an accurate plan of the present way and abutting properties including the improvements built upon it. This plan should show clearly the amount of property it is necessary to take from each abutter to accomplish this improvement, marking on the plan the dimensions of every taking to 0.01 ft. and its area to the nearest square foot as well as the existing dimensions and areas of all lots affected. These data not only give the local authorities the necessary information for their deliberations but also show each abutter the exact effect the change will have upon his property. Usually such changes are not adopted until a hearing has been given at which all interested parties may express their views.

When the ordinance is finally passed authorizing the widening and the street lines are thus " established " it is the duty of the City Engineer to mark these new lines promptly by monuments, of the legal department to " settle the damages " with the owners who have been deprived thereby of part of their property, and of the public works department to proceed with the construction work necessary to widen the street.

271. **Establishing Street Grades.** — Not infrequently the street grades will be established at the same time that the lines are established (see Art. 270, p. 324), and the legal department of the city will at that time have to settle grade damages as well as land taking damages. In some cases the courts have held that in widening a very narrow street the damage to the abutters is nil since the improvement increased the value of their remaining property to so great an extent. But when a change in street grades is made it rarely happens that improved properties in which their entrances, doorways, driveways and steps already conform to the existing grade are not damaged somewhat by a change in grade. Because of this fact it is the surveyor's duty, when the street grade is to be changed or " established," to show on his plan all approaches to improved property, elevations on driveways and a few elevations in front yards. On the street profile, he should show, not only the profile of the center line, but also that of the curb lines and property lines, the elevations of basements and first floors and steps of all buildings that are near to the street lines so that the effect of change in street grade may be at once apparent.

A description of the proposed street grade is usually put in written form for acceptance by the proper municipal authorities. When this description has been formally accepted by an order of the City Government the grade is said to have been " established." Such an order may refer to the profile by title or recorded number, or it may be a written description of the grade. The profile of each street should contain one or more cross-sections on which is indicated to what part of the cross-section the established profile refers, i.e., whether the profile grade is the grade of the center of the street, the curb, or the sidewalk at the property line.

Following is a description of an established street grade:

" Beginning at station 146 (Maple St.) at the junction of the center lines of Maple St. and Ocean Ave., at grade* 52.00, the grade line falls 0.50 per 100 for 726 ft. to grade 48.37 — thence rises 0.82 per 100 for 322 ft. to grade 51.01 — thence falls 0.50 per 100 for 122 ft. to grade 50.40 — thence falls by a vertical parabolic curve for 100 ft. as follows:

Sta.	Elev.
157 + 70	50.40
157 + 95	50.18
158 + 20	49.76
158 + 45	49.15
158 + 70	48.35

thence falls 3.60 per 100 for 239 ft. to station 161 + 09 at the junction of the center lines of Maple St. and High St., grade 39.75."

272. THE DATUM PLANE. — In every city there usually exists some established datum plane to which all elevations may be referred. In the older municipalities, it was customary to choose a datum bearing an intimate relation to the topography of the locality; a town on the seaboard chose mean sea level or mean low water (Art. 263, p. 309); inland cities often selected the mean level of some lake or even some arbitrary datum. Because of this multiplicity of data (there are over 40 in the State of Massachusetts), considerable confusion ensued in providing elevations for such state projects as highways which run from city to city. At present, the network of levels established by the U. S. Coast and Geodetic Survey and of the U. S. Geological Survey, the datum for both of which is *mean sea level*, is so comprehensive that there is little excuse for a town not using this

---

* The word *grade* is frequently used to mean the *elevation* of a point. Care should be taken not to confuse the meaning of *grade* with *rate of grade*. The latter is sometimes called *gradient*, a word which has some advantages but is not entirely satisfactory.

uniform and *scientifically* established datum. It is the present practice of both these Federal agencies to establish a permanent bench mark, whenever possible, near the center of the community so that it will serve as a starting point for all the elevations in that town. Information regarding standard bench marks established by these agencies may be obtained by writing the Director of these surveys at Washington, D. C.

273. ESTABLISHING BENCH MARKS. — When the datum has been determined, bench marks are established by the method explained in Art. 245, p. 293. The establishment, at the start, of a reliable system of bench marks is of utmost importance, in order that the elevations of all parts of the city shall refer to the same datum. In laying out construction work it is absolutely necessary that reliable bench marks shall be available and sufficiently distributed to be of use in any section of the city without requiring many set-ups of the level to connect a bench mark with the work that is to be done. An advantage gained by having them close together is that they may serve as ready checks on each other as well as on the work at hand. It is not uncommon for a bench mark to be disturbed, and, if the level work is not checked frequently on some other bench mark, an error will surely enter into all of the level work which was started from that bench.

Many of the larger cities run their principal lines of levels with a geodetic level, and wherever possible, utilize the Government bench marks determined by first order leveling. It is advisable to establish the principal bench marks in pairs to diminish the chance of a total loss of a bench mark if there is any disturbance due to construction or other cause. The two B.Ms. preferably should be on opposite sides of the street, but near enough to be seen from one set-up of the instrument.

274. STAKING OUT NEW STREETS. — In staking out a new district or a street widening, the information at hand is usually a plan of the layout which has been approved by the municipal authorities, the street lines as they appear on the plan being the " established lines."

It is the surveyor's duty to stake out these lines on the ground, connecting them properly with the established street lines of the older portion of the city. As soon as the stakes are in place and checked the street lines should be marked by monuments (Art. 277, p. 330), so that there will be no difficulty in retracing the lines as they were originally laid out. If considerable grading work is to be done in building the new streets it may not be practicable to set many of the corner bounds at first on account of the likelihood of their being disturbed. Under these circumstances it is the duty of the surveyor to reference the points by cross transit lines or by some other accurate method before construction work begins; for it is important that the layout, as recorded in the city order, shall be fixed accurately and definitely so that when the streets are brought to the proper grade and the monuments are finally set they will mark the exact position of the established street line.

275. Referencing Important Points. — On account of the liability of these important corner stakes becoming disturbed before permanent monuments can take their place, it will be highly desirable to tie them in by three or more accurate ties to permanent and well-defined physical objects. (See Art. 142, p. 121.) Since in new districts fixed structures seldom exist, and since objects like trees or fences are liable to be removed at any moment on account of building operations, it will be well to set into the ground additional reference stakes as here explained. This same method applies as well to the referencing of the center line of a highway, a railroad, a dam, a bridge, or the lines of any project where construction activities are pretty sure to disturb the important stakes.

Fig. 111 illustrates two methods of referencing the stake A. In the upper figure a row of stakes B, C, D and E are accurately placed on any convenient straight line through A that will bring them all well outside of any anticipated construction work. Accurate measurements are taken from A to all four stakes and recorded. Point A can then be checked or replaced at any time with a minimum of fieldwork.

In the second figure two lines are chosen at exactly right angles (measured with the transit) and points F and G accurately placed on one line and H and I on the other. The distances from A are measured and recorded as before. This method also admits of locating *A*, if lost, without the use of a transit as there are four different pairs of ties that intersect at right angles and which can be used to set *A* and to check its position.

Point *A* could be tied in by taking one accurate foresight on a well-defined distant object such as a church steeple and then placing points on three stakes on that line all within, say, 100 ft. of *A* and measuring from *A* to each of the three points

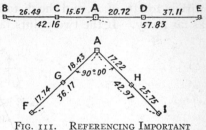

FIG. 111.   REFERENCING IMPORTANT POINTS.

to 0.01 ft. and recording them.   The foresight should be described in the notes together with the ties; if all but one of the stakes are disturbed, point *A* can still be accurately reproduced.

In Fig. 112, for example, line *J A L* was selected intentionally so that it crossed the ledge and was in exact line with the church

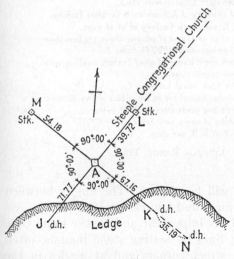

FIG. 112.   REFERENCING IMPORTANT POINTS.

steeple and so the line *A K* would cross the ledge also. The drill-hole ties are likely to be more permanent than stakes. If stakes *M* and *L* are lost point *A* is still well determined. Even though but one of these reference points remain point *A* can still be replaced.

276. Line ties, involving no measured distances, may also be used to advantage as illustrated in Fig. 113. Points *O*, *Q*, *S* and *U* are distant, well-defined and easily described natural foresights. The transit is sighted, for example, on *O* and then focused on some nearby readily described foresight on the same line; both O and the nearby foresight should be described in the notes.   Such ties give precise results only when the near foresights are, say, within 200 ft. of A, and the distant foresights are, say, ten times as far away.   If the two points (as P and O) are comparatively

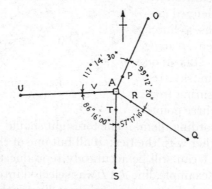

Pt. A - 3" square oak hub, copper tack.
  O - c. steeple white Methodist Church with clock.
  P - West outer corner east chimney J. A. Knowles & Co. shoe factory.
  Q - c. steel chimney L. K. Brown soap factory at ht. of guys.
  R - S. side of N. vertical edge of frame of window above big barn door
      red barn white trimmings about 200 ft. from A.
  S - W. side E. corner board, main house of grey 2-story dwelling with
      French roof and hexagonal cupola.
  T - c. conical top of water tank Ideal Laundry Co.
  U - Halfway from Nly. vert. outer face of cap on top middle of 3 ventilators
      on roof of L. E. Howe's dry goods store, Main St. to the
      Nly. face of main stem of same ventilator ----→
  V - Vane rod at gable B. & W. R..R. car shop.

FIG. 113.   LINE, OR RANGE, TIES.

near together the method will be useless.   The angles between these lines are accurately measured and checked.

277. MONUMENTS. — It is important and at the same time customary to define street lines by setting stone bounds, often called *monuments*, at the street corners and at angles in the street lines.   The bounds are set sometimes on the side lines, sometimes on the center lines, and sometimes in the sidewalks. At street intersections, one monument at the intersection of the center lines will suffice to mark both street lines, but since this point will come in the center of the road pavement where it is likely to be disturbed by traffic or by street repairing it is seldom placed there. The more practicable method is to define the street lines by marking the side lines at the angles or, where these are rounded corners, at the beginning and end of the curves or at the intersection of the two street lines. It is not necessary that all four corners of a street intersection be marked, as a bound on one corner will define the side lines of the two streets and, the width of the streets being known, the other sides can be easily determined. Nor is it necessary to place a bound at one of the corners of every street intersection, provided a street is straight for several blocks, although it is good practice to do so. If stone bounds are placed exactly on the side lines of the streets they are liable to become disturbed by building operations. It is *always* preferable, therefore, to place the bound in the sidewalk flush with the surface of the walk and at such an offset that it will be the least liable to be disturbed by building operations or by the resetting of curb stones. The best place for the bound is at a point about 2 ft. inside the curb stone but at some full number of feet from the street line. In some cities it is the practice to place them at a 2 ft. offset from the property line, but this is usually inadequate; 5 to 10 ft. away is much better practice provided these distances still bring the offset line within the limits of the sidewalk. All monuments should be placed with extreme care as regards both their accuracy of position and their stability.

278. Monuments are usually squared stone or concrete posts 4 to 8 inches square and 3 to 4 ft. long, the length depending upon the severity of the climate. In New England a monument less than 4 ft. long is likely to be disturbed by frost action. A monument may be raised or otherwise disturbed by frost even though its bottom rests on unfrozen ground. They are carefully squared on top and a drill-hole in this end marks the exact point. This drill-hole may be made either before the stone is set in place, or else after it has been so placed that its center is about in position, when the exact point may be defined by drilling a hole in its top. Frequently the hole is

filled with lead and a copper nail set in the lead is used to mark
the exact point. For nice definition of the point, a copper bolt
is inserted and two lines scratched across it at right angles; the
intersection marks the exact point. When the stone bound is
placed at the intersection of the side lines of the streets it is
sometimes located entirely in the sidewalk in such a way that its
inside corner is exactly on the intersection of the street lines.
The three other corners of the bound are usually chipped off so
that there may be no mistake as to which corner defines the line,
but the line corner frequently becomes worn off and this practice
is therefore not recommended. Some surveyors use, instead of
stone bounds, a piece of iron pipe or iron plug with a punch-hole
in the top of it, driven into the ground or embedded in cement
concrete. Long heavy stakes are employed temporarily to define
intermediate points or points of secondary importance.

279. Setting Stone Bounds. — The exact location of a stone
bound is usually marked by a tack in the top of an ordinary
wooden stake. The permanent monument which is to replace
the stake should be set before the frost has entered the ground
or before any other disturbance of the stake can have taken place.
When the bound is ready to be set the first thing to do is to
drive four temporary stakes in pairs on opposite sides of the
bound stake about two feet from it and in such a way that a line
stretched from two opposite stakes will pass over the tack in the
head of the corner stake (Fig. 114). Then tacks are set carefully in the tops of these temporary stakes in such positions that
a stretching line running from the tack on one stake to the tack
on the opposite stake will pass exactly over the tack in the bound
stake.

Then the bound stake is removed and the hole dug for the
stone bound. Care should be taken not to dig the hole any
deeper than is necessary so that the bound may be set on firm
earth. As to the position of the top of the bound with reference
to the surrounding ground, surveyors disagree. Some prefer
that the monument should stick out of the ground so that it
can be found readily; others believe that if it projects above
the surface the bound is likely to become misplaced or worn
by traffic, and that it is better therefore to set it just flush with

the ground or slightly below the natural surface. If any grading is to be done in the vicinity the bound should be set so that it will conform to the proposed grade. If a cement sidewalk is to be laid the top of the bound must fit exactly and form a part of its surface. When the hole for the bound has been dug to the proper depth it is well to stretch the strings across between the temporary stakes and plumb down roughly into the hole to determine where the center of the bound will come, so that when the monument is dropped carefully into the hole it can be placed so that it will set plumb.

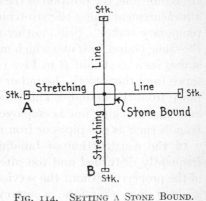

FIG. 114. SETTING A STONE BOUND.

The bound having been set in the hole, the next operation is to fill around it. This should be done with care, the material being thoroughly compacted as the filling proceeds and the bound kept in such a position that the drill-hole in the

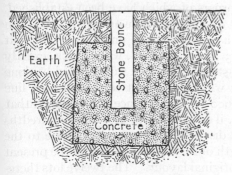

FIG. 115. SETTING BOUND WITH CONCRETE FOUNDATION.

top of it, if there is one, shall be **exactly** under the intersection of the strings. It is sometimes desirable to put in a foundation of concrete and to fill with concrete around the monument to within a foot of the surface, as shown in Fig. 115, where a more substantial bound is required, or where the ground is so soft as to furnish an insecure foundation. A bound so placed is not liable to disturbance by frost action. If the top of the bound is plain and the hole is to be drilled after the bound is in place, care should be taken to place the monument so that this hole will come close to the center of the top in order that it may present a workmanlike appearance. After the bound is set exactly in place the temporary stakes are removed.

Some surveyors prefer to use only two opposite stakes and one stretching line, the position of the monument being determined by a measurement along the stretching line from one or both of the temporary stakes. Still another method of temporarily tying in the stone bound, and one which many surveyors use, is to set two stakes such as A and B in Fig. 114, and either measure the distance from them to the bound or else set them at some even distance from the bound. This process of using temporary stakes and the stretching line is employed also in setting other types of bounds such as gas pipes or iron rods.

In the construction of buildings or fences, monuments are frequently disturbed and too often they are reset by the owner of the property without the services of a surveyor. In rerunning a street line, therefore, a surveyor should be on the lookout for such conditions, and he should be cautious in the use of any monument which he has any reason to suspect may have been misplaced.

280. STAKING OUT CITY LOTS. — In staking out the lots of a rectangular block, the corners of which have been established, the most direct method is as follows. The transit is set up on the S.B. at A (Fig. 116), a sight is taken on B, and the front corner stakes of lots 1, 2, 3, 4, etc., are set, with a tack, exactly on line, in the top of each stake. All such work should be done to the nearest 0.01 ft. It will be well first to measure the line AB, to see that it is just 600 ft. long. Since it is assumed that the S.Bs. were set exactly, if it is found to be a few hundredths over or under 600 ft., this discrepancy was probably due to the difference between the length of the tape employed on the present work and that used in the original layout. The twelve lots therefore must be laid out with equal frontages. For example, it may be a hot day when the lots are to be staked out and the tape may read on that day a distance from A to B of 599.88 ft. To allow for this each lot should be laid out 49.99 ft. wide. (See also Art. 151, p. 136 for laying out lots.)

With the instrument still at A and sighted on C, point D is

set by measuring 66 ft. from C, and then point E is placed midway between A and D. Whatever slight discrepancy there may
be in the distance between the S.B. at A and that at C is thrown
into the depth of the lots rather than into the width of the street.
The distance DA should nevertheless be checked.

By setting up the instrument at B and sighting on H, points
F and G are set. Then by setting up at F and sighting on D
the front corners of lots 13, 14, 15, etc., are determined by
giving to each lot its proper share of the measured distance

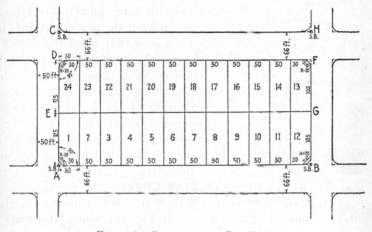

FIG. 116.   RECTANGULAR CITY-BLOCK.

FD. Another set-up of the transit at G with the line of sight on
E will allow the " back bone " to be run out and the back corners
of all the lots established. The depths of the lots can be checked
easily by taking direct measurements from the front to their
rear corner stakes.

By the method suggested above the street lines are made
straight and the slight inaccuracies which may occur in the
fieldwork are put into the back and side lines of the lots.

281. CURVED STREET LINES. — Where the streets are curved,
as is frequently the case in new residential districts, before such
lines can be established or before the lots can be defined for
deed descriptions it is necessary for the surveyor to run out the

street lines on the ground and there determine the elements of the curves that will fix them mathematically.

Curved street lines give a more pleasing effect than straight lines in suburban residential districts. On the contour map of the new district the engineer or landscape architect draws the proposed street lines so that they will properly fit the contours and at the same time give a pleasing effect. The surveyor must transpose such a layout into circular curves and tangents so

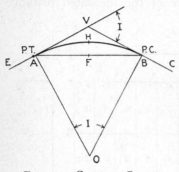

that the layout can be mathematically described. In the field he begins with some known street line, and runs out the new street lines in such a way that when the data he determines are plotted the lines will coincide with those on the layout plan. Such a mathematical determination of the street lines must be made before they can be " established " and before the dimensions of the abutting lots can be calculated.

Fig. 117.   Circular Curve.

282. ELEMENTS OF A CIRCULAR CURVE.— Before describing how to stake out a curve it will be well first to consider the elements of a simple circular curve. In Fig. 117 which represents a simple circular curve

$$OB = \quad \text{Radius} \quad = R$$
$$AHB = \quad \text{Length of Arc} \quad = L_c$$
$$AB = \quad \text{Long Chord} \quad = C$$
$$VA = VB = \text{Tangent Distance} = T$$
$$VH = \text{External Distance} = E$$
$$HF = \text{Middle Ordinate} \quad = M$$
$$I = \text{Intersection Angle, or}$$
$$\quad \text{Central Angle}$$
$$V = \text{Vertex, sometimes}$$
$$\quad \text{called `` } P.I.,\text{'' point}$$
$$\quad \text{of intersection}$$
$$P.C. = \text{Point of Curvature}$$
$$P.T. = \text{Point of Tangency}$$

From simple geometric and trigonometric relations,

$$\mathrm{Tan}\,\frac{I}{2} = \frac{T}{R}, \qquad T = R\,\tan\frac{I}{2}$$

$$\mathrm{Exsec}\,\frac{I}{2} = \frac{E}{R}, \qquad E = R\,\mathrm{exsec}\,\frac{I}{2}$$

$$\mathrm{Vers}\,\frac{I}{2} = \frac{M}{R}, \qquad M = R\,\mathrm{vers}\,\frac{I}{2}$$

$$\mathrm{Sin}\,\frac{I}{2} = \frac{C}{2R}, \qquad C = 2\,R\,\sin\frac{I}{2}$$

$$L_c = R \times \text{Circular measure of } I.^*$$

283. STAKING OUT CIRCULAR CURVES. — In Fig. 117 the two lines BC and EA are produced in the field and a point is set at their intersection V, as described in Art. 208, p. 205. The instrument is then set up at V and the central angle I carefully measured, or if point V is inaccessible other angles such as VEC and VCE may be measured from which I can be easily computed. Then the radius R, which is taken from the plan, being known, the tangent distance T is obtained by the formula, $T = R \tan \frac{1}{2} I$. Points $P.T., P.C.$ are then set, and the curve is usually laid out by the method of *deflection angles* as explained in the following article.

284. DEFLECTION ANGLES. — In laying out curves a deflection angle is usually referred to as an angle between a tangent and a chord, e.g., in Fig. 118 angles VAb, VAc, etc., are deflection

---

* In city work the curves are **actual arcs** as described above, but in railroad engineering the curves are so flat that the *Length of Curve* is measured along 100-foot chords and the sharpness of the curve is then defined by the angle subtended by a 100-foot **chord**. This angle is called the *Degree of Curve*, and is used to designate the curvature instead of the radius. Some State Highway Departments use the degree of curve system, the **length of curve** being the number of 100-foot chords and fraction. In others, the radius is specified and the length of the arc is the *actual arc*. The plans should show which system is employed. **See Table VII of arcs for radius 1.**

In the degree of curve method the central angle divided by the degree of curve will give the number of 100-ft. chords in the length of the curve, i.e., $\frac{I}{D} = L$ (in 100-ft. stations). Therefore L (in feet) $= \frac{100\,I}{D}$. For a complete discussion of railroad curves see " Railroad Curves and Earthwork," by Professor C. F. Allen, published by McGraw-Hill Book Company, New York.

angles. Since these angles are measured by half the included arc these deflection angles must be equal to half the angle at the center subtended by the same chord or arc.

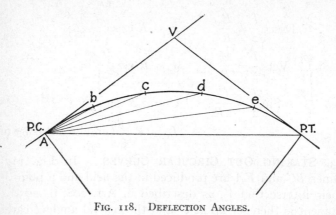

FIG. 118. DEFLECTION ANGLES.

If the total length of the curve is divided into a number of equal parts, n, the angle at the center under each of these arcs will be $\dfrac{I}{n}$, and the deflection angle for one chord will be $\dfrac{I}{2n}$, which in Fig. 118 is the angle VAb. Angle bAc = angle VAb, both being measured by one-half of equal arcs. It follows then that the deflection angle to point

$$c = 2 \times \frac{I}{2n} = \frac{I}{n}$$

$$d = 3 \times \frac{I}{2n} = \frac{3I}{2n}$$

etc.

Evidently, after the first deflection VAb is found, the other deflections can be obtained simply by adding the increment $\dfrac{I}{2n}$ to the preceding deflection angle, and this is the method which should be used. The deflection angle from the $P.C.$ to the $P.T.$ should be equal to $\dfrac{I}{2}$; this check should always be applied to the computations before they are used in laying out the curve.

The chords Ab, bc, cd, etc. are equal since their arcs are equal. With the radius and the central angle $\left(\dfrac{I}{n}\text{ for one chord}\right)$ given, the chord length can be found readily from the formula, $c = 2R \sin \dfrac{I}{2n}$. Since the angle at the center is usually small and the radius is usually large the angle I between the tangents must be measured with a precision that will give the arc or chord to 0.01 ft.

If the arc be known an approximate value for the corresponding chord length may be obtained by the useful (approximate) formula,

$$l_c - c = \frac{c^3}{24R^2} \quad \text{or} \quad = \frac{l_c^3}{24R^2} \; *$$

in which l_c is the length of the arc, c is the chord length, and R the radius.

Most of the engineers' handbooks contain tables of chords and corresponding arcs for curves of different radii, which assist greatly in shortening these computations.

When the deflection angles have been computed and checked and the chord length found, the instrument is set up at A (Fig. 118), a foresight taken on the vertex with the vernier reading 0°, and the point b set by measuring Ab and placing b on line by means of the transit on which the first deflection angle VAb

---

* The following will give some idea of the accuracy of this formula.

With $R = 100$ and $c = 25$, the formula gives $l_c = 25.065$ (correct value is 25.066).

With $R = 100$ and $c = 50$, the formula gives $l_c = 50.521$ (correct value is 50.536).

With $R = 1000$ and $c = 100$, the formula gives $l_c = 100.042$ (correct value is 100.042).

This formula will be found very useful if a slide rule is employed for the computation. Its derivation is in Appendix B, p. 699.

has been laid off. Point *c* is set by measuring *bc* and placing *c* on line given with the transit on which the second deflection angle has been laid off, and so on, until the last point (*P.T.*) has been set.

It is evident that with the transit at the *P.C.* the curve could have been laid out just as well by taking the measurements from the *P.T.* end, and some surveyors prefer to do it this way. Similarly the instrument might just as well have been set up at the *P.T.* instead of the *P.C.* and the measurements started from the *P.C.* if it were found to be more convenient.

It is sometimes necessary to set **definite station points** on the curve rather than to cut the curve up into several **equal** parts as

Description of curve	Station	Distance (Arc)	Chords			Deflection Angles	Remark
			Left	Center	Right		
			Width of Street 70 Feet.				
To Right	18+52.50	30.08	35.31	30.05	24.79	25°-47'-40"	P.T.
R = 200	18+22.42	50.00	58.59	49.87	41.14	21-29-10	
T = 96.66	17+72.42	50.00	58.59	49.87	41.14	14-19-20	
I = 51°-35'-20"	17+22.42	50.00	58.59	49.87	41.14.	7-09-40	
L_c = 180.08	16+72.42						P.C.

FIG. 119. NOTES OF A CIRCULAR CURVE.

suggested above. The principle is exactly the same as described above; but in figuring the deflection angles and the chord length to be used the computations are not quite so simple. No trouble will be experienced, however, if it is borne in mind that **the total deflection angle to any point is equal to half the central angle to that point from the *P.C.*, and that the central angle for any arc bears the same relation to the entire central angle that the arc does to the entire length of arc.** (Art. 406, p. 487.)

285. **Keeping the Notes.** — In a curved street the notes of alignment usually refer to the center line, the two side lines being parallel to the center line. All three of these lines have to be run out by the use of chords and deflection angles; Fig. 119 is an example of a compact form of notes for this work. In the first column is a description of the curve, which refers to the center line of the street. This particular curve is marked

" To Right," meaning that it deflects to the right while passing around it in the direction in which the stations run. In the third column are the distances computed as actual arcs along the center line. The next three columns headed " Chords " are the chord measurements across the curve from station to station on the left side line, the center line, and the right side line of the street, the terms left and right meaning left and right looking in the direction in which the stations run. In the column headed " Deflection Angles " are the total deflections to be laid off with the instrument set up at the *P.C.* These same deflection angles are used in running out the side lines because the chords

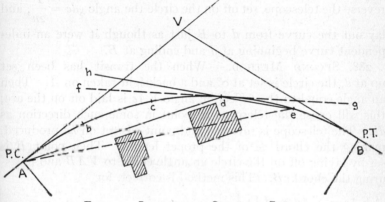

FIG. 120. INTERMEDIATE SET-UP ON CURVE.

which have been computed for the side lines run between points which are radially opposite the corresponding points on the center line. The computation of these notes will be found in Art. 406, p. 487.

286. When the Entire Curve Cannot be Laid Out from One End. - It is often impossible to see from the *P.C.* to the *P.T.* of a curve on account of intervening obstructions. In these circumstances the curve is run from the *P.C.* as far as is practicable and a transit point is set carefully on the curve; then the transit is brought forward and set up at the point thus fixed, and the curve extended beyond. There are two different methods employed for this purpose.

287. First Method. — Assume the circular curve in Fig. 120 to be laid out from A to d as described above. Point d is set carefully and the instrument then taken to that point and set up. The vernier is turned toward the 0° and beyond it until it reads the value of the deflection angle VAd. Then by using the lower clamp and tangent screw the telescope is sighted on point A. The upper plate is then unclamped and, if the telescope is turned so that the circle reads 0° the instrument will then be pointing along the direction of an auxiliary tangent df, for angles VAd and Adf are equal. It is well to note whether the instrument appears to point in the direction of the tangent at d. Then reverse the telescope, set off on the circle the angle $gde = \dfrac{I}{2n}$, and lay out the curve from d to B just as though it were an independent curve beginning at d and ending at B.

288. Second Method. — When the transit has been set up at d, the circle is set at 0° and a backsight taken on A. Then an angle equal to the deflection angle VAe is laid off on the arc; this will cause the telescope to point in some such direction as dh. The telescope is reversed and point e is set on hd produced, making the chord de of the proper length. Then point B is set by laying off on the circle an angle equal to VAB and measuring the chord eB. This method is correct, for

$$VAe = VAd + dAe$$
$$= fdA + hdf, \text{ being measured by half of equal arcs.}$$

This second method is sometimes to be preferred since the original deflection angles that were figured can be used throughout the curve.

289. Curved Street Corners. — It is the practice in many cities to curve the corners of the streets by introducing a circular curve of short radius. Where both street lines are straight the problem may be handled as explained in Art. 284, p. 337. Curves of short radius (10 to 50 ft.) may be laid out to advantage from their centers, or if the center is inaccessible, by stretching lines along the chords and erecting middle ordinates.

290. One Street Line Straight, the Other Curved. — In Fig. 121 the curved street line DEF intersects the straight stree

line AV and at this point the circular curve whose center is C'
and with a given radius r is to be introduced to round off the
corner. It is required to stake out the curve GE on the ground.
In the field any tangent line, such as FV, is run off from some
known point on the curve and intersected with AV, and the angle
β and the distance FV are measured. In the right triangle
CFV in which R and T are known, compute angle α and distance
CV. In the right triangle CAV, CV and $\gamma = \beta - \alpha$ being
known, compute CA and AV. $CA' = CA - r$; $CC' = R - r$.
In the right triangle $CA'C'$, CA' and CC' being known, compute
$A'C'$ and $A'CC' = GC'E$. Angle $ACF = 180° - \beta$. Angle

$ECF = ACF - A'CC'$, from
which the length of the arc
FE can be readily computed,
which locates the point E.
$VG = AV - A'C'$, which
locates point G of the curve
GE, and any intermediate
points can be located as
explained in the previous
articles.

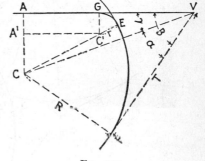

FIG. 121.

As the radius $C'E$ is often
quite short the center of the
curve can be located from
either its $P.C.$ or $P.T.$ or
both, and any intermediate points on the curve can be easily
swung in from its center.

If curve EG forms a reversed curve with FE the computations
follow the same general method described above.

291. Both Street Lines Curved. — In Fig. 122 the two curved
street lines ABD and $A'B'D'$ intersect each other, and the curve
whose center is E, with a given radius r, is introduced at the
intersection of the two street lines. It is required to locate the
curve $B'B$ on the ground. In the field the tangent DV is run
off from some known point D on the curve ABD and intersected
with a tangent $D'V$ from the curve $A'B'D'$ and angle α and distances T and T' are measured. In the right triangle CDV,
R and T being known, compute angle CVD and distance CV.

Similarly in the triangle $C'VD'$ compute angle $C'VD'$ and distance $C'V$. In the oblique triangle CVC', CV, $C'V$ and angle $CVC' = 360° - (\alpha + CVD + C'VD')$ being known, compute CC' and the angles $CC'V$ and $C'CV$. In the oblique triangle $CC'E$, $CE = R + r$, $C'E = R' - r$, and CC' being known, compute the angle $C'CE$, $CC'E$ and $C'EC$, which is the supplement of the central angle of the curve $B'B$. Angle $DCB = DCV + VCC' - C'CE$, from which arc DB can be com-

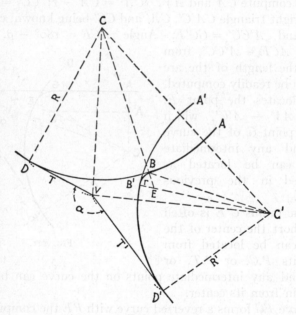

FIG. 122.

puted. Similarly angle $D'C'B' = D'C'V + VC'C - CC'E$ from which arc $D'B'$ is computed. These locate the $P.C.$ and $P.T.$ of the small curve whose center is E.

292. INTERSECTION OF CIRCULAR ARC AND STRAIGHT LINE.— This problem occurs wherever a straight property line cuts a curved street line. In the survey sufficient data must be obtained so that the distance along the curve and also the distance along the property line can be computed to the poin where it cuts the curve. The usual method is to lay out a line tangent to the curve at some known station A on the curve, Fig. 123, intersect that tangent with the property line at D, and measure the distance AD and the angle α.

The problem is to find arc AB and distance BD. The radius R is known. Draw radius OI parallel to the property line and AH and JB perpendicular to OI; then

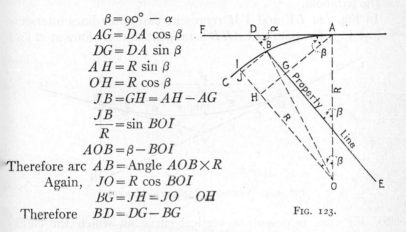

$$\beta = 90° - \alpha$$
$$AG = DA \cos \beta$$
$$DG = DA \sin \beta$$
$$AH = R \sin \beta$$
$$OH = R \cos \beta$$
$$JB = GH = AH - AG$$
$$\frac{JB}{R} = \sin BOI$$
$$AOB = \beta - BOI$$

Therefore arc $AB =$ Angle $AOB \times R$

Again, $\quad JO = R \cos BOI$
$$BG = JH = JO - OH$$

Therefore $\quad BD = DG - BG$

Fig. 123.

293. STAKING OUT STREET GRADES. — The fieldwork necessary in setting grade stakes is explained in Arts. 261–2, pp. 308B–309. When new streets are constructed the excavation or embankment first is brought to sub-grade, i.e., to the grade of the bottom of the road covering or pavement. The grade stakes set for this work are usually the center and the two side slope stakes, properly marked with the cut or fill, as described in Arts. 256–8, pp. 303–8.

As the work progresses the center stake is dug out or covered up and when the construction has progressed nearly to the sub-grade it is customary to set additional stakes, marking the elevation of the sub-grade along the center line and on each side line of the roadway. If sidewalks with curbstones are to be constructed, first the curbs are set to grade, and then the pavement grades are marked on the face of the curb, as well as on stakes in the center of the roadway and at points halfway between the curbs and center. (See Art. 296, p. 348.)

294. VERTICAL CURVES. — Where the rate of grade of a street changes, it is customary, in order to avoid an abrupt transition from one grade to the other, to introduce a vertical curve, usually from 100 ft. to 1000 ft. long, which is tangent to both grade lines. The simplest curve to lay out for this purpose is the parabola.

In Fig. 124 LV and VM represent two grade lines intersecting at V. The parabola AHB is tangent to these lines at A and

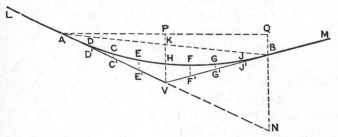

FIG. 124.   VERTICAL PARABOLIC CURVE.

B. Fig. 124 represents a vertical curve on which the elevation of nine points must be determined. The equation of the parabola is

$$y^2 = 4\,px, \text{ or } y^2 = \text{(constant)}\,x, \tag{1}$$

the x dimensions being parallel to VK (vertical) and the y dimensions being along AV. From the equation it is easy to see that **the offsets from the tangent vary as the squares of the distances along the tangent,** or $x_1 : x_2 = y_1^2 : y_2^2$. The lines VP and NQ are vertical and AQ is horizontal. Since the curve extends an equal **horizontal** distance each side of V, $AP = PQ$; and therefore $AK = KB$. $NB = 4\,VH$; $VH = 4CC'$; $CC' = 4DD'$; etc. (from equation 1).

$$NB = g \times \frac{AP}{100} + g_1 \times \frac{PQ}{100}$$

$$NB = (g + g_1) \times \frac{AQ}{200} \text{ (if } AP = PQ, \text{ the usual case)}$$

$$KV = \frac{NB}{2} \text{ (from similar triangles)}$$

but $\qquad NB = 4\,VH$ (from above)

therefore $\qquad KV = 2\,HV,$

or point H is midway between V and K.

The elevation of V is determined from the established grade. The number of 25-ft. stations will determine the distance VA and VB. The elevation of A and of B can be readily computed along their respective straight grade lines.

$$\text{Elev. } K = \frac{\text{Elev. } A + \text{Elev. } B}{2}$$

$$\text{Elev. } H = \frac{\text{Elev. } V + \text{Elev. } K}{2}$$

$$VH = \text{Elev. } H - \text{Elev. } V$$

Elevations of all the other intermediate points along the curve can be computed by finding the elevation of the points D', C', E', F', G', and J' and by adding to these elevations the ordinates $D'D$, $C'C$, $E'E$, etc.

$$D'D = J'J = \frac{VH}{16}$$

$$C'C = G'G = \frac{VH}{4}$$

$$E'E = F'F = \frac{9VH}{16}$$

295. CROSS-SECTION OF STREET. — On account of the necessity for draining the surface of a road the center is raised or " crowned " above the grade of the gutters by an amount depending on various conditions. The shape of the road surface is sometimes two planes, running straight from the gutter to a summit or ridge in the center of the street, this ridge being rounded off by rolling; but more frequently it is a curved surface in the form of a parabola or a circle. Ordinarily the width of the street is great compared with the crown, so the parabola and the circle are virtually coincident.

When a street is to be paved the curbstones are first set to proper line and grade, then stakes are set for the finished grade of the roadway. The center grade stake is frequently the only grade given and a templet, or form, which can be set on the curbs and on this center stake is used to give the form of the cross-section. The form of the templet for this work is laid out by the surveyor. If no templet is used he should set intermediate grade stakes between the center and the curb lines. Whichever method is used the surveyor must compute the necessary ordinates to give the correct shape to the surface.

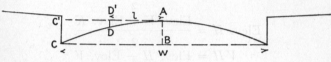

FIG. 125. CROSS-SECTION OF PAVEMENT. GUTTERS AT SAME ELEVATION.

296. Gutters at Same Elevation. — Fig. 125 represents the cross-section of a pavement and sidewalks. The crown AB is given. The ordinate DD' at any other point on the parabola

$$= C'C \times \frac{l^2}{\left(\dfrac{W}{2}\right)^2}$$ since in a parabola the offsets from a tangent

vary as the square of the distance out along the tangent (Art. 294, p. 346). But $C'C = AB$; hence, if D' is halfway from the center to the curb, $DD' = \dfrac{AB}{4}$

297. STAKING OUT CURB* LINES AND GRADES. — If the line stakes that are set for the curbstones are placed directly on the line of the curb they will be disturbed when the trench is excavated. For this reason they are usually set in the sidewalk on an offset line, say, 3 ft. from the outside edge of the curb, and at intervals of about 25 ft. The grade stakes are set at about the same interval, with their tops at grade or at some even

---

* Called edgestones in some localities

distance (6 inches or 1 foot) above or below the grade of the curb. Sometimes the grade stakes are not driven so that their tops bear any relation to the finished grade, but a horizontal chalkmark is made on the side of the stake indicating the proper grade. A stake can be marked much more quickly than the top can be driven to the exact grade.

When new curbstones are being set, or forms for concrete curbs, stakes as a rule cannot be used in old streets because the sidewalks are too hard, and even if stakes could be driven those projecting above the surface of the sidewalk would be a source of danger to pedestrians. It is customary therefore to use heavy spikes about 6 inches long. These are driven into the sidewalk on the offset line and the elevations of their tops determined by leveling. The difference between the elevation of each spike and the elevation of the curb opposite it is calculated. A list of the stations and the distances the spikes are above or below the curb is given to the foreman in charge of the work. These distances always should be transposed into feet and inches (to the nearest $\frac{1}{8}$ inch) before being given to the foreman, as it is seldom that the men employed to lay the curbstones know how to use tenths and hundredths of a foot. (See Art. 7, p. 2.)

Where there are trees or poles in line with the curbs, a nail can sometimes be set in the side of a tree on the line of the curb as well as at its grade. Points like these should be set in preference to offset stakes or spikes wherever possible, as there is little liability of the workman misinterpreting such marks. They can fasten their string directly to the nail and set the curb or forms, if the edgestone is to be of concrete, to agree with it.

Before the curbstones are ordered the surveyor usually measures the distances between trees, poles and driveways, and then makes out a schedule of the lengths of straight, of curved and of chamfered stones (opposite driveways) to be used on the job. This schedule is used in ordering the stones, and when they are delivered they should be found to fit the conditions without the necessity of cutting any of them.

298. STAKING OUT SEWERS. — The lines and grades of sewers are sometimes run out in the same way as those described for curbstones. The stakes or spikes (in hard paving) are set for line and grade on an offset line parallel to the center line of the sewer, and the difference in elevation between the spike and sewer opposite is calculated as in Art. 297.

Another method which is extensively used is to drive spikes or stakes on the center line of the sewer and, from the elevation of the ground, determine the depth of digging. The depth of digging is given to the foreman in feet and inches from the top of the spikes, or a mark is made on the stakes, indicating the depth the trench must be dug below the mark. As the excavation is completed, batter boards are placed every 25 to 50 feet along the sewer. Batter boards are horizontal boards nailed to long heavy stakes driven firmly into the ground on either side of the excavation. The tops of the cross boards are placed a full number of feet above the elevation of the flow line (inside bottom of the pipe) of the sewer. On these batter boards a nail is driven exactly in the center line of the sewer. (See Art. 262, p. 309.)

299. Rerunning Street Lines and Grades. — All kinds of work, such as the construction of fences and buildings, street improvements, and underground construction call for reproducing the street lines and grades. The work of rerunning the line is simple enough if the original S.Bs. are in place. It is not uncommon, however, to find that in excavating a cellar on a corner lot the corner bound has been disturbed or that it has been removed entirely; and before the required line can be staked out properly it may be necessary to begin at some reliable S.B. farther down the street or even on some other nearby street line.

When the line finally has been rerun it is customary to take and to record swing-offsets from the corners of the underpinning of several of the buildings located along the street and near to the line. By this record of offsets, then, this street line can be run out very easily and quickly at any future time, and any disturbance of the S.Bs. at the corners can be detected readily. **Several offsets to substantial buildings are of more permanent value than stone bounds.** In some offices these offsets to buildings are recorded directly on the street plans. Several offsets from existing buildings give one of the best means of preserving a street line.

Whenever a street line or grade is rerun full notes should be made showing all measurements taken for determining the lines or grades.

Sometimes the original street lines have been obliterated so completely that it is necessary to resurvey them and make a new record plan and a new description of them and to have these new lines " established " by a city ordinance. Such work, for example, has been done by the City of Providence since 1857 when a state law was passed requiring that accurate street lines be marked where the adjacent land was about to be built upon. To carry out this law properly the resurvey of a number of the principal streets was required and the policy then adopted has been continued.

When a new building is to be constructed the owner usually requests the City Engineer to define the street grade in front of his property. The surveyor who has charge of this work goes to the place and levels from the nearest B.M. to the site of the new building. He has in his possession the established grade of the street and its cross-section. From these he can compute the elevation of the sidewalk at those points along the street line where the grades are desired. On the fence or on stakes set on the side line of the street he marks the grade of the sidewalk at the property line, usually to a hundredth of a foot.

300. ACCIDENT PLANS. — These plans are for the purpose of showing in great detail the physical features at or near the site of an accident. It may be a railroad wreck, a street railway accident, automobile collision, injury to pedestrian due to faulty sidewalk pavement, or a murder. The surveyor's duty is to make a plan on a large scale so that it may be exhibited on the wall in a court room near the jury and can be readily seen by them without having to leave their seats. Scales of such plans are usually 1 inch = 4 ft., 1 inch = 8 ft. and 1 inch = 10 ft.; the two former scales are convenient for use by the layman who is familiar only with the use of the ordinary scale divided into inches and eighths. These plans should be shaded and colored so as to show very clearly the physical features which may relate to the case, and the buildings or windows from which witnesses may have claimed to have seen the accident. All trees and poles in the vicinity should be shown and their diameters marked on the plan. Sufficient elevations should be taken so that the surveyor can testify to the rates of grades and amount one part of the pavement is above or below another portion of the street. If the accident occurred after sundown, the location of street lights and store window lights may be important.

In coloring the plan, crayon colors will be suitable. Use the same color for the same physical features, as, for example, dark brown for bituminous-bound pavement, light brown for earth or gravel sidewalks, dark blue for curbstones, as this will define clearly the limits of the roadway, light blue for cement concrete sidewalks, yellow or orange around the fronts of wooden buildings, and red for brick buildings. Sometimes a series of letters A, B, C, lettered beside black crosses plotted at every 25 ft. or 50 ft. along the street will aid the jury in estimating distances on the plan, as well as assist the witnesses in talking about the plan.

A prominent North point should be drawn on the plan. The measurements should be taken accurately, especial attention being paid to keeping the note-book in neat form as it is sometimes introduced as evidence as well as the plan.

301. SETTING BATTER-BOARDS FOR A BUILDING. — One of the most common tasks of the surveyor is to set the batter-boards for the excavation and construction of the cellar of a new building. The dimensions of the building and the elevation at which to set it are usually obtained from the architect, although sometimes the elevation of the ground floor of the building is recorded on the plan itself. In a brick or stone building the lines to be defined are the outside neat lines of the building, and the elevation desired is usually the top of the first floor. In a wooden building the line usually given is the outside line of the brick or stone underpinning and the elevation given is the top of this underpinning on which the sill of the house is to rest. Sometimes the outside line of the sill instead of the underpinning is desired. There should be a definite understanding in regard to these points before the work of staking out is begun.

Generally there is no elevation marked on the plan and the surveyor is simply told to set the top of underpinning a certain distance above the sidewalk or above the surface of some portion of the lot. If there is an elevation referred to City Datum marked on the plan, he should level from the nearest B.M. and set the batter-boards at the grade given.

The location of the building on the lot is given either by plan or by orders from the architect or owner. Not infrequently the surveyor receives the directions to place the building so that its front line is on line with the other buildings on the street and so that it will stand a certain number of feet from one of the side lines of the lot.

His first work is to stake out the location of the building by setting temporary stakes accurately at all corners of the building, e.g., in Fig. 126, at A, B, C, D, E, and F. A stake also should be set at G so that the entire work can be checked by measuring the diagonals AG and FB, and GD and EC. These checks always should be applied where possible. Then the posts for the batter-boards are driven into the ground 3 or 4 ft. outside the line of the cel-

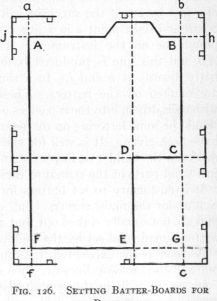

FIG. 126. SETTING BATTER-BOARDS FOR A BUILDING.

lar so that they will not be disturbed when the walls are being constructed. On these posts, which are usually of 2 inches × 4 inches scantling, 1-inch boards are nailed. These boards are set by the surveyor so that their top edges are level with the grade of the top of the underpinning or for whatever other part of the building he is giving grades. After the batter-boards are all in place they should be checked roughly by sighting across them; they should all appear at the same level. Sometimes, however, on account of the slope of the ground some of them have to be set a definite number of feet above or below grade.

Then the lines are to be marked by nails driven in the top of these batter-boards. The transit is set up on one of the corner stakes of the house at A (Fig. 126), for example, and a sight is taken on F. This line is then marked on the batter-board beyond (at f) and on the one near the transit (at a). If the batter-board is so near the transit that the telescope cannot be focused on it, then point a can be set within a hundredth of a foot by eye if the surveyor will stand outside of the batter-board and sight point a in a line determined by point f and the plumb-line on the instrument. Then a sight is taken along AB and this line is produced both ways and nails set on the batter-boards at h and j. In a similar manner all of the lines are marked on the batters. These points should be marked with nails driven into the top edges of the batter-boards and there should be some lettering on the boards to make clear which lines have been given. It is well for the surveyor also to show these marks to the builder or inspector and have it clearly understood just what parts of the structure these lines and grades govern.

It is customary to set batters for the jogs in the building as well as for the main corners; but small bay windows of dwellings are not usually staked out, but are constructed from wooden patterns made and set by the builder.

As soon as the excavation is begun the corner stakes are dug out and the building lines are then obtained by stretching lines between the nails in the opposite batter-boards. These batter-boards are preserved until the sills or first floor are in place, after which they may be removed.

It is good practice to set reference points on the main lines of the building and to place such points entirely outside of the area disturbed by construction of the new building.

302. STAKING OUT A BRIDGE SITE. — The following refers to a small bridge and its supports, such, for example, as a railroad plate girder bridge over a city street, which is supported on two concrete abutments.

A transit and tape survey of the general location, including the physical structures in the immediate vicinity and the angle between the side lines of the street and the center line of location of the railroad, will be embodied in the " site plan " that usually accompanies the construction plans of such a structure. The base-line of location of the railroad and the street lines should be run with the utmost care so that their relations shall be fixed exactly by the field measurements, because the structure and its supports are designed and located with reference to these data. Points on these lines should be tied in as explained in Art. 275, p. 328.

Fig. 127 represents the plan of one abutment of a skew bridge. The outside line of the foundation is $ABCDEFG$; the neat

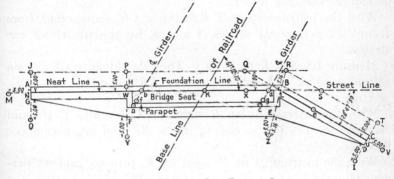

FIG. 127. STAKING OUT BRIDGE SITE.

line of the face of the abutment is $NWKLU$. These faces are vertical, but the backs are sloping.

Stakes should be set so that they will define, both in direction and in extent, the faces NL and LU. They are placed on an offset line at a sufficient distance from these neat lines so that the excavation for the foundation will not disturb them; in this instance 5 ft. from the neat line.

First take from the plan the distances AN, AG, NW, WK, KL, LU, CU and CD. Then set the temporary point K accurately by intersecting the base-line of the railroad with the street line (Art. 208, p. 205).

With the instrument at K sight along the street line and set the permanent stake (and tack) M, the temporary points L and N and two temporary points on either side of S.

With the instrument at N sight on L, turn 90° and set permanent stakes J and O.

With the instrument at J sight on a swing-offset of 5.00 ft. from L and set the permanent stake P opposite F and also two temporary stakes on either side of both Q and R.

With the instrument at L sight along the street line and turn the angle $28° 47' 50''$, check it by repetition, set the temporary point U and the permanent stakes V and Q, the latter by the stretching line method, using the two temporary points already placed on line JR on either side of Q.

With the instrument at U sight on L, turn $90°$ and set the permanent stakes T and I.

With the instrument at T sight on a 5-ft. swing-offset from L and set permanent stakes S and R by the stretching line method.

Measure LS, SR, RQ and QL. They should all equal $5 \div \sin 28° 48' = 10.38$. The check distance $LR = 5.00 \div \cos 14° 24' = 5.16$.

With the instrument at R sight on J, lay off $75° 36'$ and measure $10.32 + WF \div \cos 14° 24' = RZ$ and set permanent stake Z.

With the instrument at P, sight on R, turn $90°$ and set permanent stake Y.

By this method stakes M and S define the face of the head wall and left wing and J, P and Q are intermediate offset stakes used in placing the concrete forms exactly on the street line. Similarly Q and V define the face of the right wing and S and T are additional offset points used in setting the forms. Stakes J, O, T and I define the face of the end forms.

When construction is about to begin temporary stakes are set at A, B, C, D, E, F and G by measuring from the offset stakes. These stakes will be lost as the excavation progresses. The concrete for the foundation is poured into the hole excavated, or if forms are needed for the foundation their lines are fixed by measuring over from the offset stakes as suggested above. The elevation of the bottom and of the top of the foundation are defined by grade stakes set just outside the excavation near A, H, B and C.

When the foundation has been poured to grade and has had a day to " set up," mark on the top of it temporary points at

N, W, X, L, e and U by measuring 5 ft. from the offset stakes opposite them. The points give the form carpenter his lines for the face forms of the wall which are erected vertically on these lines. The forms for the back are set at the proper distance from the face forms as given on the plans; these back forms are battered.

Points at elevation of the bridge seat are marked directly on the forms, or else reference points are marked on the face of the forms, and the exact distance from these reference grades to the finished bridge seat is given to the foreman in charge. Since concrete shrinks, care should be taken to make proper allowance for this by having it clearly understood by the foreman that the grades given are for the finished seasoned walls.

After the bridge seat is poured mark upon it the point K and lay out the parapet end forms the proper distance from this point. When the parapet has been poured run out the center lines of the girders parallel to the base-line and mark points such as a and c on the top of the parapet and also points f and b and g and d on the bridge seat. Using these lines the bearing plates can be placed accurately on the bridge seat and their position checked by the surveyor before the bridge arrives.

The points on the parapet define the center lines of the girders which must be placed exactly on these lines so that the floor system will fit properly between the girders.

SURVEY OF CITY LOTS

303. When the survey of a City lot is to be made its purpose and the information required must first be ascertained. The plan is usually made as a basis for an architect's design or for record in the Registry of Deeds or in the Land Court (see Arts. 153–153a, pp. 137–138). Whatever the purpose of the plan the fieldwork methods are substantially alike.

Where the boundaries reasonably admit of more than one interpretation it is customary to register the maximum claim in Land Court cases, whereas if the plan is for other purposes it is advisable to adopt for boundaries only those which are so well fortified by evidence that it is reasonably sure that any Court would validate them.

304. Plan for Architect's Design. — The plan is usually drawn on a scale of one-eighth or one-quarter inch per ft. It should show the following:

1. Angles and linear dimensions of lot lines, area, and also measurements in the recorded deed of the property for comparison with measured dimensions.
2. Location of lot lines with relation to existing party-walls and thicknesses of the latter.
3. References to party-wall agreements, by Registry of Deeds book and page number. (Art. 153, p. 137.)
4. Any restrictions which prevent free use of either the whole or any portion of the lot, including rights-of-way (all to be found in recorded deeds or other recorded documents). Any evidence that illegal public use has been made of any portion of the lot such as indications that persons have been continuously crossing portions of the property. See Art. 151, p. 133.
5. Street numbers as shown on the buildings.
6. Elevations of present sidewalks and established (official) elevations and widths of sidewalks.
7. Location in streets, size, kind and elevation of inverts (inside of bottom) of sewers.
8. Names of adjacent owners.
9. Plotted location of buildings on lot, including character and number of stories of buildings.
10. Plotted location of buildings on adjacent lots near the party line, and their character. Also any encroachments of cornices, belt course, etc., of adjacent building.
11. Approximate North point. While it is the general rule for engineers to place a plan on the paper so that the North is at the top of the plan, architects usually prefer to have their plans drawn so that the main street is parallel to the bottom of the sheet.
12. Section of city and zoning district in which the lot is located.

In addition to the above information, some architects desire:

13. Elevation of ground and elevation of basements of buildings.
14. Location of existing water pipe, gas pipe, electric conduits and connections, telephone connection and other underground conduits.

305. Plan for Record. — A plan for record must be drawn to such a scale as will give the size required by the particular Registry at which it is to be recorded. In some registries plans are redrawn to fit the deed books, this being done by the engineer of the Registry. Other registries have no rules regarding size. This plan should show:

1. Linear dimensions, angles (or bearings), and area of lot.
2. Location of buildings on the lot, character and number of stories.

3. Existing party walls and their relation to the lot lines.
4. Buildings adjacent and near to party lines, marked wood, stone or brick.
5. Names of adjacent owners.
6. Street numbers as shown on the buildings.
7. References to party-wall agreements, by Registry of Deeds book and page number.   (Appendix C.)
8. Any restrictions which prevent free use of either the whole or any portion of the lot, including rights-of-way (all to be found in recorded deeds or other recorded documents).
9. Approximate North point.
10. Section of city in which lot is located.

306. Data Required for Fieldwork. — Let us suppose the plan to be made is for the use of an architect.

Data fixing the street lines and the elevation of two or more bench marks should be obtained from the office of the City Engineer.

Next, examine the Land Court records to see if any of this or adjacent property has been put through that Court, because a boundary once fixed by that Court is final.   (This of course applies only to States in which Land Courts exist.)

Next, the deeds of the property to be surveyed and usually also deeds of adjacent property should be examined and copied from Registry of Deeds records.   The substance of all recorded party-wall agreements and other agreements that may restrict the use of any part of the property should be copied also.   Sometimes this information is given by a conveyancer who has been examining the title for the client or for other interests.

With the above information in our possession actual surveying work can be commenced at the site.

307. Fieldwork. — The methods used in making the survey should be such as will insure accuracy, reasonable speed, and above all give the least chance of mistakes.   Experience has proved that the process followed in the example to be explained gives excellent results.

The parcel here shown (Fig. 128) is a typical irregular lot containing no right angles, and with party walls on each side; these vary in thickness, thereby presenting in one example most of the usual problems of a city survey of land fully occupied by a building.

Offset lines run parallel to the street lines are first marked on

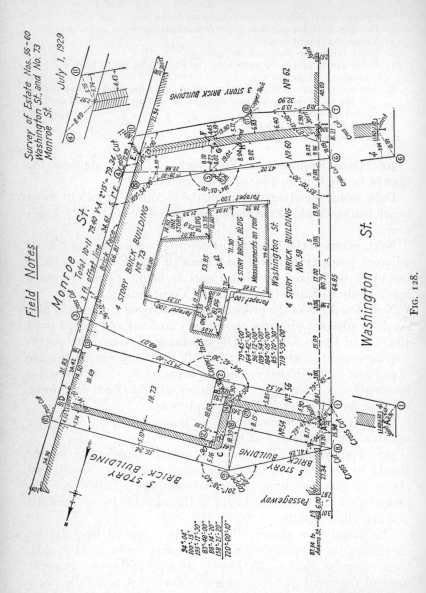

Fig. 128.

the sidewalks by carefully established points. Joining these sidewalk lines, forming a closed traverse, transit lines are run **within** the property, where sights through doorways or windows can be taken, and extending from street to street; then from these same transit points within the building, lines are run parallel to the party walls and offsets measured from these lines to the interior faces of the walls. Similarly, another traverse is formed by the sidewalk lines and lines run on the **outside** of the building parallel to the exterior faces of these walls, where possible, and offsets measured to the walls from these outside lines.

Fig. 128 illustrates the specific steps taken in making such a survey.

Let us suppose that the survey starts on Washington St., also that the City Engineer has said that the original monuments defining the street lines have disappeared, and since all of the buildings on that street are very old, occupation will fix the street lines (Art. 140, p. 118).

First set up the transit over a point at some convenient distance (say 3 ft.) from the face (at the sidewalk level) of the iron column at the joint between buildings Nos. 60 and 62 (marked I in Fig. 128). The transit is sighted on a swing-offset 3 ft. from the face of the stone post at the wall joint between Nos. 54 and 56. Then cross-cuts (thus +) or nails are put into the sidewalk on this offset line at places convenient for running traverse lines within and without the building, such as at 8, 1, 6 and 7. As it is well to avoid sighting through windows, on account of refraction of the glass, these marks should be placed opposite doors or windows which can be opened. While the instrument is sighted along the line 8-7 the transitman should select two suitable natural sights, one in each direction, preferably at a considerable distance; these he will always use thereafter. The intermediate posts facing on Washington St. and the joints in party walls are then located by offsets and ties as shown, and the frontages of the two adjacent buildings are measured to determine whether these owners have the frontages called for in their deeds. Intermediate distances from door to door are measured.

Similarly, run the offset line 10–11 on Monroe St. The City Engineer has given us a definite line for that street.

While on this offset line the fronts of the building and those immediately adjacent are located and measured as on Washington St. and cuts as 10, 3, 4 and 11 placed at convenient points for running lines into the building or for party-wall locations. It is well to measure between adjacent points and then measure the total distance as a check. There being considerable difference in elevation between points 10 and 11, and the slope of the sidewalk being uniform, the most accurate result is obtained by slope measurement, the distance being measured by the tape lying directly on the sidewalk, and the vertical angle taken by measuring the height of the axis of the telescope above point 10 and sighting on a point at the same height above point 11.

Obviously, permission to enter and take measurements in a store or occupied building always should be obtained. Managers and tenants are usually willing to allow privileges of this sort within reason, but naturally resent intrusion without permission. It is unwise, however, to give tenants information regarding the purpose of the survey. Giving the name of the engineering firm represented, denying knowledge of the purpose of the owner and referring inquiries to him is a safe policy unless one has been otherwise instructed.

Next run line 1–2 parallel to the inside face of the party wall. If the wall bends slightly make the two end offsets equal and measure one in the middle to record the bend. The brick wall is the object to be surveyed and where it is covered with sheathing it is imperative to know the thickness of that sheathing. This can be obtained by measuring through a small gimlet-hole or drill-hole made with a Yankee drill. If this cannot be measured, note its character; soft sheathing is usually 2 inches thick and plaster on the brick is usually from $\frac{1}{4}$ to 1 inch thick.

Now place point 2, a copper tack on the floor, at a convenient point with due consideration also of the position of line 2–3. The angle at 1 is read and doubled, and distance 1–2 is measured.

Set up on point 2 and measure the swing-offset to the wall joint on Washington St. (6.65). This will show directly its position with relation to the inside face of the party wall. Run line 2–12 parallel to the short wall, measure the angle at 2, the offsets, and the distance 18.69 to the wall face. Similarly, line 2–13 is laid out parallel to the party wall and the angle and swing-offsets measured. Being unable to run this line 2–13 through to Monroe St. on account of the wall, point 3 opposite a window is selected on the offset line 10–11 which was run on the Monroe St. sidewalk and the distance 2–3 and angle at 3 are measured.

Run line 6–5 parallel to the inside face of the wall and measure swing-offset 9.84 to the joint on Washington St. Set up on point 5 and run line 5–20 parallel to the wall; the small jog and the flat bend in the wall are located approximately as indicated in Fig. 128, but their exact location will be found later by calculation. Line 5–4 is run and angles measured at 5 and 4.

To the closed traverse 1–2–3–4–5–6 we have now tied the interior faces of the party walls, their street joints and the street face of the building. We must now obtain a survey of the outer faces of these party walls.

Set up on point 8 and run a line parallel to 1–2. If the offsets taken to the outer face of the wall are approximately equal, the presumption is that both angles (at 1 and 8) are correct, as walls are usually built with parallel faces, but if there is a difference in the outside offsets an angle error is probable and should be investigated.

The perpendicular distance between lines 1–2 and 8–18 is easily calculated and the sum of the offsets on both sides subtracted from the computed perpendicular distance gives the thickness of the wall. Brick walls are built in multiples of 4″; that is, they are 8″–12″–16″–20″, etc. in thickness. If the result gives a 10″ or an 18″ wall it is well to investigate as a mistake is probable. It is also advisable to measure if possible the size of the bricks in the wall being surveyed, as those laid in the 70's are usually about $7\frac{1}{2}$″ instead of 8″ long — a peculiarity which may account for an apparent error.

Similarly, set up on points 9–10–11 and lay off lines parallel to the interior faces of the party walls, measure the offsets to their outer faces; these give the wall thicknesses and also check the angles previously turned. When possible, measure the swing-offset to party-wall joint, and when it is not possible measure the distance along the street line from the transit line to the joint. It is well also to have tie measurements, when possible, to all angle points in walls, as from point 9 to 14, and from point 2 to 15. As it is impossible to run a line parallel to the wall though point 7, a line 7–16 is run approximately parallel to it and several points on that transit line are marked from which the shortest distances to the wall have been measured.

As the plan should show the limits of buildings of different heights and area ways, it is well also to take roof measurements as shown in the subsketch in Fig. 128. Roof measurements along the party walls, fronts and a few ties across the roof not only will give the sizes of the various buildings but also serve as rough checks on the survey made at the street level.

308. Calculations and Plotting of the Survey Traverses. — *1st*. Calculate the traverse by coördinates — Arts. 429–30, pp. 519–20. It should close within 1 : 10 000 or better. The error is distributed by judgment. (Art. 422, p. 506.) The balanced traverse is made a basis for the second step.

2nd. Plot the traverse on a large scale, preferably $\frac{1}{4}$ inch to a foot. Plot all walls and other details of the survey on this plan. See Fig. 129.

3rd. Add to this plan all party-wall and deed data, placing the deed dimensions of the lot within the lot and the deed dimensions of adjacent lots within their respective lots.

4th. From a study of all recorded agreements and field data determine the division lines from the evidence supporting them. In deciding which lines to select one must bear in mind that since a costly building may be erected on this lot it is well to submit all questionable boundaries to the owner, or to his attorney, and obtain from him a decision with respect to them.

5th. Calculate the coördinates of all angle points and then the azimuths and lengths of the sides adopted as the boundaries. Check the calculated azimuths by the azimuth of the field survey.

6th. Using the lines and angles as actually recorded on the finished plan, and adopting one street line as an axis, compute the entire property boundary again by the coördinate method as a final check on the finished plan.

308a. Calculation Details. — Traverse 1–2–3–4–5–6 is calculated by coördinates. Since Washington St. is a convenient base-line, we assume that the azimuth of line 6–1 is 0° and that azimuths increase clockwise. Assume the coördinates of point (1) are $x = 0$, $y = 200.00$, with the x's increasing toward the east and y's increasing toward the north. By doing so we avoid minus coördinates in future surveys of property in the same block.

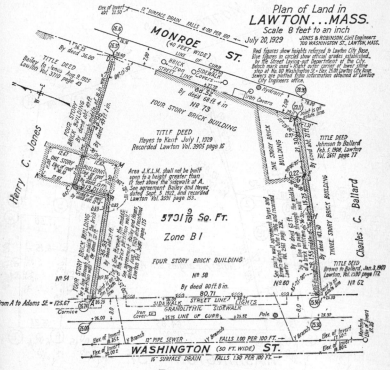

FIG. 129.

The sum of the angles was 719° 59'. Since the angles at 4 and 5 were the most liable to error, being adjacent to short sides, 30" is added to each angle.

It will be found that this traverse closes within 0.02 east and west and 0.005 north and south. If we increase the distance 5–6 by 0.01, calling it 47.03, and decrease the distance 2–3 by 0.01, calling it 48.06, the traverse will be well balanced.

Now calculate the coördinates of points 8–9–10–11–7–16;

also the perpendicular distances between lines 1–2 and 8–18, between lines 2–12 and 9–19, between 9–10 and 2–13, between 5–20 and 11–17, and from point 16 to the line 6–5. These distances form an excellent check on the two traverses and the

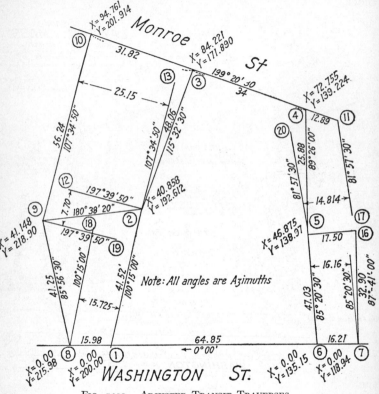

FIG. 129a. ADJUSTED TRANSIT TRAVERSES.

plot, and also permit of computing the thickness of walls. The results of the above are shown in Fig. 129a.

The survey then should be plotted; and if this is done accurately on a scale of 4 ft. to the inch, errors of 0.15 ft. or greater can be detected readily by scale.

309. Determination of Boundaries from Analysis of Evidence. — The information obtained from the Registry of Deeds is now put on the plan. (Fig. 129.)

Our title deed is the conveyance of Hayes to Kent. The names of the grantor and grantee are lettered in the middle of the plan; also the date of the transfer and the volume and page where it is recorded at the Lawton Registry,

In this instrument the line $A-B$ is described as being about 37 ft. in length and passing through the middle of the brick partition wall. This record is lettered on the plan as shown. Line $C-B$ is described as being 13 ft. in length, but no mention is made of its passing through a party wall, hence the record " By Deed 13 ft." is all that is necessary. Similarly the deed information relating to lines $C-D$, $D-E$, $E-I$ and $I-A$ is added.

Our title deed mentions two party-wall agreements, one referring to line $G-I$, the other to $A-B$; also to an agreement restricting the height of any building to be placed on area $J-K-L-M$. These agreements are very important and the substance of them should be lettered on the plan as shown in Fig. 129.

Similarly the information contained in the deeds of the adjacent owners is added to the plan. With these data before us we can now study the evidence of the boundaries.

It should be remembered that when any property line is defined in the deed by distance and also by a physical object, the latter rules in case of disagreement of the two. (See Art. 151, p. 133.)

Line $G-I$ is a line through the middle of the party wall; that was fixed by agreement, but this only applies for a length of about 43.50 ft. Ballard, the present owner of No. 62, acquired his property in two separate parcels at different times, but only the one acquired from Brown carries a party-wall agreement.

As there are two separate walls which back up on the line $E-F$ (as indicated by the cross-hatching in Fig. 129) that line is undoubtedly the property boundary. Each party is occupying to that line and these conditions have apparently existed for a sufficient time to make it the boundary by " adverse possession " even if there were no other evidence of its validity. (See Art. 151, p. 133.)

The line of Monroe St. as stated is that given by the City Engineer and is authentic.

In line $C-D$ we have more of a problem. The wall is a party-wall. It is used by both parties and there is no wall joint in the front. The sum of the two frontages from fieldnotes is 104.77, or 0.44 ft. greater than by the deeds. Furthermore, if we lay off Jones' deed distance from his northerly corner it will fall about 3 inches north of the center of the party wall, and if from the joint at E we lay off our deed distance along Monroe St. it will fall $2\frac{1}{4}$ inches south of the center of the wall.

As the center of the wall which is being used by both parties is the fairest boundary, it giving each party a greater frontage on Monroe St. than that called for in their respective deeds, the wisest thing to do is to assume it to be the boundary and call the attention of the owner to the discrepancy. As party-wall rights without a recorded agreement may prove troublesome, it is wise at this time for the two adjacent owners to sign a party-wall agreement in accord with the above decision before the proposed new building is commenced.

Line $C-B$ should be fixed in the same manner as $C-D$ as conditions are similar.

Although line $A-B$ is described as passing through the middle of the brick partition wall (which is 20 inches thick), reference to the fieldnotes shows that the street joint A is actually 0.08 ft. south of the center line of the wall.

It may be better to accept the wall joint as the corner at A and run to the center of the wall at point B, thus sacrificing a small triangular strip of land, for the purpose only of avoiding a controversy which might arise if 0.08 ft. of the front of building No. 54 were apparently cut away. But, as in the other cases, the decision of this question should be made by the owner.

On consulting the agreement between Bailey and Hayes dated Sept. 5, 1922, we find the statement "and it is further agreed that the area hereinafter described which is now covered by a one-story building and indicated as $ABCD$ on a plan by Jones & Robinson, surveyors, dated Aug. 20, 1922 and herewith recorded shall not be built over to a height greater than 12 ft. above the sidewalk on Washington St. where the land of the party of the first part adjoins the land of the party of the second part."

On consulting that plan we find that the area restricted is the one indicated by the letters *J K L M* on our plan. A note giving the substance of this restriction is therefore added to our plan.

310. Calculation of the Adopted Boundaries of the Property. — As the joints at *A* and *I* are at the lot corners we first calculate their coördinates using the ties from points 1 and 6 and the offsets from line 1–7. With 6.91 as a hypothenuse and 3.00 as a perpendicular we find the distance from 1 along line 1–7 to the foot of the perpendicular from *A*. This added to the " *y* " of 1 gives us the " *y* " of point *A* whose " *x* " is obviously 3.00. In the same way using tie 10.09 and offset 3.00 we find the coördinates of point *I*. The distance *AI* calculated from these coördinates (80.71) agrees with the measurement taken in the field.

The thickness of wall *A–B* = 15.725 − (5.90 + 8.17) = 1.655 ft. = 20 inches. Similarly the computed thickness of wall *BC* is 16 inches.

As point *B* is at the intersection of the center line of walls *A–B* and *C–B* it is 5.90 + 0.83, or 6.73, from line 1–2 and 2.93 + 0.66, or 3.59, from line 2–12.

The coördinates of point *B* may be calculated as indicated in Fig. 129b.

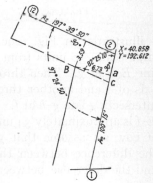

Draw *B–c* parallel to 2–12. Having the perpendicular 3.59 and the opposite angle at *c*, calculate the distance 2–*c* and then having the coördinates of 2 and the azimuth of line 2–*c* we can obtain the coördinates of *c*. Similarly, having the perpendicular 6.73 and the angle at *c*, calculate *B–c*; and then the coördinates of *B* from the azimuth and distance of line *B–c*.

FIG. 129b.

An alternative method is to calculate *a–c* and then 2–*a*. We can obtain now the coördinate of *a*, and as *a–B* is at right angles to 2–*a* we can obtain its azimuth readily and likewise the coordinates of *B*. By this second method it is only necessary to look up the sine and cosine of one azimuth, namely 100° 15′, whereas by the first method it is necessary to look up the sine and cosine of two angles, 100° 15′ and 197° 39′ 50″.

In a similar way obtain the coördinates of *C* and *D*, the latter being 5.80 from line 9–10 and 3.00 from line 10–3.

To obtain the coördinates of *E* we use the tie 8.49 from 4 and the swing-offset of 2.97. This gives us the coördinates of a point 0.03 ft. into Monroe St. which we will call *e*. We know that point *E* is 3.00 from Monroe St. traverse line and also lies

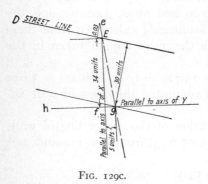

FIG. 129C.

on the line *E–F*, which is parallel to 11–17. As the angle between Monroe St. and the line 11–17 is 117° 23′, to obtain the distance from *e* to *E* we divide 0.03 by the sine of 117° 23′. With the coördinates of *e* and the azimuth and distance from *e* to *E*, we can calculate the coördinates of *E*.

A convenient graphical method of finding the difference in coördinates between *e* and *E*

is illustrated in Fig. 129c. Draw a line (using any convenient large scale) 30 units from and parallel to *D–E* and intersecting line *E–F* at *g*. Then through *g* draw a line *g–h* parallel to the axis of *y* and another through point *E* parallel to the axis of *x* intersecting line *g–h* at *f*. Using the same scale we will find that *E–f* is approximately 34 units in length and *f–g* 5 units in length. If now we assume that 30 units = 30 thousandths of a foot the difference between the *x*'s of *e* and *E* is 34 thousandths and the difference between the *y*'s of *e* and *E* is 5 thousandths of a foot.

Distance *EF* is obtained from the roof measurement of 21.33 − 0.03 = 21.30 that is, the distance from Monroe St. to the end of the party-wall. With this distance and the azimuth of *E–F*, which is the same as 11–16, we now calculate the coördinates of *F*. An exact value for the length *EF* is not important because if the jog F is 0.1 to 0.2 ft. nearer to or farther from Monroe St. it matters little.

The computed perpendicular distance between lines 11–17 and 5–20 is 14.81. If distance 5.74 at joint E is subtracted from 14.81 it gives 9.07 as the distance from E to line 5–20. Since G is in the center of the 20 inch wall G–H, it is 8.85 ft. from line 5–20. The difference between 9.07 and 8.85, or 0.22, gives the length of the line F–G, which is so short that we are safe in assuming it to be at right angles to E–F, and then compute the coördinate of G.

As indicated by the offsets, line G–H is so nearly parallel to E–F that it is better to assume it to be so and to ignore the small variation of 0.02 ft., in calculating the coördinates of H and the length of G–H. Having the coördinates of G and I the azimuth and length of GI are computed readily. With azimuths of I–H, H–I and G–I, calculate the angles of the triangle GHI and with the side G–I known we can find the other two, and then the coördinates of H and I.

From the coördinates of points A, B, C, D, E, F, G, H and I we can find the azimuths and lengths of the property lines. This gives a balanced traverse (Fig. 130).

311. Final Adjustments of Property-Line Dimensions. — Using the traverse of boundaries with lengths calculated to the nearest thousandth and the azimuth to the nearest 10 seconds, a plan of the boundary lines can then be produced that should balance.

Structural companies and architects usually calculate structural members to the nearest $\frac{1}{16}$ inch. They often prefer to have the boundary dimensions recorded on the plan, therefore, only to the nearest 0.005 ft. To accommodate this situation the lengths in the calculated boundary traverse can now be modified by adding a thousandth or two to certain lines and subtracting from others so that most of the lines will read to a full hundredth of a foot, but in a few cases to half hundredths. Using these new lengths and the old angles, compute the boundary traverse anew by coördinates, using this time a different axis. Then adjust any slight error of closure that may exist by making slight changes preferably in the angles; or by making a small change in a short side if that seems to be the more practical.

This was done in producing the final plan (Fig. 129).

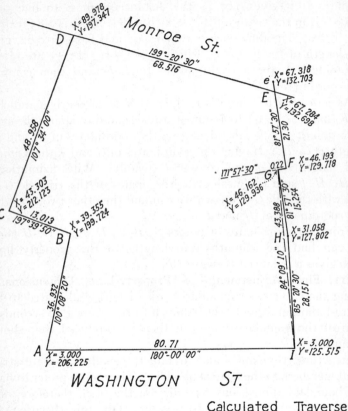

Calculated Traverse
of Boundaries

FIG. 130.

311a. Other Data Shown on Final Plan. — When sewers water pipes and various other utilities have to be shown on plan confusion will result unless each object is designated clearly For that reason it is well to use not only different colors but als different characteristics in the lines representing the various pipe etc.   Satisfactory results will be obtained by using the following representations:

Water pipes — Full blue lines thus _____

Sewers — Brown lines thus _____•____

Surface drains — Brown lines thus _____ __ _____ __

Gas pipes — Green lines thus _____ __ __ ____ ___

Elec. conduits — Red lines thus ____ __ __ __ __ __ __ __

Tel. and Tel. pipes — Red lines thus __ __ __ __ __ __ __

Present elevations are shown in red.

Official elevations are shown in blue within circles.

Deed measurements and quotations from records are shown in green.

The Bench Marks used should also be shown on the plan.

311b. Profile and Sections of Building Walls — Fieldwork. —

In obtaining the profile and sections of wall E–F–G–H–I the following method is used.   On Washington St. (see Fig. 130a) a mark is made in the vicinity of point 7 on line 1–7, so selected that when a line parallel to I–II is laid off and projected upwards it will pass through the windows of all the floors of building No. 62 and also, when run over the roof, this line can be produced to Monroe St. without meeting obstructions, such as penthouses or chimneys.   Let us suppose that point 7 fulfills these conditions.

Since it is impossible to place a point on the roof of No. 62 sighting directly from point 7 another point 7a is marked on this line on the opposite sidewalk of Washington St. and a foresight 7b is placed on the face of the building beyond point 7a.

The transit is then set up on 7a and sighted on 7 and a point 7c is marked on the roof of No. 62, far enough back from the parapet of the building to form a suitable place to set up a transit. The transit telescope should now be plunged (instrument reversed) and point 7c again marked, and, if there is any variation between the two sights, point 7c should be shifted to conform to the average between the two positions.   (See Art. 64, p. 58.)

The instrument is then set up over point 1 and sighted on 7. A leveling rod is now held horizontally with its end at point

$7c$ the right-angle offset from $7c$ to line 1–7 can be read on the rod, and the distance 7–$7c$ computed.

The transit is now set up on the roof-point $7c$, sighted on the point $7b$, and double reversed to set $7d$ near the angle at H. Offsets are measured to the wall H–I and the distance $7c$–$7d$ measured.

The transit is now set up on point $7d$, sighted on $7c$, and the angle $176°$ $36'$ $30''$ (from Fig. 130a) turned, and point $7e$ is marked on the roof near the Monroe St. wall. It is now pointed on a line parallel to G–H and F–E and offsets are measured to the face of these walls.

Line $7d$–$7e$ is produced to Monroe St. and point $7f$ is marked on the easterly sidewalk of that street, by double reversal of the transit; the distance $7d$–$7e$ is measured.

The transit is now set up over $7f$, the line $7e$–$7f$ intersected with line 3–11 at point $4a$ and the right-angle offset from point E to line $7e$–$7f$ measured.

The angle between lines $7e$–$7f$ and 3–11 is measured, the right-angle offset from $7e$ to line 3–11 measured with the rod and the objects on the roof (wall thicknesses, penthouse, sky light and chimney) measured and tied onto the roof traverse and the survey on the roof is completed.

The profile of the wall should now be taken. First establish a temporary bench mark or reference mark on the face of building No. 60 from which vertical tape measurements can be made to the roof of No. 60, the higher building.

The transit (used as a level) is now set up on the roof of No. 60 and a vertical reading taken with the tape on the bench mark established on the face of the building.

Readings should now be taken either with the tape or rod at every change in slope on the roof of No. 60 where it adjoins No. 62, at every change in the slope of the roof of No. 62 where it adjoins No. 60, on the roof of the one-story building at F and E at every change of slope in the parapet wall G–H–I, and on top of the penthouse, the chimney and the skylight.

Employing the same methods used in ascending from Washington St. another bench mark can be established on Monroe St. and the levels checked.

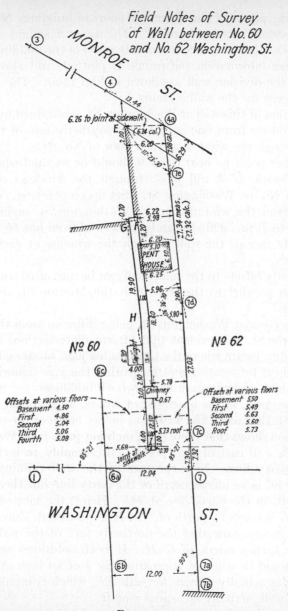

Field Notes of Survey
of Wall between No. 60
and No. 62 Washington St.

FIG. 130a.

The elevations of the basement floors of buildings No. 60 and No. 62 should now be obtained. The use of flashlight, acetylene light or candle will be needed in dark parts of the building. With the above information the profile is plotted, and also the roof plan of the division wall as shown in Fig. 130b. The next step is to survey for the wall sections.

A section of this wall at Washington St. is obtained by measuring the offsets from line $7a$–7 to the southerly face of the party-wall through the window at each floor of No. 62.

Another point $6a$ near point 6 should be marked where a line parallel with H–I will pass through the windows of all the floors of No. 60 Washington St. Set up on point $6a$, establish a point $6b$ on the westerly line of Washington St. making $6a$–$6b$ parallel to 7–$7a$. Offsets can be measured from line $6b$–$6a$ to the northerly face of the wall through the window at each floor of No. 60.

Similarly offsets to the same wall can be measured from transit lines run parallel to the wall from the Monroe St. side of the building.

The section at Washington St. being different from the section at Monroe St. it is evident that intermediate sections should be obtained to locate where the changes, or jogs, occur. These can be obtained by locating and measuring the jogs (ignoring chimneys) which occur in each floor in both buildings.

For instance, in the basement of No. 60 we find that at Washington St. the face of the wall is 14 inches north of the party line. Inspection shows that there is a 4 inch jog 30 ft. from Washington St. The wall east of that point is presumably 10 inches north of the party line. Now the face of the wall running in from Monroe St. is 12 inches north of the party line but there is a jog of 0.22 ft. in the party line at FG. Hence the face of the wall east of G is 0.078 ft. north of line H–G produced, since previous measurements show that the northerly face of the wall west of G is 10 inches north of G–H. If both solutions are correct there should be a jog of approximately $\frac{5}{8}$ of an inch at point G. The jog is actually 1 inch, for wall EF, which is intended for 12 inch wall, actually measured 0.97 ft.

With the location of all of the jogs at all the floors in building

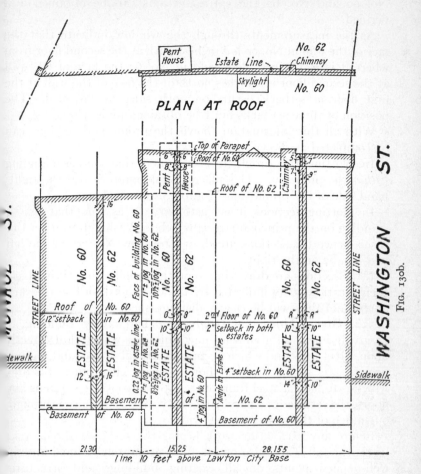

Profile and Sections of Wall between Estates
No. 60–62 Washington St., Lawton, Mass.

Scale 8 feet to an inch

August 15, 1929

Jones and Robinson, Civil Engineers
700 Washington St., Lawton, Mass.

No. 60 and No. 62 the entire sections can be obtained and verified.

As the measurements through the window indicate that the face of the wall in No. 60 is 2 inches south at the second floor from where it is at the first floor, and in No. 62 the face of the wall at the second floor is 2 inches north of the face of the wall at the first floor, a setback occurs on both sides of the wall. The position of these setbacks must be obtained by leveling.

With all this information shown the profile and sections can be completed as shown in Fig. 130b.

In plotting the profile it is assumed that one is standing *within* the property. This places Washington St. on the right-hand side of the profile and Monroe St. on the left.

In plotting sections it is customary to assume that one is standing on the principal street, which is Washington St. in this case; hence the sections are drawn to show No. 60 on the left and No. 62 on the right.

If the sections are drawn in red on the profile, which is in black, their location being indicated by the dot and dash line (marked party line) they will be clearly distinguished.

312. Giving Lines and Grades for Large City Building. — In giving lines and grades for new buildings which abut directly upon street lines and which occupy nearly all of the land, batter-boards are impracticable. For a large city office building which is to have a steel frame or reinforced concrete columns and floors, the services of a surveying party may be required throughout much of the construction period.

Before any excavation work begins the surveyor should take levels carefully, and also offsets from accurately defined lines at well-defined points on all existing buildings and structures abutting on or near the property, and as the work progresses he should rerun the levels frequently so as to discover any settlement of these structures while it is incipient. It is important that the B.M. shall be outside of any area that can possibly be disturbed by the construction.

As the work on the new building progresses he will set grade and lines for all rough excavation work, for masonry foundations of basement walls and column footings, mark all columns centers on the completed footing, set lines and grades for forms for concrete walls and piers, check their position before the concrete is poured, mark grades for each floor level at all columns, check the grade of forms for floors before they are poured, check up the elevation at many points throughout each floor before and after the forms supporting the floors have been struck and for a month or more thereafter so as to determine whether the green floor slab is sagging.

The grid lines connecting all column centers should be referenced on the architect's plan to the property lines shown on the surveyor's plan (Fig. 131). The surveyor accurately reproduces these column lines on the ground and reference marks on each column line are marked on the opposite sidewalks on a base-line parallel to the street line and on the party walls, so that each line of columns is referenced at both ends (Fig. 131). As far as possible these marks should be well outside the limits of actual construction so that they will not be disturbed. It is advisable also to set reference marks for levels at the ends of each line of columns, preferably by setting the level up, by trial, so that the middle cross-hair will be an exact number of feet above the City Datum. Then the reference marks are cut in the walls surrounding this lot and on the walls of the buildings that face the site of the new building. This insures a consistent set of reference marks readily seen from all parts of the new building site and which are dependable because all were cut at the height of the line of sight and in plain view of the levelman.

A sketch always should be given to the superintendent of construction showing all reference marks made. In construction work more mistakes are made by misunderstanding than by errors in measurements. It is advisable, therefore, to give all dimensions to the superintendent both in feet and hundredths and also in feet and inches and fractions (usually to $\frac{1}{16}$ inch).

In laying out large plants involving many buildings, connecting pipe lines, and tracks the entire layout may be referred to a rectangular coördinate system. By this means the property lines, buildings, and all points needed for purposes of construction are tied together, and points of known coördinates may be set by measuring from any convenient stations in the system.

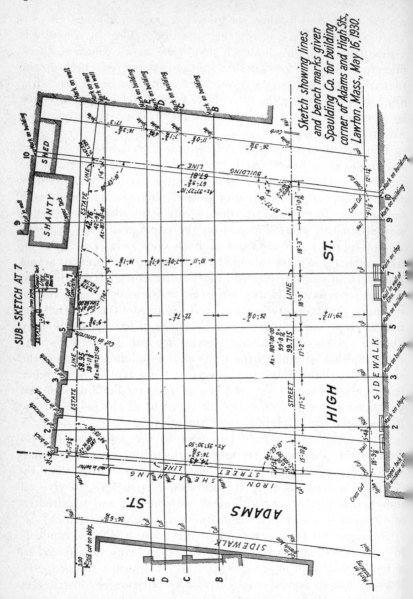

Sketch showing lines and bench marks given Spaulding Co. for building corner of Adams and High Sts., Lawton, Mass., May 16, 1930.

RECTANGULAR COÖRDINATE SYSTEM FOR SURVEYING CITIES

313. General Description. — In the survey of a city or a metropolitan district it is customary to refer all points to a system of plane rectangular coördinates. Some point within the area, preferably a station already established by triangulation, is selected as the fundamental point of the coördinate system. All distances and all coördinates are computed as though they were in a plane tangent to the earth at this point. The effect of disregarding the curvature of the earth is found to be extremely small for such areas. The true meridian through this tangent point is taken as the axis of Y for the system, and the line at right angles to it as the axis of X. All points within the area may be located with reference to this starting point. In order to avoid negative values of the coördinates, the initial point may be assigned the coördinates 10 000 N, 10 000 E, or any other convenient values. In such a system all azimuths, or bearings, refer to the initial meridian or Y axis. Consequently at all points not on the initial meridian the local meridian is not used. The direction of the Y axis is sometimes called " grid North " to distinguish it from the geographical meridian.

In the survey of the city of Baltimore (Fig. 131a) the origin was taken at the Washington Monument in the center of the city. The city map is divided into squares 1000 ft. on a side. It is also divided into blocks one mile square, each square being shown on a page of the atlas. These squares are designated by numbers north or south, east or west of the origin, as, $1S_2W$, $3N_4E$, etc. The position of a point is shown by its distance in feet from the coördinate axes, as 2020.5 N, 1105.0 E.

Among other cities that have been surveyed by this coördinate method the following may be mentioned: New York, Atlanta, Rochester, Cincinnati, Pittsburgh, and London, Ontario.

One of the advantages of a coördinate system is that if any point of known coördinates is lost it can be replaced by means of the known coördinates of other points in that district. If the stations from which it was originally located have been lost, it may be relocated from any other points whose coördinates are known. If a large area is destroyed by fire the entire district may be laid out again from points outside the devastated area. It is of utmost importance, therefore, that all stations be marked permanently.

314. Triangulation Scheme. — The principal points of the survey (control points) are usually located by triangulation, sometimes by especially accurate traverses, or both. In a triangulation system the length of one side of some triangle must be measured, then if sufficient angles are taken (with great precision) all other sides may be calculated by plane trigonometry. The shape of the triangles is important. It is difficult to lay down rules for the shape of acceptable triangles without going into the discussion from a mathematical standpoint. In general, it is necessary to avoid small angles which occur opposite the base, or known side, or opposite the side being calculated. It is not correct to say that small angles should never be admitted in the system; they should not be admitted when they enter the system in such a way as to weaken it. (See Coast and Geodetic Survey Special Publication No. 120.) In beginning such a survey it is usually possible to utilize such triangulation as already exists in the locality in question. For a method of converting the latitudes and longitudes of such triangulation stations into plane coördinates see Hosmer's *Geodesy*, and Coast and Geodetic Survey Special Publication No. 71. The triangulation may be precise enough to furnish base-lines upon which the entire system of triangles may be built up. But if the triangulation in this locality is a long distance from the base from which it was computed the errors in length may have accumulated to such an extent that the lines will not be sufficiently accurate to serve as base-lines for the city survey. It may be possible however to utilize the triangulation to furnish the general position of the survey as a whole, but it will be necessary to measure one or two special base-lines with great accuracy and to make special determinations of azimuth. Land values in cities are high, and are increasing. The precision required in a city survey is fully as high as that of any kind of survey that is made, and it is a mistake to begin such a survey with work of low precision, for if the precision of the triangulation is barely sufficient for the present purposes

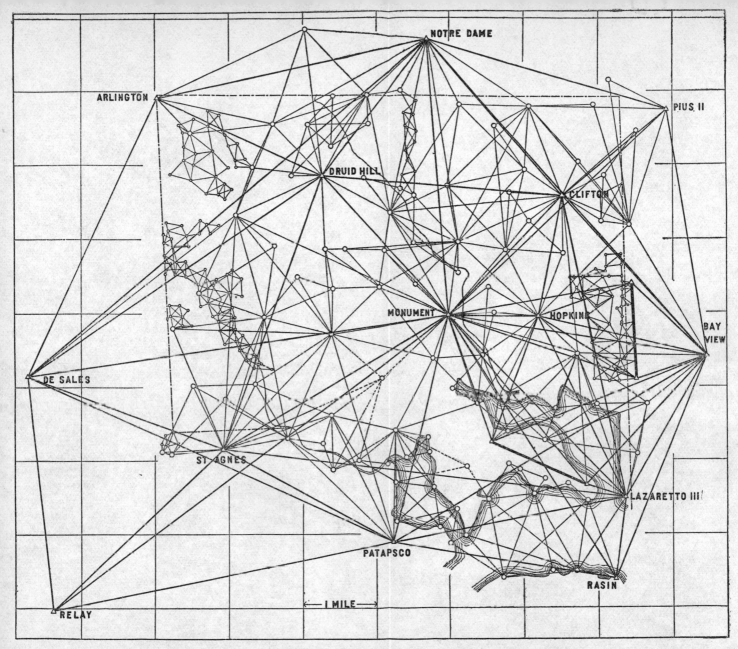

FIG. 131a.   TRIANGULATION SCHEME FOR SURVEY OF THE CITY OF BALTIMORE.
(Printed by permission of Major Joseph W. Shirley, Chief Engineer of the Topographical Survey Commission, Baltimore, Md.)

it is only a question of time when the whole system must be resurveyed.

There will in general be two classes of triangulation stations: (1) those occupied with the instrument and located with first-order precision; and (2) such points as flagpoles, church spires, or water tanks, not occupied with the instrument, but located by intersection. These latter points will be useful, but are never quite so accurate as the former. Such points may be used to locate the transit by means of the three-point problem. (See Vol. II, Chap. I.) It is of special importance in city surveys to attend to the precise centering of both the instruments and the signals over the station marks.

315. Measurement of Base-line. — The lines chosen as bases should be placed for convenience on fairly level ground, but for accurate results they should be such as will give well-shaped triangles, and the former consideration should never outweigh the latter. The base is measured with invar tapes or wires, a spring balance, and thermometers, as described in the publications already cited. The tapes should be tested at the U. S. Bureau of Standards both before and after the measurements. The measuring stakes, or the measuring tripods, should be lined in carefully with a transit, and the grade of the tape determined carefully by leveling. If two independent measurements of the base agree within about one part in 500,000 the base will be satisfactory for this work. It is not difficult, however, to secure a precision of about one in one million.

316. Measuring the Angles. — If a direction theodolite, reading to seconds by means of microscopes, can be secured for this work it will give the best results. If a repeating transit (10″ vernier) is used the angles must be measured with a sufficient number of repetitions to give angles with a probable error of, say, 0″.5. Each set of angles should consist of six angles with telescope erect and six with telescope inverted. The particular order in which the direct and reverse angle are taken may be varied somewhat. About five sets will be required on each angle. In order to distribute the readings over the circle and thereby eliminate errors of graduation each time a new set is begun the initial setting of the vernier should be advanced by an amount equal to $360°/mn$, where m is the number of verniers and n is the number of sets to be measured. Both verniers should be read and the mean taken at the completion of each half-set. Careful attention must be given to the centering and the leveling of the instrument. The signals should be such as to give no error of " phase " (side illumination) and should be exactly centered over the station mark.

317. Adjustment of the Principal Triangulation. — In a system of triangulation of such importance it is advisable to have the entire main scheme of triangles adjusted by " Least Squares." Once done it will not have to be repeated. This adjustment removes all inconsistencies and prevents accumulation of error such as would occur if errors were allowed to remain in the system. For individual triangles it will be sufficient to divide the error of closure by 3 and to apply this correction to each angle. This may be done for the preliminary computation of all triangles. The test of accuracy most easily applied is to see if the sum of three angles of each triangle is equal to 180° + any spherical excess which may be required. The spherical excess is only 1″ for each 76 square miles of area of the triangle, so, for the triangles discussed here the spherical excess will be quite small, but in some instances it will not be negligible. In first-order triangulation the error of closure of a triangle should be about 1″ or less. In city work it should not fall much below this accuracy. (See Report on Horizontal Control, Proc. Am. Soc. C. E., p. 2491, Vol. 54, No. 9, Nov. 1928.)

318. Azimuth. — Before beginning any other work it is important to obtain the azimuths of two or more lines, preferably connected with, or near to, the initial station. These azimuths must be determined with an accuracy comparable with that of the triangulation, that is, with a probable error of about 0″.5. (For the special methods required see Vol. II, Chap. II, and Coast and Geodetic Survey Spec. Pub. No. 14.) These azimuths must refer to the initial meridian. If they are observed at any station other than the initial point the amount of the convergence of the meridians must be determined and allowed for.

319. Subsidiary Triangulation. — After the principal triangulation has been completed other stations may be located, the triangles being smaller and the accuracy somewhat less, than that of the main scheme. (For specifications for $2d$ and $3d$ order triangulation see U. S. C. & G. S. Spec. Pub., 145.) The object of this is to place stations in more convenient locations from which to run traverses for locating street lines, or lot lines. If a belt of these smaller triangles starts from an accurate base-line it is advisable to close it on some other line of known length in order to check all the intermediate work.

320. Traverses. — After the triangulation has been completed, traverses may be run from one triangulation station to any other, connecting all street corners, lot corners, and other points whose location is desired. Since the coördinates of the points from which these traverses start are of a high order of precision and since the traverses close on other accurate points, it is not necessary to make the traverse measurements themselves with so great accuracy as would be necessary if there were no controlling system of triangulation. It is for this reason that the triangulation is really economical. When a traverse is closed on a fixed station the error of closure is computed and the error thrown into the traverse itself. The positions of the triangulation stations are not altered, as these are considered to have been finally fixed in the general adjustment.

321. Method of Locating Street Lines, Property Lines and Buildings. — The coördinates of all traverse stations are calculated after the traverse has been adjusted. To locate street corners, points on offset lines, or lot corners, it is only necessary to turn angles and measure distances from the traverse stations to points on the lines in question. The azimuths or bearings of all these lines may be calculated readily (always referred to the Y axis of the system). When the distance and the bearing are known the difference in coördinates (Δy) and (Δx) can be found as explained in Art. 420, p. 504. Buildings, property lines, street railways and underground conduits may be located by the various methods discussed in Chap. VI. All important points should be located from at least two different instrument stations as a check against mistakes.

EXAMPLE

Position of point a from station 3 (Fig. 131b) would be calculated as follows:

Azimuth $3 - a = 221° 10' 30''$
Dist. $3 - a = 41.29$ ft.

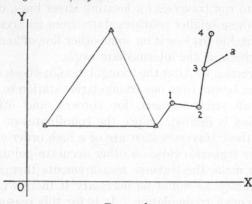

FIG. 131b.

Diff. lat.	31.08	(See Art. 420, p. 504.)
log diff. lat.	1.49246	
log cos az.	9.87662	
log dist.	1.61584	
log sin az.	9.81846	
log dep.	1.43430	
dep.	27.18	

	North	East
Coörd. of 3	2160.41	4209.20
Diffs.	+31.08	+27.18
Coörd. of a =	2191.49	4236.38

321a. Level Control. — Vertical control involves providing precise elevations referred to one well-defined datum so that their accuracy is assured. Vertical control is produced by running first-order levels (Vol. II, Chap. III) and establishing permanent bench marks placed in pairs at about one-half to one mile apart. The bench marks are placed in pairs so that both are visible from one set-up of the level instrument, thus giving an immediate check on settlement of the bench marks. The levels should be run in loops of about one mile in length on a side; the error of closure in each loop is a valuable check on the observations. The entire net should be adjusted by the method of Least Squares to give the most probable elevations and to remove all inconsistencies. From these first-order elevations, levels of low order may be conveniently run to provide grades for construction. (See Art. 100b, p. 81B.)

PROBLEMS

1. The deflection angle between two lines is 46° 24′ to the right. The lines are to be connected with a curve of 300-foot radius.

(a) Find the tangent distance to .01 ft. and the total length of arc to .01 ft.

(b) If the curve is laid out in 10 equal parts, compute the deflection angles (to ½ minute) from the tangent at the P.C. to each point and show check on the deflection angle to the P.T. Also compute the length of the short chord (to .01 ft.) to be used in laying out these points.

(c) If, instead, the curve is laid out by a series of 25-foot chords starting at the P.C., compute all the deflection angles necessary to lay out this curve and the length of the last chord to close on the P.T.

2. Compute chords to .01 ft. and deflection angles to ½ minute for center line, right, and left edges of a 40-foot pavement, on a curve of 250-foot center-line radius to the left. The center-line curve is to be staked out in 25-foot arcs starting at the P.C. The points set on the left and right edges of the pavement are to be radially opposite those on the center line. The station of the P.C. = 20 + 00.00. I = 36° 00′.

3. The grade lines shown below are to be connected by a vertical parabolic curve 400 ft. long.

(a) Compute the elevations to .01 ft. at full stations and +50 points along the curve.

Sta. 50 + 00	El. 24.60
Sta. 65 + 00	El. 57.60
Sta. 85 + 00	El. 26.80

(b) What is the elevation at Sta. 65 + 20?

4. A pavement 30 ft. wide has a parabolic surface with a total crown of 6 in. If the pavement grade elevation at the center line is 96.20, what are the elevations at quarter points between the center line and the curb?

5. Design the cross-section of a residential street, 30 feet wide, on which an unsymmetrical crown is required. The highest point of the pavement is to be elevation 656.62; it is located 12 ft. east of the face of the curb on the west side of the street. The elevation of the gutter on the west side of the street is to be 656.27 ft. The elevation of the gutter on the east side of the street is to be 655.98. Curbs are to be 7 inches in height on each side of the street. On a sheet of cross-section paper, plot the cross-section of the street. Use a horizontal scale of 8 ft. = 1 in. and a vertical scale of 1 ft. = 1 in. Determine the elevation of the top of each curb and also the elevation for each 5 ft. point across the pavement. Record the elevations on the sketch.

6. A $+4.0\%$ grade line meets a -5.5% grade line at elevation 238.92 at Sta. $48 + 00.0$. An 800-foot parabolic vertical curve is to be used to connect these grade lines.

(a) Compute and tabulate the elevations for points at every full station and $+50$ points along the curve.

(b) Determine the station and elevation of the point of highest elevation on the curve.

7. A -3 per cent grade meets a $+5$ per cent grade near an underpass. In order to maintain the minimum clearance allowed under the bridge and at the same time introduce a vertical transition curve in the grade line, it is necessary to use a curve that lies 200 ft. on one side of the vertex of the straight grade lines and 100 feet on the other. The station of the beginning of the curve (200 ft. side) is $10 + 00$ and its elevation is 746.40.

(a) Determine the elevation of each 25-foot station on the 300-foot vertical (parabolic) curve to .01 ft.

(b) If the up-hill edge of the under side of the bridge is at Sta. $12 + 50$ and at eleva. 759.23, what is the vertical clearance under the bridge at this point?

8. (a) Compute the lengths to 0.01 ft. not given on the sketch (Fig. 131c) of all straight and curved boundaries on the lots shown; also compute the area of each lot to nearest 10 s.f.

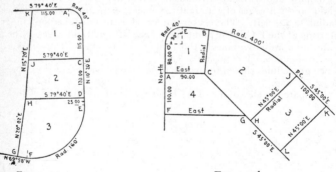

FIG. 131c. FIG. 131d.

(b) Plot the lots to a scale of 50 ft. = 1 in. and letter all dimensions, bearings and areas on the plot.

9. (a) Compute the lengths to 0.01 ft. not given on the sketch (Fig. 131d) of all straight and curved boundaries of the lots shown.

(b) Compute the area of each lot to nearest 10 s.f.

CHAPTER XI

CONTOURS — MISCELLANEOUS TOPOGRAPHICAL SURVEYING METHODS

322. The usual topographical map shows such physical features as water surfaces, limits of cultivation, fences, roads and buildings in their correct relative positions on a horizontal plane. These features of the map may be made as complete and accurate as desired by the use of horizontal distances and horizontal angles. When, however, it is desired to show on the map the vertical element, or relief of the ground, then some artificial system must be employed for this purpose. Writing the elevations on the plan does not convey to the eye a clear picture of the relief. The system used for showing the relief must fulfill two purposes. First, it should make the form of the surface apparent to the eye without great effort on the part of the user of the map; that is, the user of the map should be able to interpret the map as a model of the ground. Second, it should furnish also definite information regarding the elevations of points shown on the map.

323. Systems depending upon shadows cast by the elevated portions of the land have been used with striking effect. These make the general form of the surface apparent at once even to a person not experienced in the use of maps. Although useful for some purposes they tell nothing about actual elevations of the surface. Sometimes elevations are indicated by different tints or shades.

324. Systems depending upon the use of artificial shade lines, or *hachures*, were formerly in general use on maps. These lines show the surface form, but they do not furnish exact information regarding the heights. On many of the earlier maps issued by the Coast and Geodetic Survey this shading system was used, an excellent example being the map of Mount Desert Island (1875). Very artistic results can be produced by the use of hachure lines, but for engineering purposes they do not give information that is sufficiently exact and consequently are much less used at the present time. The use of hachures survives, however, in maps of such large areas that merely the general location of mountains can be given, as, for example, the western hemisphere, or the North American continent. It also survives in conventional symbols for eroded banks, gravel pits, and cuts and fills on a railway or a highway.

Fig. 132 shows a mountain represented by hachure lines. The short lines are drawn always in the direction of the steepest slope

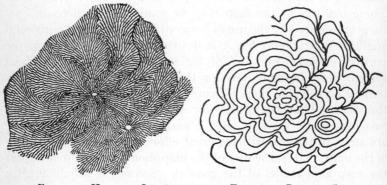

FIG. 132. HACHURE LINES.   FIG. 133. CONTOUR LINES.

of the surface. The spacing of the lines, center to center, is always the same, but the weight (width) of the lines increases with the steepness of the slope. Definite scales of slope of the surface and width of line have been worked out, a given width of line indicating a definite slope of the surface. Any such scale is of course arbitrary.

325. Contour Lines. — The system now in general use for representing the form of the surface is that employing *contour lines*, or lines passing through points of equal elevation. The elevations of the contours are known definitely, so that the elevation of any point on the ground may be derived from the map. At the same time this system makes the form apparent to the eye, even to persons that have but little familiarity with maps. The location and relative heights of the hills is apparent at once; a close spacing of the contours indicates a steep slope, while a wide spacing means a flatter slope. With a little study one can learn to visualize the terrain from the contours, and at the same time obtain an accurate elevation when he wants it. Fig. 133 shows the same mountain as is represented in Fig. 132, but represented by contour lines.

A contour line is the **intersection of a level surface with the surface of the ground.** A clearer conception of a contour line may be obtained from the following. Imagine a valley, or a de-

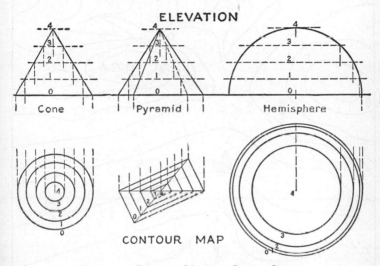

FIG. 134. CONTOUR MAPS OF SIMPLE SOLIDS.

pression in the surface of the ground, partly filled with water. The shore line of this body of water will be a contour line, because it is the intersection of a level surface with the surface of the ground. If the water stands at an elevation of 50 ft. the shore line is the 50-ft. contour. If the surface of the water were raised 5 ft. the new shore line would be the 55-ft. contour. Contour lines, if extended far enough, will therefore be closed curves, and all of the points on any one contour will have the same elevation above the datum. It is customary to take contours a whole number of feet above the datum, spacing them in regard to height, so as to make the *contour intervals* equal, e.g., a contour may be taken at every 5 ft. or every 10 ft. of elevation. Since the contours are equidistant in a vertical direction their distance apart in a horizontal direction indicates the steepness of the slope.

Fig. 134 illustrates contour maps of simple geometric solids.

Fig. 135.   Illustrating Characteristics of Contours.

326. Characteristics of Contours. — The chief characteristics of contours are illustrated in Fig. 135, and may be summed up as follows.

1. All points on any one contour have the same elevation, as at *A*.

2. Every contour closes on itself, either within or beyond

the limits of the map. If the contour does not close within the limits of the map it will run to the edge of the map, as at *B*.

3. A contour which closes within the limits of the map indicates either a summit or a depression. In depressions there will usually be found a pond or a lake; but where there is no water the contours are usually marked in some way to indicate a depression, as at *C*.

4. Contours can never cross each other except where there is an overhanging cliff, and here there must be two intersections, as at *D*. Such cases as this seldom occur.

5. On a uniform slope contours are spaced equally, as at *E*.

6. On a plane surface they are straight and parallel to each other, as at *F*.

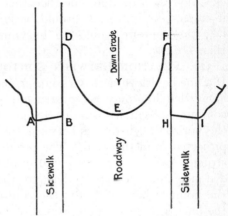

FIG. 136. CONTOUR CROSSING A STREET.

7. In crossing a valley the contours run up the valley on one side and, turning at the stream, run back on the other side, as at *G*. Since the contours are always at right angles to the lines of steepest slope they are at right angles to the thread of the stream at the point of crossing.

8. Contours cross the ridge lines (watersheds) at right angles, as at *H*.

9. In general the curve of the contour in a valley is convex toward the stream.

Fig. 136 shows a contour across an ordinary city street with sidewalks and curbstones, the street being located on a steep grade. In order to trace out the position of a contour it is necessary to keep in mind that it is a line all points on which are at the same elevation. It will be noticed that the contour from *A* to *B* crosses the sidewalk in a straight line but not perpendicular to the street line because the sidewalk is sloped toward the gutter. Turning at B it runs straight along the face of the curbstone until it strikes the gutter at D, and returns on the other side of the gutter along the surface of the road, the point E being where it swings around and travels back toward the other gutter. The other half of the street is similar. If the center of the road is at the same elevation as the top of the curb opposite, then E will be opposite B. This illustrates how contours run around valleys (gutters) and ridges (crown of street).

If the side of the street to the right (HF) were at a lower elevation than the left side then the contour at the point where it crosses the gutter, F, would be farther up the road from E, i.e., the contour would be unsymmetrical, EF being longer than DE.

327. RELATION BETWEEN CONTOUR MAP AND PROFILE. — If a line be drawn across a contour map the profile of the surface along that line may be constructed, since the points where the contours are cut by the line are points of known elevation and the horizontal distances between these points can be scaled or projected from the map. The profile shown in Fig. 137 is constructed by drawing first equidistant lines parallel to AB, their distance apart corresponding to the contour interval; from the points where AB cuts the contours, lines are projected to the lines of corresponding elevation on the profile. Conversely, if the profiles of a sufficient number of lines on the map are given it is possible to plot these lines on the map, mark the elevations of points on the lines, and from these points to sketch the contours as described in Art. 331, p. 399.

328. RELATION BETWEEN CONTOUR MAP AND SIDE ELEVATION OR PROJECTION. — A photograph of a landscape taken horizontally is actually a perspective of the landscape, but if sufficiently distant it represents **approximately** a side elevation of the country. To construct such a projection from a contour map (Fig. 138), lines are drawn perpendicular to AB, the plane of projection, and tangent to the contours. These tangent points show the limits between the visible and invisible portions of the landscape, the observer being assumed to look in a direction perpendicular to the plane AB.

329. DRAINAGE AREAS. — The drainage area that supplies a stream or a pond is bounded by the *divide line*, which is a line drawn along the ridges surrounding a depression as indicated by

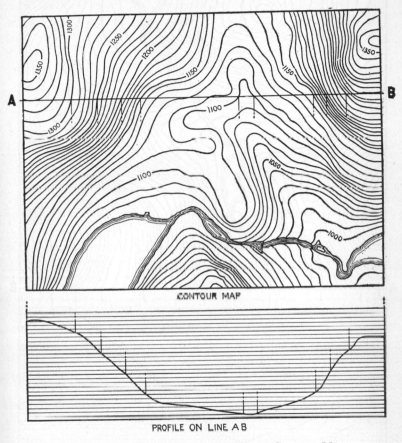

CONTOUR MAP

PROFILE ON LINE A B

FIG. 137. PROFILE CONSTRUCTED FROM A CONTOUR MAP.

the dotted line on Fig. 139. Since the perpendicular to the contour at any point is the direction of steepest slope the direction in which water will flow at any point can be determined at once by examining the contours. On the ridge there is a line (its summit) on one side of which water will flow down one of the slopes and on the other side of which it will flow down the other slope. This line is the divide line or *watershed line*.

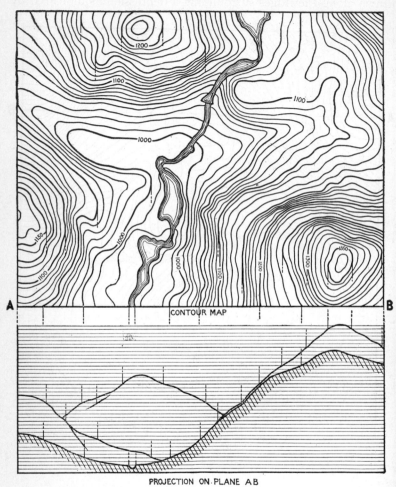

FIG. 138. SIDE ELEVATION CONSTRUCTED FROM A CONTOUR MAP.

If a dam were built as shown in Fig. 139, the elevation of the water back of the dam being 960 ft., the area actually flooded by the water at this stage is the area included within the 960-ft.

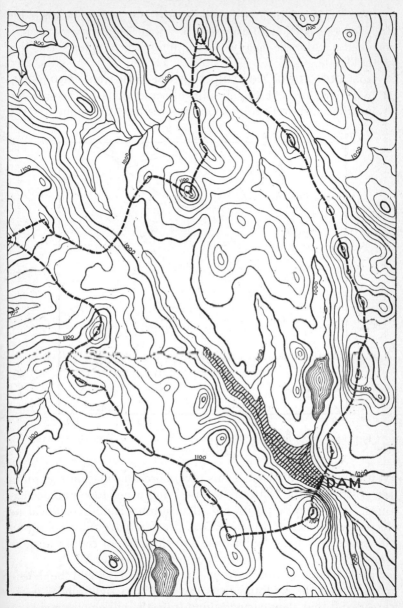

Fig. 139. Illustrating Flooded Area and Drainage Area.

contour; this is indicated by the shaded section. The drainage
area for the portion of the stream above the dam is the area
included within the heavy dotted line, which follows the line
of the divide.

**330. SKETCHING CONTOURS FROM STREAMS AND SUM-
MITS.** — The present topography of some parts of the country
is due almost entirely to erosion by streams. Consequently the

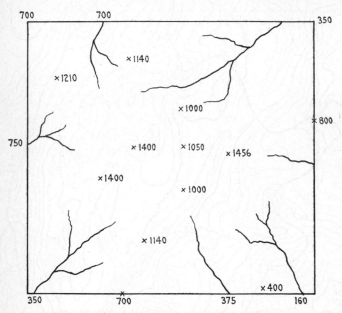

FIG. 140. MAP SHOWING THE LOCATION AND ELEVATION OF STREAMS
AND SUMMITS.

position and fall of the streams give more information regarding
the position of the contours than do any other topographic features. If a definite position of the contours is desired it will be
necessary to obtain the elevation of a few governing points on
the ridges as well as the location and elevation of the streams, as
shown in Fig. 140. (See also Volume II, Chapter VI.)

In sketching contours from these data it should be borne
in mind that the contours cross the stream at right angles to its
thread and that they curve around from the hill on either side so

as to represent the valley of the stream.   Since hills formed by erosion have rounded tops and relatively flat slopes near their bases the contours are farther apart at the top and bottom of the slope of an eroded hill than they are near the middle.   A stream is usually steeper near its source than in the lower portion and therefore the contours are closer together near the source.   This is true in general but the shape of the contours in any particular

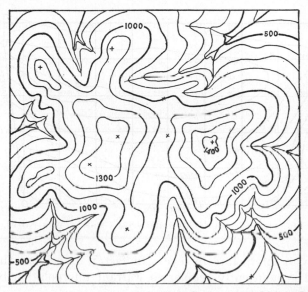

FIG. 141.   CONTOURS SKETCHED FROM THE DATA GIVEN IN THE MAP ON PAGE 398.

locality will depend upon the geological formation. Fig. 141 represents the same country as Fig. 140 but with the contours sketched on it, following out the general suggestions which have been mentioned.

331. SKETCHING CONTOURS FROM KNOWN ELEVATIONS. — A portion of the country can be cross-sectioned as described in Art. 253, p. 302, or profiles can be run on any desired lines as explained in Art. 251, p. 299. From these known elevations contours can be sketched by interpolation. This is done usually by estimation and the principle involved is the same whether the elevations were obtained by cross-sectioning or by profiles.

Fig. 142 illustrates how contours can be sketched from cross-section notes. Elevations are taken at each grid corner and also wherever there is a change of slope, so that it may be assumed that the slope of the ground is uniform between any two adjacent points. Then by simple interpolation the contours may be sketched. This interpolation may be done by geometric construction, but for most topographic work it is accurate

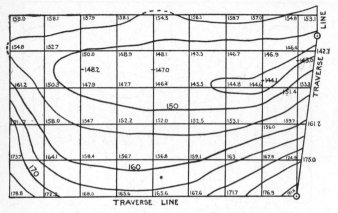

FIG. 142.   CONTOURS SKETCHED FROM CROSS-SECTION NOTES.

enough to interpolate by eye. In fact it is seldom that the ground is sufficiently regular to warrant interpolation by geometric construction.

332. MISTAKES IN SKETCHING CONTOURS. — Fig. 143 shows several examples of incorrect contour sketching. The locations of the streams on this map are assumed to be correct. The numbers on the illustration refer to the tabulation of characteristics of contours given in Art. 326, p. 392; these will assist in identifying the kind of error existing. The number 2, for instance, shows a contour line which stops short at the stream, whereas it evidently should cross the stream and continue on the other side of the valley. At 4 is a divided contour, which is an impossibility. The 7's all show places where the contours are evidently drawn without any regard to the position of the streams. For example, at the middle of the map the stream appears to be climbing up the valley, then over the saddle, and then flowing down the opposite valley.

333. CONTOUR PROBLEMS. — There are many surveying problems involving earthwork which can be solved by use of a

FIG. 143. CONTOURS INCORRECTLY SKETCHED.

contour map. As a rule the smaller the contour interval, the more accurate will be the result of such computations. Contour studies occur in a variety of problems, so numerous that it would be useless to attempt to cover the subject fully. Three typical

problems, however, are illustrated and explained; and these
contain the essential principles applicable to all contour studies.

334. EXAMPLE 1. — (Fig. 144). Given a contour map, the
surface being represented by contours shown by full lines; a
plane (extended indefinitely) is passed through the straight lines
AB and CD, which are level and parallel, AB being at elevation

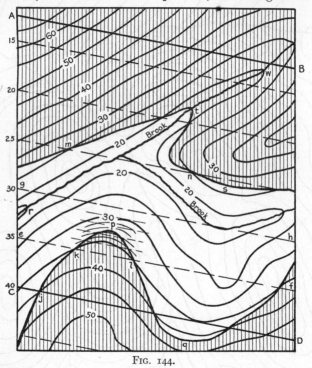

FIG. 144.

12.5 and CD being at elevation 40. It is required to find where
this plane intersects the surface, and to shade the portion which
is above the plane.

Since the proposed surface is a plane, contours on it will be
parallel to AB and CD. The elevations of AB and CD being
known, other contours, such as ef and gh, can be interpolated
between AB and CD. Their interval is made 5 ft. the same as
the contour interval for the original surface. Evidently the
point where any of these parallel lines crosses a surface con-

tour of the same elevation, as j, k, l, m, or n, is a point on the intersection of the plane with the surface. Joining these points gives the line of intersection of the plane with the original surface, which is indicated by the heavy full line on the figure. Such points as q, s, or t are determined by interpolation. Intermediate contours are drawn at one-foot intervals between the original surface contours; corresponding lines are interpolated between the straight contours that show the plane; in this way additional intersections are obtained, and the point p is deter-

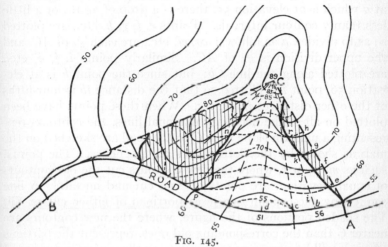

FIG. 145.

mined. Again it will be seen that point t, with reference to the parallel straight contours, is at elevation 18.5; with reference to the original contours, it will be seen that wt is about three-tenths of wr, the distance between contours, and this makes the elevation of point t equal to 18.5.

EXAMPLE 2. — Fig. 145 shows a road, and terrain on which the original contours are represented by full lines. It is desired that all of the road between A and B shall be visible from the ground at point C. Sketch on the map, and shade, the portions that will have to be cut down to fulfill this requirement.

The general method of solving this problem is to sketch a new set of contours on the map, which will represent a uniform slope from C to the nearer edge of the road. All above the surface represented by these new contours must be cut away.

First draw lines, such as Ca, Cb, and Cc, the points a, b, and c being points on the upper side of the road in such positions that it may be assumed that the slope is uniform from a to b and b to c. Along these lines interpolate points which will lie on the uniform slope from C to the road and also on the regular 5-ft. intervals which correspond to the contours. For example, along the line Ca from the summit which is at elevation 89 to the road at a which is at elevation 55, there is a drop of 34 ft., or a little less than 7 contour intervals. Points e, f, g, h, etc., are plotted so as to divide Ca as follows: ea, ef, etc., are each $\frac{5}{34}$ of AC, and the upper division is $\frac{4}{34}$ of AC. Similarly points i, j, k, etc., are plotted along the line Cb; but since the point b is at elevation 56, point i is plotted so that the distance ib is four-fifths of the other distances ij, jk, etc. When these points have been plotted on all of the necessary diagonal lines, the contours representing a uniform slope from C to the road are sketched on the map as shown by the dotted lines on the figure. The points, such as m, n, or r, where the new contours cut the old contours of equal elevation, are points of " no cut and no fill." A line connecting these points encloses portions of either cut or fill. The shaded portions of the figure, where the new contours are nearer C than the corresponding old ones, represent the portions where it will be necessary to excavate to the surface represented by the dotted contours. In the central portion of the figure, from point c to point p, the road can be seen without excavation. This problem embodies principles used in studies of military maps — to determine dead (not visible) areas.

EXAMPLE 3. — (Fig. 146). Given a contour map on which are shown the two side lines of a road, the contours being represented by full lines. The road is to be built on a 4% down grade starting at A at elevation 55. Scale 1 inch = 125 ft. Side slopes of road to be $1\frac{1}{2}$ horizontal to 1 vertical. It is desired to sketch the new contours on the slopes of the road, to sketch on the map the top and foot of slopes, and to designate the portion in embankment and the portion in excavation.

First, the new contours which are to cross the road are plotted at *ab, cd, ef, gh*. These will be 125 ft. apart, as a 4% grade falls 5 ft. in a distance of 125 ft. If the road is assumed to be level in cross-section, then these lines will cross the road at right angles to its general direction as shown in the figure. From points *a* and *b*, on either edge of the road, the new contour lines will follow along the slope, e.g., the line *ao* represents the new 50-ft. contour. Where this contour *ao* passes point *c* it is just 5 ft. above the road. Since the slope of the cut is $1\frac{1}{2}$ to 1,

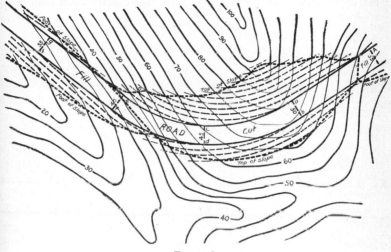

FIG. 146.

then the distance out from *c* must be $1\frac{1}{2} \times 5 = 7.5$ ft.; opposite *e* it is 10 ft. above the road and similarly the distance out from *e* must be 15 ft. Where this new 50-ft. contour meets the old 50-ft. contour at *o*, is a point at the top of the slope. Similarly all of the new contour lines, which are represented on the figure by dash lines are plotted and their intersections with the corresponding contours of the original surface give points of " no cut " or " no fill," or top of slope (in excavated portions) and foot of slope (in embankment portions). These lines are shown in the figure by heavy dotted lines. Where this heavy dotted line crosses the road it marks a " no cut " and " no fill " line, i.e., the road bed cuts the surface of the ground.

335. Locating a Grade-Line. — In locating a highway, a railway or an aqueduct on a contour map a controlling factor of the location (apart from many other practical considerations) is the " grade line." In portions of the location the grade line ascends or descends at a uniform rate; and in some places may represent the maximum gradient permissible. A uniform grade-line may be drawn on the map by first computing the horizontal distance corresponding to the contour interval and the given gradient. If, for example, it is desired to lay out on the plan a line that will

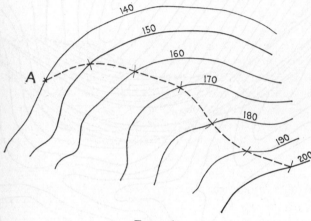

FIG. 146a.

rise at a rate of grade of 5%, or 5 ft. in 100, the contour interval is 10 ft., and the scale of the map is 400 ft. to an inch, then the horizontal distance corresponding to a 10-ft. rise (one contour interval) is 200 ft., and this is represented by one-half inch on the map. If we set on the compass (or dividers) a radius of one-half inch and intersect the successive contours with short arcs beginning at some known point, as shown in Fig. 146a, we obtain points on the contours which will lie on the 5% grade line. If the contours present irregularities it may be necessary to interpolate a contour half-way between and use a quarter-inch distance in finding the point on the interpolated contour.

336. Topographical Surveys. — This term may mean anything from a topographical survey for the purpose of locating a building, up to a survey for a topographic map of the whole country. If a large map is to be made showing contours of a large area, it is necessary first to execute a control survey, triangulation or traverse, according to circumstances, in order to tie the whole survey together accurately. This also applies to levels as well as to horizontal locations. In Chapter X is a brief description of how this is done in a city survey. The details of the topography may then be filled in by plane table, transit and stadia, or other methods, according to existing conditions. The stadia and the plane-table methods have been dealt with separately in Chapter VII.

A topographical survey affords an opportunity to use a combination of several different surveying methods. This is especially true of a large survey but may also be true of a smaller one. It is thought best, however, to deal with the different methods separately in this volume, and not to emphasize the correlation of these methods. In Vol. II the whole question of executing a control survey, and filling in the topographic or hydrographic details by appropriate methods is taken up more fully.

For small, detached surveys the purpose of which is to aid in the solution of some definite engineering problem, like the location of a bridge, the method used for obtaining the contours will usually be one of the simple, direct methods requiring only the transit and tape. In the first place, the party may not be equipped with a plane-table outfit or with stadia rods; secondly, the men may not be familiar with these methods. For a small job it would not pay to purchase special equipment and train the men in these methods. Under these circumstances the following methods, requiring not more than ordinary equipment, may be more suitable. They are methods which have been in use for a long time and require no special training beyond the simplest kind of surveying.

337. LOCATION OF POINTS FROM THE TRANSIT LINE. — Where a tape is used for measuring the distances, such objects as fences, walls, and buildings may be located as described in Chapter VI, but it will not be necessary to make the measurements with as great precision. Fig. 147 is a sample page of notes of a topographical survey where the transit and tape were

used.   On city plans, which are frequently drawn to a scale of
40 ft. to an inch, a fraction of a foot can be shown easily.   On
a topographic map the scale often is such that an error of a fraction of a foot becomes insignificant in the side measurements
from the transit line, where such errors cannot accumulate.
Sometimes it may be sufficient to obtain the distances by pacing,
and the angles or directions by means of a pocket compass.   Locations frequently may be checked by noting where range lines
intersect the transit line.   In making a **series** of measurements
it is well to take each measurement with a little greater precision
than is actually needed for plotting, in order to be sure that the
accumulated error does not become too large.

In taking measurements the surveyor should constantly keep
in mind **how the notes can be plotted;** often this will prevent
the omission of necessary measurements.   No matter whether
an accurate or only a rough survey is desired **check measurements** should be taken on all important lines.   An example of
notes of a survey, using the stadia method, is shown in Fig. 96,
p. 233.

338. Locating Contours by Cross-Sections. — A very common as well as expensive method of locating contours is that of
taking cross-sections.   Elevations on the surface of the ground
are usually taken at each cross-section corner to tenths of a foot.
From these elevations the contours may be sketched by interpolating between these known elevations as explained in Art.
331.   The accuracy may be increased materially by taking
elevations at intermediate points when it appears that the ground
does not slope uniformly between the grid points.   The size of
the squares used should depend upon the roughness of the surface
and the contour interval employed.

339. Locating Contours by Profiles. — Where the ground is
fairly smooth it is sufficient to take a few profiles on known lines,
not necessarily at right angles to each other.   These lines are
stationed and elevations are taken at every full station and
also at the points of marked change in slope.   From these data
the contours are sketched on the map by interpolation as described in Art. 331.   This sketching should be done in the field
while the terrain is before the eyes of the topographer.

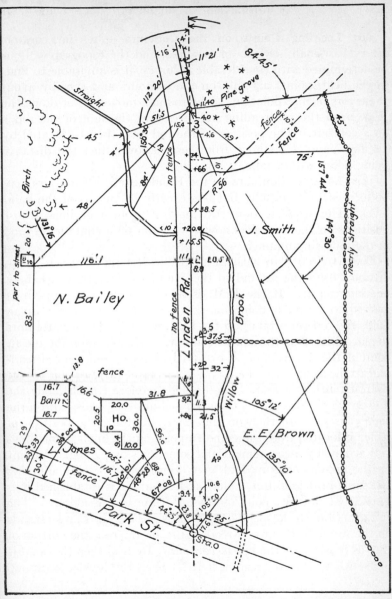

FIG. 147. FIELD-NOTES OF A PORTION OF A TOPOGRAPHICAL SURVEY
WITH TRANSIT AND TAPE.

409

340. Locating Points on the Contours. — If the contour interval is small, say one or two feet, and the topography is to be determined with considerable accuracy, it is advisable to find, in the field, points actually on the contours and thereby avoid the errors of interpolation. The rodman moves up or down the slope until the rod-reading indicates that the foot of the rod is on a contour. The position of the rod may then be located by an angle and a distance from some known line, the distance being taken with a tape or by stadia.

341. Locating Contours by the Hand Level. — Contours may be located more rapidly but less exactly by means of the hand level. The work is done by making profiles of lines whose positions on the map are known. A point on a contour is found in the following manner.

The first step is to measure to the nearest tenth of a foot the distance from the ground to the eye of the leveler, which may be, say, 5.4 ft. If the B.M. is at elevation 143.43 and it is desired to locate a point on the 140-ft. contour, the rodman holds the rod (or a tape) on the B.M. while the leveler attempts to place himself on the 140-ft. contour. When he is on the 140-ft. contour the elevation of his eye (H.I.) is 145.4 and the rod-reading at the B.M. must be $145.4 - 143.43 = 1.97$, or 2.0 to the nearest tenth of a foot. The leveler therefore travels along the line on which the point is to be located until he reads 1.97 on the rod. His feet are then on the 140-ft. contour, the position of which is located from some known point on the line. Sometimes this is done by measurement and sometimes by pacing. A point on the 145-ft. contour could have been located first by applying the same principle, but if the 140-ft. contour is established it is very easy to locate a point on the 145-ft. contour as follows. The distance from the leveler's feet to his eye being 5.4 ft., if he stands on the 140-ft. contour and reads 0.4 ft. on the rod, the bottom of the rod must be on the 145-ft. contour. By trial then the point is found where the rod reads 0.4 ft.* Then the leveler walks up

---

* For very rough work sometimes the rod is not used, the leveler simply estimating where the rod-reading will come on the rodman's body and placing him so that his feet will be on the proper contour.

the hill and, standing on the point just found, places the rodman on the next higher contour by the same process.

In working down the hill to locate the 135-ft. contour, if the leveler is standing on the 140-ft. contour, the rod will be on the 135-ft. contour when it reads 10.4 ft. Or, when the 140-ft. contour has been found by the leveler the rodman comes forward and holds the rod on this spot and the leveler backs down the hill until he reads 0.4 ft. on the rod; he is then standing on the 135-ft. contour. Some prefer to cut a stick just 5 ft. long and hold the hand level on the top of it in taking sights.

The points thus found at regular contour elevations are then plotted on the corresponding lines and the contours sketched by joining points of equal elevation by lines which represent as nearly as possible all the irregularities of the ground between such points. Where the lines that are profiled are far apart or where the country is very rough it is frequently necessary, in order to obtain the correct position of the contours, to locate extra points on them between these profiled lines. The extra points are located by right-angle offsets from the lines. Most of this work is plotted in the field upon paper ruled in small squares to facilitate sketching. Where practicable it is well always to sketch the contours in the field rather than in the office.

341a. Locating Contours by Cruising with Compass and Clinometer. — In dense woods or underbrush the cruising and sketching method herein described will often give results sufficiently close for the purpose in hand and will effect saving in time and money.

Traverse lines are first run through clearings in the woods at intervals of 1000 to 3000 ft., preferably parallel to each other, and profiles of these lines are made by direct leveling or by stadia. The traverse lines are plotted, thus cutting the area into enclosed smaller areas; the topographical details of these are surveyed as follows.

Starting on one of the control lines, sketch the contours by eye on both sides of the cleared lines for a short distance into the woods. The topographer then cruises the country between these control lines by running range lines by hand compass (usually at right angles to the control lines) at, say 100 to 300 ft. intervals, starting from one traverse line and with the elevation determined by leveling, and running at right angles through the woods to the next line, sketching contours for 100 ft. or more on either side of the range line as he goes, using the Locke level or clinometer for determining elevations, and checking these elevations, as well as his position, at the other traverse line ahead. A small hand sketching board is used for this work. Then he returns on the next range to the first control line, obtaining as he does so all of the topography in the belt which he has covered. These data are then transcribed directly onto a plan which has been left on the first control line. The topographer then proceeds to the next pair of ranges running, say south on one and back north on the other, checking out at each time on elevation and distance and on his position east and west on the control line, as he reaches the clearing where the traverse line was run. At the end of each cruised line he adjusts any errors in elevations and distance which may appear, provided they are not so great as to indicate a serious mistake. This method gives an independent control through the traverse on all of the topography. It provides a check on all of the cruising work and it gives a fairly accurately located contour even in heavily wooded districts. The transcription of the contours drawn on the sketching board onto the larger plan in the field discloses any apparent error; this should be corrected immediately in the field.

342. Location of Streams and Shore-Line. — A transit traverse run approximately parallel to a stream or a shore-line will form a base from which the shore-line can be located by right angle offset lines measured to bends and to other selected points along the shore-line. Sometimes a boulder or a tree can be identified at a bend of the shore-line and angles can be taken to it from two different transit points thus locating the bend by the intersection of the two lines. If these located points are plotted on a small sketching board the topographer can then sketch by eye the details of the shore-line between these located points and thereby produce a faithful map.

Shore-lines of ponds can be located economically from traverse lines run on the ice in winter. From the pond side of the shore its shape and characteristic changes can be seen more clearly.

The shore line required may be the high-water mark or the low-water mark, the average shore-line or the shore on the day the survey is made. If the shores are flat slopes the positions of these different lines may be several feet apart. The surveyor should ascertain before making the survey which shore-line is required; and his field-notes and the plan should show clearly which line is being located.

Where the high-water mark is required and the survey is made during a period of low water, it is often difficult to distinguish the high-water mark, particularly on marshy shores. Usually it is possible, however, to determine the elevation of high water from stains on some wharf or ledge or boulders lying in the water, and then to trace out the contour corresponding to that elevation on those portions of the shore-line where the high-water mark is indistinct, as described in Art. 340, p. 410.

PROBLEMS

1. (a) From the map shown in Fig. 137 draw a profile along the line indicated by the lower border. Vertical scale, 1 inch = 200 ft.

(b) Draw a profile along a line drawn from the upper left to the lower right corner. For the vertical scale let $\frac{1}{20}$ in. = one contour interval.

(c) Assume a straight line drawn from the lower left corner of the contour map to a point midway between A and B, and from that point to the upper right corner of the map.

Draw a profile of this broken line. Use vertical scale of 1 inch = 200 ft.

2. Assume that the side borders on the map shown in Fig. 138 are meridians with North toward the top of the page. Draw the side elevation (or projection) looking from the North toward the South. Vertical scale, 1 inch = 200 ft.

3. If the scale of the map shown in Fig. 139 is 1 inch = 1 mile, determine the number of square miles in the drainage area by means of the method explained in the second paragraph of Art. 404, p. 486.

4. In Fig. 146, if the road had been level and at Elev. 62 ft., plot the intersection of the side slopes and the surface.

5. In Fig. 144, if the elevation of A is 5 feet and the line BC is level at Elev. 25 ft., draw the intersection of the plane defined by ABC and the surface.

CHAPTER XII

MINE SURVEYING

343. GENERAL REMARKS. — In this chapter the usual limitations and difficulties met with in surveying a mine are pointed out and some of the instruments and common methods described. A brief description is given also of the methods of establishing the boundaries of mining claims in the United States.

Mine surveys are made for the purpose of determining the relation of mine workings to the boundaries of the property, obtaining data from which to establish direction for proceeding with the workings, determining the amount of material taken from the mine and the probable amount of available ore that can be worked, obtaining data from which graphical representation of mine workings may be made, and aiding in efficient operation of the mine.

344. DEFINITIONS OF MINING TERMS. — The following terms are in common use in mine surveying.

Adit. An approximately horizontal underground passageway running from the surface into the mine workings and used for drainage and ventilation.

Apex. The portion of the surface of the undisturbed rock formation which is included between the walls or sides of the mineral deposit.

Bed. A stratum in the earth's crust which has been formed or deposited in a nearly horizontal layer.

Back. Top of a passageway (same as roof).

Chute. A narrow, inclined passage used for drawing off broken ore from a stope or raise.

Collar. Timbers around top of shaft.

Compartment. One of the smaller passageways of a large shaft divided by timber partitions. Fig. 153, p. 431, is the plan of a three compartment shaft.

Connection. A passageway which is driven from one accessible part of the mine to another.

Cross-cut. A horizontal passageway across or approximately at right angles to the strike.

Dip. The inclination of any rock plane to the horizon.

Drift. A horizontal passageway following the vein.

Fault. A fracture in the earth's crust along which slipping or shearing has occurred.

Floor. The bottom of the passageway or of a seam or bed.

Heading. Any preliminary passageway driven to explore the mine or to facilitate the future operations.

Heave. The distance between the two parts of the same vein which is divided by a fault, measured along the strike of the fault.

Levels. Horizontal passageways run at different levels along the deposit or adjacent to it for working the mine.

Manhole. A small passage from one level into the next level above or below, or into stopes.

Mill-hole. A passage between a stope and a level through which the ore is conveyed.

Ore Shoot. A rich aggregation of ore within a vein.

Outcrop. That portion of the vein which is exposed on the surface of the ground.

Prop. A piece of timber which prevents any rock in the roof from falling, sometimes called a post.

Raise. A passage driven steeply upward from any portion of the mine.

Roof. The top of a passageway or of a seam or bed.

Room. A place other than a passageway from which material has been extracted. The term usually refers to bed deposits.

Seam. A bed of mineral or a small vein.

Stopes. Rooms formed by the excavation of ore above or below a level, sometimes filled with broken ore or rock.

Strike. The direction (bearing) of a horizontal line in the plane of a deposit. The strike is always at right angles to the dip.

Stull. A piece of timber wedged in crosswise between the side walls of a passageway.

Throw. The vertical distance between the planes representing two parts of the same vein which is divided by a fault. The term is used only in regard to deposits which are nearly horizontal.

Tunnel. A horizontal working passageway open at both ends.

Vein. (Also *lode*, *ledge*, *lead*, etc.) A mineral body of the flattened shape.

Wall. The rock on each side of the mineral body. The upper wall is called the " hanging wall," and the lower the " foot wall."

Winze. A subsidiary shaft not starting from the surface.

MINING INSTRUMENTS

Owing to the confined nature and steep inclination of many of the passages in a mine through which the survey lines have to be carried, it is necessary to use specially constructed instruments.

345. MINING TRANSITS. — In modern mining all of the accurate angle measurements are taken with a transit, several forms of which are designed for this purpose. The essential features are lightness and adaptability for measuring accurate azimuths of nearly vertical or of very short sights. If the telescope is of low power the illumination of the field is better and its focal length is usually shorter, both of which are conveniences in mine surveying. The transit should be provided with a full vertical circle which should be enclosed in a metal case to protect the graduations from dripping water. In sighting highly inclined lines a striding level will be found useful, but the horizontal axis of the transit must be so designed that the striding level will fit upon it.

With an ordinary transit one cannot take a downward sight more steeply inclined than $55°$ or $60°$ to the horizon. Various attachments have been devised for sighting more steeply inclined lines, the object being to permit a sight to be taken over the edge of the horizontal circle of the instrument. This is usually accomplished by attaching an auxiliary telescope to the side or to the top of the main telescope of the engineers' transit, so that the instrument will afford all the advantages of the ordinary transit and also will make it possible to sight even down a vertical shaft.

346. Eccentric Telescopes. — Some mining transits are constructed so that an auxiliary telescope may be attached to an end extension of the horizontal axis, such an instrument being known as a *side telescope transit*. In another type of transit, called the *top telescope transit*, the auxiliary telescope is mounted above the main telescope. The distance between the centers of the main and auxiliary telescopes is called the *eccentricity*. Some instruments (Fig. 148) are made with an interchangeable telescope which can be attached at either the top or the side of the main telescope. In such an instrument no correction for eccentricity of the auxiliary telescope is necessary, provided the horizontal angles are measured with the top telescope and the vertical angles are measured with the side telescope.

In comparing the merits of the various forms of attachment it must be remembered that the object to be accomplished is to transfer the meridian accurately from one station to another, these stations sometimes being close together in plan but distant in elevation.

The side telescope has the merit of being easy to operate. Since this telescope is detachable the transit need not be encumbered with it when the main telescope can be used, which is the case in most of the surveying required in mines. When this attachment is used the effect of eccentricity in the measured azimuths is eliminated by the reversal method described below.

When a top telescope is attached the main telescope cannot be inverted. With such a transit the correction for eccentricity must be applied to all altitude readings.

When it is not important to double the angle azimuths may be carried more rapidly by means of the top telescope than with the side telescope, but it is good practice to double all of the angles of a traverse.

The interchangeable side and top telescope is in common use. Some prefer to use the side telescope only, the vertical angles being measured directly and the horizontal angles being measured by repeating the angles and reversing the telescope at the same time, so that if four angles are read, for example, the result of the fourth reading divided by 4 will give the angle whose vertex is at the point over which the instrument is set.

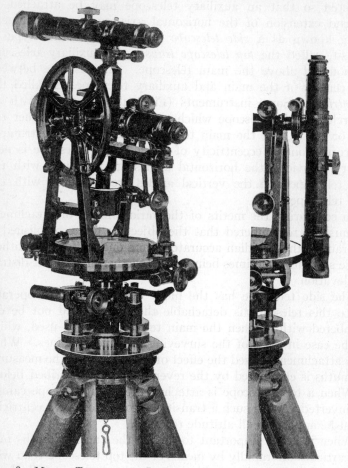

FIG. 148. MINING TRANSIT WITH INTERCHANGEABLE SIDE AND TOP TELESCOPE.
(From photographs loaned by C. L. Berger & Sons, by permission.)

If the instrument is used as just described then the top telescope is used only for lining in points along the shaft. Others prefer to use the top telescope for all work; the azimuths are measured directly and only the vertical angles require correction.

347. Correction for Eccentricity. — If the side telescope is used in measuring a single azimuth or if the top telescope is used for measuring vertical angles, a correction for eccentricity must be made. The correction for either angle may be made by regarding the line between the centers of the eccentric and main telescopes as one of the lines of the traverse. Instead of making this eccentric distance a line of the traverse, it may

sometimes be more convenient to eliminate it by sighting the auxiliary telescope at an auxiliary point which bears the same relation to the station point as the center of the auxiliary telescope bears to the center of the main telescope. It is also possible, when the horizontal distance to the point sighted is known, to compute a correction to apply to the angle measured by the auxiliary telescope which will make it equal to the angle which would have been measured had the main telescope been used.

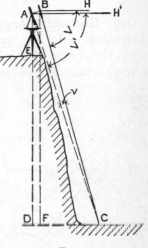

348. Vertical Angle Correction for Eccentricity of Top Telescope. — In Fig. 149 the vertical angle V has been

FIG. 149.

taken by means of the top telescope to point C in the bottom of a shaft. The distance AC was measured, A being the horizontal axis of the main telescope. The distances desired are DC and AD. HB and $H'A$ are both horizontal,

$$\text{then } V' = V - v$$

where V is the angle measured by the top telescope, v is the angular correction for eccentricity, and V' is the corrected angle.

$$\text{Since } \sin v = \frac{AB}{AC} = \frac{\text{Distance between telescopes}}{\text{Distance measured}}$$

we may construct a table for any instrument giving the values of v for different measured distances.

The vertical and horizontal components of AC are then

$$AD = AC \sin V' = AC \sin (V - v)$$
and
$$DC = AC \cos V' = AC \cos (V - v)$$

Had the measured distance been BC instead of AC then

$$AD = \qquad\qquad BC \sin V - AB \cos V$$
and
$$DC = CF + FD = BC \cos V + AB \sin V$$

349. Horizontal Angle Correction for Eccentricity of Side Telescope. —

In Fig. 150, the center of the small circle represents the center of the instrument, and the line of sight of the eccentric telescope is tangent to this circle. Angle H has been

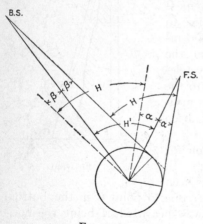

measured with the side telescope and H' is the angle which would have been obtained had it been measured with the main telescope. The difference in direction between the lines from the F.S. to the side telescope and to the main telescope is the angle α, and the difference in direction between the lines from the B.S. to the side and to the main telescope is the angle β. By the construction indicated in the figure

FIG. 150.

the angle formed between the two dash lines is equal to the angle measured with the side telescope. The required true angle H' therefore is equal to $H - \beta + \alpha$. Since the usual practice is to measure all horizontal angles as azimuths in a clockwise direction, the true horizontal angle will equal the angle measured with the side telescope minus the correction angle for the B.S. plus the correction angle for the F.S. These correction angles α and β obviously balance when the horizontal distances from the center of the instrument to the F.S. and the B.S. are equal.

The cotangent of the correction angle for either case equals the horizontal distance from the center of the instrument to the point sighted divided by the distances between the main and side telescopes.

350. ADJUSTMENTS OF MINING TRANSITS. — It is assumed that all ordinary adjustments of the transit have been made. In addition, the adjustment of the object slide (Art. 77, p. 69) is of unusual importance, because often in mining work the azimuth has to be transferred through very short horizontal sights, or inclined sights with short horizontal component. Exceptional care must be taken to make the horizontal axis of the telescope truly horizontal and the line of sight exactly perpendicular to it.

The side telescope is generally adjusted by first making its line of sight parallel to the axis of the side telescope tube. This is done by the cross-hair adjustment and the aid of a pair of fixed wyes in which the tube is rotated; it is the same adjustment as for the level, Art. 121, p. 95. It is assumed that the instrument maker has made the optical axis parallel to the axis of the tube.

Secondly, the line of sight is made parallel to that of the main telescope. In the instrument shown in Fig. 148, this adjustment is made by moving the cross-hairs, but there is another style of instrument which has a trivet placed between the auxiliary telescope and the main part of the transit and in this instrument the adjustment is made by the adjusting screws on the trivet. The former instrument is cheaper, more rigid and less liable to get out of adjustment. To make this adjustment sight on a piece of paper upon which are drawn two vertical marks connected by a horizontal line, the distance between the marks being equal to the distance between the telescopes. The plane of the paper should be placed at right angles to the line of sight and about 200 ft. distant. The vertical cross-hair of the main telescope is sighted at one of the vertical lines by means of the clamp and tangent screw of the plates and then the vertical cross-hair of the side telescope is sighted at the other line by adjusting the vertical cross-hair of the side telescope, if the instrument is like that shown in Fig. 148. This adjustment of the vertical cross-hair may affect the first adjustment, but its effect is usually so slight as to be negligible. If, however, the instrument has trivet plates, this adjustment is made by means of the trivet plate adjustment screws on the side telescope.

The side telescope and main telescope are then brought into the same plane at right angles to the vertical plane as follows: The horizontal cross-hair of the main telescope is sighted at some point, preferably a distant one; then the horizontal cross-hair of the side telescope is sighted at the same point by means of the tangent screw on the side telescope.

As the adjustment of the side telescope is not direct, but made by comparison with the main telescope, and as this may not be in perfect adjustment, the instrument should be used in both the direct and reversed positions if accurate results are required.

The top telescope is adjusted in much the same manner as the side telescope.

351. COMBINED SOLAR ATTACHMENT AND TOP TELESCOPE.
— A special top telescope is sometimes made to do the duty of a solar attachment also; but it is now generally admitted that better meridian determinations can be made by direct solar observations with the main telescope, and the surveyor is advised not to get any such complex attachment for mining work.

352. FITTINGS OF MINING TRANSITS.
— A mining transit should have (1) a reflector for illuminating the cross-hairs (2) a diagonal or prismatic eyepiece which makes it possible to take any upward sight not exceeding about 60° above the horizon or to take sights where, because of the close proximity of walls, it is impossible to place one's eye directly behind the eyepiece, and (3) a tripod with extension legs; (4) a plumb-bob with an interior reel for adjusting the length of plumb-bob string is a convenience.

The bracket and trivet shown in Fig. 151, although not essential, are very useful attachments, especially for work in shafts and for low set-ups of the instrument. Another convenient form of bracket is that in which the ring holding the base of the transit can be slid along horizontally on the bracket instead of being fixed at the end as in Fig. 151. This permits greater lateral movement and facilitates setting the transit over or under a point. In the bracket shown in Fig. 151 it is necessary to attach it at the start in such a position that the center of its cir-

cular base is so near the point that the exact setting can be
made entirely by the shifting head of the transit.

353. Compasses used in Mines. — The transit has taken,
to a great extent, the place of the old miner's dial in which the
compass was the main feature. This is partly because, in

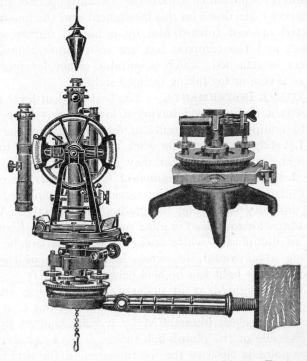

FIG. 151.   BRACKET AND TRIVET USED WITH MINING TRANSITS.
(From the catalogue of C. L. Berger & Sons, by permission.)

modern mines, so much heavy machinery and often electric
lights and motor cars are used that the compass needle cannot
be depended upon even to its ordinary degree of accuracy, and
furthermore the advantages afforded by a transit as compared
with a compass are so great as to make the difference in cost
of the two instruments a matter of minor importance.

Compasses often are used, however, for reconnoissance surveys and sometimes also for filling in the details.   They are

made in many sizes and of different designs. A compass with a plain needle is preferable to one with a swinging card, since the former can be brought to rest more quickly and is more accurate by reason of the smaller amount of weight on the center bearing. One of the excellent forms of compass for details and reconnoissance work is the " Brunton pocket transit." The observer looks down on this instrument and the line of sight is reflected upward toward him by a hinged mirror so that the object and the compass box are seen simultaneously. A clinometer is attached, which is suitable either for measuring the dip of a vein or for taking inclined sights.

354. OTHER INSTRUMENTS. — The best kind of level for use in mines is a dumpy level having a low power telescope. It should be equipped with a reflector for illuminating the cross-hairs. Leveling rods for mine work are made similar to ordinary leveling rods, except that they are shorter, the 3-ft. and the 5-ft. lengths being the commonest. These rods are usually of the Philadelphia pattern, the target being employed when there is difficulty in reading the graduations directly. A good form of target for rods used in mine surveys has a slit silhouetted against an illuminated white background. This can be made by cutting a horizontal slit across half the face of the level target so that the light can be held behind it.

The objects sighted at in underground surveying must be illuminated. An ordinary plumb-bob hung in front of a white card or tracing cloth illuminated by a light held in front of and at one side of the plumb-bob makes a good signal. Even when the point is close to the instrument and the atmosphere is clear a white card held behind the plumb-bob string is of great aid to the transitman. Signals in which there is a burning light, such, for example, as a plummet lamp, are sometimes used, the sight being taken on the wick of the lamp.

The equipment should contain at least two tapes, a 50- or 100-foot steel tape graduated to hundredths, and another tape of such length that the longest slope measurements required, such as those from level to level, can be made in one measurement. Tapes 200 or 300 ft. in length are suitable for this purpose. It is frequently impracticable to hold a tape level and obtain the measurement by plumbing because of darkness in the mine. For this reason inclined measurements are commonly used. A short pocket tape is convenient for measuring the height of instrument, height of point and offsets. The open form of reel shown in Fig. 1, p. 3, should be used because tapes used in mines often become wet and dirty.

UNDERGROUND SURVEYING*

355. TRANSFERRING A MERIDIAN INTO A MINE. — There are two general methods of transferring a meridian into a mine: first, by means of the main telescope or an auxiliary telescope on the transit, and, second, by means of plumb-lines hung in a shaft. If the mine is entered by an adit or a tunnel the passage-way is usually so nearly level that the meridian can be transferred into the mine by setting up the transit at the mouth of the adit and, after taking a backsight on a fixed station on the surface, taking a foresight into the adit and establishing a point within the mine. If the entrance is by a shaft which is highly inclined, but not vertical, the same general method is employed except that the auxiliary telescope will be required.

When the shaft is vertical it is still possible to use the transit and its auxiliary telescope, but a more accurate method is to use long plumb-lines hung in the shaft. If the mine has but one shaft it is necessary to suspend two plumb-lines (sometimes three or four) in the shaft. If the mine has two or more shafts a point may be located at the bottom of each shaft by plumbing down from the top. Then a traverse can be run in the mine connecting these underground points and another traverse on the surface connecting the corresponding points at the tops of the shafts; in this way a closed traverse is formed connecting all of the points.

356. Transferring Meridian Down Shaft by Use of Transit. — It is of the utmost importance that the line defining the direction of the shaft (shaft line) should be accurately established because it is the line on which all underground traverses depend and it

---

* See " Coal Mine Surveying and Engineering," Eng. News, Feb. 9, 1911, and April 13, 1911.

is also the line of reference for extending the shaft.   It is marked
by a series of shaft plugs (stations) set in the hanging wall which
are established as the shaft excavation progresses.   It is good
practice to have three or more stations in the shaft between
levels.

Station o (Fig. 151a) is set in the foot wall at the collar of the
shaft.   Its position is located by connecting it with the traverse
on the surface.   With the transit at o and a backsight on the previous surface station, horizontal and vertical angles are laid off so

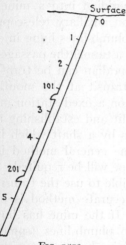

as to give the predetermined direction of
the shaft line.   Shaft plugs are set in line
in the hanging wall at 1, 2, 101, 3, 4, 201
and 5 and their positions computed.
(Art. 365, p. 439.)   As the excavation of
the shaft progresses other lower shaft
stations are set in a similar manner.   Because of the impracticability of sighting
over long distances and making long
measurements in a shaft these lower
stations will not be located from o but as
follows.   To locate 5 the instrument is
set under shaft plug 3 and sighted on 201
and checked by taking a sight on 4.
Station 5 is then lined in and set.   The
advantage of the foregoing procedure
is that after the sights on 201 and 4

FIG. 151a.

have been taken the inclination of the telescope has to be changed
little if at all in order to set 5 in line.   This minimizes the effect
of errors caused by the instrument being slightly out of adjustment.   In all precise work and where highly inclined sights are
necessary the instrument should be in good adjustment and a
stride level should be used to insure the horizontality of the
horizontal axis.   This level is more sensitive than the plate
bubbles and therefore more effective.

If the instrument is not equipped with a stride level, the vertical axis may be made more truly vertical by means of the telescope level which is more sensitive than the plate levels.   First,
level the instrument as nearly as possible by means of the plate

bubbles, then place the telescope over an opposite set of leveling screws, and by means of the vertical clamp and tangent screw bring the telescope bubble to the center; then turn the telescope 180° in azimuth and if the telescope bubble moves away from the center bring it halfway back to its central position by means of the plate leveling screws, and bring it the rest of the way to its central position by means of the tangent screw of the vertical arc. Repeat this process with the telescope in line with the other pair of leveling screws.

In addition to establishing the shaft stations as described above, stations such as 101 and 201 are set in such a position that the transit may be set under them (sometimes on a bracket) at such a height that sights may be taken to points established in the levels. When it is necessary to use an auxiliary telescope for this purpose the side telescope is recommended. The backsight may be taken on a shaft plug, either above or below the transit, whichever is the more convenient, and the angle turned to the station in the level. When the side telescope is used it should be used in both the direct and reversed position, the true angle at the center being half the second reading (Art. 349, p. 420).

Sometimes an azimuth is carried into the workings by stretching a horizontal wire across the bottom of the shaft and as far back into the workings as possible, the wire being carefully aligned by the instrument at the top. This method may admit of even more accuracy than that of taking a backsight to the surface from a station established in the bottom of the mine. Errors caused by a slight inclination of the horizontal axis are not important when this method is used, and for that reason it is also useful when a sensitive striding level is not to be had. The effect of a slight inclination of the horizontal axis is simply to shift the line a little to one side of, but parallel to, the true position.

356a. Errors in Steep Sights. — When sighting up or down a steep mine shaft there are two errors in the adjustment of the transit that may introduce appreciable error into the horizontal angles, although they usually have but little effect in ordinary work. These are (1) the inclination of the horizontal axis to the true horizontal line, and (2) the error of the line of collimation (line of sight).

The inclination of the horizontal axis to the true horizon is always small. In ordinary work the telescope is inclined to the horizon by an angle of but a few degrees, and for such vertical angles the effect on a horizontal angle is but a small part of this error of adjustment. In such work as triangulation, or any work where accuracy is of importance it is customary to eliminate this error by using the transit in both positions and to use the mean result. The error in the horizontal angle is equal to i (tan h − tan h') where i is the inclination, h the angular altitude to one point and h' the altitude of the other. For an inclination of 10″ and vertical angles of 10° and 0° this error is

$$10'' (\tan 10° - \tan 0°) = 1''.76$$

For 89° and 0° the error is 9′ 33″.

The effect of an error in the line of collimation on a horizontal angle is similar. It may be found by the relation c (sec h − sec h'); the line of sight making an angle of 90° − c with the horizontal axis. If the error c is 10 seconds and the altitudes are 89° and 0° the resulting error in the horizontal angles is

$$10'' (\sec 89° - \sec 0°) = 9' 23''$$

If the altitudes were 10° and 0° the resulting error in the horizontal angle would be only 0.15 second.

356b. Error Due to Angle Between Inner and Outer Centers of Transit. — Errors that are of no practical importance in ordinary transit work may become serious errors in such work as sighting up or down steep mine shafts, or in astronomical observation where the angular altitudes are likely to be high, because the small errors are multiplied by large factors.

An error which comes within this class is that caused by the failure of the geometric axes of the inner and outer centers of the transit to coincide exactly. If the inner and outer conical surfaces of the outer center do not have the same (or parallel) geometric axes the metal is thicker on one side than on the other.

In Fig. 151b it will be seen that the outer center (to which the graduated circle is attached) is thicker at the top on the right side; the (dotted) axis of the outer surface is to the right of the (full line) axis of the inner surface. When the inner center is held with one hand and the outer center revolved with the other hand the axis of the inner center describes a conical surface. When angles are measured by the repetition method the inner axis gradually moves in this conical surface and the angles are affected by this error.

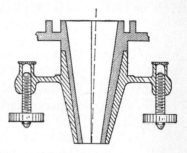

A transit may be tested for this error either by means of the telescope or by a spirit level placed on the instrument. If the horizontal hair is sighted on a point, and the upper circle held with one hand while the lower circle is revolved with the other hand, then any lack of coincidence of the two axes will be revealed by an up-and-down motion of the cross-hair. Similarly,

FIG. 151b. SHOWING ANGLE BETWEEN AXES OF INNER AND OUTER CENTERS.

if a sensitive level is placed on the upper circle and the axis rotated as before the bubble will show a slight backward and forward movement. By noting the vernier readings corresponding to the two extreme positions of the cross-hair or the bubble it is possible to determine the direction of the plane through the two axes. This error will be small in all well-made instruments. But even an error of 5″ may be a serious one on very steep sights because it will be multiplied by so great a factor.* It is possible to arrange a program of observations which will eliminate this error by making several measurements of the angle, the initial readings being distributed uniformly around the circle; and using the instrument in both the direct and the reversed positions.

---

* For a discussion of this error see a paper by Professor L. H. Cooke of the Royal School of Mines, London, entitled "Methods of measuring Horizontal Angles that involve Steep or Precipitous Sighting in their Measurement," Institution of Mining and Metallurgy, 31st session, 1921–1922. (London.)

357. Plumbing the Meridian Down a Vertical Shaft.[*] — To the mine surveyor the plumb-line is an instrument of precision, excelling even the transit under some conditions, and the work of transferring the meridian down a vertical shaft usually can be accomplished more accurately by the plumb-line than by any other method.

The method usually followed is to suspend two bobs (sometimes three or four) from points located at the collar of the shaft and

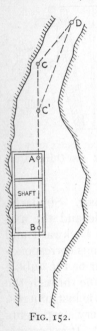

FIG. 152.

whose positions have been accurately determined from the surface surveys. The azimuth of the line joining the two points at the collar of the shaft is the azimuth of the plane defined by the plumb-lines. If the instrument is taken underground and set up at C (Fig. 152) and "jiggled"; that is, moved until the line of sight CA and the two wires A and B are in the same vertical plane then the azimuth of the line CAB becomes known. The distances BC, AC and BA should be measured and the latter should be equal to the distance between the two points established at the collar. The distance from the wires of the plumb-lines to the transit should be chosen so that it will be unnecessary to move the objective far when focusing. Since this condition is seldom possible, the object glass slide should be in excellent adjustment. When the instrument is in the same vertical plane as the wires a point is established over or under the instrument

and an angle turned to another station as D further along the level, thus furnishing a permanent line in the level whose azimuth is readily computed. By measuring CD the position of L

---

[*] See references listed on pp. 457–9, this volume.

See also Colliery Engineer and Metal Miner, Vol. XVII, p. 23; Colliery Engineer Vol. XIV, p. 92, and School of Mines Quarterly, Vol. III, pp. 269–77.

so far been opened only by one shaft. If there is a second
[sh]aft or an adit, it is, of course, only necessary to plumb or
[oth]erwise transfer the position down each shaft; the com-
[pu]ted distance between these points then becomes a base-line
[of] substantial length. In Fig. 154 the traverse ABCD is run
[ou]t on the surface to connect the two shafts at A and D. The
[po]ints A and D are plumbed down the shafts and the correspond-
[in]g points A' and D' established at the bottom. An underground
[tr]averse A'G'F'E'D' is then run out. In the surface traverse
[th]e length and azimuth of AD and in the underground traverse
[th]e length and azimuth of A'D' are missing. The horizontal

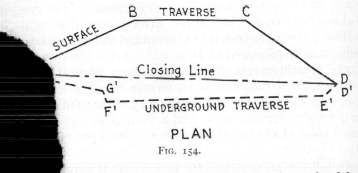

PLAN

FIG. 154.

[a]zimuth of each of these lines can be determined from
[respect]ive traverses as explained in Art. 434, p. 525. The
[tra]verse is referred to the true meridian, and, since
[not] yet known in regard to the direction of the meridian
[of] the underground traverse is referred to an assumed
[one.] The true azimuth of A'D' is the same as the azimuth
[p]rovided the plumbing down the shaft has been done
[correct]ly. The difference between the true and assumed azi-
[muth]s of A'D' is a correction to be applied to the azimuths of
[a]ll of the lines of this underground traverse.

360. UNDERGROUND TRAVERSES. — Surveying in a mine is
[ne]cessarily a process of traversing, for only the working passages
[a]re available for lines of survey. The line of traverse is often
[run] so that the longest possible sight may be taken. In the tor-
[t]uous passages of a mine it is frequently necessary to take very
[s]hort sights on the main traverse and since the azimuth is trans-

may be calculated. It is good practice to check the position of
D by " jiggling in " at a second point C'.

The plumb-lines should be as small in diameter as the weight
will permit. They are usually of copper, annealed iron or
piano wire.* With regard to the size of plumb-bob and wire
there is a great difference of opinion. The plumb-bobs should
be heavy enough to straighten out all bends in the wire. They
should be immersed in oil or water or an oil emulsion, so as to
stop their swinging in the shortest possible time, and the receptacle in which the plumb-bobs are immersed should be covered
in order to protect the surface of the liquid from water dripping
down the shaft. All air
currents should be checked
so far as possible, since experience has shown that in
deep shafts they have considerable effect upon the
plumb-lines. Great care
should be taken to see that
no part of the wires comes
in contact with the shaft.

When once the plumb-
lines are hung the meridian
may be transferred to all
the levels of the mine once
and for all time, so that a

FIG. 153. TRIANGULATION AT JUNCTION OF
SHAFT AND LEVEL.

little extra precaution and time given to this operation are
worth while. The surveyor should always keep in mind the
fact that in plumbing the meridian down the mine the direction
of the meridian is of much more importance than the actual
position of the points themselves, because an error due to an
incorrect direction of the meridian may be multiplied many
hundreds of times in carrying the traverse through the mine.

When the level or cross-cut runs in a direction with respect
to the shaft such as is shown in Fig. 153, then the triangulation

* See Eng. and Min. Jour., Vol. LV, p. 179, Feb. 25, 1893; Proc. Inst. of C. E.,
Vol. CXLII, p. 334; School of Mines Quarterly, Vol. XI, p. 333, and Colliery
Engineer, Vol. XVI, p. 31.

method is employed. Points A and B are the plumb-bobs and point C is where the transit is set up. A slight error in the distance AB merely affects the computed lengths of AC and BC, whereas a small error in the **direction** of AB may produce large error in the positions of distant points in the workings. The point C therefore is chosen as far from the shaft as possible even though the angle C is small.

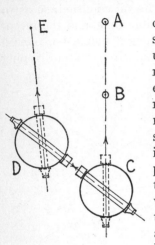

FIG. 153a. COLLIMATOR METHOD.

357a. Collimator Method. — When carrying a meridian into a mine the space at the bottom of the shaft is usually so cramped that great care must be exercised to avoid a large error in the azimuths carried into the mine. By the following method accurate work may be done even in a small space. The two wires are suspended in the usual manner and their swing properly damped. (Art. 357.) The transit is placed at C in line with the wires A and B (Fig. 153a). Since the telescope cannot be focused on both at the same time the instrument is lined in by focusing first on one and then on the other and moving the transit until the centers of the wires are in line.* A second transit is placed at D, which may be but 3 or 4 ft. away. By pointing the two telescopes toward each other and focusing for long distance the hairs of each telescope may be viewed by the other. (See Art. 128b, p. 102.) The angle then may be turned from CBA to the line of sight of the second transit. (This is not necessarily the angle BCD.) Next the angle is turned by the second transit from the sight line of the first transit to the line DE, which should be fairly long. The second transit might have been turned a few minutes right or left when first pointed toward the transit at C, but the transit at C would have to be turned the same amount

right or left in order to sight the vertical cross-hair the angles themselves might be changed their su constant. In order to eliminate errors in the run jective of the transit at C, as well as the other errors ment, the telescope should be inverted and the process The angles may be measured by repetition, and any progra but it is essential that the angles at C should be con with the angles in the corresponding position of the transit The transit at D might be pointed in any arbitrary direc (within certain limits) and left in that position while ang are being measured at C. But the vertical cross-hair of th transit at C must be carefully sighted again at the cross-ha of the second transit before the latter is moved from its fir position. After the transit at C is sighted and clamped, th angles may be measured at D.

358. Measurements of Distances down Vertical If the depth of the shaft is no greater than the le tape, then the zero end of the tape may be lowered small weight attached to it, and a vertical measure from a point at the top of the shaft to a level line of lished by the transit set up in the bottom of the s he distance is greater than the tape-length it may along the guides for the cage or skip, or it may b by means of a long wire. The difficulty in meas vertical shafts by means of long tapes or wires is that t on account of their weight. The amount the tape str be determined as follows. If a tape is suspended fro balance the pointer will register the total weight o this is twice the average tension in the tape. Conseq he pull is increased by attaching a weight W to the end tape the average tension is $W + \frac{1}{2}$ (weight of tape). Knowi his average amount of pull the actual length of tape can b ound by stretching the tape out on a floor and testing it a described in Art. 19, p. 13, giving it the same amount of pull.

359. Transferring a Meridian into a Mine when there ar Two Shafts.† — The above methods presuppose that the min

---

* See footnote on p. 429.

* See Colliery Engineer, Vol. XVI, p. 53.
† See Colliery Engineer, Vol. XIV, p. 53.

may be calculated. It is good practice to check the position of D by " jiggling in " at a second point C'.

The plumb-lines should be as small in diameter as the weight will permit. They are usually of copper, annealed iron or piano wire.* With regard to the size of plumb-bob and wire there is a great difference of opinion. The plumb-bobs should be heavy enough to straighten out all bends in the wire. They should be immersed in oil or water or an oil emulsion, so as to stop their swinging in the shortest possible time, and the receptacle in which the plumb-bobs are immersed should be covered in order to protect the surface of the liquid from water dripping down the shaft. All air currents should be checked so far as possible, since experience has shown that in deep shafts they have considerable effect upon the plumb-lines. Great care should be taken to see that no part of the wires comes in contact with the shaft.

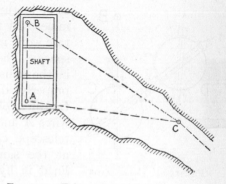

FIG. 153. TRIANGULATION AT JUNCTION OF SHAFT AND LEVEL.

When once the plumb-lines are hung the meridian may be transferred to all the levels of the mine once and for all time, so that a little extra precaution and time given to this operation are worth while. The surveyor should always keep in mind the fact that in plumbing the meridian down the mine the direction of the meridian is of much more importance than the actual position of the points themselves, because an error due to an incorrect direction of the meridian may be multiplied many hundreds of times in carrying the traverse through the mine.

When the level or cross-cut runs in a direction with respect to the shaft such as is shown in Fig. 153, then the triangulation

---

* See Eng. and Min. Jour., Vol. LV, p. 179, Feb. 25, 1893; Proc. Inst. of C. E., Vol. CXLII, p. 334; School of Mines Quarterly, Vol. XI, p. 333, and Colliery Engineer, Vol. XVI, p. 31.

method is employed.   Points A and B are the plumb-bobs and point C is where the transit is set up.   A slight error in the **distance** AB merely affects the computed lengths of AC and BC, whereas a small error in the **direction** of AB may produce large error in the positions of distant points in the workings. The point C therefore is chosen as far from the shaft as possible even though the angle C is small.

357a. Collimator Method. — When carrying a meridian into a mine the space at the bottom of the shaft is usually so cramped that great care must be exercised to avoid a large error in the azimuths carried into the mine.   By the following method accurate work may be done even in a small space.   The two wires are suspended in the usual manner and their swing properly damped. (Art. 357.)   The transit is placed at C in line with the wires A and B (Fig. 153a).   Since the telescope cannot be focused on both at the same time the instrument is lined in by focusing first on one and then on the other and moving the transit until the centers of the wires are in line.*   A second transit is placed at D, which may be but 3 or 4 ft. away. By pointing the two telescopes toward each other and focusing for long distance the hairs of each telescope may be viewed by the other.   (See Art. 128b, p. 102.) The angle then may be turned from CBA to the line of sight of the second transit.   (This is not necessarily the angle BCD.) Next the angle is turned by the second transit from the sight line of the first transit to the line DE, which should be fairly long.   The second transit might have been turned a few minutes right or left when first pointed toward the transit at C, but the transit at C would have to be turned the same amount

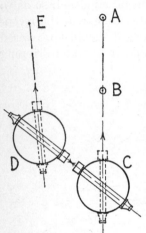

FIG. 153a. COLLIMATOR METHOD.

---

* See footnote on p. 429.

right or left in order to sight the vertical cross-hair of D, so while the angles themselves might be changed their sum would be constant. In order to eliminate errors in the run of the objective of the transit at C, as well as the other errors of adjustment, the telescope should be inverted and the process repeated. The angles may be measured by repetition, and any program used, but it is essential that the angles at C should be combined with the angles in the corresponding position of the transit at D. The transit at D might be pointed in any arbitrary direction (within certain limits) and left in that position while angles are being measured at C. But the vertical cross-hair of the transit at C must be carefully sighted again at the cross-hair of the second transit before the latter is moved from its first position. After the transit at C is sighted and clamped, then the angles may be measured at D.

358. Measurements of Distances down Vertical Shafts.* — If the depth of the shaft is no greater than the length of the tape, then the zero end of the tape may be lowered by having a small weight attached to it, and a vertical measurement taken from a point at the top of the shaft to a level line of sight established by the transit set up in the bottom of the shaft. When the distance is greater than the tape-length it may be measured along the guides for the cage or skip, or it may be measured by means of a long wire. The difficulty in measuring deep vertical shafts by means of long tapes or wires is that they stretch on account of their weight. The amount the tape stretches may be determined as follows. If a tape is suspended from a spring balance the pointer will register the total weight of the tape; this is twice the average tension in the tape. Consequently if the pull is increased by attaching a weight W to the end of the tape the average tension is $W + \frac{1}{2}$ (weight of tape). Knowing this average amount of pull the actual length of tape can be found by stretching the tape out on a floor and testing it as described in Art. 19, p. 13, giving it the same amount of pull.

359. Transferring a Meridian into a Mine when there are Two Shafts.† — The above methods presuppose that the mine

---

* See Colliery Engineer, Vol. XVI, p. 53.
† See Colliery Engineer, Vol. XIV, p. 53.

has so far been opened only by one shaft. If there is a second shaft or an adit, it is, of course, only necessary to plumb or otherwise transfer the position down each shaft; the computed distance between these points then becomes a base-line of substantial length. In Fig. 154 the traverse $ABCD$ is run out on the surface to connect the two shafts at A and D. The points A and D are plumbed down the shafts and the corresponding points A' and D' established at the bottom. An underground traverse $A'G'F'E'D'$ is then run out. In the surface traverse the length and azimuth of AD and in the underground traverse the length and azimuth of $A'D'$ are missing. The horizontal

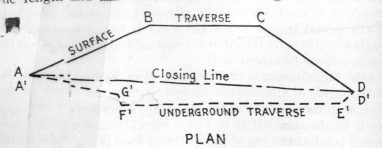

PLAN

Fig. 154.

length and azimuth of each of these lines can be determined from their respective traverses as explained in Art. 434, p. 525. The surface traverse is referred to the true meridian, and, since nothing is yet known in regard to the direction of the meridian in the mine, the underground traverse is referred to an assumed meridian. The true azimuth of $A'D'$ is the same as the azimuth of AD, provided the plumbing down the shaft has been done accurately. The difference between the true and assumed azimuths of $A'D'$ is a correction to be applied to the azimuths of all of the lines of this underground traverse.

360. UNDERGROUND TRAVERSES. — Surveying in a mine is necessarily a process of traversing, for only the working passages are available for lines of survey. The line of traverse is often run so that the longest possible sight may be taken. In the tortuous passages of a mine it is frequently necessary to take very short sights on the main traverse and since the azimuth is transferred to distant connections through these short lines great care should be exercised; and instrumental errors should be eliminated by reversing the telescope and using the mean of the two results. After the main traverses have been run, the surface boundaries may be established accurately underground and the stopes and working places surveyed by more convenient and less accurate methods, from the traverse stations already established.

It is often very convenient in underground work to take the azimuth from an estimated general direction (or strike) of the vein; for the direction of the meridian is of no importance in the actual working of a mine, while the direction of most of the passages usually will vary only a few degrees from the strike; this will simplify the traverse calculations.

Accurate traverses should be carried into all important workings of the mine; these include the shafts, levels, cross-cuts, raises and winzes. Permanent transit points should be established in the shaft at every level; in an inclined shaft it is good practice to put in one or two points on line between the levels to hold the direction of the shaft. Offset distances called " rights " and " lefts " are measured on each side of the traverse line within the mine workings for the purpose of locating the limits of the workings. The floor of passages is defined by determining the elevation of the necessary number of points, and the roof by measurements from points located on the floor.* Elevations are defined within the mine either by direct leveling, as in leveling out on the surface, or by means of inclined distances and vertical angles. Secondary openings, such as stopes, are surveyed by running the lines from the main traverse through a chute or mill-hole, from which the necessary dimensions and angles are taken to define the shape and extent of the stope holes. †   Sometimes these stopes are surveyed by use of the compass and clinometer. Where long stopes are to be surveyed a transit line is run from a station in a level up through a chute at one end of the stope, carried along through the stope, and then

---

* See Colliery Engineer, Vol. XIV, p. 197; also School of Mines Quarterly, Vol. XI, p. 334.

† See Eng. and Min. Jour., Jan. 27, 1900;   Proc. Inst. of Mine Surveyors, Vol. II, and Min. and Sci. Press, April 3, 1910.

down through another chute at the other end closing on another
station in the level.

The field-notes of these details are usually kept in the form
of sketches which show the traverse line that forms the skeleton of the survey and the measured offsets and angles which
locate the points needed to define the boundaries of the hole.*
It is often necessary to draw sketches showing the opening both
in elevation and in plan and to add descriptive remarks sufficient
to make the sketch clear to any surveyor even though he is
unfamiliar with that particular place in the mine.

361. Traverse Stations and Station Marks. — The places
chosen for stations should be in protected places and located

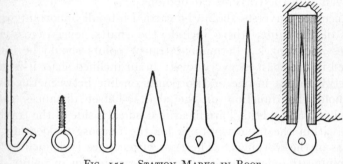

FIG. 155.   STATION MARKS IN ROOF.

where they will not be liable to be tampered with or disturbed.
They are often marked by a drill-hole with a plug and spad of
some kind, a nail, a spike or a boiler rivet.

A satisfactory station mark may be made by drilling in the
roof (or back) of a passageway a hole about $1\frac{1}{2}$ inches in diameter
and driving a tight-fitting wooden plug into the hole; a mark
of some kind is made on the end of the plug.   These marks are
commonly a spad (or spud) which is made by flattening the
head of a horseshoe nail and drilling a hole about $\frac{1}{8}$ inch in diameter through it.   Other roof marks commonly used are an eye
pin, a screw-eye, a staple or a bent nail.   (See Fig. 155.)   These
station marks can be attached to the caps of the mine timber,
but timbers are liable to be moved.

---

* See Colliery Engineer, Vol. XIV, pp. 38 and 197.

Owing to the workings in the mine these overhead marks sometimes cannot be employed; then the stations are established on the floor. Floor station marks are commonly a short stout spike or a sharpened boiler rivet driven into a tie of the track. In the heads of these spikes a small drill-hole is made to distinguish them from other spikes. For a temporary mark a punch mark on the rail, a mark on a block of lead or iron or a chalk mark is often used.

In sighting overhead stations a plumb-line is suspended and the angle and distances taken to a mark on a plumb-line, such as to the top of plumb-bob, to a knot in the line, or to a bit of candle grease fastened to the line. When the station is on the floor a pencil may be sighted, and if the station mark has a small drill-hole in it a small finish nail can be inserted, upon which to sight.

All such points must be illuminated. This may be done by holding a piece of tracing cloth back of the station mark, behind which is a flashlight or a lighted candle; this causes the nail or pencil held upon the station mark to be silhouetted against a white surface. Often a candle or a flashlight held to one side of the object sighted will illuminate it sufficiently, especially if a sheet of white paper is held behind it. Many devices such as plummet lamps and special illuminated targets on tripods are sometimes used.

Besides the devices which mark the exact station point a white ring is often painted around them to aid in finding the point. Another method is to paint an arrow on the wall, pointing toward the station. It is good practice to paint the number of the station near by, either on the hanging wall or on the foot wall. In some mines a small copper, brass or aluminum tag upon which the station number is stamped is attached near the station mark.

The method of numbering stations sometimes depends upon their positions and sometimes it does not.* Where the station number relates to its position in the mine one of the methods is to number all points on the first level from 100 to 199, on the second level from 200 to 299, and so on, as is done in the field-notes on pp. 442–4. Another method is to designate the station

---

* See Eng. and Min. Jour., Sept. 8, 1906; also Min. and Sci. Press, Oct. 24, 1903.

as 1206 N or 1318 S, if the workings are about North and South; the first number would mean station 6 on the 12th level north of the shaft. Where the numbering of the stations has nothing to do with its location they are usually numbered consecutively. A book containing the number, location and description of all stations should be kept up to date, and if the mine has more than one shaft this fact should be indicated in the notes or in the station numbers.

362. Setting up the Transit. — If the point to be occupied is on the floor the transit is set up in the usual manner; if it is in the roof a temporary point can be marked on the floor by plumbing down from the roof point, and then the transit set up over the temporary floor point. If the point is in the roof, however, the usual method is to suspend the plumb-line from the point and set the instrument up under it. Most instruments have a mark on the telescope barrel over the intersection of the center lines of the horizontal axis and the telescope. This point is set approximately under the plumb-bob and the instrument leveled, the telescope is brought to a horizontal position by the telescope bubble, and then by means of the adjustable head the point is brought directly under the plumb-bob.

363. TRAVERSING. — In running the traverses in levels, drifts and horizontal, or nearly horizontal passages, the work is done the same as on the surface and under these conditions the main telescope of the transit can be used. The angles are measured either as direct angles, and **doubled for a check,** or measured as azimuths. (See Art. 144, p. 123.) Vertical angles are read in the ordinary manner, but care should be taken to determine the index correction. Whenever the vertical circle is read with the telescope both direct and inverted, the index correction should be determined and applied to each reading to eliminate errors produced by plate bubbles. The mean of these two corrected angles is the true value. Where it is necessary to use an eccentric telescope the proper correction for eccentricity must be applied as described in Arts. 348 and 349, pp. 419–420.

364. The following method is in use in several mines and requires no reduction for eccentricity. The side telescope alone is used, the vernier is set on zero and a backsight taken on the first point, the upper motion is unclamped and the second point sighted with the vertical and horizontal cross-hairs; the horizontal and vertical angles are then read. The lower motion is unclamped, the telescope inverted, and the first point sighted again; the upper motion is unclamped and the second point sighted as before. Again the horizontal and vertical angles are read. The first horizontal angle read does not give the true angle, but half of the second angle reading does give the true horizontal angle; and the mean of the two vertical angles read gives the true vertical angle. In practice the vertical angle is generally read but once, the index correction being applied. The above method is illustrated in the notes on pp. 442–4.

365. Since nearly all traverse measurements are made as inclined measurements, and since vertical angles often are used together with the distances for obtaining elevations, it is frequently necessary to measure the H.I. (*height of instrument*) and the H.Pt. (*height of point*) above or below the station mark. If the transit is set **above** the station the H.I. is recorded + (plus), and if the transit is set **under** the station the H.I. is recorded − (minus); but if the point sighted is **below** the station the H.Pt. is recorded + (plus), and if it is **above** the station the H.Pt. is recorded − (minus).

The vertical distance is obtained by computing the " sine distance," which is the inclined distance × the sine of the vertical angle, and then applying to that distance the proper correction, depending upon the amount and the sign of the H.I. and H.Pt. distances. For example, Fig. 156 indicates a set-up of the instrument under a point in the roof; the vertical angle was taken to the top of the plumb-bob hung from another point in the roof. Here the H.I. is minus and H.Pt. is plus.

Fig. 157 illustrates a set-up where the instrument station is in the roof, the station ahead is in the floor, and the vertical angle was taken directly to the point in the floor; here the H.I. is a minus quantity. There are several different combinations which arise, but no difficulty will be experienced if the relative position of the points is visualized before the computations are made.

The horizontal distances are usually obtained by computing

the "cosine distance," that is, the inclined distance × the cosine of the vertical angle. The reason why the cosine instead of the versed sine is so frequently used in obtaining the horizontal

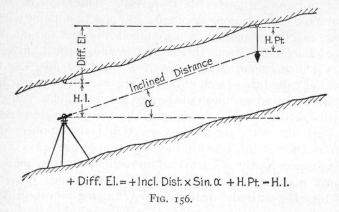

+ Diff. El. = + Incl. Dist. × Sin. α + H. Pt. − H. I.

FIG. 156.

distance is because its logarithm can be taken from the tables at the same opening as the log sine, which is used for the vertical distance. But when the horizontal distance alone is required and the vertical angle is small, the versed sine method explained in Arts. 12, p. 9, and 390, p. 474 should be used.

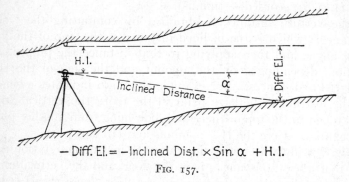

− Diff. El. = − Inclined Dist. × Sin. α + H. I.

FIG. 157.

The field-notes on pp. 442–4 illustrate this common method of running mine traverses.

366. A somewhat less common method of traversing is to use three tripods having leveling heads and centering plates like those of the transit. The transit fits on to any of these heads, and while it is attached to one of them the other two are surmounted by *lamp targets* in which the sighting center has exactly the same position that the sighting center of the transit would have if set on the same tripod. These tripods are placed vertically over or under the stations and the transit is attached to the middle one. When the transit head is moved from the middle to the foremost tripod a target takes the place formerly occupied by the transit, and the hindmost tripod is brought ahead of the transit and set up on the new forward station.

367. Traverse Notes. — As in all classes of surveying the form of notes differs with local practice and the personal preference of the surveyor. A common and useful form is shown on pp. 442–4. In these notes the first column shows that the instrument was first set up at station o, the second and third columns state that a B.S. was taken on a monument with the horizontal circle set at o° oo′, a F.S. taken to station 2 and horizontal angle read as 88° 03′; then, without changing the circle reading, a B.S. was taken on the Mon., and then another F.S. taken on station 2 and the double angle read was 176° 08′, half of which is the true angle. All horizontal angles are read here as azimuths, in a clockwise direction from a B.S. on the station designated in the " Pt." column. The fourth column states that the distance 651.01 was measured horizontally instead of on the slope, which latter is the usual custom and would have been used here had the tape been long enough. The fifth, sixth and seventh columns state that the vertical angle was a single reading of a depression angle taken to a point that was distant above station 2 an amount equal to the distance the center of the instrument was above station o. The description of the points sighted is in the last column.

The next set of readings shows that the transit was set at the same station o, and the horizontal angle read and " doubled "; the single reading of the angle was considerably different from half of the double reading, owing to the fact that the sight was down the shaft, as indicated by the vertical angle, and so highly inclined that an auxiliary telescope (here a side telescope) had to be used. In the column headed " H.Pt." is recorded + 3.27,

TRAVERSE NOTES OF BEAR CREEK MINE, WEST BOWLDER, MONTANA.

Sta.	Pt.	Hor. Angle.	Slope Dist.	Vert. Angle.	H.Pt.	H.I.	Remarks.
o	Mon.	0° 00′				+ 4.68	Coördinates Mon.
	2	88° 03′	651.01	− 0° 58′	− 4.68		= Lat. + 1476.82
	Mon.	" "	(Hor.)				Dep. − 647.87
	2	176° 08′					Hor. Dist. O to Mon. = 764.27
*o	Mon.	0° 00′				+ 4.68	Elev. Mon. = 560.28, R.R.
	101	357° 01′	117.38	−80° 10′	+ 3.27		= 4.92
	Mon.	" "					O = pt. on collar of shaft.
	101	355° 40′					Bearing O to Mon. = due N.
101	o	0° 00′				− 6.23	2 = Top of air shaft to 1st level.
	102	269° 55′	230.83	+ 0° 45′	+ 3.42		101 = Shaft plug 1st level.
	o	" "					* Side telescope.
	102	179° 50′					102 = Spad in roof 1st level.
101	o	0° 00′				− 6.23	
	201	179° 54′	112.65	−80° 09′	+ 4.14		201 = Shaft plug 2nd level.
	o	" "					Side telescope.
	201	359° 52′					
102	101	0° 00′				− 2.85	
	103	181° 30′	153.51	+ 0° 55′	+ 3.75		103 = Spad in roof 1st level.
	101	" "					
	103	3° 00′					
102	101	0° 00′				− 2.85	
	107	181° 25′	75.03	+ 0° 52′	+ 3.16		107 = Spad in roof 1st level.
	101	" "					
	107	2° 50′					
103	102	0° 00′				− 3.16	
	104	181° 32′	105.68	+ 0° 39′	+ 4.01		104 = Spad in roof 1st level.
	102	" "					
	104	3° 04′					
104	103	0° 00′				− 3.75	
	105	181° 01′	162.13	+ 0° 48′	+ 4.26		105 = Spad in roof 1st level at
	103	" "					foot of air shaft.
	105	2° 02′					
105	104	0° 00′				− 3.92	
	2	270° 30′	92.36	+88° 25′	0.00		Side telescope.
	104	" "					
	2	194° 14′					
105	104	0° 00′				− 3.92	
	Breast	179° 50′	15.9	0° 00′			
201	101	0° 00′				− 6.22	
	301	180° 00′	115.78	−80° 32′	+ 2.93		301 = shaft plug at 3rd level.
	101	" "					Side telescope.
	301	360° 00′					
201	101	0° 00′				− 6.22	
	202	268° 06′	167.48	+ 0° 53′	+ 1.96		202 = Spad in roof 2nd level.
	101	" "					
	202	176° 12′					

TRAVERSE NOTES OF BEAR CREEK MINE, WEST BOWLDER, MONTANA (*Continued*).

Sta.	Pt.	Hor. Angle.	Slope Dist.	Vert. Angle.	H.Pt.	H.I.	Remarks.
201	101	0° 00′				− 6.22	
	205	88° 00′	196.02	+ 0° 47′	+ 3.01		205 = Spad in stull 2nd level.
	101	" "					
	205	176° 00′					
202	201	0° 00′				− 4.92	
	208	182° 28′	138.07	+ 0° 44′	+ 1.09		208 = Spad in roof at raise 2nd level.
	201	" "					
	208	4° 56′					
202	201	0° 00′				− 4.92	
	203	182° 28′	106.37	+ 0° 47′	+ 1.03		203 = Spad in roof 2nd level.
	201	" "					
	203	4° 56′					
203	202	0° 00′				− 3.68	
	204	182° 35′	176.93	− 0° 29′	0.00		204 = Spike in floor at breast 2nd level.
	202	" "					
	204	5° 11′					
208	202	0° 00′				− 3.04	Side telescope.
	107	268° 01′	121.03	+77°59′	+3.26		
	202	" "					
	107	177° 08′					
205	201	0° 00′				− 4.28	
	206	180° 24′	216.87	+ 0° 48′	+ 3.69		206 = Spad in roof 2nd level.
	201	" "					
	206	0° 48′					
206	205	0° 00′				− 4.23	
	209	180° 44′	117.72	+ 0° 41′	+ 3.18		209 = Spad in roof over winze 2nd level.
	205	" "					
	209	1° 30′					
206	205	0° 00′					
	Breast	181° 04′	152.00				
301	201	0° 00′				− 6.78	
	302	268° 34′	304.02	− 0° 10′	0.00		302 = Spad in floor in raise 3rd level.
	201	" "					
	302	177° 08′					
301	201	0° 00′				− 6.78	
	303	268° 34′	315.83	+ 0° 48′	+ 3.16		303 = Spad in roof 3rd level.
	201	" "					
	303	177° 08′					
301	201	0° 00′				− 6.78	
	305	88° 54′	194.63	+ 0° 50′	+ 4.02		305 = Spad in roof 3rd level.
	201	" "					
	305	177° 48′					
301	201	0° 00′				− 6.78	
	401	180°02′	116.82	−80° 10′	+ 3.02		401 = Shaft plug 4th level. Side telescope.
	201	" "					
	401	360° 00′					

TRAVERSE NOTES OF BEAR CREEK MINE, WEST BOWLDER, MONTANA (*Continued*).

Sta.	Pt.	Hor. Angle.	Slope Dist.	Vert. Angle.	H.Pt.	H.I.	Remarks.
302	301	0° 00′				− 4.16	
	208	266° 56′	123.48	+79° 30′	+ 4.03		Side telescope.
	301	" "					
	208	175° 18′					
303	301	0° 00′				− 4.16	
	304	184° 33′	288.92	+ 0° 12	0.00		304 = Spike in floor, breast 3 ft. beyond.
	301	" "					
	304	°9 06′					
305	301	0° 00′				− 4.16	
	306	182° 12′	186.10	+ 0° 46′	+ 2.16		306 = Spad in roof 3rd level.
	301	" "					
	306	4° 24′					
306	305	0° 00′				− 1.52	
	307	180° 56′	150.16	+ 0° 43′	0.00		307 = Spike in floor at winze 3rd level.
	305	" "					
	307	1° 52′					
307	306	0° 00′				+ 4.77	
	209	87° 11′	120.49	+71° 11′	0.00		Breast 15′ beyond 307. Side telescope.
	306	" "					
	209	175° 02′					
401	301	0° 00′				− 6.72	
	402	268° 02′	219.73	+ 0° 48′	+ 2.08		402 = Spad in roof 4th level.
	301	" "					
	402	176° 04′					
401	301	0° 00′				− 6.72	
	406	90° 24′	116.39	− 1° 02′	+ 1.98		406 = Spike in floor 4th level, breast 2′ beyond.
	301	" "					
	406	180° 48′					
401	301	0° 00′				− 6.72	
	Bot. shft.	180° 00′	49.7	−80° 10′	0.00		
402	401	0° 00′				− 2.01	
	403	184° 08′	84.83	+ 0° 45′	+ 3.24		403 = Sta. in roof at raise 4th level.
	401	" "					
	403	8° 16′					
402	401	0° 00′				− 2.01	
	404	184° 08′	92.62	+ 0° 42′	+ 2.68		404 = Spad in roof 4th level.
	401	" "					
	404	8° 16′					
403	402	0° 00′				− 2.68	
	302	269° 08′	111.68	+81° 24′	+ 2.61		
	402	" "					Side telescope.
	302	179° 56′					
404	402	0° 00′				− 3.01	
	405	182° 49′	217.66	+ 0° 13′	0.00		405 = Spike in floor 4th level, breast 3′ beyond.
	402	" "					
	405	5° 38′					

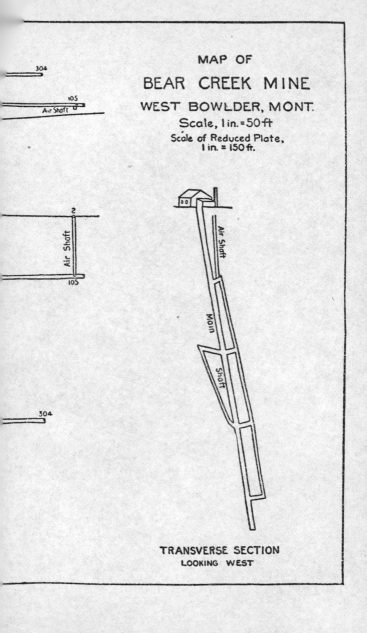

MAP OF

BEAR CREEK MINE

WEST BOWLDER, MONT.

Scale, 1 in. = 50 ft

Scale of Reduced Plate,
1 in. = 150 ft.

304

105
Air Shaft

2

Air Shaft

105

Air Shaft

Main

Shaft

304

TRANSVERSE SECTION
LOOKING WEST

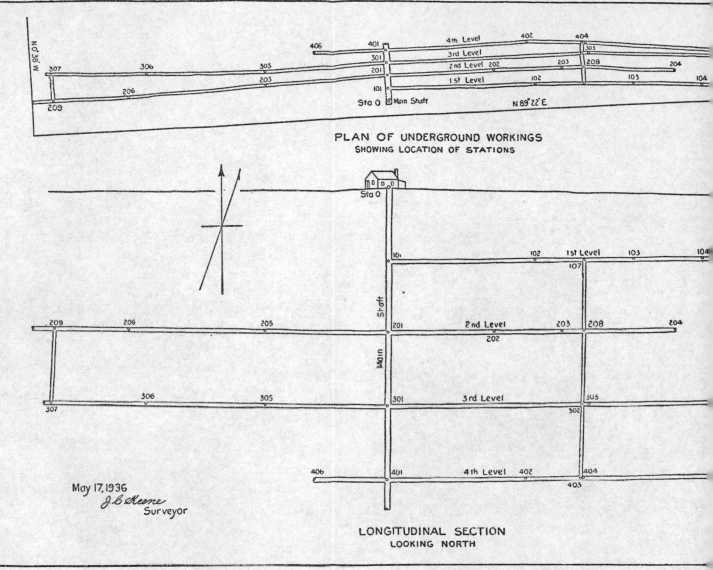

PLAN OF UNDERGROUND WORKINGS
SHOWING LOCATION OF STATIONS

LONGITUDINAL SECTION
LOOKING NORTH

May 17, 1936
J. C. Keene
Surveyor

FIG. 158. PLOT OF A MINE SURVEY.

which means that the vertical angle was taken to a point, on
a plumb-line hung from station 102, that was 3.27 ft. below the
station mark. (Art. 365, p. 439.) Throughout this traverse the
main telescope was used, except on highly inclined sights, when
the side telescope was used as indicated in the " Remarks "
and by the horizontal angle readings. Had the top telescope
been used and the angles accurately measured the first reading
of the horizontal angle would have been half of the " double
angle," but the vertical angles would all have had to be corrected for eccentricity of the telescope, as explained in Art. 348,
p. 419. In the method used in these notes no eccentricity correction is necessary.

The measurements which locate the walls of the workings have
been omitted purposely from the foregoing notes for the sake of
simplicity. A plot of the mine in which this traverse was run
is shown in Fig. 158.

368. Station, Computation, and Coördinate Books. — Besides the field note-book, most mining engineers keep three other
survey record books, a book containing a description and location of all traverse stations, one containing the computations of
all traverses and other surveys, and a coördinate book containing
the computed values of the coördinates of station points.

369. Station record books are commonly kept in the form
shown below. These notes show that station 1001 is in C shaft,

STATION RECORD.

Station.	Notes.	Coörd.	Comp.	Date.	Remarks.
1001	C shaft	2– 1	60–83	2–10–15	Shaft plug 10th level
1013	B 10 N	1–19	59–77	2–14–15	Plug in stope

its coördinates are on p. 1 of Coördinate Book No. 2, the computations relating to this point are on p. 83 of Computation Book
60, and that the point was set on Feb. 10, 1915.

370. The computation book is usually a book of unruled pages
with pasteboard covers. At the top of the pages should be entered the title of the computation, the coördinates and elevation
of the station from which the computations start, the bearing of

Main Shaft Line. Coörd. Mon. = $\begin{cases} \text{Lat.} + 1476.82 \\ \text{Dep.} - 647.87 \end{cases}$ Coörd. Bk. 76, p. 43.

May 20, 1906. J. C. Keene.

Elev. 560.28   Main Shaft Fieldbook.

o − 2   N 88° 04′ E

Lat.	Dep.	Elev.		Bearings.
8.52810	9.99975	560.28 = Mon.	H.D. = 651.01	o — Mon. = due N
2.81359	2.81359	+4.92	V ∠ = 0° 58′	88° 04′
1.34169	2.81334	565.20	8.22720 tan	o − 2 = N 88° 04′ E
		−4.68	2.81359	
+21.96	+650.64	560.52 = o	1.04079	
+712.55	−647.87	−10.98		
+734.51	+2.77	549.54 = 2	V.D. = −10.98	

o − 101   N 2° 10′ W

Lat.	Dep.	Elev.		Bearings.
9.99969	8.57757	560.52 = o	V ∠ = −80° 10′ 9.23244	o — Mon. = due N
1.30204	1.30204	+4.68	S.D. = 117.38 2.06960	360°
1.30173	9.87961	565.20	1.30204	357° 50′
		−115.66	H.D. = 20.05 2.06960	o − 101 = N 2° 10′ W
+20.03	−0.76	449.54	2.06317	
+712.55	−647.87	+3.27	V.D. = −115.66 115.66	
+732.58	−648.63	452.81 = 101		

101 − 102   N 87° 45′ E

Lat.	Dep.	Elev.		Bearings.
8.59395	9.99967	452.81 = 101	9.99996	101 − o = S 2° 10′ E
2.36325	2.36325	−6.23	2.36329	269° 55′
0.95720	2.36292	446.58	2.36325	267° 45′
		+3.02	H.D. = 230.81 230.81	180°
+9.06	+230.63	449.60	V ∠ = +0° 45′ 8.11693	101 − 102 = N 87° 45′ E
+732.58	−648.63	+3.42	S.D. = 230.83 2.36329	
+741.64	−418.00	453.02 = 102	0.48022	
			V.D. = + 3.02	

=3TH LEVEL NORTH B SHAFT.

Sta.	Bearing	Dist. Hor.	Latitude N	Latitude S	Departure E	Departure W	Total Latitude	Total Departure	Total Elev.	Elev. Plat.	N Bk. No.	N Bk. P	C Bk. No.	C Bk. P	Date.	Sta.	Remarks.
699							+1266.78	−547.32	−788.95							699	
801	S 29°41′ E	23.40		20.33	11.59		+1245.45	−535.73	−789.05							801	6″ Spike in tie
866	S 68 02 E	33.43		12.50	31.00		+1233.95	−504.73	−789.26							866	"

FIG. 159a. COÖRDINATE BOOK.

the B.S. line, where the coördinates used are to be found in the Coördinate Book, the shaft and level under which the data will be found headed in the field-notes, the date and the name of the computer. Fig. 159 is the beginning of the computations of the notes on pp. 442–4.

In computing horizontal distances log cosines of vertical angles are used rather than log versed sines, because the former can be taken from the same page of the tables as the log sines which are used for computing the vertical distances. The vertical distance of the first course from station 0 to 2 was obtained through the tangent of the angle, because the distance measured was the horizontal distance.

371. The Coördinate Book may be ruled and columns headed as shown in Fig. 159a. In it are recorded the results of the computations in the proper columns.

Columns headed " Latitude " and "Departure " are computed as explained in Chap. XIV. The minus signs before the numbers in the " Elev." column indicated that the points are below the datum plane.

The column headed " Elev. Plat." is used for recording the

elevation of base of rail at the shaft; the following four columns are for recording the field note-book number and page and the computation book number and page.

372. MINE MAPS. — The maps of a mine are frequently the only means of clearly conveying information regarding the shape and extent of the workings.* They should be made so as to show in the clearest possible manner the passages and stope-holes, their extent as well as their location. Since in different mines the veins of deposit have different amounts of dip and different directions of strike, considerable judgment must be exercised in the choice of planes upon which to project the plans of the workings so that their location and extent will be shown in the clearest possible manner.

The usual plans prepared for a mine are

(1) Surface plan.
(2) Underground workings in plan.
(3) Underground workings in longitudinal section.
(4) Underground workings in transverse section.
(5) Map of stopes.
(6) Assay map.
(7) Geological data.

(1) The surface plan should show the boundaries, roads, joining railroad, buildings, mine dump, drains and water supply.

(2) The underground plan is a projection on a horizontal plane. It should show all underground workings such as the shafts, levels, cross-cuts, winzes, raises, stopes, faults, ore shoots, mill-holes, and sometimes the geology; the progress should be shown by different colors, by difference in character of lines or by dates lettered on the plan.

In mines where the dip is 70° or greater the plan is often complicated because lines on one level overlap lines representing other levels. To avoid this confusion each level should be plotted in plan separately. In Fig. 158 all levels are shown on one plan because the stopes are not plotted on that plan and hence there is no overlapping of lines on different levels.

---

* See article on Accurate Underground Plans, in Canadian Engineer, May, 1902.

When the dip is less than 60° to 70° the plan of the entire mine can usually be plotted on one sheet, and if the levels are colored differently the plan is more easily understood.

(3) The longitudinal section may be either a vertical section, as in Fig. 158, or a section lying in the plane of the dip, in which case it is called a " plan on the vein." In the former the true vertical distance between levels is shown, whereas in the latter the levels are shown at distances apart equal to the slope distances along the shaft. Even though the levels are usually constructed on a grade of about 1 per cent for drainage and haulage they are often plotted on the longitudinal section as level passages.

This longitudinal section should show all workings shown on the plan (see [2] above) and should show the progress of the work in a clear manner, especially in the stopes.

If the vein is fairly regular and the coördinate planes are taken with the assumed north and south along the strike, then the longitudinal section represents the levels in their true lengths.

(4) The transverse section is usually plotted in a plane at right angles to the plan and longitudinal section. It is well in some cases to plot several transverse sections, each one a separate sheet, in order that their lines may not overlap and produce a confusing drawing. If the longitudinal plan is in a vertical plane through the strike, then the transverse plane is at right angles to this plane and on it the shaft would show in its true length.

(5) In some mines stope maps are kept showing in detail the size and shape of each stope as a separate map and indicating upon the plan the progress made. These working plots may be either vertical, horizontal, or parallel to the vein or seam. In any case, the thickness of the deposit is recorded at frequent intervals together with other particulars, such as thickness of waste or value of ore. These thicknesses are all measured at right angles to the plane of the working plan, so that when multiplied by the area on the plot, the cubic contents of any section is obtained. Where the ore occurs in irregular masses, not conforming particularly to any one plane, the above system does not apply and some other method must be devised by the surveyor. The best way of estimating amounts not mined is

to sketch their probable extent on such a chart from the data available and to make use of the area and thickness method as suggested above.

(6) Assay plans are made from the plan and longitudinal section of the mine on which is plotted the location from which assay samples have been removed.*

(7) A plan showing geological data should show the boundaries of the various formations, the planes of bedding and the foliation, the fault planes with their displacement, and all veins and dikes encountered.† These data could of course be shown to some extent by three coördinate planes as in solid geometry, but it is usually better to plot the geological data taken in each level. Any inclined rock surface is then represented by a series of contour lines corresponding to the levels from which the information is actually obtained. Strikes, dips, and intersections may then be determined by use of a protractor, a scale and a table of cotangents.

In a metal mine a plan of each level, when filled in with all the geological data, will have as much detail as can be shown conveniently. It is usual to make a geological plan of each level separately on thin tracing paper so that any two or possibly three consecutive ones may be superimposed. The particular position, strike, and dip of any ore shoot or surface may then be found as easily as though they were all plotted on the same piece of paper.

The scale of the surface map is usually 100 or 200 ft. to an inch. The general plans of underground workings are often 50 ft. to an inch and the detail stope plans are 20 ft. or 10 ft. to an inch. The general underground plans can best be plotted by the coördinates of the station points. The coördinates can be laid out on the plan and then if it changes scale by shrinking or swelling it does not affect the accuracy of the plan, for the new station points located in workings as they progress are plotted by coördinates from the nearest of the coördinate points originally plotted on the map. Since these maps are used so frequently and for so long a period, it is advisable to plot them on the best quality of mounted paper available.

---

* See Min. and Sci. Press, Sept. 3, 1904.
† See Mining Reporter, Vol. XLVIII, p. 181.

373. MINE MODELS. — These may be constructed of wood and glass. A wooden box without a top is built first. Horizontal strips of wood are fastened to the inside of the box at distances apart equal to the vertical distances (to scale) between the levels. On each of these horizontal strips a sheet of glass is placed on which has been accurately painted the horizontal projection of that particular level. The glass should be treated first with a coat of copal varnish or gelatine so that it will take the paint or ink. Strips of glass are inserted between the horizontal sheets to represent a shaft or winze.

374. LAYING OUT MINING WORK. — Drifts or cross-cuts are laid out by putting in two nails or hooks in the roof, not too near together, from which the miner can hang two plumb-lines and sight the center of the heading he is to run.

Vertical shafts are carefully plumbed on the inside of the frames, and frame by frame, as these are put in. It is best to hang the plumb-line from several frames above the bottom one, as these upper ones are more likely to have ceased to move. Hang the line an even fraction of an inch each way from the true position of the corners and note any accidental variation in the last frame set, so that in future work, if it is desired to hang the plumb-line from this frame, its error of position can be allowed for. The dimensions of a shaft or drift are given either " in the clear," meaning net measurements inside all timbers, or " over all," meaning gross measurement outside all timber and lagging.

375. UNDERGROUND SURVEYING PROBLEMS. — In the practice of mine surveying, problems are constantly arising which tax the ability and ingenuity of the surveyor, although the actual solution of most of them is quite simple. A few of the common problems met with in such work are given below.

376. To Find an Ore Shoot by Driving a Level. — The pitch being given by its altitude and azimuth, this serves as a course from any point on the ore shoot whose coördinates are known. The difference in elevation between this point and that of the level to be driven is divided by the sine of the altitude (or vertical angle) of the ore shoot, which gives the slope distance along the ore shoot. The horizontal coördinates of the point where the level will intersect the ore shoot may then be calculated.

377. To Lay Out a Connection in a Mine. — Here the problem is to determine the bearing (or azimuth) and the vertical angle and the distance to run from point A in a mine to point B in another portion of the mine. A traverse can be run from A to B through the passages already cut in the mine, and all the distances reduced to horizontal distances which, together with the azimuths, form a traverse in which the length of the closing line AB (horizontal projection) and its azimuth are missing. These can easily be computed by the method explained in Art.

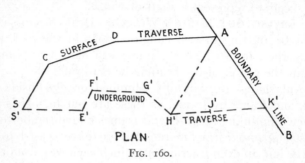

PLAN

Fig. 160.

434, p. 525. The difference in elevation between the actual points A and B together with the length of the horizontal projection of AB will give the vertical angle; from these data the direction and distance between the points A and B can be computed.

378. To Establish a Boundary Line of the Claim Underground. — In Fig. 160 points A and B are on the boundary of the claim. The shaft is located at S, and it is desired to prolong the underground working in the drift $H'J'$ to a point K' vertically under the boundary line. The surface traverse $BADCS$ is run out, point S is plumbed down to S', and the meridian transferred into the mine. Then the underground traverse $S'E'F'G'H'J'$ is run out. The horizontal projections of all the measured lines on both traverses are computed (or measured), and the length of the level line AH' and its bearing can be calculated as described in Art. 434, p. 525. In the horizontal triangle $AH'K'$, AH' and all the angles being known, the line $H'K'$ can readily be computed. If the drift $H'J'$ is not level the distance from H'

along the drift to the boundary plane will be equal to the horizontal distance H' K' divided by the cosine of the vertical angle.

379. BOREHOLE SURVEYING. — The exploration of ore-bearing property is often carried on by drilling deep holes. These may be made for the purpose of determining the character of the rock, as well as to form air passages or drainage holes. The holes sometimes vary considerably from a straight line and their direction can only be plotted by determining at various points in their length their slope depth, bearing and dip.

The length is readily obtained by measuring the length of the rods used in drilling, or a wire with a weight attached may be lowered and then measured.

Many devices have been used for determining the bearing and dip. The simplest consists of a phosphor-bronze shell, similar to a piece of pipe about ten inches long and one and one-half inches outside diameter (the diameter depends to a certain extent on the diameter of the drill-hole). The inside diameter is slightly larger than one and one-eighth inches. One end of this shell is closed permanently, while the other may be closed by means of a plug or left open as desired; when in use this plug is screwed in tightly. On the other end of the plug is a thread to which drill rods may be attached, or a hole through which a wire may be fastened. The device may then be lowered into the hole.

To determine the dip and bearing, a piece of glass tubing is used which is about six inches long and whose inside diameter is uniform and whose outside diameter is such that it will just fit in the shell. In the center of this tube is placed a tightly fitting rubber stopper, dividing the tube into two parts. The lower half is partially filled with hydrofluoric acid, and corked. The upper part is partially filled with liquid gelatin, and a small compass-needle, suspended in a frame to which a piece of cork is attached, is placed in the gelatin. The tube is then corked and placed in the shell, which can be lowered to any desired depth. This is then allowed to remain in the hole until the acid has had time to act on the glass, and the gelatin to harden. The acid etches the glass, and the angle it makes with the vertical may be measured by placing the glass tube in a special instrument for that purpose. Knowing this angle, the dip may be computed.

The bearing is obtained as follows. The cork is of sufficient size so as to float the compass and frame, the compass, however, being always surrounded by the gelatin. The latter should be of such consistency that it will not harden until some time after the instrument is in place. This will then allow the magnetic needle to coincide with the magnetic meridian. When the gelatin hardens it holds the needle in place, and the bearing of the hole at that point may be determined by noting the position of the needle when the tube has been withdrawn from the hole. If several results are obtained at different depths, the coördinates of these points may be computed, and plans made if necessary.

Another instrument sometimes used is similar to the above, but both compartments are partially filled with gelatin. A compass is placed in one, and a small suspended plumb-bob is placed in the other.

Another instrument used for this purpose, more elaborate than the former, contains a compass and plumb-bob which are photographed when the instrument is at any desired depth. A sensitized paper, a small electric lamp and battery for illuminating the bob and compass, and a watch are lowered with the instrument, the watch being so constructed that it makes the exposure automatically.

380. TUNNEL AND SUBWAY SURVEYS. — The simplest case of tunnel construction is that of an aqueduct built on a straight grade and line. A surface traverse forming a long straight line may be run from portal to portal to establish accurate points on the center line of the tunnel in the vicinity of its portals for the purpose of projecting the tunnel from each end toward the center. On this surface line all points are fixed with great accuracy to insure that the directions of the lines at each end of the tunnel are in the same straight line, and also to locate intermediate shafts when the work is to be carried on from shafts as well as from the portals. The line is transferred down the shafts by the plumbing method described in Art. 357, p. 430. The surface line directly above the center line of the tunnel may be run first as a random straight line and then points set on the center line by offsets, or it may be necessary to run a traverse between the portals and then compute the closing side, which is the center line. (Art. 434, p. 525.) Large transits with circles 7 to 9 inches in diameter and horizontal circles reading to the nearest 10" are often used for this work. As the work of tunneling progresses the lines at both portals are extended into the tunnel by means of the transit, and accurate roof points are put in from which plumb-lines are hung to fix the direction for the workmen to follow in carrying on the excavation. The elevations are carried along by means of the ordinary leveling instrument.

A topographic survey is made for the purpose of preparing a profile along the line of the tunnel to show the amount of cover over the tunnel, the best locations for vertical or inclined shafts, and the geological structure through which the tunnel will pierce.

When the tunnel is to extend under a river it is often necessary to establish its alignment by a system of triangulation. This method was employed when surveying for the Hudson River Tunnel of the Pennsylvania Railroad, the Simplon Tunnel and St. Gothard Tunnel in Switzerland.

When it is necessary to introduce curves into the tunnel alignment they are laid out by the common method of deflection angles, and are projected forward by use of the largest chords which can be sighted. The deflection angles are laid off and then measured by repetition and corrected as explained in Art. 61, p. 57. These problems frequently occur in city subway layouts, but since there are usually many shafts in such construction there is ample opportunity to transfer surface points into the underground work to serve as checks.

The great variety of conditions existing in tunnel and subway alignments has brought forth many special surveying details, too numerous to mention in this treatise. Following are several references to engineering periodicals in which some of the special surveying methods used in tunnel and subway projects are described.

Hoosac Tunnel, Massachusets, on Boston & Maine R.R.
　　"Manual for Railroad Engineers," by Vose, pp. 69–70.
　　Colliery Engineer, Vol. XVI, p. 52.

Musconetcong Tunnel, New Jersey, on Lehigh Valley, R.R.
    Trans. A. I. Mining Engineers, Feb. 1875, Vol. III, p. 231, by H. S. Drinker.

Simplon Tunnel, Italy.
    Eng. News, Dec. 21, 1905, Triangulation and Construction Surveys.
    Eng. News, Aug. 13, 20 and 27, 1903.
    Schweizeriche Bauzeitung, March 14, 1908, by M. Rosenmund.

Lötschburg Tunnel, Switzerland.
    Schweizeriche Bauzeitung, Aug. 26, 1911.

Vosburg, Pennsylvania, on Lehigh Valley Railroad.
    "The Vosburg Tunnel," by Leo Von Rosenberg, 1887.

Cascade Tunnel, Washington, on Great Northern Ry.
    Eng. News, Jan. 10, 1901, by John F. Stevens.
    Eng. & Contr., Aug. 1927, by H. B. Alvord.
    Journal Boston Soc. of Civil Engineers, March, 1927.
    Proc. A. S. C. E., Feb. 1931, Vol. 57, p. 194.
    Describes triangulation and base-line survey.
    Illustrations show instruments used and triangulation network.
    Typical calculations of triangulation are shown.

New Croton Aqueduct, New York.
    Trans. A. S. C. E., Vol. XXIII, 1890, pp. 17–30, by F. W. Watkins.

New York Rapid Transit Subways.
    Trans. A. S. C. E., Vol. XXIII, 1890, p. 31, by Edward Wegmann, Jr.
    Eng. Rec., Sept. 19, 1903.   Eng. News, Dec. 4, 1902; June 11, 1903.

Sewer Tunnel at Columbus, Ohio.   Surveying Under Compressed Air.
    Civil Engineering, Jan. 1933, by O. Bonney.
    Describes method for transferring lines and grades down shafts by holing
        through headings into compressed air chambers.

Napean Tunnel, New South Wales.
    Proc. Ins. of C. E., 1888, Vol. XCII, pp. 259–67, by T. W. Keele.

Gunnison Tunnel, Uncompahgre Valley Project, Colorado.
    Eng. Rec., Aug. 28, 1909, by I. W. McConnell.

Cincinnati Water Works Tunnel.
    Eng. Rec., March 4, 1905, by J. A. Hiller.

Hudson River Tunnel, Pennsylvania Railroad, New York.
    Eng. News, Dec. 13, 1906, by James Forgie.
    Eng. News, Feb. 28, 1907, by James Forgie.

East River Tunnels, New York.
    Eng. Rec., July 28, 1906.   Eng. News, Oct. 5, 1916, by C. M. Holland.
    Describes carrying line from surface to tunnel, and particularly the alignment
        of shields being driven into soft material — several good illustrations.

Little Tom Tunnel, Norfolk & Western Ry.
    Eng. News, Apr. 19, 1900, by Emile Low.

Scranton Tunnel, Pennsylvania, on the Lackawanna & Wyoming Valley R.R.
    Trans. A. S. C. E., May 1906, Vol. XVI, p. 221.

Strawberry Tunnel, Strawberry Valley Irrigation Project, Utah.
    Eng. News-Record, Dec. 7, 1917, by L. M. Hammond.
    Describes a unique method of defining line in tunnel partly filled with water.

Edison Electric Illuminating Co., of Boston.

Eng. & Contr., Dec. 19, 1917, by H. B. Pratt.

Describes survey with transit hung inverted from roof of tunnel.

Andes Copper Mining Co., Potreillos, Chile.

Eng. & Miners Jour., Feb. 24, 1923, by J. E. Harding. Describes driving a tunnel from surface of ground to connect with another tunnel driven from mine workings underground. Triangulation not satisfactory for computing the course of tunnel — a surface survey required. Difficulties encountered because of striking water — tape and lens affected by moisture, requiring special handling.

Three Mile Water Supply Tunnel, Providence, R. I., Water Supply.

Eng. News-Record, Oct. 8, 1925, by R. R. Bradbury. A comprehensive article covering surface alignment, establishing tunnel alignment, dropping line into tunnel, use of tunnel lamp and protractor rod, running out curve, precise taping.

Mount Royal Tunnel, Canadian National Ry., Montreal, Canada.

Eng. Rec., May 10, 1913, by J. L. Busfield. Eng. & Contr., Oct. 21, 1914.

Describes precise survey around mountain to find distance between portals.

Linwood Ave. and Lake St. Tunnels, Milwaukee, Wis.

Eng. News, June 15, 1916.

Describes an " instrument table " for setting up transit or level without blocking haulage track; and also type of markers used in tunnel roof.

Land and Lake Water Tunnel at Chicago, Ill.

Eng. News-Record, July 26, 1917. Describes triangulation to locate borings, transferring line down shafts, use of telephone for signalling, special device for setting up instrument under ground.

Colorado River Aqueduct of Metropolitan Water District of Southern California. — Tunnel Cross Sections and Clearances.

Civil Engineering, Jan. 1934, by B. A. Eddy.

Describes taking cross-sections of a tunnel by means of a large pantograph which traces contour of the tunnel rim directly on to cross-section paper.

Civil Engineering, Jan. 1936, By E. L. Crawford.

Describes method for checking cross-sections and detecting protrusions.

Application of Precise Surveying to Tunnel Construction.

Canadian Engineer, June and July 1936, by F. S. Hutton.

A comprehensive treatise on the technique of surface and underground surveys for tunnels, describing triangulation for control, dropping lines and levels down a shaft, laying out a curve underground, passing through lock into compressed air chamber, and methods for marking points and handling instruments to obtain the necessary precision.

SURFACE SURVEYING

381. SURFACE SURVEYING IN RUGGED MOUNTAIN REGIONS.
— In accurate work, such as the surveying of mining claims for patent,* the ordinary mining transit may be used. Measurements are made with a steel wire tape, 300 to 500 ft. long and marked every 10 ft. (or 20 ft.); it is used with a short aux-

---

* By patent proceedings is meant the proceedings necessary to obtain from the government a fee simple deed to the mining claim.

iliary steel ribbon tape which is divided to hundredths of a foot. Over rough ground it is not practicable to measure horizontal distances by use of plumb-lines. Slope measurements are taken from the horizontal axis of the instrument to the point at which the telescope is sighted, care being taken not to over-stretch the tape or to kink it. (Art. 12, p. 9.) The most accurate work is done by stretching the tape with a tension handle (a spring balance) which can be attached by a clamp to any part of the tape. Where it is feasible, just enough tension is given so that the stretch of the tape compensates for the short-age due to sag. Sometimes assistants will have to hold the middle point, or the points at one-third and two-thirds the length of the tape, up to the line of sight, giving at the same time enough pull to make the sag equal in the different sections of the tape.

In making general maps of a mining district, only monu-ments and important locations need be shown accurately. This accurate work, which is the first to be done, forms a skeleton on which to make a general map. The topography can be filled in by using a transit fitted with stadia hairs and a compass.

The best topographical data in mountainous country are ob-tained by running traverses along the ridges and valleys; these are also usually the best places to travel. Much sketching is nec-essary and the work should be plotted by the surveyor himself each day as the work proceeds. In this work a rough deter-mination of the topography is sufficient, since the plans are usu-ally plotted to the scale of $\frac{1}{10000}$ or smaller, and therefore such instruments as the hand compass, clinometer, and aneroid baro-meter can be used. With such instruments one man can do the entire work. The plane-table cannot be used to advantage in wooded mountain or in mine surveying, but photographic survey-ing may often prove useful in filling in details of topography.

382. Mine Boundaries—Location Survey—Lode Loca-tion.* — In most countries mineral rights are defined by vertical planes through lines marked out on the surface. Title to metal-liferous lands, however, as granted by the United States,

---

* For further information with regard to this subject see the Manual of Instruc-tions for the Survey of the Mineral Land of the United States, issued by the Com-missioner of the General Land Office, Washington, D. C.

conveys the right to all minerals included in the downward prolongation of the portions of veins cut off by the vertical end bounding planes, i.e., a vein can be worked in the dip indefinitely, but in the direction of the strike it is limited by the end bounding planes of the claim.

The federal law allows a claim to cover 1500 ft. measured along the direction of a vein and 300 ft. on each side of it. These dimensions, which constitute the maximum, can be reduced by local laws. Fig. 161 shows the measurements made in

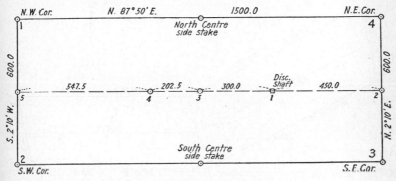

FIG. 161. PLAN OF LODE CLAIM.

staking out a claim 1500 ft. long and 600 ft. wide, the ends being perpendicular to the center line. The discovery was made at the point marked " discovery shaft." The direction of the center line follows the supposed direction of the strike of the vein. The claimant decided to limit his claim on the east end 450 ft. from the discovery shaft. The center line was therefore extended 1050 ft. westward, for he is entitled to a claim 1500 ft. long. At stations 2 and 5 right angles were turned off and the four corners set. When measuring from the discovery shaft westward the center point (station 3) was set as a means of establishing the center side stakes. The corner stakes and the center side lines of a claim are marked with the number of the corner and the name of the claim. Bearings and ties are taken to patent corners of other (adjoining) claims, or, bearings from one corner of the claim are taken to mountain peaks or other permanent points. A location certificate is then made out stating the name of claimant, date, place, extent and description of claim (metes and bounds); this is sent to the county recorder.

The end lines of claims are not necessarily perpendicular to the center line; they may make any angle, for example, to fit an adjoining claim, but the two end lines must be parallel. Claims not infrequently have angles as shown in (Fig. 161a), or the side line may be broken lines. Where a claim conflicts with another it may stop short of the full distance allowed by

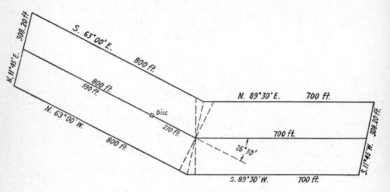

Fig. 161a.　Plan of Lode Claim.

law. In order to guard against troublesome litigation, an effort is sometimes made to surround a valuable claim with others, thus forming a " group." The more valuable claim is then protected as regards all " extralateral rights."

383. SURVEYING FOR PATENT.*— The surveying of claims for patent from the United States Government can only be obtained by those who have received appointment of United States Deputy Mineral Surveyor and they must have an order from the Surveyor General of the state or territory in which the claims are located before making any such survey.

In surveying for patent much more accurate work has to be done than when merely locating a claim. Before applying for an order for a patent survey the claim survey should be examined

---

* For more detailed information see "Mineral Land Surveying," by James Underhill (published by John Wiley & Sons).

to see that it is correct and closes accurately. Any inconsistencies should be removed, and the description made to agree with the lines intended in the claim. If the dimensions on the ground are subsequently found to differ slightly from those in the certificate an error of a few feet or a few minutes of an angle will usually be permitted. The claimant then deposits the fees for the Surveyor General's office, and makes application for the survey, accompanied by certified copies of the certificates of location. If the location certificates are found correct the order is issued. Otherwise the certificates are returned for correction.

The mineral surveyor then executes the survey just as for a claim location survey except as to accuracy of measurements and manner of marking corners. An error of one part in two thousand is permitted by the Surveyor General. The corners are monumented with stones, rock in place, or by marked trees. Sometimes a witness corner is set on line when it is not possible to set a regular corner monument. The survey is tied in (from Cor. No. 1) to a Section corner or to some U. S. locating monument. The workings and improvements (such as shafts, tunnels, buildings, etc.) are tied in to the corners and are shown on the plan. An estimate of the value of these improvements must be made and must be shown to be at least $500 per claim.

Placer claims may be taken in 20 acre tracts, the bounding lines of which must conform with the general system of survey lines established by the Government, but if such survey has not been extended to the district, they must be bounded by true meridian and east and west lines. The survey of coal land is subject to somewhat similar rules.

PROBLEMS

1. From a station at the mouth of a tunnel a line is run in the tunnel, azimuth 37° 24′, slope distance 424.34, vertical angle + 2° 10′, H.I. + 4.62, H.Pt. 0.0; thence azimuth 62° 42′, slope distance 278.53, vertical angle + 2° 18′, H.I. + 4.21, H.Pt. + 3.12, to breast. From the same station at tunnel a line is run on the surface, azimuth 98° 33′, slope distance 318.57, vertical angle − 3° 22′, H.I. + 4.87, H.Pt. 0.0; thence azimuth 38° 02′, slope distance 647.82, vertical angle + 14° 13′, H.I. + 4.73, H.Pt. 0.0, to the center of a vertical shaft. How deep must the shaft be to meet a connecting drift run on a grade of + 2.4% from a point in the floor at

the breast of tunnel which is 7.0 ft. vertically under the roof point, and what is the slope length and azimuth of this drift?

2. The strike of a certain vein at point of outcrop is N 43° E and the dip is 71° 50' to S.E. From this point of outcrop a surface line is run, N 83° 15' E, slope distance 248.12, vertical angle − 12° 34'; thence S 2° 54' E, slope distance 208.52, vertical angle − 14° 34', to a point from which the tunnel is to be driven in the direction N 71° W and with a grade of + 3.8% until it intersects the vein. All vertical angles were taken to points above the station sighted equal to the distance the horizontal axis of the transit was above the station point under the instrument.

(a) What would be the slope length of such a tunnel?

(b) What would be the slope length and bearing of the shortest possible tunnel run on a + 1.3% grade to intersect the vein?

3. A vein has a strike of S 67° W and its dip is 55°. What is the bearing of a line lying in the plane of the vein and having a vertical angle of − 44°?

4. Given the following field-notes.

Sta.	Pt.	Hor. Angle.	Slope Dist.	Vert. Angle.	H.Pt.	H.I.	Remarks.
O	X	0° 00'				+ 5.64	O = pt. in collar. X = pt. due S of Sta. O. Bearing O − 100 = due S
	100	0° 00'	106.21	− 67° 40'	+ 14.91		Pt. in roof
O	100	0° 00'				+ 5.64	
	I	89° 40'	308.95	0° 00'	− 5.41		Pt. on collar
100	0	0° 00'				− 15.12	
	101	269° 50'	80.74	+ 1° 04'	+ 2.61		Pt. in roof
101	100	0° 00'				− 3.22	
	102	175° 40'	113.40	+ 0° 27'	+ 2.18		Pt. in roof
I	0	0° 00'				+ 5.41	
	103	90° 20'	105.01	− 67° 07'	+ 15.02		Pt. in roof
103	I	0° 00'				− 13.13	
	104	94° 16'	99.98	− 1° 06'	− 3.71		Pt. in tie in floor

All horizontal angles were measured clockwise, the first pointing being made on the B.S.

Compute the horizontal distance and slope distance, to nearest 0.01 ft., from station 102 to station 104.

Compute the vertical angle and bearing, to the nearest minute, from station 102 to station 104.

5. A vertical winze has been sunk below the level of a tunnel. It is desired to sink a vertical shaft from the surface to connect with the winze. Station X is established at the mouth of the tunnel and station Y is near the site of the proposed shaft. Y bears S 88° 58' 56" W, 896.79 ft. from X. The following are the

notes of the survey reduced to horizontal distances connecting X and the winze corners A, B, C, and D:

Instrument Station.	Mean Deflection.	Horizontal Distance.	Stations Sighted.
X	0° 00′	896.79	Y
X	134° 55′ 26″ L	403.08	1
1	74° 05′ 06″ L	587.20	2
2	32° 23′ 43″ L	67.00	3
3	54° 43′ 47″ R	44.80	4
4	39° 51′ 57″ R	41.07	5
5	31° 10′ 10″ R	19.57	Cor. A
	31° 10′ 10″ R	27.24	Cor. B
	39° 43′ 40″ R	21.47	Cor. C
	24° 02′ 40″ R	25.77	Cor. D

Required the bearings and horizontal distances from Y to points vertically over the winze corners.

6. From station M at the mouth of a tunnel a traverse is run in the tunnel, azimuth 20° 35′, distance 352.16, vertical angle + 1° 02′, H.I. + 4.71, H.Pt. + 3.42 to point A; thence azimuth 61° 07′, distance 528.24, vertical angle + 0° 40′, H.I. − 3.62, H.Pt. + 4.07, to point B at the breast of the tunnel. From M a surface traverse is run, azimuth 25° 10′, distance 578.34, vertical angle + 4° 25′ to point C; thence azimuth 11° 15′, distance 407.62, vertical angle + 14° 20′ to point D, which is the center of a vertical shaft 129 ft. deep. In sighting surface points the vertical angles were in all cases read to points above the stations sighted equal to the distance the horizontal axis of the telescope was above the station point under the instrument.

Find the azimuth, vertical angle and slope distance of the line from the point at the bottom of the shaft to the roof point at breast of the tunnel.

7. Assuming the transit to be in perfect adjustment what is the error in horizontal angle in sighting down a 500-ft. shaft, when the vertical angle is − 89° and the telescope cannot be sighted closer than 3 seconds along the inclined line?

8. A vein has a dip of 38° to the W and a strike of N 9° 35′ E. A drift in vein is driven N 14° 30′ E. What is the per cent of grade of the drift?

9. A drift is constructed N 38° E on a 3% grade in the plane of a vein whose strike is N 57° E. What is the dip of the vein?

10. A vein has a dip of 57°. A drift is driven N 37° W in the plane of the vein on a grade of 5%. What is the strike of the vein?

PART III

COMPUTATIONS

CHAPTER XIII

GENERAL PRINCIPLES. — MISCELLANEOUS PROBLEMS. EARTHWORK COMPUTATIONS

384. GENERAL REMARKS. — The ultimate purpose of many surveys is to obtain certain numerical results to represent quantities such as areas or volumes. In the section on Surveying Methods it has been pointed out that in all surveys there should be a proper relation between the precision of measurement of the angles and distances. To secure final results to any given degree of precision, the measurements in the field must be taken with sufficient precision to yield such results. In computing from a given set of field-notes the surveyor should first determine how many places of figures he should use in the computations, the aim being to obtain all the accuracy which the field measurements will yield without wasting time by using more significant figures than are necessary. Professor Silas W. Holman* in the preface to his " Computation Rules and Logarithms " says: — " It would probably be within safe limits to assert that one-half of the time expended in computations is wasted through the use of an excessive number of places of figures, and through failure to employ logarithms."

Final results should be carried to as many significant figures as the data will warrant and no more. In order to insure the desired precision in the last figure of the result it will usually be necessary to carry the intermediate work one place further than is required for the final result.

385. The number of significant figures in the result of an observation is the number of digits that are known. For instance, if a distance is recorded as 24 000 ft. when its value was obtained to the nearest thousand feet only, it contains but two

---

* See " Elements of the Precision of Measurements and Graphical Methods," by Professor H. M. Goodwin, published by McGraw-Hill Book Co., New York.

significant figures. The zeros are simply put in to show the place of the decimal point If, however, the distance has been measured to the nearest foot and found to be 24 000 ft. there are five significant figures, for the zeros are here as significant as the 2 or 4. Similarly a measurement such as 0.00047 contains but two significant figures, the zeros simply designating the position of the decimal point, for, had this same value been recorded in a unit $\frac{1}{100000}$ as large the result would have been 47.

Again, if a series of measurements is taken between two points to hundredths of a foot and three of the results are 4.88, 5.05 and 5.00 it is evident that each of these distances contains three significant figures; if each one is multiplied by 1.246 the results are 6.08, 6.29 and 6.23, respectively. But had the measurements been taken to the nearest tenth of a foot and found to be 4.9, 5.1, and 5.0, these values when multiplied by 1.246 should appear as 6.1, 6.4 and 6.2. This illustration indicates the proper use of significant figures. Since the measurements 4.9, 5.1, and 5.0 are in error in the third figure (maximum error = 0.05) the factor 1.246 should be taken as 1.25. Similarly in the use of such a constant as 3.1415927 it is a waste of time to use more significant figures in the constant than are known in the number with which it is to be combined.

386. In deciding how many places of decimals to use in the trigonometric functions the student should examine the tabular differences and determine what percentage error is introduced by any error in an angle. For example, suppose an angle of a triangle to have been measured in the field to the nearest minute. There may be an error of 30 seconds in this angle, and it will be seen from the table of natural sines that the tabular difference for one minute in the fourth decimal place varies from 3 for a small angle to less than 1 for a large angle, and that the variation is about the same for cosines, and for tangents and cotangents of angles under 45°. Then for half a minute the difference will be, on an average, about 1 in the fourth place. Therefore, in general, four places will give results consistent with the precision of the angles. But if there are several steps in the computations it is advisable to use five-place tables to insure correct results in the fourth place. Similarly, five-place tables of functions will, in general, give angles to the nearest 10 seconds, and six-place tables to the nearest second. These are only average results and are intended to give the student a suggestion as to how to decide for himself whether to use four-, five- or six-place tables. Time can be saved by using four-place tables where only four places are required rather than using six-place tables and dropping off the unnecessary digits; however, if six-place tables have " tables of proportional parts " for interpolation, then the time saved by these may more than offset the use of more than the required number of places in the functions.

387. The following simple examples illustrate the uselessness of measuring the distances with a precision which is inconsistent with that of the angles, when the angles are to be used in the computation of other distances. Given the measurements shown on Fig. 162. If the angle B was measured to the nearest minute only there may be an error of 30 seconds in this angle and the tabular difference for 30 seconds for the sine and cosine of this angle in four-place tables is 0.0001; therefore use four-place tables. It is evident that the 0.02 on the hypotenuse distance is of no value whatever in determining the length of the other two sides a and b, that the 0.6 being the fourth significant figure should be retained, and that the resulting length of a or b will not be reliable to more than four significant figures.

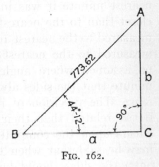

FIG. 162.

$$\log 773.6 = 2.8885 \qquad \log 773.6 = 2.8885$$
$$\log \cos 44° \ 12' = \underline{9.8555} \qquad \log \sin 44° \ 12' = \underline{9.8433}$$
$$\log a = 2.7440 \qquad \log b = 2.7318$$
$$a = 554.6 \qquad b = 539.3$$

If it be assumed, however, that the angle B is measured by repetition and found to be $44° \ 12' \ 25''$ the error in the original angle then was about $25''$. By using the same value for the hypotenuse (773.6) and six-place tables to secure greater precision the value of a is 554.5 and of b 539.4. Comparing these results with those obtained above will give a good idea of the error in length of these lines due to reading the angle to the nearest minute only and also a proper conception of the fallacy of computing with tables of more than four places when the angles are read to the nearest minute only. The difference between the values of a and b obtained by use of the angle 44° 12′ and similar results by use of 44° 12′ 25″ is due entirely to the 25″ and not to the fact that four-place tables were used in the former case and six-place tables in the latter, for in both the result has been obtained to four significant figures only.

It is also evident that when the angle B was measured to the nearest minute it was inconsistent to measure the hypotenuse closer than to the nearest tenth of a foot. But if angle B was measured to the nearest 10 seconds the line AB should have been measured to the nearest hundredth. It should not, however, be assumed where angles are measured only to the nearest minute that the sides always should be recorded to tenths of a foot. The precision of measured distances and angles should be so related that their respective errors should have equal effects upon the computed results. As a general statement it may be said that when the angles are read to nearest minute only, the sides should be measured to four significant figures; with angle to nearest 10 seconds they should be measured to five significant figures; and with angles measured to 1 second the sides should be measured to six significant figures. Where small angles are involved in the computations they must be measured with greater precision. All the sides of a large triangle might be measured to hundredths of a foot, the angles being recorded to the nearest minute only, and the distances alone used for the computations, the measured angles serving merely as checks; this, of course, is practicable at times.

388. In Fig. 163 we are to determine the length of a long line from a short one and the error in the short line is therefore magnified several times. The same degree of precision should be secured in the measured line BC as is desired in the computed lines AC or AB, which, it will be assumed, is required to four significant figures. In order that the measurements of line BC

and angle *A* may be consistent with the precision of the required result, *BC* should be measured to the nearest hundredth of a foot and angle *A* to the nearest quarter of a minute, because the tangent of angles of about 4° varies 0.0003 per minute. In this computation four-place tables should be used and

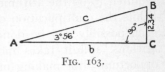

FIG. 163.

the value obtained for *AC* or *AB* should be recorded only to four significant figures.

$$\log 12.34 = 1.0913$$
$$\log \tan 3° 56' = \underline{8.8373}$$
$$\log AC = 2.2540$$
$$AC = 179.5$$

If *AC* is desired to the nearest hundredth of a foot the angle *A* must be determined closely by repetition, but this will not give the length *AC* to the nearest hundredth unless *BC* has been measured closer than to the nearest hundredth; for, suppose there is an error of 0.005 ft. in the measurement of *BC*, then the line *AC* being about 15 times as long as *BC* will have an error of 0.075 ft. no matter how exact the angle at *A* may be measured. In other words, if *AC* is desired correct to five significant figures *BC* should contain five significant figures. Evidently the practical way of obtaining an exact value for the inaccessible distance *AC* is to measure *AB* to the nearest hundredth, and to compute *AC* from *AB* and *BC*, using the angle at *A* as a check on the measured distances. In both of the above examples it is assumed that the 90° is exact.

389. LOGARITHMIC OR NATURAL FUNCTIONS. — The question as to whether logarithmic or natural functions shall be used will depend upon the nature of the computation. Many surveyors have become so accustomed to using natural functions that they often use them when logarithms would require less work and offer fewer opportunities for mistakes. Each method has its proper place, and the computer must decide which will be the better under any circumstances. The use of logarithms saves time spent in actual computation because the process is simpler, but, on the other hand, looking up the logarithms consumes time. The result is often, however, a saving of time over that required to do the arithmetical work of multiplying or dividing. While the multiplication of two numbers of three or four digits each possibly can be done directly more quickly than by logarithms, still it takes more mental effort and there is more opportunity for making mistakes; but if several such multiplications are to be made logarithms are almost always preferable. Furthermore when there are several multiplications of the same number logarithms will save time since the logarithm of this common number has to be taken from the table but once. Frequently, however, the computation is so simple that the use of logarithms would be almost absurd, e.g., the multiplication of any number by a simple number like 20, 25, 150, or 500. If a function of an angle is to be multiplied or divided by any such number the natural function should be used.

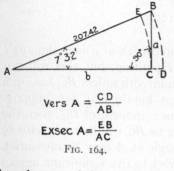

$$\text{Vers } A = \frac{CD}{AB}$$

$$\text{Exsec } A = \frac{EB}{AC}$$

Fig. 164.

390. SHORT CUTS. — The solution of a right triangle, when one of the angles is small, involving the use of the cosine of this small angle, often can be more easily obtained by the use of the versed sine or external secant of the angle. In Fig. 164

$$AB = 207.42$$
$$A = 7° 32'$$
$$AC = 207.42 \cos 7° 32' \quad (1)$$
$$\text{But } AC = AB - CD$$
$$= 207.42 - 207.42 \text{ vers } 7° 32' \quad (2)$$
$$= 207.42 - 207.42 \times 0.00863$$
$$(207.42 \times 0.00863 = 1.79 \text{ by slide rule.})$$
$$= 207.42 - 1.79$$
$$= 205.63$$

Obviously, when the angle is quite small, the result of the multiplication indicated in (2) can be taken from the table to the nearest hundredth of a foot with much less effort than is required for the computation called for in (1). In fact, the computation in (2) can often be done more quickly by the use of natural numbers than by logarithms, and usually the slide rule will give results sufficiently exact (Art. 394, p. 476).

Had AC been given (205.63) and the angle A ($7° 32'$), then

$$AB = \frac{205.63}{\cos 7° 32'}$$

But $AB = AE + EB$

$$= 205.63 + 205.63 \text{ exsec } 7° 32'$$
$$= 205.63 + 205.63 \times 0.00871$$

(205.63 × 0.00871 = 1.79, by slide rule.)

$$= 205.63 + 1.79$$
$$= 207.42$$

391. There are many " short cuts " in arithmetical work which are of great value to the computer, and the student should endeavor to learn the most common and simple ones. The following are a few illustrations.

$$247 \times 25 = \frac{247 \times 100}{4} = \frac{24700}{4}$$

$$682 \times 50 = \frac{68200}{2}$$

$$694 \times 150 = 69400 + 34700$$

$$927 \times 62.5 = 92700 \times \tfrac{5}{8}$$

$$672 \times 1002.3 = 672000 + 1344 + 201.6$$

$$547 \times .9968 = 547 (1 - .0032) = 547 - 5.47 \times .32$$

$$\frac{43}{60} = \frac{4.3}{6} \text{ (reducing minutes to decimals of a degree)}$$

$$\frac{843}{12.5} = 8.43 \times 8$$

The student should cultivate the habit of performing mentally as much of the work as can be done without fatigue, delay, or danger of mistakes. No hard and fast rule can be laid down in this matter, as some persons have more aptitude than others for work of this kind. Such subtractions as 180° − 36° 47′ 18″ always should be performed mentally. Also in taking the co-logarithm of a number from a table of logarithms the result should be written down directly.

392. ARRANGEMENT OF COMPUTATIONS. — All surveying computations should be kept in a special computation book. At the head of the page should appear the title of the work, the number and page of the field note-book from which the data are copied, the names of the computer and checker, and the date. The work should be arranged neatly and systematically so that every part of the computations can be traced by any one who is familiar with such work. Where possible the work should be so arranged that numbers will have to be written but once. Each important value, each column, etc., should be labeled so that it can be readily found. In large offices it is found more satisfactory to use separate sheets for computations. These may be bound in covers, each job being a book by itself. It is important that each separate sheet contain enough information to identify it if it becomes separated from the rest.

393. CHECKS. — It is very important that all calculations should be checked, not merely at the end of the computation but also at as many intermediate steps as possible. In this way a great waste of time may be prevented and serious mistakes avoided. One good method of checking is to perform the operations when possible by two independent methods, for example, by the use of logarithms and by natural functions. Very often two men do the computing, one man's work acting as a check on that of the other. The two may work by the same or by different methods, and the results may be compared at intervals. **Every part of the work should be done independently, from the copying of data out of the note-book to the final results.** It is not uncommon to find two men computing the same area where only one of them looks up the logarithms. If a mistake is made in looking up the logarithms the results may check but they are wrong. Each computer also should check his work roughly by estimating approximately what the result should be.

394. SLIDE RULE. — A valuable aid in checking calculations is an instrument known as the *slide rule*, which enables the computer to multiply and divide numbers by logarithms by a purely mechanical process. It is really the equivalent of a table of logarithms. It consists of a wooden rule, usually about 10 inches long, having a groove in one side in which runs a small wooden strip called the slide. On one face of the rule are placed two scales, *A* and *D*, Fig. 165, one above and one below the slide *BC*. These are constructed by plotting logarithms of numbers by subdividing a unit of some convenient length, say 10 inches. For example, the log of 1 is 0, so this is taken as the left end of the scale and the number 1 placed at this point. The log of 2, to three significant figures, is 0.301, and a line is placed therefore at a distance equal to .301 of the 10 inches, or 3.01 inches, and marked with the number 2. Similarly at 4.77 (log 3 = 0.477) a line is marked 3. The space between 1 and 2 is subdivided by plotting log 1.1, log 1.2, etc. The subdivision is continued until the spaces are as small as will admit of rapid and accurate reading of the scale.

It is customary to make the spacing on the upper scale just half that on the lower, i.e., if 10 inches is chosen as the unit for the lower scale, then the unit for the upper scale will be 5 inches. Since the length of this upper scale is only half the length of the rule there are usually two scales exactly alike marked on the upper part of the rule, the right end of one coinciding with the left end of the other.

On the slide are two scales, *B* and *C*, exact duplicates of *A* and *D* on the rule. A *runner* is usually attached to the rule for convenience in setting and reading the scales. This runner is a small metal or glass slide which fits over the face of the rule in such a way that it can be slid along the rule and set at any reading of

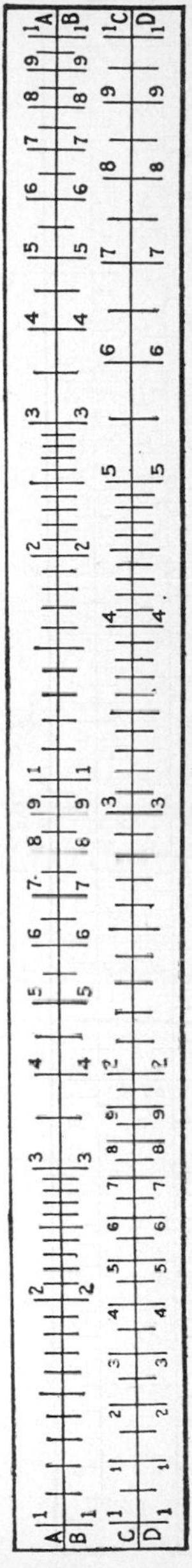

Fig. 165.

Fig. 166.

the scale. It is usually provided with a fine line running crosswise of the rule which is used in marking the exact setting.

Multiplication or division of numbers is performed by adding or subtracting the scale distances corresponding to these numbers. Adding two scale distances is equivalent to adding two logarithms. For example, if the left end of scale C, Fig. 166, is set opposite the number 2 of the scale D, then opposite the number 3 on scale C, is found the product, 6, on scale D. The distances which have been added are those corresponding to log 2 and log 3 respectively. The sum of these distances is the distance corresponding to log 6. Division is performed by placing the divisor on scale C over the dividend on scale D and reading the result, opposite the end of the scale C on the scale D.

Fig. 166 shows the position of the scales for dividing 6 by 3. The scales A and B may be used in a like manner. It is evident that, by setting the runner on the result of one operation and then moving the slide so that one of its ends coincides with the runner setting, continued multiplication and division can be performed without the necessity of reading intermediate results.

Scale D may be used in connection with scale A for obtaining squares or extracting square roots. Since the spaces on scale A are one-half those on scale D the number 4 on scale A is opposite number 2 on scale D, 9 is opposite 3, and so on, every number on scale A being the square of the corresponding number on scale D. Other scales, generally log sines and log tangents, are placed on the reverse side of the slide, so that trigonometric calculations also can be performed with this instrument. Results obtained with the ordinary 10-inch slide rule are usually correct to 3 significant figures, so that this slide rule is the equivalent of three-place logarithm tables.

395. Calculating Machines. — The statements made in the preceding articles (384–393) apply to computations made by simple arithmetic or by means of logarithms. The practice today in most engineering offices is to use calculating machines for nearly all computations. Addition, subtraction, multiplication and division may be performed on these machines, and the results carried out to as many as 8 (in some machines 10) places. Many calculations that are laborious by means of logarithms, such as traverse and land subdivision calculations, may be performed on the calculating machine with about the same speed as the ordinary slide rule, and without the loss of significant figures. In machine calculations the natural trigonometric functions are used; these natural functions are available in seven-place tables tabulated for 10″ of angle.* In most plane surveying calculations the angles are not used closer than to the nearest 10″ so that with these seven-place tables interpolation is unnecessary. This saves time and avoids chances for error in the interpolation.

In the computations of closed traverses it is customary to use rectangular coördinates running N & S and E & W (called Latitudes and Departures). In calculating these Lats. and Deps. the sine and cosine of the bearing angle is multiplied by the length of the traverse line. These calculations can be readily made with a computing machine employing natural functions. The machine is also a great convenience throughout all the computations required in determining the area of a closed traverse. When one number is to be multiplied by a series of numbers, the constant multipliers can be placed on the keyboard, and then multiplied by all the other numbers in sequence without re-setting the common multiplier. This facilitates such calculations as those for the volumes of prisms, areas by offsets, or offsets from a random line.

Where the machines are frequently used, the motor-driven type will prove more economical than the hand-operated type in the

---

* Natural Trigonometric Functions, by R. E. Benson.

long run. The operation of these machines is easy to learn, so that rodmen or tapemen who may not know how to use logarithms can quickly learn how to perform all ordinary operations on the machine, and therefore be profitably employed in the office when fieldwork is not in progress.

396. REDUCING THE FIELD-NOTES FOR COMPUTATIONS. — Before any of the computations are made the measurements must be corrected for systematic and constant errors, such as temperature of the tape, sag, errors in length of tape, alignment errors. The errors in the angles are balanced by altering the value of those angles which were taken from short sights since the angular errors are most likely to occur in these. Whenever distances have been measured on slope, these distances are reduced to horizontal by multiplying them by the versed sine of the vertical angle and subtracting the result from the **corrected** slope distance, the correction for error in the tape being made **before** this is done. Sometimes instead of a vertical angle the slope distance and the difference in elevation between the points are the data contained in the field-notes. In this case the formula given in Art. 21, p. 14, should ordinarily be used.

397. CURVED BOUNDARY BY OFFSETS. — The offsets to the brook (Fig. 53, p. 115) were taken at regular intervals in one portion of the survey and in another portion offsets were taken at the points where the direction of the brook changes. The offsets which were taken at regular intervals give a series of trapezoids with equal altitudes the area of which can be obtained by one computation. Although there are several approximate rules for this computation the two most common are what are known as the *Trapezoidal Rule* and *Simpson's One-Third Rule*.

398. Trapezoidal Rule. — If the figure is considered as made up of a series of trapezoids, all having the same base, the total area can be found by the following rule:

$$\text{Area} = d\left(\frac{h_e}{2} + \Sigma h + \frac{h_e{}'}{2}\right)$$

where d = common distance between offsets,
h_e and $h_e{}'$ = end offsets of the series of trapezoids,
and Σh = sum of the intermediate offsets.

399. Simpson's One-Third Rule. — In the development of this formula the curved line is assumed to be a parabolic curve. It is claimed by some that this affords results more nearly correct than the Trapezoidal Rule. The latter is probably sufficiently exact for most problems of this kind, where the offsets at best can give but an approximate location of the crooked boundary, which is frequently a brook or a crooked wall the middle of which must be estimated.

Simpson's One-Third Rule is as follows:

$$\text{Area} = \frac{d}{3}(h_e + 2\Sigma h_{odd} + 4\Sigma h_{even} + h_e')$$

where d = common distance between offsets,

h_e and h_e' = end offsets of the series, 1st and last offsets,

$2\Sigma h_{odd}$ = twice the sum of all the odd offsets
(the 3d, 5th, 7th, etc., from the end)

$4\Sigma h_{even}$ = four times the sum of all the even offsets (the 2d, 4th, 6th, etc., from the end).

This rule may be derived by taking any three consecutive offsets and passing through their extremities a parabola whose axis is parallel to the offsets. The area of the parabolic segment formed by the chord and the curve is known to be two-thirds the area of the (circumscribed) parallelogram bounded by the chord, a parallel tangent, and the end offsets extended. The area of this segment added to the area of the trapezoid formed by the first and third offset is the area of the two strips. Combining several such pairs of strips the above expression is obtained.

In order to apply this rule it is evidently necessary to have an **even** number of strips; if the number of strips is odd, all but one end strip may be computed by this rule and the extra strip treated as a trapezoid and computed separately. If there is a triangle or a trapezoid at the end of the series which has a base greater or less than d it must be computed separately also.

Fig. 167 shows the computation of a series by both methods and also the computation of several trapezoids and triangles at the ends of the series.   The data are taken from the field-notes in Fig. 53, p. 115.

400. STRAIGHTENING CROOKED BOUNDARY LINES. — In Fig. 168, $AEFGH$ represents a curved boundary between two tracts of land, and it is desired to run a line from A so as to make

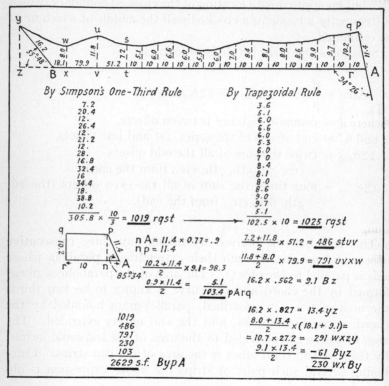

FIG. 167.

the boundary a straight line and to leave each tract of the same area as before.

The trial line AB is first run, and the distance AB, the angles at A and B, and the necessary offsets to the curved boundary are measured in the field.   Then the areas of the property between this trial line and the curved line are computed as explained in the previous articles.   The sum of the fractional areas on one side of the trial line and the sum of the areas on the other side of it should be equal. If not made so by the trial line, the difference between these sums is the area of a correction triangle ABC which must be taken from one tract and added to the other because the trial line has taken this difference from one of the tracts and it should therefore be restored. The area and the base AB being

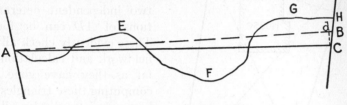

FIG. 168. STRAIGHTENING A CROOKED BOUNDARY

known the altitude dC can be computed. Then in the triangle ABC, the lines BC and AC and the angle at A are calculated; and the line AC is staked out, its calculated length being checked by measuring the line AC in the field and the angle at A being checked by the measured distance BC.

401. AREA BY TRIANGLES. — If the field has been surveyed by setting the transit in the middle of the field and taking angles between the corners (Art. 138, p. 117), the areas of the triangles may be found by the trigonometric formula:

$$\text{Area} = \tfrac{1}{2}\, a\, b \sin C,$$

where C is the angle included between the sides a and b.

If all three sides of any of the triangles have been measured or if the field has been surveyed with the tape alone (Art. 139, p. 118), the area of the triangles can be found by the trigonometric formula given in Table X at the bottom of p. 682.

402. AREA OF A QUADRILATERAL BY TRIANGLES. — Most city lots have four sides, and while some standard coördinate method such as those described in Chap. XIV is often employed in computing their areas, it is not uncommon to divide these quadrilaterals into simple triangles and to use this for computing the area and checking the geometric exactness of the fieldwork.

In Fig. 169, *ABCD* represents an ordinary city lot in which all the sides and angles have been measured. It is evident that the diagonal *BC* can be computed either from *BD*, *CD*, and the

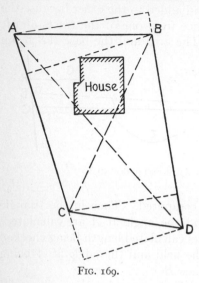

FIG. 169.

angle *D*, or from *AB*, *AC*, and the angle *A*. These two determinations of *BC* should check each other. Similarly two independent determinations of *AD* can be found. These evidently check all the fieldwork and calculations as far as they have gone. In computing these triangles the best way is to resolve all the work into right triangle calculations, as suggested by the dotted lines on the figure which show two pairs of perpendiculars, one pair for triangles *ABC* and *BCD*, and another pair for triangles

ADC and *ABD*. Not only is this method more simple than to use the oblique triangle formulas, but it gives at the same time altitude distances which are useful in computing the area of the lot. The area can be obtained by calculating the area of one pair of triangles and checked readily by calculating the other pair.

403. Area of Curved Corner Lot. — In Fig. 170 *ABF-HGDE* is the boundary of a corner lot, all the angles and distances of which have been determined in the field. The area of *ABCDE* can be com-

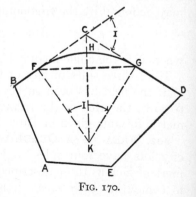

FIG. 170.

puted easily by the method explained in Art. 424, p. 510. Then the area of *FCGH* must be subtracted from the traverse area.

The angle I is known and the radius KF of the curve is given or can be computed from data such as CH or CF obtained in the field (Art. 282, p. 336).

$$KFHG = \frac{FHG \times HK}{2} = \frac{I° \times 0.0174533^* \times (HK)^2}{2}$$

$$KFCG = FC \times FK$$

$$FCGH = KFCG - KFHG$$

$$= KG(CG - FHG \div 2)$$

$$= \text{Radius} \left(\text{Tangent} - \tfrac{1}{2} \text{Arc} \right)$$

The area of $FCGH$ could have been calculated by computing the area of the triangle FCG and then subtracting the area of the segment FHG from it. The area of this segment, however, cannot be calculated accurately by any short formula. An approximate formula for the area of a segment is

Area of Circular Segment $= \tfrac{2}{3} MC$ (approximately), where M is the middle ordinate and C is the chord length.

$$M = \frac{C^2 \dagger}{8\,R} \quad \text{(approximately)}.$$

---

* The length of the arc of curve whose radius is 1 and whose central angle is 1° is 0.0174533, which will give results to six significant figures, provided I and R are correct to six significant figures. The total arc for any central angle may be found from Table VII, p. 673, by first finding the total arc for a radius of 1 and then multiplying by the radius of the curve.

† In Fig. 171, $OB = $ Radius of circular curve.

$CH = $ Middle Ordinate for chord AB.
CD is drawn tangent to the curve.

$DB = $ Tangent Offset for chord CB.
OE is drawn perpendicular to CB.
In the two similar triangles OEB and CBD,
$DB : CB = BE : OB$

$$DB : CB = \frac{CB}{2} : OB$$

$$DB = \frac{CB^2}{2\,OB}$$

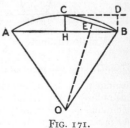

FIG. 171.

Offset from Tangent $= \dfrac{(\text{Chord})^2}{2 \times \text{Radius}}$ (τ)

But $DB = CH$, and $AB = 2 \times CB$ (approximately).

Expressed in terms of C and R,

Area of Circular Segment $= \dfrac{C^3}{12R}$ (approximately).

These formulas are fairly accurate when M is very small as compared with C. They are most useful, however, as a check on computations made by the preceding method.

404. Rough Checks on Areas. — If the traverse has been plotted to scale, it can be divided easily into simple figures such as rectangles or triangles, their dimensions scaled from the plan, and their areas computed, thereby giving an independent rough check on the area.

A piece of tracing paper or cloth ruled into small squares can be placed over the plot of the area and a count made of the number of squares and fractional parts included within the area desired. Then, the area of one square being known, an approximate area of the figure may be obtained. This method is particularly applicable to areas with irregular boundaries.

405. Planimeter. — One of the commonest ways of checking the area of a traverse is to obtain its area by means of an instrument called the *planimeter*. It is a small instrument consisting of an arm, carrying a tracing point, which is fastened to the frame of the instrument; the arm can be adjusted to any desired length. The frame touches the paper at only three points: the anchor point, the tracing point, and the circumference of a small wheel which is free to revolve. On the rim of this wheel is a scale and beside it is a vernier which is used in reading the scale.

$$\therefore CH = \dfrac{\left(\dfrac{AB}{2}\right)^2}{2\,OB} = \dfrac{AB^2}{8\,OB} \text{(approximately)}$$

Middle Ordinate $= \dfrac{(\text{Chord})^2}{8 \times \text{Radius}}$ (approximately) (2)

The following will give some idea of the accuracy of this formula:

When radius = 20 ft. and chord = 10 ft., M = 0.625 (correct value is 0.635).
When radius = 100 ft. and chord = 25 ft., M = 0.781 (correct value is 0.784).
When radius = 100 ft. and chord = 100 ft., M = 12.500 (correct value is 13.397).
When radius = 1000 ft. and chord = 100 ft., M = 1.250 (correct value is 1.251).

It is evident from the above that this formula will not give accurate results when the chord is large in comparison with the radius.

The length of the arm can be regulated by setting it, at the proper reading on a scale which is marked on the arm, so that a unit on the wheel scale will represent any desired unit area on the plan, such as a square inch or a square centimeter. (See Appendix A on the Planimeter.)

In using the instrument the anchor point is set at some convenient position on the drawing **outside** of the area to be measured and then the tracing point is run around the perimeter of the area to be determined. The reading on the wheel is recorded when the tracer is at the starting point. The tracer, in passing around the perimeter, should be kept as **closely as possible** on the boundary line and should return **exactly** to the starting point. Then the scale is again read, and the difference between the two readings is the area that has been traced out, expressed in some unit depending on the length of the arm. The result can be transposed easily into the unit of the scale of the map.

Usually the settings for the scale on the arm are furnished by the maker for various units of area. It is safer to test this setting by running the instrument around a known area, such as 4 square inches and determining the interval passed over by the wheel by making several tests and by setting the anchor point at different positions. This interval divided by 4 will be the value of one square inch of plan area and this is equivalent to a certain number of square feet of surface, depending upon the scale of the map. It is important that the sides of the trial square should be laid off so that they agree with the present scale of the map which, owing to swelling or shrinking of the paper, is frequently not quite the same as when it was first drawn (Art. 514, p. 593).[*]

406. DEFLECTION ANGLES AND CHORDS FOR A CIRCULAR CURVE. — The computations shown in Fig. 172 refer to the notes in Fig. 119, p. 340. In the discussion of the simple curve as applied to city surveying (Art. 282, p. 336) will be found the for-

---

[*] When areas are desired from U. S. Geological Survey maps on which are shown parallels of latitude and longitude it is best to refer all planimetered areas to the areas of a quadrilateral, say, 1° on a side. The area of such quadrilateral can be taken from a publication entitled Geological Tables and Formulas, by S. S. Gannett, Bulletin No. 650, U. S. Geological Survey, and by simple proportion the desired area found.

mulas which have been used in the computations in Fig. 172. The length of the curve L_c is found by taking from Table VII ("Lengths of Circular Arcs: Radius = 1"), the length of an arc

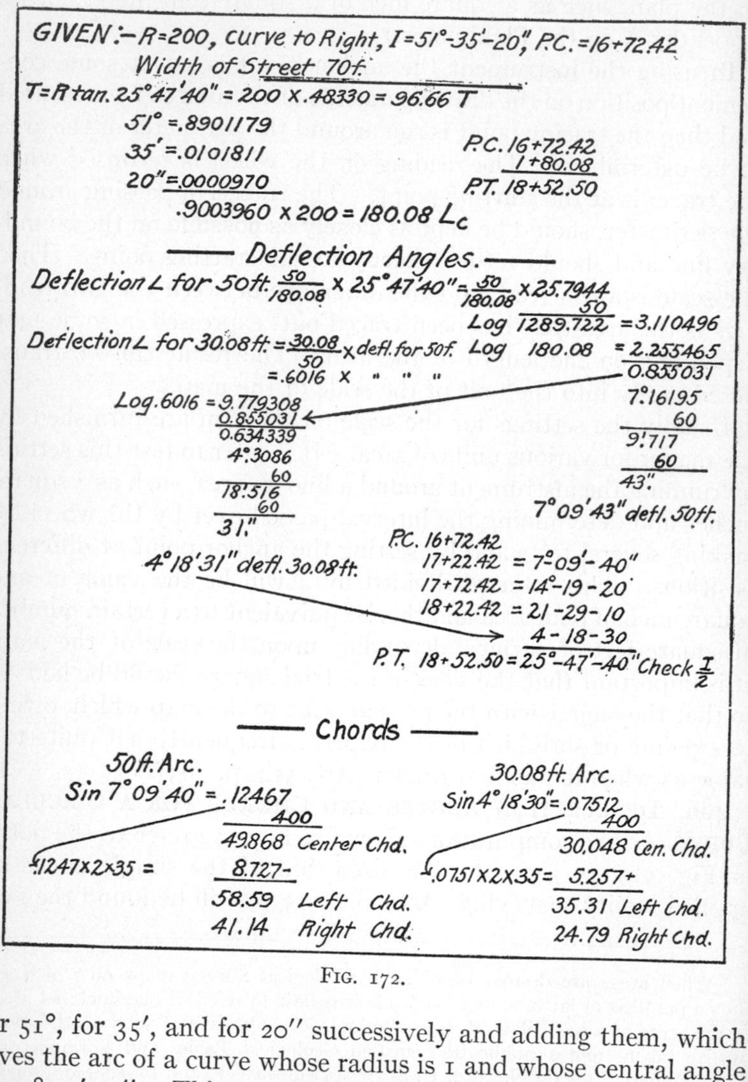

FIG. 172.

for 51°, for 35′, and for 20″ successively and adding them, which gives the arc of a curve whose radius is 1 and whose central angle is 51° 35′ 20″. This, multiplied by the radius (200), gives the value of L_c, which is added to the station of the P.C. to obtain the station of the P.T.

407. COMPUTATION OF ASTRONOMICAL OBSERVATIONS. — The computations relating to observations for meridian and latitude will be found in Chapter VIII.

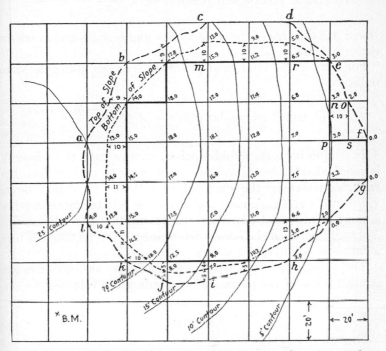

Bank drops vertically for 4 ft. from Top of Slope, unless otherwise noted.

FIG. 173.   PLAN OF PORTION OF A BORROW-PIT.

COMPUTATION OF VOLUME

408. BORROW-PITS. — Fig. 173 is a plan of a borrow-pit divided into squares by the cross-section method. The contours depict the original surface, before any excavation had been done. At the corners of the squares are given the depths of cut in feet and tenths.

Each of the squares represents a plan of a truncated rectangular (square) prism whose volume may be taken as the average of the four corner heights multiplied by the area of the cross-section, or, expressed as a formula,

$$\text{Vol. trunc. rectangular prism} = A \times \frac{h_1 + h_2 + h_3 + h_4}{4}$$

where A is the area of the cross-section and h_1, h_2, h_3 and h_4 are the corner heights.

For a truncated triangular prism, such as *eno*, using the same notation,

$$\text{Vol. trunc. triangular prism} = A \times \frac{h_1 + h_2 + h_3}{3}$$

In computing a trapezoidal prism, such as *nofp*, the trapezoid is subdivided in one of two ways; it may be divided into two triangles either by the diagonal *nf*, or by *op*, or it may be divided into a rectangle *nosp* and a triangle *osf*; the latter method is more nearly consistent with the assumption that the surface is straight between the points determined. If a rectangle is used a cut must be interpolated at *s*.

The slightly irregular lines such as *de*, *ef*, are considered as straight lines for the purpose of computing the volume.

EXAMPLE 1

Computation of cut at point *m*

> Original surface elevation   17.4 from contours.
> New elevation after excavation   1.5
>   cut 15.9 ft.

EXAMPLE 2

Subdivision of *epf* (first method). The area V_1 (Fig. 173a) is calculated as a triangular prism,

$$V_1 = \frac{2'.0 + 3'.0 + 3'.0}{3} \times \frac{100}{27} = 9.88 \text{ cu. yds.}$$

The area *nofp* is then divided into a rectangle *nosp* and a triangle *ofs* (Fig. 173b) the interpolated elevation at *s* being $1'.5$. Then

$$V_4 = \frac{3'.0 + 2'.0 + 1'.5 + 3'.0}{4} \times \frac{200}{27} = 17.59 \text{ cu. yds.}$$

and

$$V_5 = \frac{2'.0 + 0'.0 + 1'.5}{3} \times \frac{100}{27} = 4.32 \text{ cu. yds.}$$

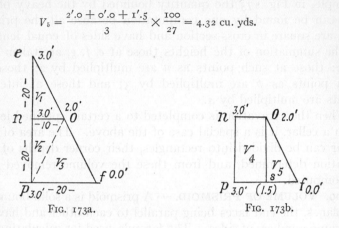

FIG. 173a.　　　　FIG. 173b.

EXAMPLE 3

Subdivision of epf (second method). The volume V_1 is the same as before. The solid $nofp$ is divided into two triangular prisms by a diagonal nf or op (Fig. 173a).

If the diagonal op is selected, then

$$V_2 = \frac{3'.0 + 3'.0 + 2'.0}{3} \times \frac{100}{27} = 9.88 \text{ cu. yds.}$$

and

$$V_3 = \frac{3'.0 + 2'.0 + 0'.0}{3} \times \frac{200}{27} = 12.35 \text{ cu. yds.}$$

Unless the proper diagonal was selected in the field there is no way of knowing which one fits the ground more nearly. This assumption of a diagonal may, therefore, be farther from the truth than the assumption of a rectangle and a triangle. If the other diagonal (nf) be assumed the two volumes are 6.17 and 14.81, giving a total of 20.98 cu. yds. as compared with 22.23 cu. yds. obtained by the use of op. The first method (square and triangle) gives 21.91 cu. yds.

When there are a number of prisms with the same cross-section, as shown in Fig. 173, these rectangular prisms can be computed as one solid by assembling them as follows:— Add all corner heights which occur in one prism only; then add all corner heights which occur in two prisms and multiply their sum by 2; then add all corner heights occurring in three prisms and multiply the sum by 3; finally multiply the sum of the heights occurring in four prisms by 4. The grand total is then multiplied by the area of one square and divided by 4. For example, in Fig. 173 the quantity bounded by the heavy black line can be found by one computation because all the prisms in it are square in cross-section and have sides of equal length. In the summation of the heights those at e, f, g, are taken but once; those at such points as n are multiplied by 2; those at such points as p are multiplied by 3; and those at interior points are multiplied by 4.

When the excavation is completed to a certain specified level, as in a cellar, it is a special case of the above. The area of the cellar can be divided into rectangles, their corner depths of excavation determined, and from these the volume removed can be computed.

409. VOLUME OF PRISMOID. — A prismoid is a solid bounded by planes, the end faces being parallel to each other and having the same numbers of sides. The formula used for calculating its volume is found to apply also to figures whose lateral faces are warped surfaces and also certain other curved surfaces. The data obtained from field notes are usually in the form of cross-sections taken at right angles to some general line of the construction, thereby dividing the earthwork into prismoidal solids with their bases parallel and their sides either plane or warped surfaces.

410. End Area Formula. — The simplest method of computing the volume of a prismoidal solid is to average the areas of the two bases and multiply by the distance between them, i.e.,

$$V = \frac{A_1 + A_2}{2} \times l \qquad (End\text{-}Area\ Formula)$$

in which A_1 and A_2 are the areas of the two end bases and l is the distance between them. This method is used to a very great extent throughout the country for earthwork computations, although it does not give sufficiently accurate results for certain classes of work, such, for example, as masonry. As a rule the end-area formula gives somewhat larger volumes than the prismoidal formula.

411. Prismoidal Formula. — The correct volume of a prismoid is expressed by the *Prismoidal Formula:**

$$V = \frac{l}{6}(A_1 + 4A_m + A_2)$$

in which l is the distance between the two bases, A_1 and A_2; and A_m is the "*middle area*," i.e., the area half-way between the two bases. The dimensions of the middle section are found by averaging the dimensions of the end sections. The middle area is computed from the dimensions of this middle section; it should **not** be taken as the mean of A_1 and A_2.

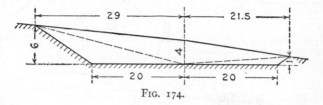

FIG. 174.

412. Railway or Highway Cross-Sections. — When these formulas are applied to the quantities between cross-sections of a railway or a highway the end areas can be computed easily from the field-notes by dividing the sections into triangles as shown in Fig. 174.

Notes of section: $\dfrac{29.0}{+6.0}$ $\quad +4.0 \quad$ $\dfrac{21.5}{+1.0}$

$$\text{Area} = \frac{4 \times (21.5 + 29)}{2} + \frac{20 \times (1 + 6)}{2}$$

$$= 2 \times 50.5 + 10 \times 7 = 171.$$

It is also the custom with some surveyors to plot each section carefully to scale and to obtain its area by use of the planimeter (Art. 405, p. 486). This is probably the most practical method when the sections are very irregular and also when they are required as a record of the rate of progress of the construction work.

---

* For demonstration see "Curves and Earthwork," by C. F. Allen, published by McGraw-Hill Book Co., New York.

There are several other methods employed in computing earthwork but the above are by far the most common.

Several sets of Earthwork Tables and Diagrams have been published which reduce materially the work of computation.

413. ESTIMATES FOR GRADING. — Estimates for grading may be made conveniently by means of a topographic map.

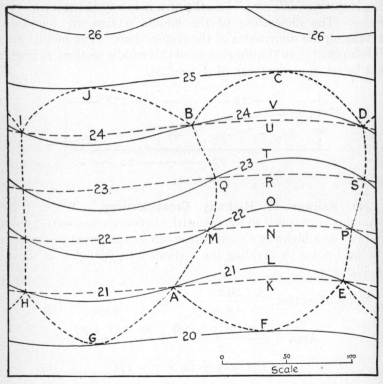

FIG. 175.

On this map will appear the contours of the original surface. The contours representing the finished surface are also sketched upon the map; the smaller the interval between the contours the more precise will be the result. In Fig. 175 the full lines represent the contours of the original surface, which is to be altered so that when the necessary cutting and filling have been done the new surface will have the appearance indicated by the dash contours. At contour 20 and at contour 25 no grading is to be done. On the plan, first sketch the lines $ABCDEF$ and $AGHIJB$ which are lines of " no cut " and " no fill," i.e., lines which enclose areas that are either to be excavated or filled. The amount of excavation and embankment must be computed separately. In sketching such lines the lines AB, ED, and HI, as will be seen, follow the intersection of the original contours with the new ones, since at these points there is no cut or fill. There are no direct data on the plan which define where the earthwork ends at C but the assumption is here made that the fill will run out to meet the original surface at about the next contour at C. In this example the fill must run out somewhere between the 24-ft. contour and the 25-ft. contour, for if it ran beyond the 25-ft. contour there would be another new 25-ft. contour shown on the plan. Therefore the line BCD has been sketched to represent the limits of the fill in that vicinity; similarly EFA, AGH, and IJB have been sketched.

There are three general methods of computing the earthwork from the data given on the plan; (1) by computing directly the amount of cut or fill between successive contours, (2) by assuming a horizontal plane below the lowest part of the earthwork and computing the volume of the earth between this plane and the original surface, then computing the volume between the same plane and the finished surface; the difference between these two volumes will be the amount of earthwork, or (3) by drawing on the plan a line of no cut or fill, a line representing, say, 5-ft. cut or fill, a line representing 10-ft. cut or fill and so on. Then compute the volume between these successive 5-ft. layers.

414. (1) Referring to Fig. 175 and applying the first method, the volume of the solid $AMPE$ is that of a solid having two parallel end planes $AKEL$ (a plane at elevation 21) being the lower, and $MNPO$ (a plane at elevation 22) being the upper plane. The altitude between these two end planes will be the difference in elevation between 21 and 22, or will be 1 ft.

The areas of the horizontal planes $AKEL$, $MNPO$, $QRST$, and $BUDV$ may be obtained by planimeter (Art. 405, p. 486) or otherwise, and the volume of the solid $AKEL$-$MNPO$ may be obtained by the End Area Method (Art. 410, p. 492), its altitude being 1 ft. If it is desired to obtain the volume by the use of the Prismoidal Formula the volume of the solid $A\,KEL$-$QRST$ may be found by using $A\,KEL$ as one base, $QRST$ as the other, and $M\,NPO$ as the middle area, the altitude, or length, of the solid being the difference between 21 and 23, or 2 ft. While neither of these methods is mathematically exact, they are the ones usually employed for this kind of a problem. The solid $A\,KEL$-F may be considered to be a pyramid with a base $A\,KEL$ and an altitude of 1 ft.

EXAMPLE

In Fig. 175 the amount of fill on the area $ABCDEF$ is computed below.
Area $AELK$ = 900 sq. ft. $900 \times \tfrac{1}{3} =$ 300 cu. ft. (Pyramid)

" $MNPO$ = 1000 $\dfrac{900 + 1000}{2} \times 1 =$ 950.

" $QRST$ = 1020 $\dfrac{1000 + 1020}{2} \times 1 =$ 1010.

" $BUVD$ = 680 $\dfrac{1020 + 680}{2} \times 1 =$ 850.

                         $680 \times \tfrac{1}{3} =$ 227   (Pyramid)
                              3)3337 cu. ft.
                              9)1112
                               124 cu. yds. Total Fill.

415. (2) Referring again to Fig. 175 and applying the second method, the area of $ABCDEF$ is found (by planimeter); this is the area of a plane at, say, elevation 20, since none of the fill extends below contour 20. Then the area of $ABCDEL$ is found, which is the area of the plane cutting the original ground at elevation 21. Similarly the areas of $MBCDPO$, $QBCDST$, and $BCDV$ are found. The volume of the solids between these planes may be computed by the End Area Method or by use of the Prismoidal Formula, alternate contour planes being used as middle areas, as explained in the preceding paragraph. The volume of solid whose base is $BCDV$ is a pyramid whose altitude is the vertical distance between the 24-ft. contour and point C, which is 1 ft.

By the same general method the areas of $ABCDEK$, $MBCDPN$, etc., which refer to the new surface of the ground, may be obtained, and the volume of the solids between successive contour planes computed. The difference between this quantity and the quantity between a plane at elevation 20 and the original surface will give the amount of fill.

While in this particular problem the first method is the shorter, still there are cases where the second method will be somewhat simpler. It is particularly useful when the actual amount of cut or fill is not desired but when it is required to know if the proposed alterations will require more or less earth than can be easily obtained on the premises and, if so, about how much the excess will be. Under these circumstances the portions of cut and fill will not have to be computed separately. A line is drawn around the limits of the entire area where the grading is to be done, the volume between an assumed plane and the original surface is found, and then the volume between the same plane and the proposed surface. The difference between the two values will give the amount of excess of earthwork.

416. (3) Fig. 176 illustrates a third method of computing earthwork from the data given on a topographic map. The original contours are shown in full lines and the contours of the proposed surface in dash lines. Through the intersection of the new contours with the original ones is drawn the line of " no cut " (zero line), the line where the cut is just 5 ft. (marked 5), the line of 10-ft. cut (marked 10), etc. These dotted curves enclose areas which are the horizontal projections of irregular surfaces which are parallel to the final surface and at 5 ft., 10 ft., 15 ft., etc., above the final surface. The solids included between these 5-ft. irregular surfaces are layers of earth each 5 ft. thick, and their volumes may be computed by either the End Area Method or by the Prismoidal Formula as explained in the preceding paragraphs. The areas of these horizontal projections are obtained from the map and the vertical dimensions of the solids are the contour intervals.

417. ROUGH ESTIMATES. — Rough estimates of the quantity of earthwork are often required for preliminary estimates of the cost of construction or for monthly estimates of the amount of work done. For preliminary estimates of road construction, very frequently the notes of alignment and the profile of the center line are the only information at hand. From this profile the center cuts or fills can be obtained, and the cross-sections can be

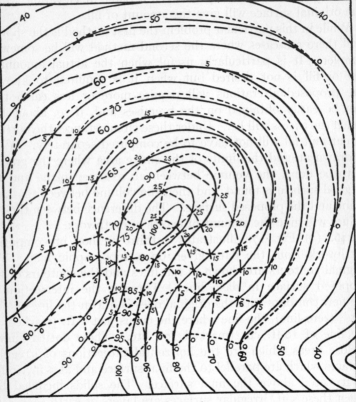

FIG. 176.

assumed to be level sections (Art. 258, p. 305) and computed b the End-Area Method. The slight errors resulting will b corrected in the final estimate.

In obtaining the required data from which to make an a proximate estimate of the quantity of earthwork, the engine has an opportunity to exercise his judgment to an unusual degre Rough estimates do not, as a rule, call for a large amount of fiel work. It is important that as few measurements as possible should be taken and that these should also be at the proper places to give complete data and to allow simple computations. Too often engineers, as soon as they arrive on the work and before making a study of their problems, begin to take measurements, consequently they return to the office after hours of hard work with a mass of figures from which it will take several more hours to compute the quantities. Whereas, a few moments' thought given to the choosing of the proper measurements to be taken in the field would give data which could be computed in a few minutes by use of the slide rule, affording results sufficiently accurate for rough estimates.

PROBLEMS

1. A series of perpendicular offsets are taken from a straight line to a curved boundary line. The offsets are 15 ft. apart and were taken in the following order: 6.8, 7.2, 4.6, 5.7, 7.1, 6.3, and 6.8.

(a) Find the area between the straight and curved lines by the Trapezoidal Rule.

(b) Find the same area by Simpson's One-Third Rule.

2. It is desired to substitute for a curved boundary line a straight line which shall part off the same areas as the curved line. A trial straight line AB has been run; its bearing is S 10° 15′ W, its length is 418.5 ft., and point B is on a boundary line CD which has a bearing S 80° W. The sum of the areas between the trial line and the crooked boundary on the easterly side is 2657. ft.; on the westerly side it is 7891. ft. It is required to determine the distance BX along CD such that AX shall be the straight boundary line desired. Also find the length of the line AX.

3. In the quadrilateral $ACBD$ the distances and angles which were taken in the field are as follows:

$$A\,B = 50.63 \qquad A\,B\,C = 105° 39′ 00″$$
$$B\,C = 163.78 \qquad B\,A\,D = 89° 37′ 30″$$
$$C\,D = 93.80$$
$$D\,A = 160.24$$
$$D\,B = 167.73$$

Check the fieldwork by computations, and figure the area of the quadrilateral by using right triangles entirely.

4. Two street lines intersect at an angle (deflection angle) of 48° 17′ 30″. The corner lot is rounded off by a circular curve of 40-ft. radius.

(a) Find the length of this curve to the nearest $\frac{1}{100}$ ft.

(b) Find the area of the land included between the curve and the two tangents to the curve (the two street lines produced).

5. Find the quantity in cubic yards, in the borrow-pit shown in Fig. 173; the squares are 20 ft. on a side. Bank is vertical 4 ft. down from top of slope; then

slopes uniformly to "foot of slope," except where the depths are marked in figures. Here the slope is to be taken as uniform from top to bottom.

6. At station 6 a rectangular trench was measured and found to be 3 ft. wide and 4 ft. deep. At stations 6 + 70 it was found to be 3.2 ft. wide and 8.6 ft. deep.

(a) Find by use of the Prismoidal Formula the quantity of earthwork between stations 6 and 6 + 70. Result in cubic yards.

(b) Find the volume of the same by End-Area Method.

7. The following is a set of notes of the earthwork of a road excavation.

$$12 \quad \frac{27.0}{+8.0} \qquad +4.2 \qquad \frac{23.4}{+5.6}$$

$$11 + 60 \quad \frac{30.0}{+10.0} \quad \frac{15.0}{+4.5} \quad +4.0 \quad \frac{15.0}{+7.5} \quad \frac{24.0}{+6.0}$$

$$\text{Sta. } 11 \quad \frac{21.0}{+4.0} \qquad +6.0 \qquad \frac{25.8}{+7.2}$$

The base of the road is 30 ft. and the slopes are $1\frac{1}{2}$ to 1.

Find by the End-Area Method the quantity of earthwork from station 11 to station 12. Result in cubic yards.

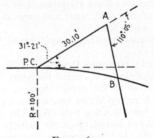

FIG. 176a.

8. A pyramid has a square base 8 ft. on a side, the height of the pyramid being 12 ft. What is the error (in cubic feet) in the volume computed by the "end-area method"?

9. In Fig. 176a compute the distances from B to A and to P.C. (See Art. 292.)

CHAPTER XIV

CALCULATIONS RELATING TO TRAVERSES

418. CALCULATION OF TRAVERSE. — Traverses are run for a definite purpose which in turn determines the precision required and hence the methods that must be employed to obtain that precision. No survey is mathematically perfect. In a compass traverse, the bearings may be several minutes in error and the distances are usually measured without great precision; such a closed traverse in all probability would not meet the geometric requirements of a closed figure. Even in closed traverses observed with high precision there will be small errors in both angles and distances, and these precise surveys will not mathematically close until adjustments are made to the dimensions. These adjustments will be explained later.

Before " calculating the traverse " all linear distances should be corrected for all constant and systematic errors, and if slope measurements have been made, they should be reduced to the horizontal. (See Chap. I.) If any of the errors are so small that they do not influence the precision required they may be omitted.

Before leaving the field the angles should be added to see that the sum equals the proper number of right angles (if interior angles are measured), or that the algebraic sum of the deflection angles equals 360°, or is as near the correct value as is consistent with the precision used in measuring the angles. If, for example, the angles are measured to the nearest half-minute, the maximum uncertainty in any angle is ±15″, which is a compensating error because it is as likely that the true angle is 15″ too small as 15″ too large. On this basis, the allowable error in the sum of the angles for a nine-sided traverse is $\sqrt{9} \times 15'' = 45''$. Hence if the sum of the angles come within 45″ of the correct value, then the angles have been measured within the limits to be expected. If the difference were 2 or 3 minutes, the angles have probably been carelessly measured; if the difference is still greater, then a mistake is indicated which should be located and corrected before leaving the field.

In order to avoid large errors and mistakes linear distances are checked by measuring the lines forward and backward; the angles should be at the least doubled for a check. By these means a field check is obtained on each individual measurement.

For traverses that do not close the angles may be checked by astronomical methods (Chapter VIII) or the methods explained in Art. 447, p. 533.

The calculation of traverses is usually carried out by means of rectangular coördinates. Before these coördinates can be found it is necessary to adopt some meridian, or axis of Y, and then to find the bearings, or the azimuths, of all the lines of the traverse with reference to this meridian. The best reference meridian to use is the **true meridian,** or geographical meridian, passing through some point of the survey. This gives bearings which are unchanging, and also permits showing the survey in its correct relation to all other surveys in the locality that also show the true meridian. (Methods of determining the true meridian are given in Chapter VIII.) If, however, the survey was made with a magnetic compass, or if the direction of the true meridian cannot be ascertained, then the magnetic meridian may be used. If the direction of neither the magnetic nor the true meridian is known, any direction may be assumed arbitrarily as a meridian, or Y axis, and bearings or azimuths referred to this direction.

Unless the azimuths have been obtained in the field by the method of Art. 144, p. 123, they must be calculated from the measured angles. If the deflection angles have been measured the azimuths may be found quickly by starting with one known (or assumed) azimuth and **adding the deflections algebraically** right deflection angles being taken as positive, and left deflections as negative. This method is illustrated in the example on p. 504.

419. Balancing the Traverse Angles. — The first step in calculating a closed traverse of a transit survey is to balance the angles, i.e., the angles should be made to fulfill the geometric conditions of the figure. While the angles of a traverse may have all been read with the same care, they may not all be equally accurate, because of difficulty that may exist in centering the instrument over the station or in sighting on points requiring plumbing. On long lines the errors from the above causes are small, but on short lines they are large. Where the conditions under which the angles have been measured are known, the angular error should be distributed on the angles that were difficult to measure. If all the angles are assumed to be measured with the same accuracy the error should be placed on the angles dependent on the short side or sides.

The following shows the balancing of the angles of the survey shown in Fig. 53, p. 115. It will be noticed by referring to p. 115 that there is a very short line running between sta. D and E. It is therefore more likely that small errors in angle occurred at the angle D and E because a slight inaccuracy in setting up the instrument at these stations and in taking the short sight to the adjacent station is likely to produce a small error in the measured angle. This survey should be balanced as follows.

Sta.	Defl. Angles		Corrected Dist.
B	87° 30′ L		179.2
C	91 09 L		164.6
D		91° 29′ R	99.7
E	92 00 L		169.3
F	95 17 L		286.2
A	85 34 L		299.2
Sums	451° 30′ L	91° 29′ R ;	Diff. 360° 01′

This survey has an error in angle of only 01′ indicating an accurate survey. To be geometrically correct the algebraic sum should be 360°. Inasmuch as the angles are measured to minutes no smaller value than a minute in the adjustment of angles should be made. The angle at Station D (adjacent to shortest side) should be changed to read 91° 30′ R. If, in this same survey, the angles had been read to half minutes and the total error was still one minute, then a correction of one-half minute would be added to the angle D and one-half minute subtracted from angle E, both of which lie next to a short line.

Using the balanced angles, bearings or azimuths are computed as in table on p. 504, for the survey on p. 115.

The bearings and azimuths of the first line should be recomputed from the last bearing and azimuth; this is a check which should not be neglected.

The following table shows the calculations of the bearings and the azimuths for the survey shown on p. 115.

Line.	Bearing.	Azimuth.
A — B	North	180° 00′
B	87° 30′ L	87 30 L
B — C	N 87° 30′ W	92° 30′
C	91 09 L	91 09 L
	178 39	
C — D	S 1° 21′ W	1° 21′
D	91 30 R	91 30 R
	92 51	
D — E	N 87° 09′ W	92° 51′
E	92 00 L	92 00 L
	179 09	
E — F	S 0° 51′ W	0° 51′
F	95 17 L	95 17 L
	94 26	
F — A	N 85° 34′ E	265° 34′
A	85 34 L	85 34 L
A — B	N 00 00	180° 00′ (Check)

420. CALCULATING THE DIFFERENCE OF LATITUDE (LAT.) AND DEPARTURE (DEP.).

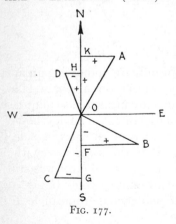

FIG. 177.

— After the bearings or azimuths have been computed, the next step in obtaining the coördinates is the calculation of the *latitudes* and *departures*. The latitude of any line is its projection on a north and south line and the departure of the line is its projection on an east and west line. Latitudes are also termed *latitude difference, difference of Y's* and departures are termed *departure difference, longitude difference* and *difference of X's*. In Fig. 177 the latitude of *OA* is *OK* of *OB* is *OF*, of *OC* is *OG* and of *OD* is *OH*. The departure of *OA* is *KA*, of *OB* is *FB*, of *OC* is *GC* and of *OD* is *HD*. North latitudes are designated N or + and south latitudes S or −. East departures are designated E or + and west departures W or −; thus for a line with a northeast bearing both latitude and departure would be positive; if the bearing were southwest both latitude and departure would be negative.

From Fig. 177 it is readily seen that when the *bearing* and *length* of a line are known the latitude and departure may be computed by solving a right triangle, i.e.,

> **Lat. = Dist. × cos bearing,**
> **Dep. = Dist. × sin bearing;**
> **or, Diff. of Y = Dist. × cos azimuth,**
> **Diff. of X = Dist. × sin azimuth.**

Example: Dist. = 186.3, bearing N 27° 31′ E (azimuth = 207° 31′)

$$\text{Lat.} = + \text{165.2 (N)}$$
$$\log \text{Lat.} = 2.21807$$
$$\log \cos \text{bearing} = 9.94786$$
$$\log 186.3 = 2.27021$$
$$\log \sin \text{bearing} = 9.66465$$
$$\log \text{Dep.} = 1.93486$$
$$\text{Dep.} = + \text{86.1 (E)}$$

421. Computation of the Error of Closure of a Traverse. —

Since all the measurements in a survey are subject to error, any traverse which supposedly returns to its starting point will not do so in reality, but there will be a short line of unknown length and direction connecting the first and last points of the traverse; this short line is caused by the accumulation of errors.

If the calculated traverse returns mathematically to the starting point then the sum of the + Lats. and the − Lats. should be exactly equal and, similarly, the sum of the + Deps. and the − Deps. should be exactly equal. The amounts by which they fail to balance are the Lat. and Dep. of the line of closure. This distance is sometimes called the "linear error of closure" and reflects the algebraic sum of all the accidental errors of measurement both in angles and distances.

Suppose the difference of latitude and of departure between the first and final point is Lat. + 0.14 ft. and Dep. − 0.06 ft. This means that the calculated position of the final point is 0.14 ft. N and 0.06 ft. W of the first point. The distance between the first point and the computed positions of the last point, i.e., the "error of closure," is found thus

$$\sqrt{0.06^2 + 0.14^2} = 0.15 \text{ ft.}$$

This closure distance, however, does not indicate the precision of the measurements until compared with the total distance around the field. Therefore a more useful and convenient measure of the accuracy is the ratio of the two, that is, the linear error of closure divided by the perimeter of the figure. This is often expressed as a fraction whose numerator is unity, as $\frac{1}{5000}$. Such a fraction states that the error of the survey is one part in 5000 parts and tells at once the quality of the work. This ratio is sometimes referred to as the "*error of closure.*"

After the sums of the N and S Lats. and of the E and W Deps. have been found they should be examined to see if they differ sufficiently to indicate a large **mistake** in the fieldwork.

If a large difference is discovered the first step would be to check all the calculations to make sure that the mistake is not in the calculations themselves. If after this recomputation the error of closure still does not come within the required limits the distances must be remeasured in the field. (See Art. 436, p. 526.)

422. Distribution of the Errors of Latitude and Departure, or "Balancing" a Closed Survey. — Before any quantities such as coördinates, dimensions, or areas, are calculated from the data of a closed survey the errors must be distributed so that a mathematically closed polygon is obtained. There are several rules which may be used for accomplishing this result.

In any closed figure the algebraic sum of the Lats. must equal zero and the algebraic sum of the Deps. must equal zero. If they do not, then corrections should be added to or subtracted from the Lats. and Deps. so as to make these sums zero.

(1) If the survey has been made by use of a compass and a chain the error in position of a point is assumed to be due as much to the error in bearing as to the error in distance, a reasonable assumption for these instruments. Hence the "compass rule," first given by Dr. Nathaniel Bowditch.

The correction to be applied to the $\begin{Bmatrix} latitude \\ departure \end{Bmatrix}$ *of any course is to the total error in* $\begin{Bmatrix} latitude \\ departure \end{Bmatrix}$ *as the length of the course is to the perimeter of the polygon.*

This rule is mathematically correct for the assumption made, that is, it fulfils the requirements of the method of least squares.

(2) If the survey is made with a transit and tape then it is reasonable to assume that the resulting error is due more to taping than to the transit work. First the angles are balanced as explained on p. 502, before the Lats. and Deps. are computed. The errors in Lat. and Dep. may then be distributed by what is called the " transit rule ": —

The correction to be applied to the $\begin{Bmatrix} latitude \\ departure \end{Bmatrix}$ *of any course is to the total error in* $\begin{Bmatrix} latitude \\ departure \end{Bmatrix}$ *as the* $\begin{Bmatrix} latitude \\ departure \end{Bmatrix}$ *of that course is to the sum of all the* $\begin{Bmatrix} latitudes \\ departures \end{Bmatrix}$ *(without regard to algebraic sign).*

This rule is not mathematically correct. It is supposed to alter the distances more than the bearings, but it will not do so under all conditions. It will, of course, give a closed figure.

Professor C. L. Crandall* proposed a rule for adjusting surveys which though not simple of application does have the advantage of being theoretically correct. H. S. Rappleye† also proposed a rule for adjusting transit and stadia traverses, in which the error in the distance is likely to be large when compared with the error in the angles. This method, like Crandall's, is based on the Method of Least Squares. On p. 513 is a survey balanced by the Bowditch rule. On p. 517 is a survey balanced by arbitrary distribution. On p. 528 is a survey balanced by the transit rule, but in this illustration the amount of the error is so small that the actual distribution is largely arbitrary.

With reference to the selection of a rule for balancing a traverse it should be observed that it is more important from a practical standpoint that the polygon should be closed than that it should be closed by any particular method. If the survey is made to close, then all the resulting (computed) dimensions will be consistent, and errors will not accumulate from the computations.

In regard to what is and what is not revealed by the error of

---

* See Geodesy and Least Squares by Crandall.
† See Procs. Amer. Soc. Civ. Eng. Nov. 1929, Vol. 55, No. 9, p. 2301.

closure it should be observed that *the constant errors are not reflected* in the error of closure. If, for example, the tape is 0.01 ft. too long and a correction for this constant error has not been applied to the distances the computed closure is not affected thereby. If the temperature of the tape is constant throughout the survey and a temperature correction is not applied to the recorded distances, similarly, it will not affect the closure. If, however, the tape temperature is recorded at a certain amount and the distances corrected accordingly but, as a matter of fact, the temperature changes during the work, then the effect of the variations in temperature enter as a part of the error of closure. This error of closure is made up chiefly of errors of an accidental nature. Notice that small accidental errors in determining the corrections for temperature, sag, pull, etc. remain in the final result, and appear in the error of closure.

In each of the preceding rules it is assumed that all measurements are equally well made and therefore that all lines are to be given the same weight in balancing. Such conditions rarely occur, however, in practice. One line may have been measured over level ground with the tape supported throughout its length; another may have required plumbing over steep slopes using short lengths of tape; and still another line may have been measured through dense bushes where it was impossible to keep the tape exactly straight. Such conditions may justify assigning most, if not all, of the error of closure to the Lats. and Deps. of these difficult lines. At any rate, wherever there is definite knowledge concerning the difficulties of measuring particular lines it is advisable to assign greater corrections to such lines than to others, that is, to assign arbitrarily to such lines the proportional part of the error that it is believed they should have. The rules given above for balancing may always be used as guides even when they are not applied strictly. They may be used in distributing any remaining error not arbitrarily assigned. With any method the corrections are applied so as to diminish the sum in the Lat. (or Dep.) column that is too large and increase the sum in the column that is too small.

During the process of making the field survey it is valuable to make notes in the field book of places where it was difficult to measure the angles accurately and also the lines where difficulty was met in making the measured distances. These facts aid greatly in determining how to distribute errors of closure in the calculated Lats. and Deps.

Another fact to be considered in the balancing of closed traverses is that such errors as that of " lining in " the intermediate points, judging whether the tape is horizontal, measuring around trees or bushes, all tend to make the recorded distances too long. When tapemen are careless about pulling the tape taut the recorded distance will be too long from this cause also. It is considered better, as a general rule, to shorten the Lats. and Deps. in the " long " columns than to lengthen those in the " short " columns. If, however, the lines are clear and an excessive tension is used then the recorded lengths may be too short.

It should be noticed that a strict adherence to any rule requires that the total error, which may be but a few hundredths (or a few tenths), shall be designated in thousandths in order to express the correction for each line. As it is inadvisable to carry such small fractions the whole matter often comes down to a more or less arbitrary distribution of the error of closure.

When calculating the corrections it should be noted that it is unnecessary to work out the complete proportion for each correction; if the total error is divided by the perimeter (compass rule) or by the sum of the latitudes or departures (transit rule) the result is the constant *correction per foot or per tape-length*, according to the unit used. If this is multiplied by the distances (or latitudes and departures) in succession the corrections are obtained. This may be done mentally or by slide rule. The number of feet per 0.01 ft. correction may be obtained by inverting the ratio of the error of closure and dividing by 100.

423. Graphical Adjustment of Error of Closure in a Traverse. — The graphical method of adjustment affords a simple means of making traverse adjustments. If a traverse $ABCDEA'$ (Fig. 177a) has been plotted by bearings and distances (or developed graphically by the plane table method) there will be a certain error of closure, AA'. To adjust the traverse graphically, construct a straight line AA' representing the length of the perimeter of the traverse with the points B, C, D, and E plotted on this straight line in proportion to the distances of these points from the starting point A. At point A' construct line $A'a$ parallel to the error of closure and equal to this error at any convenient scale. Draw Aa; this gives the *correction triangle* $A A' a$. Lines Bb, Cc, Dd, and Ee are drawn parallel to $A'a$, and each one of these lines represents the correction (direction and distance) to be applied at points B, C, D, and E on the original traverse to give the adjusted positions b, c, d, and e, thus closing the traverse.

The correction triangle may be constructed to adjust any closed traverse. The base of the triangle may be plotted to one scale and the error of closure may be magnified by plotting to

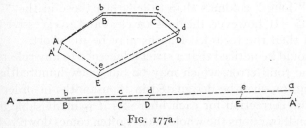

Fig. 177a.

another. If the base of the triangle AA' is drawn as an E and W line, then the altitude of a above the base is the error of closure in latitude and the perpendicular distance of a to the left or right of A' is the error in departure. Similarly the errors in latitude and departure may be scaled from the diagram at points B, C, D, and E.

424. Calculation of the Area of a Closed Figure by the Double-Meridian-Distance Method. — In calculating the area by this method it is convenient to refer to a meridian through the most westerly point of the survey. If in Fig. 178 we drop perpendiculars from each corner to the meridian FY there are formed six trapezoids or triangles, one for each side in the figure. The total area inclosed is equal to $(ABwq + BCtw + CDst) - (DErs + EFr + FAq)$; that is, in this figure the sum of all the areas determined by lines running northward minus the sum of all the areas determined by lines running southward. These are known as *north areas* and *south areas* (or $+$ areas and $-$ areas). In computing the areas of these trapezoids it is convenient to find the *double areas* first. The final algebraic sum of the double areas must be divided by 2. The area of any trapezoid equals the average distance of the extremities of the line from the (initial) meridian multiplied by the length of the projection of the line on the meridian. The average distance of the ends of the line from the meridian is known as the *meridian distance* of the course, i.e., the meridian distance of the middle point of the course. In computing the double areas twice this

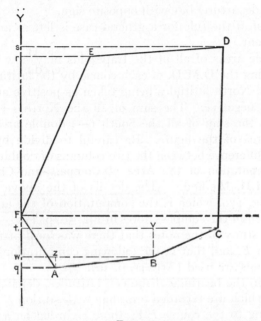

FIG. 178.

distance, or the *double meridian distance* (D.M.D.), is used; this is equal to the sum of the distances of the ends of the course from the meridian. In arranging the data for computing the double meridian distances the courses must be tabulated in consecutive order around the traverse, whether they were so taken in the field or not. The D.M.D. of the course FA is qA, which is also, in this case, the departure of the course FA. The D.M.D. of AB is $qA + wB = 2qA + zB$, that is, the D.M.D of the course FA + the departure of course FA + the departure of course AB. Hence the following rules:

(1) The D.M.D. of the first course (starting from the reference meridian) equals the departure of the course itself.

(2) The D.M.D. of any course equals the D.M.D. of the preceding course plus the departure of the preceding course plus the departure of the course itself.

(3) The D.M.D. of the last course should be numerically equal to its departure, but with opposite sign.

(The proof of the rule for a general case is left as an exercise for the student.)

The double areas of all of the trapezoids may now be found by multiplying the D.M.D. of each course by the latitude of the same course, North latitudes being taken as positive and South latitudes as negative. The sum of all the North (+) double areas minus the sum of all the South (−) double areas equals twice the area of the figure. Be careful to **divide by 2** after finding the difference between the two columns of double areas.

425. Computation of the Area of Compass-and-Chain Survey by D.M.D. Method. — The details of the above are illustrated in Fig. 179, which is the computation of the area of the traverse given in the compass notes in Fig. 50, p. 111. It will be seen from a study of the notes that there was local attraction of $\frac{1}{2}°$ at station B, and that in the following computations the corrected bearings are used (Art. 41, p. 30).

In Fig. 179 the bearings, distances, latitudes, departures, and D.M.D.'s, which are recorded on a line with station F are those corresponding to the course FA; those recorded on a line with station A refer to the course AB; etc. After the bearings and distances are entered in the table the places which are to be blank in the remaining columns are cancelled as shown; this is a check against putting the results of the computations in the wrong spaces. In computing the latitudes and departures the *log distance* is first entered; the *log sin bearing* is written below this and the *log cos bearing* is written above. To obtain the *log latitude* add the upper two logarithms; to obtain the *log departure* add the lower two logarithms. When the latitude and departure of a course have been obtained see if the results appear

Area of Wood Lot of John Smith Bk.14-P.27. Harvey Oct.12,1935.

Sta.	Bearing	Dist. (Chains)	Latitude N+	Latitude S-	Departure E+	Departure W-	Balanced Lat.	Balanced Dep.	D.M.D.	Double Area +	Double Area -
F	S 32¼ E	11.18	—	9.45	5.97	—	-9.44	+5.97	5.97	—	56.4
A	East	17.79	—	—	17.79	—	+0.01	+17.78	29.72	0.3	—
B	N 58¼ E	13.58	7.15	—	11.55	—	+7.16	+11.54	59.04	422.7	—
C	N 1½ E	32.42	32.41	—	0.85	—	+32.43	+0.83	71.41	2315.8	—
D	S 85¾ W	23.80	—	1.76	—	23.73	-1.75	-23.74	48.50	—	84.9
E	S 23½ W	31.00	—	28.43	—	12.36	-28.41	-12.38	12.38	—	351.7

129.77 39.56 39.64 36.16 36.09
39.56 36.09
Error in Lat. .08   .07 Error in Dep.

Closing Linear Error = √8²+7² = 10 Links

"Error of Closure" = 0.1/129 = 1 in 1300.

2738.8 493.0
493.0
2) 2245.8
1123. sq.ch.
112.3 acres

	F	A	B	C	D	E
Lat.	9.45	0	7.15	32.41	1.76	28.43
Log Lat.	0.9756		0.8541	1.5107	0.2465	1.4538
Log Cos Bear.	9.9272		9.7212	9.9999	8.8699	9.9624
Log Dist.	1.0484		1.1329	1.5108	1.3766	1.4914
Log Sin Bear.	9.7272		9.9296	8.4179	9.9988	9.6007
Log Dep.	0.7756		1.0625	9.9287	1.3754	1.0921
Dep.	5.97	17.79	11.55	0.85	23.73	12.36

D.M.D.s
5.97 F
5.97
17.78
29.72 A
17.78
11.54
59.04 B
11.54
.83
71.41 C
+ .83
72.24
-23.74
48.50 D
-23.74
24.76
-12.38
12.38 E Check

Areas

F
5.97
9.44
2388
2388
5373
56.4

A
29.72
.01
.3

B
59.04
7.16
354.24
5904
41328
422.7

C
32.43
71.41
3243
12972
3243
22701
2315.8

D
48.5
1.75
2425
3395
485
84.9

E
28.41
12.38
22728
8523
5682
2841
351.7

FIG. 179. AREA OF COMPASS AND CHAIN SURVEY BY DOUBLE-MERIDIAN-DISTANCE METHOD.

to be consistent with the given bearing and distance; when the bearing of a course is less than 45° its latitude is greater than its departure and *vice versa*.

Before the D.M.D. method can be applied properly the errors of the latitudes and departures should be so distributed that the figure becomes a closed polygon. In this traverse we should use the " Compass rule," p. 506. In the example (Fig. 179) the total error in latitudes is 0.08 chain. If we divide this by the perimeter of the field, 129.77 ch., we obtain 0.062 link as the correction for each chain length in the distance. Another way to express this correction is to divide the perimeter by 8, obtaining 16.2 ch. in the distance for a correction of one link (or .01 ch.) in the latitudes. Similarly, the corrections to the departures are 0.054 link per chain or one link for every 18.5 ch. These balanced latitudes and departures may be carried over into special columns, or, if preferred, the corrections may be made in red ink in the original columns.

From the balanced departures we compute next the D.M.D. of each course as shown in the next column to the right. Observe that the last D.M.D. (on line with point *F*) as computed from the preceding one is exactly equal to the departure of the last course but with opposite sign. This checks the computation of the D.M.D.'s. This check cannot be obtained unless the departures are exactly balanced. Any error in balancing the departures will appear as twice this amount in the check of the D.M.D.'s. This is one reason why the survey should be balanced even if the theoretically best rule is not used.

The partial areas are now obtained by multiplying each D.M.D. by corresponding latitude and placing the product in the *double area* columns, those having *N* latitudes being placed in the column of north (+) double areas, and those having *S* latitudes in the column of south (−) double areas. The sums of these columns differ by 2245.8. One half of this or 1123. is the area of the field in square chains, which equals 112.3 acres. By proceeding around the field in the **reverse** direction both of the letters of all the bearings would be changed, and the column of south double areas would then be the larger. The number of square units in the area would be the same.

426. Double Parallel Distance. — There is no particular reason for using the trapezoids formed by projecting the courses on to the meridian rather than those formed by projecting them on to the other axis. In the second case the *Double Parallel Distance* (*D.P.D*) should be computed, and the result multiplied by the departure for each course.

Sta.	Bearing	Dist. (Chains)	Balanced Lat	Balanced Dep	D.P.D.	Double Areas +	Double Areas −
A	East	17.79	+0.01	+17.78	+0.01	0.2	
B	N58¼E	13.58	+7.16	+11.54	+7.18	82.9	
C	N1½E	32.42	+32.43	+0.83	+46.77	38.8	
D	S85¾W	23.80	−1.75	−23.74	+77.45		1838.7
E	S23½W	31.00	−28.41	−12.38	+47.29		585.5
F	S32¼E	11.18	−9.44	+5.97	+9.44	56.4	

```
                                              178.3      2424.2
 DPD's            Areas                                   178.3
 0.01 A                                              2│2245.9
 0.01        A          B            C              1123.sq.ch.
 7.16       17.78      11.54        46.77            112.3 Acres
 7.18 B       .01       7.18         .83
 7.16         .2       92.32       140.31
 32.43                 11.54       374.16
 46.77 C               80.18        38.8
 32.43                 82.9
 79.20                    D           E           F
 1.75                    77.45       47.29        5.97
 77.45 D                 23.74       12.38        9.44
 −30.16                  309.80     378.32        2388
 47.29 E                 542.15     141.87        2388
 −37.85                  2323.5      94.58        53.73
 9.44 F Check           15490       47.29        56.4
                       1838.7       585.5
```

FIG. 180. AREA OF COMPASS SURVEY BY DOUBLE PARALLEL DISTANCES.

In the D.M.D. method the computations have been checked at every step with the exception of the multiplication of the D.M.D.'s by the latitudes. A check on this part of the work can be obtained by figuring the area also by use of the D.P.D.'s. This furnishes an example of a very desirable method of checking, as a different set of figures is used in computing the double areas, and the opportunity for repeating an error is thus avoided.

Fig. 180 shows the computation by the D.P.D. method of the area of the same survey as is calculated by the D.M.D. method in Fig. 179.

427. Computation of Area of a Transit and Tape Survey. — Before beginning the computation of the latitudes and departures the angles should be tested and balanced and the bearings calculated as described in Art. 419, and the distances should all be reduced to horizontal and corrected for error of tape and any other known errors which should be considered.

Fig. 181 shows the computation of the survey given in Fig. 52, p. 113. The arrangement of the computation is the same as that shown in Fig. 179. The latitudes and departures in this survey are computed with five-place (in some instances six-place) trigonometric functions. If the angles had been measured by a 30″ or a 20″ transit or by repetition, to a small fraction of a minute, a seven-place or a six-place logarithmic table (10″ intervals) might profitably be employed; the logarithms will not be reliable to seven places, of course, and in fact the seventh place need not even be written down, but much interpolation may be avoided if such tables are used.*

The latitudes and departures may be balanced according to the principle explained in Art. 422. As stated before, however, the surveyor's knowledge of circumstances will usually enable him to balance his survey more intelligently than by following a rule blindly. In Fig. 52, p. 113, it will be observed that certain measurements were questioned because of an uncertainty about the accuracy. In balancing the latitudes (Fig. 181) this information is used, and the error of closure thrown chiefly into these lines (*BC, GH*, and *KA*). The remainder of the area computation is the same as that described in Art. 425.

If it is desired to know the distances and bearings which are consistent with the corrected latitudes and departures these may be found as explained in Art. 433.

428. The computation shown in Fig. 186 is that of the survey given in Fig. 53, p. 115. The traverse was run with a transit

---

* Some prefer to obtain the latitudes and departures from "Traverse Tables," such as Gurden's Tables, in which the bearings are given for every minute and distances from 1 to 100.

Area J. H. Bradley Estate – Bk 42, p37.
Fuller June 7, 1936
Wilcox – Checker

Sta	Bearing	Dist. (feet)	Latitude N+	S-	Departure E+	W-	Balanced Lat.	Dep.	DMD	Double Area +	-
H	S38-07-15E	103.75		81.62	64.05		-81.62	+64.05	64.05		5228
J	N86-52-30E	96.75	5.27		96.61		+5.27	+96.61	224.71	1184	
K	S39-18-30E	420.77		325.57	266.56		-325.55	+266.55	587.87		191381
A	N62-31-30E	208.64	96.26		185.11		+96.26	+185.11	1039.53	100066	
B	N25-56-30W	436.79	392.78			191.08	+392.77	-191.06	1033.58	405959	
C	S87-01-15W	56.48		2.94		56.40	-2.94	-56.40	786.12		2311
D	S53-22-00W	98.80		58.95		79.28	-58.95	-79.28	650.44		38343
E	N36-38-00W	68.62	55.07			40.94	+55.07	-40.94	530.22	29199	
F	N59-29-00W	95.10	48.29			81.93	+48.29	-81.93	407.35	19671	
G	S51-40-45W	207.41		128.61		162.72	-128.60	-162.71	162.71		20925
		1193.11	591.67	597.69	612.33	612.35				556079.	258188

Error in Lat. 0.02   Error in Dep. 0.02

$$\text{"Error of Closure"} = \frac{\sqrt{2^2 + 2^2}}{179311} = \frac{1}{63,500}$$

556079.
258188.
2) 297891.
148946 sq. ft: Area

Deflection Angles

	Right	Left
A		78-10
B		88-28
C		67-02 (67-02-15)
D		33-39-15
E	90-00	
F		22-51
G		68-50-15
H		89-48
J		55-00-15
K	53-49	
	143-49	500-228-45
		143-49
		359-59-45

Error in Angles 0°-00'-15"
Add 0-15 to angle C

Bearings

E   N 36-38 W
    22-51
F   N 59-29 W
    68-50-15
    128-19-15
    180°
G   S 51-40-45 W
    89-48
H   S 38-07-15 E
    55-00-15
    93-07-30
    180
J   N 86-52-30 E
    53-49
    140-41-30
    180
K   S 39-18-30 E
    78-10
    117-28-30
    180
A   N 62-31-30 E
    88-28
B   N 25-56-30 W
    67-02-15
    92-58-45
    180
C   S 87-01-15 W
    33-39-15
D   S 53-22   W
    90
E   N 36-38   W

D.M.D

H   64.05
    64.05
    96.61
J   224.71
    96.61
    266.35
K   587.87
    266.35
    185.11
A   1039.53
    185.11
    1224.64
    -191.06
B   1033.58
    -247.46
C   786.12
    -135.68
D   650.44
    -120.22
E   530.22
    -122.87
F   407.35
    -244.64
G   162.71

FIG. 181. AREA OF A TRANSIT AND TAPE SURVEY BY DOUBLE-MERIDIAN-DISTANCE METHOD.

(The remainder of the computation is in Fig. 182.)

and a tape, the angles being taken to the nearest minute and distance to the nearest tenth of a foot. In balancing the latitudes and departures the " transit rule " is used, since there is nothing in the notes to indicate that any distances are probably more accurate than others. The error of 1′ in the angles is put at station D, adjacent to a short line.

Latitudes and Departures

	H	J	K	A	B
Lat.	81.62	5.27	325.57	96.26	392.78
Log Lat.	1.911803	0.72216	2.512645	1.983439	2.594149
Log Cos. Bear.	9.895815	8.73651	9.888600	9.664041	9.953876
Log Dist.	2.015988	1.98565	2.624045	2.319398	2.640273
Log Sin. Bear.	9.790512	9.99935	9.801742	9.948027	9.640934
Log Dep.	1.806500	1.98500	2.425787	2.267425	2.281207
Dep	64.05	96.61	266.56	185.11	191.08

	C	D	E	F	G
Lat.	2.94	58.95	55.07	48.29	128.61
Log Lat.	0.46767	1.77051	1.74088	1.68386	2.109267
Log Cos. Bear	8.71578	9.77575	9.90443	9.70568	9.792437
Log Dist.	1.75189	1.99476	1.83645	1.97818	2.316830
Log Sin Bear	9.99941	9.90443	9.77575	9.93525	9.894621
Log Dep.	1.75130	1.89919	1.61220	1.91343	2.211451
Dep	56.40	79.28	40.94	81.93	162.72

Double Areas

	H	J	K	A	B
Log DMD	1.80650	2.35162	2.769281	3.016837	3.014344
Log Lat	1.91180	0.72181	2.512618	1.983446	2.594138
Log Area	3.71830	3.07343	5.281899	5.000283	5.608482
Area	5228	1184	191381	100066	405959

	C	D	E	F	G
Log DMD	2.89549	2.813207	2.724456	2.609968	2.211415
Log Lat.	0.46835	1.770484	1.740915	1.683857	2.109241
Log Area	3.36384	4.583691	4.465371	4.293825	4.320656
Area	·2311	38343	29199	19671	20925

FIG. 182.

(These computations go with Fig. 181.)

It will be observed that the distances used in computing the latitudes and departures are slightly different from those which appear in the field-notes (Fig. 53); this is because the distances have been corrected for erroneous length of tape before beginning the calculation. The intermediate steps in the computation are the same as in the preceding traverse.

429. CALCULATION OF RECTANGULAR COÖRDINATES OF THE STATIONS OF A SURVEY. — In many of the larger cities and metropolitan districts the rectangular coördinate system of surveying is used. In this system the position of each corner of the different lots is fixed by X and Y coördinates referred to two lines at right angles to each other, usually some meridian and a line perpendicular to it. The advantage of this system lies in the fact that as all surveys refer to the same origin they are tied to each other, and any lot may be re-located by means of the known coördinates of its corners, even if all points in the immediate vicinity have been lost.

Generally the coördinate lines run N and S, and E and W, but when the rectangular system has been adopted for laying out city streets, and they do not run N and S, it may be more convenient to assume coördinate axes parallel to the street lines.

The coördinate system may be applied conveniently to any survey involving a large number of points. The origin of the coördinates may be taken at the first station or at any other point whose relation to the first station is known. The X coördinates of the successive points are obtained by adding algebraically the corresponding departure, or difference of X. The Y coördinates are obtained similarly from the latitudes of the successive lines. These X and Y coördinates are often called the **total departures** and **total latitudes** of the survey points.

Example: In the example shown on page 525 the coördinates of the points A, B, C, and D referred to A would be computed as follows:

Point	Y		X	
A	o	(assumed)	o	(assumed)
B	− 242.3		− 319.4	
	+ <u>301.9</u>		− <u>430.9</u>	
C	+ 59.6		− 750.3	
	+ <u>318.6</u>		+ <u>226.3</u>	
D	+ 378.2		− 524.0	

Negative coördinates for B might have been avoided by adopting some other station as an origin, as, for instance, B itself or a point 1000 ft. south and 1000 ft. west of A.

430. Calculation of the Coördinates of the Corners of a Closed Survey. — The origin may be one of the survey stations, such, for example, as the most westerly or the most southerly station, or it may be at the intersection of a meridian through the most westerly and a perpendicular through the most southerly points. All of the coördinates will be positive if this last suggestion is adopted. The coördinates are calculated exactly as in the preceding article. There is an opportunity here to check the calculations by recomputing the coördinates of the first point from

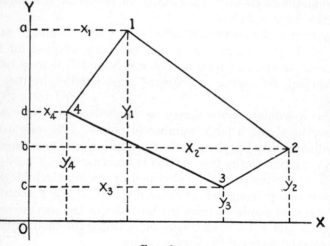

Fig. 183.

those of the last and observing whether the original value is again obtained. For an example of this calculation see Fig. 196, p. 566.

431. Calculation of the Area of a Closed Traverse when the X, Y Coördinates of All of the Corners are Known. — Assuming that the rectangular coördinates of the corners have been found by the method of Art. 429 we may obtain the area by means of these X and Y coördinates alone. It is not essential that all the coördinates should have been found from the same closed traverse, except for the check given by such a survey. If the coördinates have been determined accurately by any means the area will be accurate.

In Fig. 183 the area of the field 1, 2, 3, 4 is equal to the algebraic sum of the trapezoids

$$(a, 1, 2, b) + (b, 2, 3, c) - (a, 1, 4, d) - (d, 4, 3, c)$$

Expressed as an equation in terms of the coördinates the area is

$$1, 2, 3, 4 = (y_1 - y_2)\frac{x_1 + x_2}{2} + (y_2 - y_3)\frac{x_2 + x_3}{2}$$

$$- (y_4 - y_3)\frac{x_4 + x_3}{2} - (y_1 - y_4)\frac{x_1 + x_4}{2} \qquad (1)$$

$$= \tfrac{1}{2}\{y_1(x_2 - x_4) + y_2(x_3 - x_1) + y_3(x_4 - x_2) + y_4(x_1 - x_3)\} \qquad (2)$$

From this last equation is derived the following rule for obtaining the area of a closed field from the coördinates of its corners:

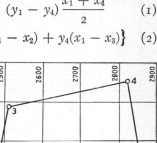

(1) Number the corners consecutively around the field.

(2) Multiply each $\begin{Bmatrix}\text{abscissa} \\ \text{ordinate}\end{Bmatrix}$ by the difference between the

Fig. 184.

following and the preceding $\begin{Bmatrix}\text{ordinates} \\ \text{abscissas}\end{Bmatrix}$, always subtracting the following from the preceding (or always subtracting the preceding from the following), and take **half the sum** of the products.

Fig. 184a illustrates the computation of an area (Fig. 184) from the coördinates of its corners. For convenience each Y has been diminished by 3000 ft. before multiplying by the corresponding difference in X's. Observe that the correctness of the subtractions may be checked by finding the sum for the fourth column, which should equal zero.

Equation (1) may be developed into the following form:

$$1, 2, 3, 4 = \tfrac{1}{2}(x_2 y_1 - x_1 y_2 + x_3 y_2 - x_2 y_3 + x_4 y_3 - x_3 y_4 + x_1 y_4 - x_4 y_1) \qquad (3)$$

When this formula is to be used the coördinates may be arranged in the following simple manner:

$$1, 2, 3, 4 = \tfrac{1}{2}\left(\frac{x_1}{y_1} \diagdown \frac{x_2}{y_2} \diagdown \frac{x_3}{y_3} \diagdown \frac{x_4}{y_4} \cdots \cdots \diagdown \frac{x_1}{y_1}\right) \qquad (4)$$

From equation (3) it will be seen that the area is equal to the sum of the products of the coördinates joined by **full** lines in (4) **minus** the sum of the products of the coördinates joined by **broken** lines.

Corner	North (Y) (Feet)	East (X) (Feet)	Diff. Adj. X's	+ Areas	− Areas
1	3304.29	2601.71	+ 372.91	113,473	
2	3462.91	2486.21	+ 90.55	41,917	
3	3591.20	2511.16	− 333.79		197,337
4	3651.81	2820.00	− 347.96		226,804
5	3470.19	2859.12	+ 218.29	102,638	

$$\begin{array}{rr} 258,028 & 424,141 \\ & 258,028 \\ \hline 2 & \overline{)166,113} \\ \hline & 83,056 \text{ Sq. Ft.} \end{array}$$

Fig. 184a. Area of Lot from Coördinates of Its Corners.

This formula involves the multiplications of larger numbers than in (2), but does not require any intermediate subtractions.

432. Calculation of Distance and Bearing from Lat. and Dep. — If the Lat. and Dep. of any line are known the Distance and Bearing (or azimuth) may be found by means of the right triangle shown in Fig. 177, the relations being

$$\tan \text{Bearing} = \frac{\text{Dep.}}{\text{Lat.}}$$

$$\text{Dist.} = \frac{\text{Dep.}}{\sin \text{Bearing}} = \frac{\text{Lat.}}{\cos \text{Bearing}}$$

The distance may be calculated from either the Lat. or the Dep.; it is best to obtain it from both so as to have a check. The relation $\text{Dist.} = \sqrt{\text{Lat.}^2 + \text{Dep.}^2}$ also will give the distance, but is less convenient to use than those given first. If the bearing is near 0° or near 90° the approximate formula of Art. 21, footnote, will give the distance quickly and accurately (slide-rule computation).

433. Calculation of the Length and Bearing which are Consistent with the Balanced Latitudes and Departures. — In describing property in a deed it is important to use bearings and distances which represent the best that can be obtained from the measurements. Since we have adjusted the traverse so as to increase the accuracy of the Lats. and Deps. it is of almost equal importance to calculate distances and bearings which are consistent with these new Lats. and Deps. If this calculation is to be made in a direct manner it will be necessary to use the same number of decimal places in the logarithms as was used in the original calculation. The corrected latitude and the corrected departure of any course are taken as the sides of a right triangle and the distance and bearing computed as in Art. 420. By the use of formulas giving corrections to the length and bearing it is possible to arrive at the same results by a slide-rule computation. The correction to the distance is given by

$$dl = dL \cos B + dD \sin B$$

$$\left(\text{or } dl = dL \frac{L}{l} + dD \frac{D}{l} \right)$$

in which the corrections to latitude and departure, dL and dD, are to be taken as positive if added to north latitudes or to east departures; the algebraic signs of $\sin B$ and $\cos B$ must be found by treating the angle as though it were in the first quadrant when NE, second quadrant when SE, etc.

The correction to the bearing is given by

$$dB = \frac{dL \sin B}{l \sin 1'} + \frac{dD \cos B}{l \sin 1'}$$

[in which $\sin 1' = 0.000291$]

These formulas may be derived by differentiation of the equations

$$l^2 = L^2 + D^2$$

and

$$B = \tan^{-1} \frac{D}{L}$$

The relationships given in this article may be readily demonstrated graphically.

Example: $B = S\ 34°\ 10'\ W,$ $l = 401.2,$ $L = -331.95,$ $D = -225.32,$ $dL = +.07,$ $dD = +.03.$

(1) Direct Solution.

$$\text{corrected } D = 225.29 \log 2.35273$$
$$\text{corrected } L = 331.88 \log \underline{2.52099}$$
$$9.83174$$
$$B = 34°\ 10'\ 07''$$
$$\log \cos B = 9.91771$$
$$\log l = 2.60328$$
$$l = 401.13$$

(2) Solution by Corrections.

$$dl = (+.07) \times (-.83) + (+.03) \times (-.56)$$
$$= -.075$$
$$l = 401.20 - .075 = 401.125 \text{ (or 401.13)} \qquad \text{(Check)}$$
$$dB = -\frac{(+.07)\,(-.56)}{401 \times .00029} + \frac{(+.03)\,(-.83)}{401 \times .00029}$$
$$= +0'.124 = +7''.4$$
$$\therefore B = 34°\ 10'\ 07'' \text{ (or } 34°\ 10'.1) \qquad \text{(Check)}$$

These corrections may be found also by the graphical method given in Art. 310, p. 370.

434. Calculation of Closing Side from Lats. and Deps. of Several Lines. — Suppose that A, B, C, and D are connected by angles and distances and that the Lat. and Dep. of each line have been computed, as shown below.

Example.

LINE	BEARINGS.	DIST., FEET.	LATS.		DEPS.	
			N.	S.	E.	W.
$A-B$	S 52° 49' W	400.9		242.3		319.4
$B-C$	N 54 59 W	526.1	301.9			430.9
$C-D$	N 35 23 E	390.8	318.6		226.3	
		sums	620.5	242.3	226.3	750.3
			242.3			226.3
		diffs.	378.2			524.0

It is desired to find the distance from A to D and the bearing of this line. The total difference of latitude of A and D is the difference in the sums of the two latitude columns, or 378.2. Similarly the total difference of departure is 524.0. These two coördinates determine the direction and distance from A to D exactly as though AD were one of the lines of the traverse.

$$\log 524.0 = 2.71933$$
$$\log 378.2 = \underline{2.57772}$$
$$\log \tan \text{Bear. of } AD = 0.14161$$
$$\text{Bear. of } AD = 54° 10'.8$$
$$\text{or N } 54° 10'.8 \text{ W (az. } = 125° 49'.2)$$

$\log 524.0 = 2.71933$	$\log 378.2 = 2.57772$
$\log \sin \text{Bear.} = \underline{9.90894}$	$\log \cos \text{Bear.} = \underline{9.76733}$
$\log \text{Dist.} = 2.81039$	$\log \text{Dist.} = 2.81039$
Dist. $AD = 646.2$ ft.	Dist. $AD = 646.2$ ft. (Check)

The preceding principle may be applied to the problem of finding the closing side of a figure in which the measurement of the length and bearing of one side have been omitted. Suppose, for example, that the outer boundary of a piece of property has been surveyed and that it is desired to divide the lot by a straight line joining two of the corners. The length and bearing of this proposed line may be computed from either part of the traverse in exactly the same manner that AD was determined in the preceding example. It should be observed, however, that when this method is applied to measurements which have not been checked by closing a circuit any errors existing in the measured lines may enter directly into the computed length and bearing of this line AD, for an error which causes the circuit to fail to close may lie in one of the distances or angles upon which the computed line depends.

435. Calculation of the Length and Bearing of Line between Two Stations from their Coördinates. — If the coördinates of two points are known the distance and bearing may be found by the method explained in Art. 434. The difference of y's is the same as the total difference in latitudes and the difference of x's is the total difference in departure. The length and bearing are then found from the right triangle, as shown in the example of Art. 434.

436. DETECTING MISTAKES. — Mistakes in fieldwork may often be detected by means of the calculations. One of the easiest mistakes to make in surveying is to omit a whole tape-length in counting. If such a mistake were made and the latitudes and departures were computed, the linear error of closure of the survey would prove to be about a tape-length. In order to find in which line this mistake probably occurred compute the bearing of this linear error of closure and examine the traverse to find a line having a bearing the same or nearly the same. The error in departure divided by the error in latitude equals the **tangent of the bearing of the line** that represents the error of closure of the traverse. The errors of the survey, of course, will prevent these bearings from agreeing exactly. If two mistakes have been made it may be difficult and sometimes impossible to determine where they occurred. When an error of this sort is indicated by the computation the line should be remeasured. It is bad practice to change an observed measurement because it is found by calculation to disagree with other measured distances.

It may, and frequently does, happen that there are several lines in the traverse that have about the same bearing. In such a case it is impossible to tell in which of these lines the mistake occurred. But if a cut-off line is measured, as was suggested in Art. 145, p. 124, and one portion of the survey balances, then the other part will contain the mistake. By proceeding in this way the number of lines in which the mistake could occur is reduced so that its location can be determined and checked by field measurement.

437. Use of Coördinates for Calculating the Length and Direction of a Property Line not Coincident with a Transit Line. — Suppose that EF (Fig. 185) is a transit line (coördinates of E and F known) from which M and N have been located by angles and distances. From the coördinates of E and the direction and distance to M we may compute the coördinates of M.

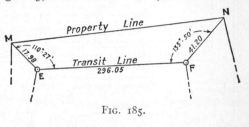

Fig. 185.

Similarly from F we may obtain the coördinates of N. Then from the coördinates of the two points the length and bearing of MN may be found as explained in the preceding article.

This problem is met frequently in the survey of land for deed description. When this is so, the lines ME and FN must be measured with the same precision as the lines of the original closed traverse. Likewise the angles must be carefully measured. Since there is no direct check on the length and bearing of the line MN similar to the checks in a closed traverse, the computations for this property line should be made independently by different computers

438. Fractional Areas. — Areas which lie between the traverse and the property line itself and are to be added to or subtracted from the area of the traverse, will ordinarily be either triangles or quadrilaterals, except where there are curved boundaries, either regular or irregular; these latter will be dealt with separately. Where the property corner is tied to a nearby transit station by an angle and a distance, the area to be added or subtracted is that of a quadrilateral in which three sides and the two included angles are known. (See the figure $iBCf$ in Fig. 186.) The area may be found by dropping perpendiculars from the corners

i and f onto the transit line BC (extended if necessary), thus making a combination of a trapezoid and two right triangles. By solving the two right triangles sufficient dimensions will be obtained to give all three areas.   The length and direction of

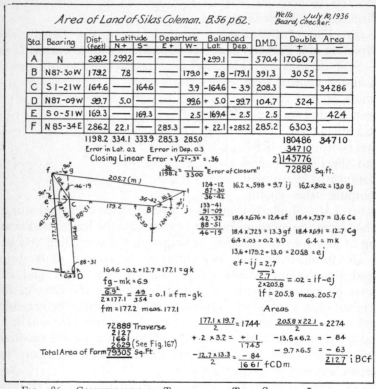

FIG. 186.   COMPUTATION OF TRANSIT AND TAPE SURVEY, INCLUDING FRACTIONAL AREA.

(See field data of this traverse in Fig. 53, p. 115.)

the property line fi may be found from these same dimensions, or by the coördinate method suggested in Art. 437.

If the area to be added or subtracted is a triangle it is necessary to obtain sufficient data to " solve " the triangle and compute its area.   If this is foreseen in the field the measurements may usually be taken so as to avoid much calculation.

If the area to be added (or subtracted) is bounded in part by a circular curve its area may be obtained by the method explained in Art. 403, p. 484. (For a discussion of circular curves see Art. 282, p. 336 *et seq.*)

If the area to be added or subtracted is bounded by an irregular curve it must be computed as described in Arts. 397-9, pp. 480-1.

439. SUPPLYING MISSING DATA. — If any two parts of a traverse, either distance or bearings, are missing, it is possible to supply these missing parts by computation and thus obtain a complete set of notes for the traverse. Since the algebraic sum of the latitudes must be zero we may write an equation of the forms $\Sigma l \cos B = 0$; similarly for the departures, $\Sigma l \sin B = 0$. In each equation there may be (the same) two missing parts. A solution of these equations simultaneously will give the missing parts. In practice this method is seldom applied but geometric solutions are preferred.

The solutions of the different cases may be classified according to whether the two missing parts are in the same line, in any two adjacent lines, or in two non-adjacent lines.

440. When the bearing and length of the same line are missing, then the two parts are computed at once from the latitude and departure of this course, as was explained in Arts. 434 and 435. This case is of frequent occurrence in the subdivision of land.

When the missing parts occur in adjacent lines we may draw a line joining the extremities of the known part of the traverse, leaving a triangle containing the unknown parts. The solution of this triangle gives the required parts. For example, suppose that a lot *ABCDEFGH* (Fig. 187) is crossed by a line *XY* and the distance *Dm* and the angle *DmY* have been measured. *ABCDmnA* is a closed traverse in which the two distances *mn* and *An* are missing. If we draw *Am* we have a continuous traverse *ABCDmA* in which *mA* is unknown both in direction and distance. These two missing parts may be computed by the method of Art. 434. Then in the triangle *Amn* we know *Am* and all of the angles and may therefore compute the distances *An* and *mn*. If the angles were missing instead of the lengths the solution of the triangle would give these angles. This case occurs frequently when a new (proposed) line is projected across the boundaries of an existing lot, as when taking land for a highway or a railway.

If the missing parts occur in non-adjacent sides, such for example as HG and EF, we may suppose G to be moved to H and F

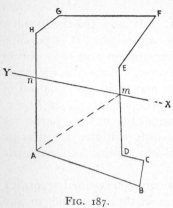

FIG. 187.

to be moved an equal and parallel distance FF'. Then we may compute the traverse $HABCDEFF'H$ as in the preceding case (triangle EFF') and find the length of bearing of FF', which will be the same as for GH.

441. The solutions of the other cases of missing data are not so simple, as they involve the use of simultaneous equations; they will not be discussed here.

442. Besides the three cases mentioned above there are some special cases which can be solved. The following example is typical of this kind of problem. In Fig. 188 the lines and angles measured are shown by full lines. The bearing of AB is given. Here one side and two angles are missing. The solution is as follows. In the triangle EAB find EB, EBA, and AEB. In the triangle EDC find EC, DCE, and DEC. Then in the triangle EBC, in which EC, EB, and EBC are known, find ECB, CEB, and BC. All

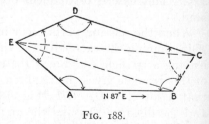

FIG. 188.

the angles and sides are then known. Examples of this type will be found in Problems 21 and 22, p. 537.

443. THE SUBDIVISION OF LAND. — There are many different problems which may arise in the subdivision of land and which may be solved simply by the application of the principles of trigonometry. A few of these problems are so common and so frequently involved in the working out of more complicated cases that their solution will be given.

444. To Cut Off from a Traverse a Given Area by a Straight Line starting from a Known Point on the Traverse. — In Fig. 189, *ABCDE* represents the traverse which has been plotted and whose area has been computed. It is desired to cut off a certain area by a line running from *F*, which is at a known distance from *A* or *E*. The line *FG'* is drawn on the plan so as to make the area *FG' DE* approximately equal to the desired area. The line *DG'* is scaled off and the scaled distance used as a trial length. Then the side *FG'* and its bearing can be found by the method explained in Art. 440, p. 529, and the area *FEDG'* computed in the usual manner. The difference between the required area and the area of *FEDG'* is the amount to be added to or subtracted from *FEDG'*. If this correction area is a minus area then *GFG'* will represent the correction triangle. In this triangle the base *FG'* and its area being known the altitude *hG* and the distances *GG'* and *FG* can be readily computed. In the traverse *FGDE*, which is the required area, the length of the missing side *FG* and its bearing can be supplied.

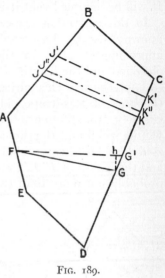

Fig. 189.

Instead of using the trial line *FG'* the line *FD* might have been first assumed and the correction triangle would then be *FDG*. This method has the advantage of containing one less side in the first trial area, but the correction triangle is large, whereas in the method explained above the correction triangle is small, which may be of advantage in that part of the computation.

445. To Cut Off from a Traverse a Given Area by a Line running in a Given Direction. — In Fig. 189, *ABCDE* represents a closed traverse from which a given area is to be cut off by a line running at a given angle (BJK) with AB. On the plot of the traverse draw the line $J'K'$ in the given direction cutting off $J'BCK'$ which is, as nearly as can be judged, the required area. Scale the distance BJ' and use this trial distance in the computations. Then compute the distance $J'K'$ and the area of $J'BCK'$ by the method suggested in Art. 442, i.e., by dividing $J'BCK'$ into two oblique triangles. The difference between this area and the required area is then found; this is a correction trapezoid to be added to or subtracted from $J'BCK'$. It will be assumed that it is to be added to $J'BCK'$.

In this correction trapezoid the area and one base $J'K'$ are known; also the base angles, J' and K'. From these data an approximate value for the altitude of the trapezoid can be obtained and the length of the other base $K''J''$ of the trapezoid computed from this altitude and the length of $J'K'$. Then the area of this trapezoid $J'K'K''J''$ can be determined accurately; the difference between this and the required correction will be small and the dimensions of the second correction trapezoid $J''K''K'J'$ can probably be computed readily from its area, and the length of $J''K''$, which are known. By successive trials, probably not more than two, the correct line JK can be found.

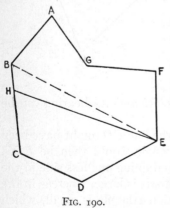

FIG. 190.

If lines AB and CD are approximately parallel the trapezoid is nearly a parallelogram and then its correct altitude can be quickly determined.

446. To Find the Area Cut off from a Traverse by a Line running in a Given Direction from a Given Point in the Traverse. — This problem may be readily solved by drawing a line from the given point in the traverse to the corner which lies nearest the other extremity of the cut-off line. The area of the traverse thus formed is then computed, and this area corrected by means of a correction triangle.

In Fig. 190, $ABCDEFG$ represents a plot of a field. It is desired to run the line from E in a given direction EH and to compute the area $HEFGAB$ cut off by this line. The latitude and departure of points B and E being known the bearing and length of BE and the area of $ABEFG$ can be computed. Then the area and the remaining sides of the triangle BEH can be obtained from BE and the angles at B and E.

It is obvious that the solution of such problems as these is greatly facilitated by plotting the traverse before attempting the computations.

447. COMPUTATION OF AZIMUTHS WHEN CHECKING ANGLES TO A DISTANT OBJECT. — In this kind of problem the coördinates of all the points along the traverse can be computed with reference to some coördinate axes. At A and B (Fig. 190a) angles have been taken to S, and from these angles the coördinates of point S, referred to AB and a line perpendicular to AB as axes, can be computed (Art. 439, p. 519). Coördinates of S referred to the same axes should have the same value when figured from BC as a base when calculated from the base CD, and so on. If, however, when computed by means of angles at D and E, the point falls

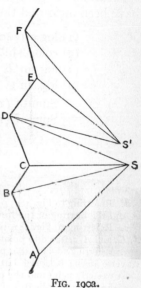

FIG. 190a.

at S', and angles E and F give its location also at S' there is evidence of a mistake in the traverse at station D. If the two locations of S and S' are such that a line between them is parallel to either CD or DE, the mistake was probably made in the measurement of the length of the line parallel to SS' and the distance SS' should be approximately equal to the amount of the mistake in measurement. If, however, SS' is not parallel to either CD or DE the mistake probably lies in the angle at D.

448. CALCULATION OF TRIANGULATION. — In a triangulation system the base-line is the only line whose length is known at the start. The sides of any triangle are found from the law of sines, as follows:

$$\frac{\sin A}{\sin B} = \frac{a}{b} \qquad\qquad \frac{a \sin B}{\sin A} = b$$

$$\frac{\sin A}{\sin C} = \frac{a}{c} \qquad\qquad \frac{a \sin C}{\sin A} = c$$

Assuming a to be the base and the angles A, B, and C to have been measured the calculations are arranged as follows:

(1) log a (1400.74)   = 3.1463575
(2) colog sin A (57° 42′ 16″)   = 0.0729874
(3) log sin B (61° 17′ 53″)   = 9.9430639
(4) log sin C (60° 59′ 51″)   = 9.9418088

Sum of (1) (2) (3) log b = 3.1624088
Sum of (1) (2) (4) log c = 3.1611537

PROBLEMS

1. Referring to Fig. 181, p. 517, calculate the distance between points H and A and the bearing of the line. (Use the balanced Lat. and Deps.)

2. Referring to Fig. 181, p. 517, calculate the coördinates (x and y) of points J, K, and A, referred to point H as an origin.

3. Referring to Fig. 186, p. 528, calculate the coördinates of all points of the traverse (using balanced Lat. and Dep.) referred to the meridian through the most westerly point and the perpendicular through the most southerly point.

4. From the coördinates of problem 3 calculate bearing and length of AD.

5. Using the coördinates of problem 3 and the data of Fig. 53, calculate the coördinates of the corners near points C and B; from the coördinates find the length and bearing of the property line itself.

6. In Fig. 186, p. 528, calculate the new bearings and distances consistent with the balanced latitudes and departures.

7. Following is a "closed" compass and chain survey. Calculate the area by the coördinate method and by the D.M.D. method

Station.	Bearing.	Distance.
1	S 40° W	17.50 chains
2	N 45° W	22.25
3	N 36°¼ E	31.25
4	North	13.50
5	S 81° E	46.50
6	S 8°½ W	34.25
7	West	32.50

8. Following is a closed transit and tape traverse. Calculate the area by the coördinate method and by the D.M.D. methods.

Station.	Deflection Angle.	Distance.
A	52° 49′ R	400.9 ft.
B	72 12 R	526.1
C	90 22 R	390.8
D	85 11 L	339.6
E	123 17 R	816.7
F	106 30 R	829.5

9. Calculate the following areas by both methods.

Station.	Deflection Angle.	Distance.
1	124° 31′ R	118.17 ft.
2	69 07 R	106.18
3	20 56 L	91.39
4	126 23 R	156.55
5	100 54 R	82.19
6	39 59 L	121.67

10. Station.	Deflection Angle.	Bearing.	Distance.
1	74° 43′½ R	N 22° 28′ E	229.15
2	125 22′½ R		105.29
3	15 29′¼ R		148.75
4	34 24′ L		276.68
5	9 53′½ L		247.67
6	172 11′ R		457.68
7	16 31′ R		242.02

11. Station.	Deflection.	Bearing.	Distance.
1	91° 41′ 30″ R	N 65° 51′ W	319.15
2	120 03′ 30″ R		168.40
3	11 14′ L		498.80
4	151 23′ R		394.18
5	8 07′ R		229.35

In this problem 100-ft. tape is 0.067 ft. short at 62° F., 12 lbs. pull.

12. Station.	Deflecting Angle.	Bearing.	Distance.
1	40° 08′ R	N 25° 43′ 30″ W	140.74
2	2° 34′ L		100.97
3	0° 58′½ R		145.74
4	51° 51′ R		84.87
5	7° 49′½ R		301.32
6	82° 39′½ R		527.70
7	107° 57′ R		498.90
8	11° 14′½ R		168.37
9	59° 56′½ R		24.35

100-ft. tape is 0.089 ft. short at 62° F., 12 lbs. pull.

13. Referring to Fig. 52, p. 113, if lines ED and BC are prolonged to intersect at C', a property corner, what is the area of the triangle that must be added to the area of the traverse? Referring to the same figure (52), if the property corner is on JH prolonged, 50.00 ft. from H, and another corner is 65.10 ft. from G, defl. angle from $FG = 31° 10′$ *left*, what is the area that must be added to the area of the traverse?

14. From the data in Fig 181, p. 517, compute by the double meridian distance method the area of the traverse $ABCDEK$. See also Fig. 52, p. 113.

15. In the following traverse there are two mistakes. Find where they occur and determine their amounts.

Station.	Observed Bearing.	Deflection Angle.	Distance (Feet).	Calculated Bearings.	Remarks.
A	N 34° E	164° 14′ R	240.2	N 34° 00′ E	
B	S 73°½ E	62° 16′ R	163.7		
C	S 10°¼ W	84° 22′ R	207.6		$CE = 188.1$
D	N 26° ½ W	142° 49′ R	273.1		$BCE = 34° 14′$
E	S 52° W	103° 41′ L	147.4		$DEC = 81° 25′$

16. The following is a set of notes of an irregular boundary of a lot of land. It is desired to straighten this crooked boundary line by substituting a straight line running from B to the line EF. Find the bearing of the new boundary line and its length; also the distance along EF from point E to the point where the new line cuts EF.

Station	Bearing	Distance (Feet)
A	S 89° 14′ E	373.62
B	N 13° 10′ E	100.27
C	N 0° 17′ W	91.26
D	N 27° 39′ E	112.48
E	N 72° 12′ W	346.07
F	S 5° 07′ W	272.42
	etc.	etc.

17. (a) In the lot of land, *ABCD*, the lines *AB* and *DC* both have a bearing of N 23° E; the bearing of *AD* is due East; *AD* is 600 ft., *AB* is 272.7 ft., and *DC* is 484.6 ft. Find the length of a line *EF* parallel to *AB* which will cut off an area *ABFE* equal to half an acre. Also find the length of the lines *AE*, and *BF*. (b) What is the area of *EFCD*?

18. Given the notes of a traverse, which does not close, as follows: —

Station	Deflection Angle	
o		
6 + 40	6° 17′ L	Find the length of a straight line from o to 20 + 64 and the angle it makes with the line from o to 6 + 40.
9 + 20	18° 43′ L	
14 + 55	12° 47′ R	
17 + 18	45° 24′ L	
20 + 64	68° 06′ R	

19. Compute the area of the following traverse by coördinates.

Station.	Deflection Angle.	Bearing.	Distance (Feet).
A	78° 10′ 00″ L		208.64
B	88° 28′ 00″ L		436.79
C	67° 02′ 15″ L		56.48
D	33° 39′ 15″ L		98.80
E	90° 00′ 00″ R		68.62
F	22° 51′ 00″ L		95.10
G	68° 50′ 15″ L	N 36° 14′ 00″ W	207.41
H	89° 48′ 00″ L		103.75
I	55° 00′ 15″ L		96.75
J	53° 49′ 00″ R		420.77

20. The line *Ax* has a bearing S 51° 10′ E, and line *Ex* has a bearing N 21° 04′ E. *A* and *E* are connected by the following traverse: *AB*, S 60° 51′ W, 102.69 ft.; *BC*, S 0° 59′ E, 298.65 ft.; *CD*, S 89° 01′ E, 101.20 ft. ; *DE*, N 80° 52′ E, 148.28 ft. Compute the distances *Ax* and *Ex*.

21. On a street line *ACE* whose bearing is S 89° 10′ E, the distance *AC* is 50.00 ft. and *CE* is 101.50 ft. The side line *AG* of a house lot has a bearing of S 2° 05′ W. Point *B* is on this side line and is 31.25 ft. from *A*. The opposite side of the lot, *CH* has a bearing S 1° 20′ W, and the side line of the next lot, *EI* has a bearing S 1° 10′ E. From *B* a line having a bearing N 89° 16′ E cuts these side lines, at points *B*, *D* and *F*. Compute distances *CD*, *BD*, *EF*, and *DF*.

22. A traverse run from *A* to *D* has the following bearings and distances: *AB*, S 26° 19′ E, 91.2 ft.; *BC*, S 89° 58′ E, 216.00 ft.; *CD*, N 1° 19′ E, 371.25 ft. Point *E* is 191.00 ft. from *A* and 212.10 ft. from *D*. Compute the bearings of *AE* and *DE*, and the angles *EAD*, *EDA* and *AED*.

23. A corner city lot *ABCDE* has the following interior angles. *A* = 7° 15′, *B* = 94° 50′, *C* = 91° 22′, *D* = 120° 27′, *E* = 226° 06′. The measured sides are

$AB = 583.58$, $BC = 102.88$, $CD = 153.01$, $DE = 86.85$, $EA = 391.42$. Bearing of AB is N 66° 50' E. At the corner B the lot is rounded by a circular curve of 20.00 ft. radius; point B is at the vertex of this curve. Compute the area of the lot.

24. Compute the area enclosed by the following traverse.

Station	Deflection Angle	Bearing	Distance
1	79° 13' R	North	1278.2 ft.
2	76 21 R		230.6
3	17 03 R		383.4
4	22 00 L		500.2
5	113 38 R		850.3
6	18 58 L		881.1
7	114 45 R		1241.5

25. Compute the area enclosed by the following traverse.

Station	Deflection Angle	Bearing	Distance
1	99° 49' R		854.1 ft.
2	100 06 R		203.9
3	19 47 L		250.7
4	22 10 R		479.6
5	32 54 L	S 1° 39' W	454.0
6	112 06 R		687.3
7	78 32 R		1341.6

PART IV

PLOTTING

CHAPTER XV

DRAFTING INSTRUMENTS AND MATERIALS — PROCESS PRINTS

It is assumed in this section that the student is familiar with the ordinary drawing instruments such as the T-square, triangles, dividers, compasses, and scales, as well as with their use.

ENGINEERING DRAFTING INSTRUMENTS

449. There are several drafting instruments which are used by engineers and surveyors but which are not so generally employed in other kinds of drafting work. The most common of these are described briefly in the following articles.

450. STRAIGHT-EDGE. — Engineering drawings are made with greater accuracy than much of the drafting work of other professions. In fact many engineering drawings are limited in precision only by the eyesight of the draftsman. It is evident, then, that to use a T-square which is run up and down the more or less uneven edge of a drawing board will not produce drawings of sufficient accuracy. For this reason in many classes of engineering work the edge of the drawing board is not relied upon. Furthermore, in most plots of surveying work the lines are not parallel or perpendicular to each other except by chance, but run at any angle which the notes require; and there is therefore not so much call for the use of a T-square as there is in architectural, machine, or structural drawings. Drawings are usually laid out by starting from some straight line drawn on the paper by means of a straight-edge, which is simply a flat piece of steel or wood like the blade of a T-square. Steel straight-edges are more accurate and are more commonly used by engineering draftsmen than the wooden ones, the edges of which are likely to nick or warp and become untrue. They can be obtained of almost any length and of any desired weight, the common length being about 3 ft. Wooden straight-edges and blades of T-squares are made with a celluloid edge about $\frac{1}{4}$ inch wide, which, on account of its transparency, is of great advantage to the draftsman.

451. ENGINEER'S SCALE. — Engineer's plans usually are made on scales of 10, 20, 30, etc. feet to an inch. In the engineer's scale, therefore, the inch is divided into 10, 20, 30, etc. parts, instead of into eighths and sixteenths. Engineer's scales are made 3, 6, 12, 18, and 24 inches long. One form is the flat wooden rule with both edges beveled and a scale marked on each bevel. Some flat rules are beveled on both faces and on both edges of each face, thereby giving four scales on one rule. Still another common form is the triangular scale having six different scales, one on each edge of the three faces. In such rules the scales are usually 20, 30, 40, 50, 60, and 80 ft. or 10, 20, 30, 40, 50, and 60 ft. to an inch. Scales are made having the inch divided into 100 parts, but in plotting a map which is on a scale of 100 ft. to an inch the work is probably done more easily and quite as accurately by using a scale of 10, 20, or 50 divisions to an inch and estimating the fractional part of a division. A 20-ft. or 50-ft. scale is more satisfactory for precision than a 10-ft. scale when it is desired to plot on a scale of 100 ft. to the inch. A plan on a 200-ft. scale is always plotted by using a 20-ft. scale, a 300-ft. plan by using a 30-ft. scale, etc.

A map covering a large area, like that of a state, for example, must be plotted to a very small scale, and this is usually given in the form of a ratio such as 1 to 20 000, 1 to 62 500, etc., meaning that one unit on the map is $\frac{1}{20\,000}$, $\frac{1}{62\,500}$, etc. of the corresponding distance on the ground; this is sometimes called the *natural* or the *fractional** scale. For plotting such maps specially constructed scales with decimal subdivisions are used.

452. PROTRACTOR. — A *protractor* is a graduated arc made of metal, paper, celluloid, or horn, and is used in plotting angles. There are many varieties of protractor, most of them being either circular or semicircular.

453. Semicircular Protractor. — Probably the most common is the semicircular protractor, which is usually divided into de-

---

* Called also the representative fraction, *R.F.*

grees, half-degrees, and sometimes into quarter-degrees. Fig. 191 represents a seimicircular protractor divided into degrees. In plotting an angle with this protractor the bottom line of the

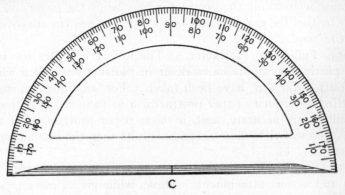

FIG. 191. SEMICIRCULAR PROTRACTOR.

instrument is made to coincide with the line from which the angle is to be laid off, and the center of the protractor, point C, is made to coincide with the point on the line. On the outside of

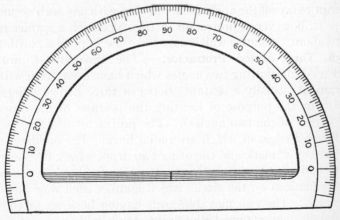

FIG. 192. SEMICIRCULAR PROTRACTOR.

the arc a mark is made on the drawing at the desired reading. The protractor is then removed from the drawing and the line drawn on the plan.

Instead of having the 0° and 180° of the protractor on its lower edge some instruments are made as shown in Fig. 192. This form is claimed by some draftsmen to be more convenient, because in handling the protractor by placing the fingers on the base neither the graduations nor the line on the plan are covered by the hand.

454. Full-Circle Protractor. — The full-circle protractor is of use particularly in stadia work or in plotting any notes where azimuths over 180° have been taken. For such work as stadia plotting an ordinary paper protractor 8 to 12 inches in diameter is sufficiently accurate, and, in fact, paper protractors of this size often will yield more accurate results than the smaller metal ones.

455. Some of the metal protractors are provided with an arm and vernier attachment. These, while giving more precise results, require more time for manipulation, and a plain metal protractor with a diameter of, say, 8 inches will give sufficiently close results for all ordinary work. As a matter of fact a protractor with a vernier reading to minutes can be set much closer than the line can be drawn, and it is therefore a waste of time to attempt to lay off the angles on a drawing with any such accuracy. There is, however, a protractor of this type with a vernier reading to about 5 minutes which may be of use in precise plotting.

456. Three-Armed Protractor. — The three-armed protractor is used for plotting two angles which have been taken with an instrument (usually a sextant) between three known points (in pairs), for the purpose of locating the position of the observer (the vertex of the two angles). The protractor has three arms, the beveled edges of which are radial lines. The middle arm is fixed at the 0° mark and the other two arms, which are movable, can be laid off at any desired angle from the fixed arm by means of the graduations on the circle, which number each way from the fixed arm. The two movable arms having been set at the desired angles and clamped, the protractor is laid on the plan and shifted about until each of the three known points (which have already been plotted on the plan) lies on a beveled edge of one of the three arms of the protractor. When the protractor is in this position its center locates the point desired, which is then marked by a needle point. Only one location of this center point can be obtained except when the three known points lie in the circumference of a circle that passes also through the vertex. In these circumstances the location becomes indeterminate.

457. It is well in purchasing a protractor to test it to see that the center point lies on a straight line between the o° and 180° marks, that the edge of the protractor is the arc of a true circle, and that the graduations are uniform.

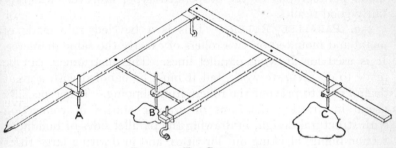

FIG. 193. THE PANTOGRAPH.

458. PANTOGRAPH. — This instrument is composed of several flat pieces of metal or wood joined in such a way as to form a parallelogram. In Fig. 193 the point A is fixed and points B and C are movable. The supports at A and B may be interchangeably fitted with a pencil point or a tracing point. If, in Fig. 193, an enlargement is being made, the tracing point would be at B and the pencil point at C. If a reduction was desired the points would be interchanged. The other bearing points shown in the figure are only for the purpose of supporting the instrument. The two movable points at B and C are so attached to the instrument that they will trace out exactly similar figures. The essential condition is that all three points A, B, and C must lie in a straight line and each point must be on one of the three different sides (or sides produced) of a jointed parallelogram. It is evident then that by changing the relative positions of these points, by moving them up or down the arms of the parallelogram, but always keeping the points on a straight line, the scale of the copy can be made to bear any desired relation to the scale of the original drawing. These instruments are usually provided with scales marked on the arms indicating the proper settings for various reductions or enlargements. The simpler types have reducing and enlarging ratios ranging from 8 : 1 to $1\frac{1}{8}$: 1 or vice versa. The more complicated types have all ratios from 1 : 1 to 1 : 20 or vice versa. Very accurate results cannot as a rule be obtained with a pantograph because there is lost motion in the several joints of the instrument. Some of the expensive metal pantographs of the suspended type, however, will give fairly good results.

459. PARALLEL RULER. — This is a beveled rule made of metal and mounted on two rollers of exactly the same diameter. It is used for drawing parallel lines. This instrument can be made to do accurate work, but it must be handled with a great deal of care to prevent the rollers from slipping. It is especially useful in drafting diagrams of graphic statics in connection with structural design, in drawing the parallel sides of buildings, section lining, blocking out for titles, and in drafting large titles that require mechanical lettering.

460. BEAM COMPASS. — This is an instrument used for drawing the arcs of circles whose radii are longer than can be set out with the ordinary compass drafting instrument. It is composed of a strip of wood or metal with two metal attachments which can be fastened to it. One of these attachments carries a needle point, and the other, which is usually provided with a slow-motion screw for exact settings, carries a pencil or a pen. This instrument is particularly useful in laying out large rectangles such as are called for when surveys are plotted by coördinates (Art. 484, p. 563).

461. CONTOUR PEN. — This pen is constructed very much like an ordinary right-line ruling pen except that it has a metal shaft, running through the entire length of the holder, to which the pen is attached. The shaft revolves inside of the holder, and the pen is so shaped that it drags behind taking a position in the direction in which it is being moved. It is used for drawing irregular curved lines such as contours or shore lines. Not a little practice is required before one can use a pen of this type accurately. When skill in its use is once acquired, however, a plan can be easily made on which the contours all have a uniform weight of line giving a very satisfactory appearance. The purpose of a contour line is to show the facts as to the land surface, and this pen should not be used unless it is found by trial that it does the work in hand properly. Accuracy is more important than appearance.

462. PROPORTIONAL DIVIDERS. — Proportional dividers are virtually an ordinary pair of dividers with both legs prolonged through the pivot-point thereby forming another pair of legs above the pivot. The pivot can be pushed up and down in a slot in the legs and clamped in any desired position, thereby altering the relative lengths of the two pairs of legs. The sliding is accomplished in some dividers by a rack-and-pinion motion. There are marks on the legs showing the proper settings for the pivot so that the space between one pair of points will bear any desired ratio to the space between the other pair. The marks on the legs should not be accepted as correct, but should be tested by actual trial. By means of this instrument a drawing can be enlarged or reduced to a definite scale without the use of the engineer's scale.

462a. The Section Liner. — This is an instrument used for drawing cross-section lines, or hatching lines, which are equidistant and parallel. One kind consists of a triangle which slides in contact with a short straight-edge, the amount of motion being regulated by an adjustable stop. In drawing the lines the triangle and the straight-edge are shifted alternately along the plan. In another kind the ruling edge is on a pivoted arm and by varying the angle between the ruling edge and the straight-edge different spacings of the lines may be obtained. Another type of the movable arm pattern has a device by means of which the spacing of the lines may be made double or treble the usual spacing.

463. RAILROAD CURVES, FRENCH CURVES, FLEXIBLE CURVE, AND SPLINE. — For drawing arcs of curves of long radii, such as occur on railroad plans and on plans of curved streets, in city work, curves made of wood, hard rubber, celluloid, or metal are used; these come in sets of about one hundred, with radii varying from about 2 inches to 300 inches. The metal curves are the most common and are made with the inside and outside edges of the same radii both edges being beveled. When a pencil line is drawn the beveled edges may be used against the paper, and when ink lines are drawn the curve can be turned over so that the beveled edges are up, thus preventing the ink from running in under the curve on the paper. Some curves for railroad work are made with a short straight edge tangent to the curve at one end and with the point where the curve begins marked by a line across it.

464. Irregular curves, called *French Curves*, are of a variety of shapes. They are made of wood, hard rubber, and celluloid, and are used to guide the pencil or pen in tracing out irregular curved lines on the map.

465. A *Flexible Curve* consists of a strip of rubber fastened to a flexible metal back. This curve can be twisted to conform to any irregular curved line on the map and can then be used as a guide against which the pencil or pen is held in tracing out the curve.

466. A *Spline* is a long thin flexible piece of wood, hard rubber, celluloid, or metal which can be bent so as to conform to a curve. It is usually held in position by specially designed weights with light metal arms which fit into a thin groove in the top edge of the spline. This instrument is used by naval architects for drawing long flat irregular curves such as occur in ship designs. In engineering drafting it is used in drawing the lines of arches, which frequently are not circular.

DRAWING PAPERS

467. The drawing papers used by surveyors may be divided into four general classes: (1) those used for plotting plans, (2) tracing paper or tracing cloth which is used for copying drawings, (3) cross-section and profile papers, and (4) process papers.

468. DRAWING PAPER FOR PLANS. — There are numerous grades of drawing paper ranging from very cheap " detail " to heavy paper mounted on cloth, called " mounted paper." For rough plots which are to be copied later or which are for temporary use only, a manila detail paper is frequently used; but where the drawing is to be of a more permanent character a heavy white or manila paper is used. Still more permanent plans, such as the plan of a survey of a city, should be plotted on heavy mounted paper. In order to be satisfactory a paper should have a surface that is not too porous to take ink nicely, and a fiber such that after scratching with a knife or rubbing with an ink eraser, the surface will still take ink effectively. No paper, however, after scratching can be expected to take bottle red ink, which permeates the fiber with extraordinary ease. Another material that has met with favor, and is used in place of mounted paper, is " unprepared blue-print cloth." It is white, very strong and durable, with an exceptionally good surface for drawing with ink, making it particularly good for record drawings.

469. TRACING PAPER AND TRACING CLOTH. — In making copies of drawings, a thin transparent paper called *tracing paper* is often used. It is not tough enough to withstand rough handling and is used only for drawings of a temporary character. There are, however, certain kinds of transparent bond paper in use which will withstand considerable hard usage.

470. For more permanent drawings a *tracing cloth* is used, made of a very uniform quality of linen coated with a preparation to render it transparent. Most tracing cloth as it comes from the manufacturer will not take the ink readily, and it is necessary to rub powdered chalk or talc powder over the entire surface of the cloth before inking the drawing. After the surface chalk is brushed off, the tracing cloth is ready for use. Tracing linen generally has one side glazed and the other dull. Pencil lines can be drawn on the rough side, but the smooth side will not take even a very soft pencil; either side may be used, however, for ink drawings. Some draftsmen prefer to use the glazed side but the dull side is more commonly used. A tracing inked on the glazed side may be tinted on the dull side either by crayons or by a wash; the latter will cockle the cloth unless it is put on quite " dry." It is easier to erase from the glazed than from the dull side, but the dull side will stand more erasing and gives more uniform lines.

Erasure of ink lines from a tracing, as well as from any drawing paper, is a delicate undertaking. Success will result if the following suggestions are observed carefully: with a smooth sharp knife pick off the ink from the paper; this can be done almost without touching the paper. When nearly all of the ink is off, rub the line with a pencil eraser. This will take off the rest of the line except perhaps a few specks of ink which can be removed readily by a sharp knife. This method of erasing takes more time than the ordinary method of rubbing with an ink eraser until the line has disappeared, but it leaves the paper in much better condition to take another line. It is impossible to obtain good results by this method unless the knife has an edge which is both smooth and sharp. Where the surface of the tracing cloth has been damaged the application of a thin coating of collodion on the damaged portion will produce a surface that will take the ink.

In making a tracing of another tracing it will be found that the lines can be seen more readily if a white paper is put under the lower tracing. It frequently happens that it is necessary to make a tracing of a blueprint. The white lines of the blueprint are not easily seen through the tracing linen. An arrangement that will assist greatly in such work is to have a piece of plate glass set into the top at one end of a drawing table in such a way that it forms part of the top of the table. The blueprint is placed over this glass and the light shining through from the under side of the glass and through the blueprint will make the white lines easily visible for copying. An electric light placed beneath the glass will prove satisfactory on dull days or for evening work. This device is also useful for tracing negative photostats or airplane photographs.

It is common practice, after a survey is made and before or during the computation of it, to plot the field-notes accurately on detail paper and later to copy the plot on tracing cloth, which is the final drawing of the survey.

From these tracing drawings any number of process prints can be made, the tracing taking the place of the negative used in photographic printing.   (Arts. 473-4.)

471. CROSS-SECTION AND PROFILE PAPERS. — Paper divided into square inches which, in turn, are divided into small subdivisions is used to plot cross-sections of earthwork and for many other purposes. The inch squares are usually divided into $\frac{1}{5}''$, $\frac{1}{8}''$, $\frac{1}{10}''$, $\frac{1}{12}''$, or $\frac{1}{16}''$. Cross-section paper can also be obtained according to the metric system, or with logarithmic divisions. Cross-section paper usually comes in sheets.

472. *Profile Paper* which, as the name implies, is used for plotting profiles comes in rolls of 10 yds. or more. The vertical divisions are usually much smaller than the horizontal divisions, which makes it easier to plot the elevations accurately. The horizontal distances to be plotted occur mostly at full station points; these are represented on the profile by the vertical rulings on the paper.

Both the cross-section and the profile papers come in colors (usually red, green, blue, orange, or burnt sienna), so that a black or a red ink line (the two most commonly used) will show up distinctly on the paper. These papers can be obtained also of very thin transparent material or in tracing cloth form, suitable for use in making process prints. Profile papers usually come in long rolls 20 inches wide. Special papers and cloth for highway plans are available with profile rulings on the lower half of the sheet only. These conform to the standards of the Bureau of Public Roads and are called " Federal Aid Sheets."

REPRODUCING PLANS

473. Blueprints. — The simplest and cheapest method for reproducing plans from tracings is the blueprint process. In this method light is passed through the tracing onto a sheet of sensitized paper. The light affects the sensitized coating chemically causing it to turn blue after washing. The portions of the sheet that were under the lines and lettering of the plan are shielded from the light and turn white in the washing; the result is a reproduction of the original plan in white on a blue background.

It is possible to make blueprints by hand using a simple frame and sunlight as the light source. The blueprint business is so well organized and wides read, however, that machine-made prints can be readily obtained from concerns specializing in this work. As a rule these machine-made prints will be cheaper and of more reliable quality than can be produced by hand methods.

Even if the job is a long way from the nearest blueprint house, the business can still be handled promptly by mail. Organizations that have much blueprinting to do, usually own and operate their own machines.

Most blueprints are made on paper. They may be made directly upon cloth, if so desired. The advantages of the cloth prints are that they do not shrink so badly as the paper prints and they are more durable. Prints which are to be used on construction work where they are sure to get rough usage are sometimes made on cloth. Both cloth and paper shrink so much, however, that scaled dimensions are unreliable.

Drawings on bond paper or photostats which are too opaque for blueprinting may be rendered transparent by soaking them in a solution of carbon tetrachloride and mineral oil; but this treatment leaves the drawings slightly greasy. They may stain other drawings or papers that come in contact with them, and therefore this process is an expedient rather than recommended practice.

473a. Vandyke Prints. — In order to obtain positive prints (i.e., a white background) by the blueprint process, a Vandyke negative is first made. The tracing is printed with the ink lines in contact with the Vandyke paper. Where the light penetrates the tracing the coating on the Vandyke paper is affected chemically so that after washing and fixing in a solution of hyposulphate of soda the background turns a dark brown and the lines appear white. The Vandyke print is then used as a tracing was used in the blueprint process described above. The light now only penetrates through the white lines producing blue lines on a white background.

One of the advantages of this process is that, as soon as a Vandyke has been made from the tracing, the tracing can be filed away and kept in excellent condition, the Vandyke being used in making all prints. A print of the Vandyke on Vandyke paper gives a permanent reproduction of the original plan in deep brown lines on a white background.

Another advantage of prints from a Vandyke is that additions may be made to the prints in pencil or ink which will show clearly on the white background; this is not true of the ordinary blueprint, on which corrections must be made with a bleaching fluid, colored crayon, or water-color.

In recent years processes have been perfected for producing positive (black lines on white) prints directly as described below. These processes have to a large extent superseded the Vandyke method.

474. Black and White Prints. — Two successful processes have been developed for producing positive prints directly from tracings. One of these processes employs a developing solution without washing, the second method is a dry process employing ammonia fumes as the developing agent. Both of these processes give black lines on a white background and reproduce tracings very closely to scale without the troublesome shrinkage characteristics of blueprints. Prints by these processes have superseded blueprints for many purposes where readability is important. They are subject to fading over a period of years.

475. Reproducing Tracings. — Tracings may be reproduced on sensitized tracing cloth by first making a brown print negative, which is placed over the sensitized cloth and printed by the usual blueprint process. The cloth is given a waterproofing coating so that it is unaffected by the washing process.

Tracings may also be reproduced photographically on a sensitized cloth. By this method, it is possible to reduce the scale of the map, and it is also possible to assemble plans of the same scale into one tracing, likewise material may be blanked out or added to the original tracing merely by placing inserts over the portions to be blanked out or changed. This process is expensive in relation to other processes, but it affords a means for reducing, altering and assembling plans which would be very costly if done by drafting.

There is a process of reproducing tracing cloth drawings on various kinds of material, such as tracing cloth, tracing paper, drawing paper, cardboard, water-color paper, or even on ordinary cotton cloth; this process of reproduction has a trade mark of " Gelitho." These " Gelitho " prints are made from a gelatin plate instead of from an expensive stone necessary in ordinary lithography work. The advantages of this method are that the prints are true to scale. They do not curl as they are not treated with a fixative or waterproofing solution, and as printers' ink is used they make a permanent record. Constant use in making blueprints, or handling in the drafting room does not seem to affect their surface.

476. Photostats. — There is a method of reproducing documents, plans, or pictures, by photography, which has some advantages over other forms of reproduction. This is known as the " Photostat " method. The original drawing does not have to be a transparent material. For this work a special camera is used which contains a roll of prepared sensitized paper. The first print made from a white plan with black lines is in the form of a negative with white lines on a black background. For many purposes these negatives are satisfactory, but if positive prints are desired, the negatives are rephotographed. Photostats of blueprints give black lines on white background directly. By adjusting the camera and lenses, enlargements or reductions can be obtained.

Photostat prints are unreliable for scaling because they shrink so much and so unevenly. It is always advisable to have a graphical scale on the plan that is to be photostated. Then if the reduction or enlargement is not exactly correct, the graphical scale will, nevertheless, fit the plan.

Field-notes that can be released for only a short time can be photostated, even though in pencil lines, and the copy used in the office while the original is sent back into the field. The printing, developing, and fixing of these prints takes but a few minutes.

Plans can be made up from blueprints of several plans pasted together, forming a large compiled map, and then photostated to any desired scale, thus producing at little cost an assembly of several plans. Similarly a photograph can be attached to the face of a drawing before being photostated thus giving a plan and photograph on the single sheet.

The photostat process is rapidly coming into extensive use. It has a wide field of usefulness, because at small cost it gives a faithful copy of any document or plan.

It is illegal to make photostats of certain documents and copyrighted material without first obtaining permission from th owners. Engineers should be cautious not to make such copies without proper authority.

The photostat process may also be used to produce transparent negatives which are printed by the blueprint process giving prints with blue lines on a white background. These negatives are used in much the same way as a Vandyke print. They have certain advantages, however. The original does not have to be transparent, the scale can be changed as desired, and the resulting negative is on heavier paper than the Vandyke and not likely to tear. The prints from transparent negatives are very attractive in appearance and look well in engineering reports.

477. Offset Printing Process. — Where a hundred or more positive prints are required on paper, the offset printing method will prove quick and economical. The original need not be transparent since the plate used for printing is produced photographically. The scale of the plan may be changed as desired. Best results are obtained from ink drawings, although pencil drawings with firm black lines can also be reproduced satisfactorily. There are several large reproduction companies which offer a nation-wide service on the mail-order plan. The offset process has several trade names, such as photo-offset, photolitho, planograph, etc. This method is particularly valuable for reproducing land subdivision plans for use in sales promotion, and also for reducing construction drawings to a scale suitable for binding with specifications.

478. INKS AND WATER-COLORS. — Bottled ink, prepared in various colors, is used extensively on engineering drawings. The so-called " waterproof " inks differ from other inks in that a water-color wash can be put over the lines without causing them to " run." Bottled black inks are quite satisfactory for all drawings. Formerly it was the custom, on work requiring fine, sharp hair-lines, to use India stick ink. This was prepared fresh for each drawing by grinding it with a little water in a saucer made for this purpose. This is rarely or never done at the present time.

While the bottled black inks are fairly well prepared, the red inks are very unsatisfactory. They will sometimes run on paper where only very slight erasures have been made; in fact, on some of the cheaper papers red ink will always run. For tracing purposes red ink is wholly unsatisfactory, as it is impossible to obtain a good reproduction of a red ink line by any of the process prints. Where red lines are needed the use of *scarlet vermilion water-color* will be found to give not only a brilliant red line on the tracing, but also " body " enough in the color so that the lines will print fully as well as the black ink lines. Scarlet vermilion water-color will give much better lines on any paper than the bottled red inks. Only enough water should be used to make the water-color flow well in the pen. Other water-colors are used in the place of the bottled colored inks, such as *Prussian blue* instead of bottled blue ink, or *burnt sienna* instead of brown ink, and these give much better results.

Frequently it is necessary to make additions on blueprints in white, red, or yellow. A white line can be put on easily by using *Chinese white* water-color; but sometimes a bleaching fluid is used, which bleaches out the blue leaving the white paper visible. The best color for a red line on blueprints is scarlet vermilion water-color; and for a yellow line none of the ordinary yellow water-colors gives as brilliant lines as *middle chrome yellow*.

Another satisfactory method of making notes and additions to blueprints is to use a ready-mixed preparation commonly used by artists in making show cards and posters. It is cheaper than water-colors, and is manufactured in a great variety of colors. Although these colors are satisfactory for use on flat drawings, they will crack or crumble if the plan is rolled and unrolled many times.

For tinting drawings, water-colors and dilute inks are used Effective tinting may be done on tracings by using colored pencils on the rough side of the linen.

CHAPTER XVI

METHODS OF PLOTTING*

479. LAYING OUT A PLAN. — Laying out a plan requires careful work. If a good-looking plan is to be obtained this part of the work must be done with not a little judgment. Besides the plan of the survey or property the drawing must have a title, and sometimes notes and a needle to show the direction of the meridian. These must all be arranged so that the entire drawing when completed will have a symmetrical appearance. Often the plot is of such awkward shape that it is difficult to lay out the drawing so that it will look well, and even then the draftsman's artistic instincts are taxed to the utmost to produce a satisfactory result.

480. Scale. — In many cases the scale of the plan as well as the general arrangement of its parts must be chosen by the engineer. Surveys of large extent which do not contain many details, such, for example, as the preliminary survey for a railroad, may be drawn to a scale of 400 ft. to an inch. A plan of a large piece of woodland or a topographical map of a section of a town may be represented on a scale of from 100 ft. to 400 ft. to an inch. A plan of a city lot for a deed is represented on a 20-ft. to 80-ft. scale; and city streets, such as sewer plans and the like, are frequently drawn to a scale of 20 ft. to 40 ft. to an inch. Sometimes on plans of construction work drawings of different scale are made on the same sheet. The drawing for a conduit, for example, may be represented by a general plan on a scale of 80 ft. to an inch, while on the same sheet the conduit may be shown in section on a scale of 4 ft. to an inch.

The field maps of the U. S. Coast and Geodetic Survey are plotted on scales of $\frac{1}{20000}$ or $\frac{1}{10000}$, but some special maps are

---

* For a brief description of different projections for maps of large areas, such as states or counties, see Volume II, Chapter XII.

made on scales as large as $\frac{1}{2000}$. The field maps of the U. S. Geological Survey are plotted to various scales and reduced on the lithograph sheets to $\frac{1}{62500}$ or $\frac{1}{125000}$.

These remarks in regard to scales are not to be considered in any sense as hard and fast rules to govern all conditions. They are suggested simply to give some idea of the existing practice in this matter.

METHODS OF PLOTTING TRAVERSES

481. PLOTTING BY PROTRACTOR AND SCALE. — The most common method of plotting angles is by use of the protractor (Art. 452, p. 542), and of plotting distances, by use of the engineer's scale. Every traverse consists of a series of straight lines and angles, which can be plotted by a protractor in the following manner: First, the survey to be mapped should be sketched out roughly to scale, in order to ascertain its extent and shape so as to decide the size of paper necessary for any given scale of drawing and to determine its general position on the sheet; this will fix the direction of the first line of the traverse, to be used as a starting line for the entire drawing. After this has been done, the first line is drawn in the proper place on the paper, its length is scaled off by using the proper scale, and its two extremities accurately marked by pencil dots or by means of a needle point, and surrounded by a light penciled circle. The line should be drawn so that it will extend beyond the next angle point a distance greater than the radius of the protractor, this extension of line being used when the next angle is laid off with the protractor.

The protractor is placed so that its center is exactly on the second angle point and so that **both** the 0° and 180° marks of the protractor exactly coincide with the line. The traverse angle taken from the field-notes is plotted, the protractor removed, the line drawn, and the length of the second course carefully scaled. Then the protractor is placed along this new line and opposite the third point, the angle at that point is laid off, the next line drawn, and the distance scaled. By this process the entire traverse is plotted.

482. Checks. — On all plotting work, just as on all field-work and computations, frequent checks should be applied to insure accuracy.

If the traverse is a closed traverse the plot, of course, should close on the paper.* If it does not and the error of closure is in a direction parallel to any one of the lines, there is probably a mistake in plotting the length of that line. If there is no indication of this sort the mistake may be either in scaling, in laying off the angles, or in both. In such a case the entire plot should be checked unless there is some reason to think that a certain line may have been laid off at the wrong angle, in which event that questionable angle should be replotted. The bearings of all the lines of the traverse can be computed with reference to the magnetic or to any assumed meridian; any line can be produced to meet the meridian line, and this angle measured and checked. Similarly, the bearing of the last line of a traverse which does not close can be computed and the angle the last line makes with the meridian measured. If it checks the computed angle it is evident that no error has been made in the angles unless mistakes were made that exactly balance each other, which is not probable. In this way, by " cutting into " the drawing here and there, the angular error, if there is one, can be quickly " run down," without laying out all of the angles again and so possibly repeating the mistake that was originally made. The angles measured in applying this check have different values from the ones first laid out, and the chance of repeating the original mistake is thereby eliminated. If no error is found to exist in the angles, the distances should next be checked. This can be done in two ways, and in some drawings both of these checks should be applied.

First, scale each line separately setting down the results independently upon a sheet of paper. After these are all recorded

---

* Instead of plotting every line of the traverse from its preceding line and returning, in the case of a closed traverse, to the beginning of the starting line, it may be well to plot half the traverse from one end of the starting line and the other half from the other end; the check will then come at a point about half-way around the traverse. The advantage of this method lies in the fact that accumulative errors are to some extent avoided since they are carried through only half as many courses.

(and not before), compare the lengths with the lengths of lines as taken from the field-notes. No error should be allowed to pass if it is large enough to be readily plotted by the use of the scale.

Second, take a long straight piece of paper, lay this on the drawing, and mark off the length of the first line on the edge of the paper; then mark off the length of the second line starting from the mark which denotes the end of the first line, and proceed in a similar way to the end of the traverse. Apply the scale to the strip of paper and read the station of each mark; record each of these independently and afterwards compare them with the field-notes. The entire length of line should check within a reasonable amount depending upon the scale; the allowable error can be determined as explained in Art. 23, p. 16.

By checking angles and distances by the above methods errors of any consequence can be avoided; in any case **a draftsman should not allow a drawing to leave his hands which has not been properly checked and is not known to be correct.**

When the traverse is not closed, such checks as have been described above must **always** be applied and also the checks mentioned in the last paragraph of Art. 491, p. 570; otherwise there is no assurance whatever that the plan is correct. It is especially necessary to check the bearings of lines frequently, so that the accumulation of small errors may not become appreciable.

483. Protractor and T-square. — While the ordinary T-square is not much used in plotting engineering plans, there are some occasions where it is convenient to use it. Where a traverse has been run by bearings or by deflection angles the T-square with a shifting head can be conveniently used in connection with a protractor for plotting the angles by bearings.

The paper is fastened to a drawing board having a metal edge which insures one straight edge to the board. A meridian line is drawn on the paper, and the shifting head of the T-square is fastened so that the blade coincides with the meridian line. Then as the T-square is slid up and down the edge of the drawing board its blade always takes a direction parallel to the meridian. By means of the protractor shown in Fig. 192 the bearing of each line can be readily laid off or checked as illustrated by Fig. 194 and the distances laid off with the scale. In order to secure a satisfactory check, the deflection angles should be laid off directly from the previous line, and the bearings checked by means of the T-square and protractor.

It is evident that the bearings of the lines may be computed just as well from any assumed meridian as from the magnetic or true meridian; and that the drawing can be fastened to the board in such a way that the T-square can be conveniently used. This method is especially applicable to compass surveys as it ob-

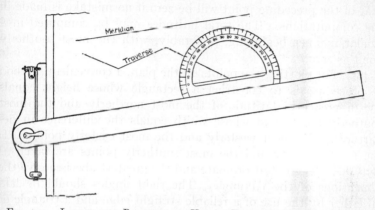

FIG. 194. LAYING OFF BEARINGS BY USE OF T-SQUARE AND PROTRACTOR.

viates the necessity of drawing a new meridian line through each angle point.

This method can be easily applied also as a means of checking any of the angles of a traverse which have been plotted by any of the ordinary methods.

484. PLOTTING BY RECTANGULAR COÖRDINATES. — In plotting by this system all points in the traverse are referred to a pair of coördinate axes. For convenience these axes are often the same as those used in calculating the area enclosed by the traverse. The advantages of this method are, (1) that all measurements are made by means of the scale only and (2) that the plotting may be readily checked.

To plot a survey of a field by rectangular coördinates, first calculate the *total latitude* and the *total departure*, that is, the ordinate and the abscissa, of each point in the survey. If the meridian through the most westerly point and the perpendicular through the most southerly point are chosen as the axes negative signs in the coördinates will be avoided. The coördinates of the transit points are computed by beginning with the most westerly point, whose total departure is zero, and adding successively the departure of each of the courses around the traverse. *East* departures are called *positive* and *West* departures *negative.* The total departure of the starting point as computed from that of the preceding point will be zero if no mistake is made in the computations. The total latitudes may be computed in a similar manner beginning, preferably, with the most southerly point as zero.

485. For plotting the points on the plan, a convenient method of procedure is to construct a rectangle whose height equals the difference in latitude of the most northerly and the most southerly points and whose width equals the difference in departure of the most westerly and the most easterly points. If the most westerly and the most southerly points are taken as zero then the greatest ordinate and the greatest abscissa give the dimensions of the rectangle. The right angles should be laid off either by the use of a reliable straight-edge and a triangle or by the beam compass.

486. The better method, however, is to construct the perpendiculars by means of a straight-edge and a triangle. It is not at all necessary, although it is always desirable, that the triangle shall be accurate. It should be used in the following manner: It is first placed against the straight-edge, as shown by the full lines in Fig. 195, and a point A, marked on the paper Point C is also marked opposite a certain definite part of the triangle. Then the triangle is reversed to the dotted position and brought so that its edge coincides with point A, and then point B is marked opposite point C, as nearly as can be judged A point D is plotted midway between B and C and the line AD is then drawn which is perpendicular to the straight-edge. If the triangle is accurate point B will fall on point C, so that this is a method of testing the accuracy of the right angle of any triangle. If it is found to be inaccurate it should be sent to an instrument maker and be "trued up." A few cents spent in keeping drafting instruments in shape will save hours of time trying to locate small errors, which are often due to the inaccuracy of the instruments used.

If the compass is used the right angle may be laid off by geometric construction. On account of the difficulty of judging the points of intersection of the arcs, very careful work is required to obtain good results with the compass.

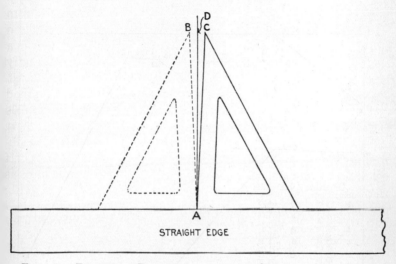

FIG. 195. ERECTING A PERPENDICULAR WITH A STRAIGHT-EDGE AND AN INACCURATE TRIANGLE.

Since the accuracy of all of the subsequent work of a coördinate plot depends upon the accuracy with which the rectangle is constructed, great care should be taken to check this part of the work. The opposite sides of the rectangle should be equal and the two diagonals should be equal, and these conditions should be tested by scaling or with a beam compass before continuing with the plot.

487. After the rectangle has been constructed, all points in the survey can be plotted by use of the scale and straight-edge. To plot any point, lay off its total latitude on both the easterly and the westerly of the two meridian lines of the rectangle, beginning at the southerly line of the rectangle. Draw a line

through both of these points by means of a straight-edge.*
Then lay off along this line the total departure, beginning at the
westerly side of the rectangle, thus obtaining the desired position
of the point.

The computations of the total latitudes and departures and
the method of plotting a traverse by the Coördinate Method are

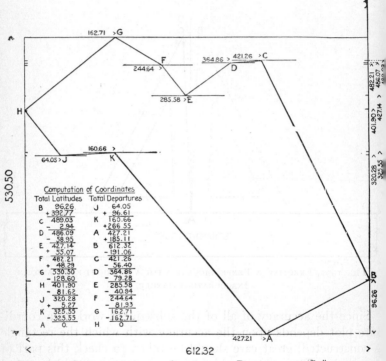

FIG. 196. COMPUTATIONS AND PLOTTING BY RECTANGULAR COÖRDINATES.

shown in Fig. 196. This is the survey which is shown in the
calculations in Fig. 181, p. 517, and in the form of notes in Fig.
52, p. 113.

---

* Accurate work, of course, cannot be obtained with a straight-edge that
not true. A straight-edge can easily be tested by drawing a fine pencil line on th
paper along one edge of the straight-edge; then turn the straight-edge over c
its other side, fit the same edge to the two ends of the pencil line, and see if th
edge coincides with the line.

488. Checks. — When the transit points have been plotted, the scaled distance between consecutive points should equal the distance measured in the field. It sometimes happens that some of the transit lines run so nearly parallel to one of the axes that the distances will scale the right amount even though a mistake has been made in laying off one of the coördinates. If so any appreciable error can be detected by testing the bearings of the lines by means of a protractor. These two tests, together with the scaled distances of any cut-off lines which may have been measured in the field (Art. 145, p. 124), form a good check on the accuracy of the plotting. Since all of the points are plotted independently errors cannot accumulate. If it is found that any scaled distance fails to check with the measured distance it is probable that one of the two adjacent lines will also fail to check and that the point common to the two erroneous lines is in the wrong position.

It should be remembered that everything depends upon the accuracy of the rectangle and that nothing should be plotted until it is certain that the right angles have been laid off accurately.

489. Plotting by rectangular coördinates is the most accurate of all the methods usually employed. For plans of closed traverses, where the latitudes and departures have been computed in connection with the calculation of its area, this coördinate method of plotting is frequently used. It can be applied equally well to a traverse which does not close, but such traverses are usually plotted by the Tangent Method, or the Chord Method, as explained in the following articles.

490. PLOTTING BY TANGENTS. — The traverse should first be plotted approximately on some convenient small scale by use of the protractor and scale, to ascertain its extent and shape. The importance of this little plot is often overlooked, with the result that when the plan is completed it is found to be too close to one edge of the paper or otherwise awkwardly located on the sheet. It takes only a few moments to draw such a sketch, and unless the draftsman is sure of the shape and extent of the plot he should always determine it in some such manner before the plan is started.

The directions of all the lines are referred to some meridian and the bearings determined with an accuracy consistent with the measured angles. From the auxiliary plot it can be decided where to start the first course of the traverse on the paper and in what direction to draw the meridian, so that the lines of the completed traverse will be well balanced with the edges of the sheet, and so that the needle will be pointing, in a general way, toward the top of the drawing rather than toward the bottom.

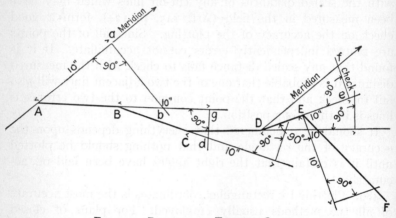

FIG. 197. PLOTTING BY TANGENT OFFSETS.

The bearing of the first line is plotted as follows (Fig. 197): Lay off on the meridian line a length Aa of at least 10 inches and erect a perpendicular at a on the right-hand side of the meridian if the bearing of the first course is east, and on the left-hand side if it is west. Look up in the table of natural functions the tangent of the bearing of the first course and scale off this distance ab on the perpendicular.* Draw Ab which is

---

* These distances and also the 10-inch base-lines are all laid off by use of the engineer's scale. By using the 10-ft. or 100-ft. scale the tangents can be laid off without any computation, whereas with the other scales the tangent must be multiplied by some number, e.g., by 2 if the 20-ft. scale is used, by 3 if the 30-ft. scale is used, etc., taking care in the pointing off.

If it is deemed unnecessary to use a base as long as 10 inches, one can be laid off at the "10" mark on any engineer's scale and the tangent distances laid off by using the same scale, e.g., if a 20-ft. scale is used the "10" mark will give a base-line 5 inches long.

the direction of the first course. On this line scale off AB, the length of the first course. On this line produced lay off Bg equal to 10 inches and erect a perpendicular, scaling off on the perpendicular the length gd equal to the tangent of the **deflection angle** at B. This determines the direction of BC from the first course. The remaining lines of the traverse are plotted in the same manner, using each time the deflection angle.

491. Checks. — Unless the survey is a closed traverse checks must be occasionally applied. Every third or fourth course should be checked by finding the angle between it and the meridian line. This angle should be found by the same method (tangent offset method) and by using a base of 10 inches as in plotting the angles. In checking the course De, for example, a meridian is drawn through D parallel to Aa, De is scaled off 10 inches, and a perpendicular ef erected. The distance ef is scaled and from the table of tangents the angle fDe is obtained. If the angle that the course makes with the meridian line disagrees with the calculated bearing of that course by any large amount, say, 10 minutes of angle or more, the previous courses should be replotted. If the error is less than 10 minutes the course which is being checked should be drawn in the correct direction so that even the slight error discovered may not be carried further along in the plot. Then after the plotting has proceeded for three or four more courses the check is again applied.

The bearings of the lines can be checked by use of the protractor and this will detect errors of any large size, but this method will not disclose small errors; moreover, if it is desired to have the plot, when completed, as accurate as could be expected from the precise method employed, it is entirely inconsistent to check by use of a method far less accurate than the one used in making the plot. For this reason the checks on the direction of the lines are applied with the same care and by the same method as was used in the original layout of the angles.

Occasionally it is more convenient to plot the complement of an angle rather than the angle itself, as was done in plotting the line EF. When doing this the right angle erected at E must be laid off with great care, preferably by the method explained in Art. 486, p. 564.

It is evident that the direction of each course could have been plotted by drawing a meridian line through the transit points and by laying off the **bearings** by the tangent method. But if such a method were used there would be no single check applied that would check all the previous courses; this check is an important feature of the method explained above.

If the traverse is not closed the lengths of the lines of the traverse should **always** be checked by the methods explained in Art. 482, p. 561.

When plotting a traverse which does not close a series of checks may be obtained as follows: compute the coördinates of

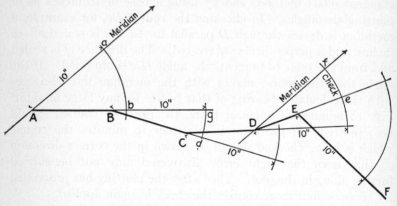

FIG. 198. PLOTTING BY CHORDS.

all of the transit stations, and the length and bearing of the closing line. Plot the initial and final points by coördinates, as well as a few of the intermediate stations. Then plot the traverse by the Tangent Method, checking upon the plotted points as they are reached.

492. PLOTTING BY CHORDS. — This method, which is employed by many draftsmen in plotting traverse lines, is fairly good although probably not so accurate as the Coördinate or so convenient as the Tangent Methods.

Fig. 198 represents the traverse *ABCDEF* which has been plotted by chords. It is the same traverse that is shown in Fig. 197.

On the meridian line the distance Aa is scaled off equal to 10 inches and the arc ab swung from A as a center by use of the ordinary pencil compass. Then from a table of chords* the length of the chord ab is found for the angle aAb. The point b is sometimes located by setting the dividers at the distances ab and with a as a center intersecting the arc ab at b; but the more accurate method is to scale from point a the chord distance and mark the point b on the arc. Then the line Ab is drawn and AB scaled off on it. With B as a center the arc gd is drawn and the chord gd, corresponding to the deflection angle at B, is scaled off. Bd is then drawn and BC scaled off on it. In the same way the entire traverse is plotted.

493. Use of the Sine. — It is evident that the chord

$$ab = 2 \times 10 \times \sin \frac{A}{2} \,;$$

hence, if a table of chords is not available, a table of sines (always easily obtainable) can be used. The sine of half the angle can be taken from the tables and multiplied by 20 mentally. Some draftsmen use the table of sines and a radius of 5 inches to avoid the multiplication. This is not recommended because a base of 5 inches is not long enough to insure an accurate drawing. The necessity of multiplying by 2 can easily be done away with by laying off the radius with a 20-ft. scale and scaling off the sine of the angle with a 10-ft. scale.

With dividers of the ordinary size it is impossible to lay out an arc with a 10-inch radius. Either beam compasses must be used or the radius employed must be shorter, so short, in fact, that it will frequently be better to resort to the Tangent Method.

494. Checks. — Since this method is usually applied to traverses which do not close it is desirable to check every fourth or fifth course so that a mistake will not be carried too far before it is discovered and thereby cause a waste of time. In Fig. 198 it is desired to check the calculated bearing of De. The meridian

---

* Tables of chords can be found in Trautwine's "Civil Engineer's Pocket Book," published by John Wiley & Sons, New York.

Df is drawn through *D* parallel to *Aa*, the arc *fe* is swung with *D* as a center and with a radius of 10 inches, and the chord *ef* is scaled. From the table of chords (or sines) the angle *fDe* (the bearing) can be found. It should agree reasonably well with the calculated bearing. The degree of precision to be expected when plotting by chords is a little less than that suggested for the Tangent Method in Art. 490, unless the beam compass is used. The Tangent Method, especially if the right angles are laid off by reversing the triangle, gives more accurate results than the Chord Method, for the use of the ordinary compass in the Chord Method is a fruitful source of error unless it is handled with the utmost care.

METHOD OF PLOTTING DETAILS

495. BUILDINGS, FENCES, STREAMS, ETC. — The previous articles have dealt with the plotting of the traverse lines only, and these in many instances form merely the skeleton of the final plan. In the field the details of the survey are located from the transit line; and, in a similar manner, the details are located on the plan from the traverse line which has been plotted already.

Buildings, fences, shore-lines, streams, etc. are all plotted by means of the scale for distances and the protractor for the angles. Often a smaller protractor is used for this sort of work than for the traverse lines. This is permissible, for the lines which locate the details are usually short in comparison with the traverse lines and the resulting error is small; furthermore any slight error in the location of a detail will not as a rule affect the rest of the drawing, whereas an error in a transit line will have an effect on all of the rest of the drawing. The plotting of buildings has been taken up in connection with their location. (See Chapter VI.)

In plotting a set of notes where several angles have been taken at one point, such as in stadia surveying, it is well to plot all of the angles first, marking them by number or by their value, and then to plot the distances with the scale.

496. CONTOURS. — Where contours are located by the cross-section method (Art. 331, p. 399), this cross-section system is laid out in soft penciled lines on the drawing. The elevations which were taken are written at their respective points on the plan and then the contours desired are sketched. The ground is assumed to slope uniformly between adjacent elevations, and, by interpolation between these points, the location of the contours on the plan can be made. When the contours have been located, the cross-section lines and elevations are erased unless the plan is intended to be used as a working drawing. As a rule all useful data, such as construction lines and dimensions, are left on a working drawing.

When the contours are located by any other means the principle is the same. The points whose elevations have been determined are plotted by scale and protractor, and the contours are interpolated between the elevations and sketched on the plan.

497. CROSS-SECTIONS. — In plotting on cross-section paper, the rulings of the paper are used as the scale, and all the dimensions of the cross-section, which are to be plotted, are laid off by counting the number of squares on the cross-section paper.

Cross-sections for earthwork computations are plotted to a natural scale of either 10 ft. or 5 ft. to the inch (the latter scale being adopted usually only when the amount of cut or fill is small). These cross-sections should always be plotted **UP** the sheet.

Progress records of construction, such as for a highway or a dam, are often kept by plotting the cross-section at each station and marking on each section in colored ink the progress of the work over certain periods, such as a week or a month. In this way monthly estimates can be readily made, each month being represented by a different color or a different style of line.

Where a series of cross-sections like this are to be plotted the station number and the elevation of the finished grade are recorded just under or over the section. To avoid mistakes in numbering the sections this should be done at the time of plotting the section. The areas of the sections and quantities of earthwork or masonry are usually recorded on the sections, together with any other data which may be of use in calculating volumes.

498. PROFILES. — Profiles are almost always plotted on profile paper, although occasionally they are plotted on the same sheet with the plan so that the two can be readily compared, the plan being shown at the top of the sheet on plain paper and the profile at the bottom on profile paper. Sometimes the plan is placed below the profile.

The profile is intended to show (graphically) relative elevations. In most surveys the differences in elevation are so small in comparison with the horizontal distances that it is necessary to exaggerate the vertical scale of the profile so that the elevations can be read from the profile with a reasonable degree of accuracy. The horizontal scale of the profile should be the same as the scale of the plan, but the vertical scale should be exaggerated, say, 5 to 20 times the horizontal scale, depending upon how close it is desired to read the elevations from the drawing. If the horizontal scale of the profile is 80 ft. to an inch its vertical scale should probably be 20, 10, or 8 ft. to an inch.

499. In plotting any profile the first step is to lay it out properly on the paper, i.e., to decide, from an examination of the range of the elevations, where to start it on the paper so that it will look well when completed, and so that any additions or studies which may be drawn on it subsequently will come within the limits of the paper. Station o of the profile should come on one of the heavy vertical lines at the left of the paper, and the heavy horizontal lines should represent some even elevation such as 100, 125, 150, etc.

The profile is plotted by using the rulings of the profile paper as a scale; it is drawn in pencil first and afterward inked in. It will be found, if these profile papers are carefully measured with a scale, that owing to the shrinkage of the paper the divisions frequently do not scale as long as they should. In plotting a profile or section on such paper no attempt is made to use a scale; the scale of the paper is assumed to be correct and the intermediate points are plotted by estimation, which can almost always be done accurately since the rulings of the paper are quite close together.

The data for a profile of the ground generally consist of levels taken in the field at such points that the ground may be assumed to run straight between adjacent elevations. For this reason, in drawing the profile, the points where the slope of the ground changes should not be rounded off. On the other hand the ground probably does not come to a sharp angle at that point. The profile should be plotted therefore as a series of free-hand straight lines drawn so that the angles are not emphasized. When a profile is made from a contour map, the line should be a smooth, rather than an angular line.

500. Profiles of the surface of the ground are generally made for the purpose of studying some proposed construction which is represented on the profile by a grade line, consisting usually of a series of straight lines. The points where the gradient changes are plotted and connected by straight ruled lines unless the proposed grade should happen to be a vertical curve (Art. 294, p. 346). Vertical lines are also drawn from the bottom of the profile to the grade line at these points. Notes of alignment are recorded at the bottom of the profile as shown in Fig. 198a.

501. "Breaking" the Profile. — When the difference of elevation is such that the profile line, if continued, would run off the top or the bottom of the paper, the profile line may be stopped at some vertical line, preferably a heavy line, and resumed at the same vertical line, say 20 ft. or 50 ft. lower or higher, as the case may require. The numbering of horizontal lines to the right of this point should then be changed to correspond.

502. Checks. — After plotting the surface and grade elevations in pencil, read off from the profile the station and elevation of each point as plotted and record both the station and elevation on a piece of paper. Compare these readings with the data given and make the necessary corrections. Time can be saved if one man reads off the station and elevation from the profile while a second man compares the readings with the note-book. A quick method of **plotting** profiles is to have one man read the notes while the other man plots them, but when the profile is being **checked** this method should not be used; the man, preferably the one who did not do the plotting, should **read from the profile as plotted** and these readings should be compared with the note-book.

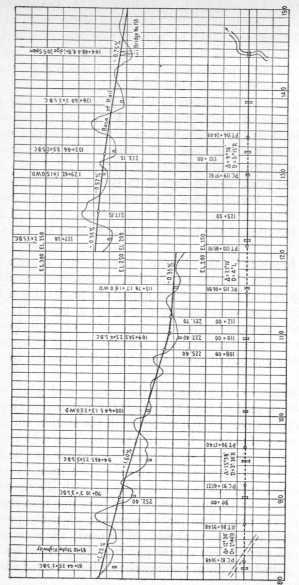

Fig. 198a. Profile of Railway.

PROBLEMS

1. Plot the surveys given in Fig. 50, p. 111, and in Fig. 53, p. 115 by Protractor and Scale, Rectangular Coördinates, Tangents, or Chords.

2. Plot by use of Scale and Protractor the notes given in Fig. 147, p. 409.

CHAPTER XVII

FINISHING AND FILING DRAWINGS*

503. WHAT SHOULD APPEAR ON A DRAWING. — Drawings are made for a great variety of purposes, so that the data which a plan should contain depend entirely upon the use to which it is to be put. There are, however, several important things which should appear on every engineering drawing. In the first place, it should have a complete title, and this should be a brief description of the drawing. The title should state whether the drawing is a plan, cross-section, profile, etc.; what it represents — a lot of land, a sewer, a railroad, etc.; the name of the owner; the place; the date; the scale; and the name of the surveyor and his address. Besides the title, some plans, such as land plans, always require the names of owners of abutting property, and a meridian (needle). Notes are frequently added giving such information as is necessary to interpret the plan. All essential dimensions are lettered in their proper places.

Besides these it is well to insert in some inconspicuous place (preferably near the border) the number of the note-book and the page from which the notes were plotted, and also the initials of the draftsman who made the drawing and of the man who checked it.

Fig. 199 represents a land plan which contains all of the essentials; it is a plot of the land shown in the form of notes in Fig. 52, p. 113; its computations are on p. 517; and its working plot is illustrated by Fig. 196, p. 566.

504. TRAVERSE LINES. — The convenient use of a plan sometimes requires the traverse line to be shown on the completed drawing. It is usually shown as a full colored line, each of the angle points being represented by a very small circle of the

---

* For methods of finishing topographic and hydrographic maps see Volume II, Chapter XIII.

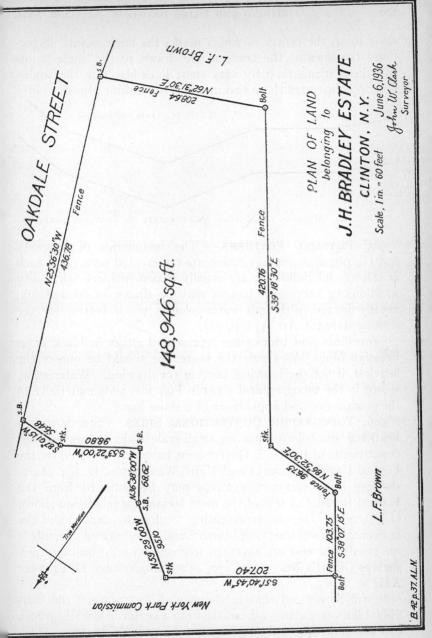

FIG. 199. COMPLETED LAND PLAN.
(Scale of Reduced Drawing, 1 inch = 120 feet.)

same color, the center of which marks the angle point. Sometimes the lines of the traverse are drawn to the angle points
and these are marked by very short lines bisecting the angles.
Fig. 200 illustrates these two methods of marking transit points.

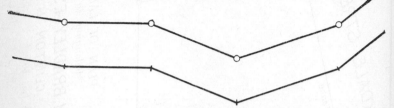

Fig. 200.   Methods of Making Angle Points on Traverse Lines.

505. Physical Features. — The boundaries of property
and the physical features which are represented on a plan, such
as streets and buildings, are usually drawn in black ink. Any
additions or proposed changes may be drawn in colored ink,
usually in red, although water-color is much better, for the
reasons stated in Art. 478, p. 555.

Shore lines and brooks are represented either in black or in
Prussian blue. As a rule the shore line should be one of the
heaviest, if not the heaviest line, on the drawing. Waterlining,
shown in the topographical signs in Fig. 201, adds materially to
the prominence and appearance of a shore line.

506. Topographic Conventional Signs. — Standard conventional symbols for use on small-scale maps by the various
departments of the U. S. Government have been adopted by the
Federal Board of Surveys and Maps, Washington, D. C.; charts
showing these standard symbols may be obtained from the
Federal Board. A few of the more common symbols are shown
in Fig. 201. The one representing " cultivated land " and the
horizontal lines of the " salt marsh " and " fresh marsh " symbols
are ruled; the rest are executed freehand with an ordinary pen
such as Gillott's No. 303 or 170. (See also Volume II, Chapter
XIII.)

It will be noticed that in the symbol for " grass " the individual lines of a group all radiate from a center below the group,
and also that they end on a horizontal line at the bottom. This

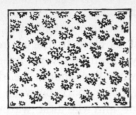

DECIDUOUS TREES (OAK).

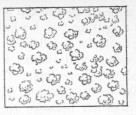

DECIDUOUS TREES (ROUND LEAF.)

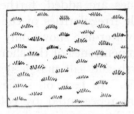

GRASS.

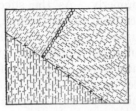

CULTIVATED LAND.

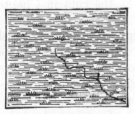

FRESH MARSH.

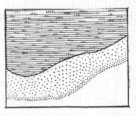

SALT MARSH — SAND.

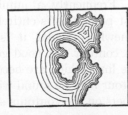

WATERLINING.

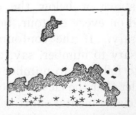

LEDGES — EVERGREEN TREES.

FIG. 201. TOPOGRAPHIC CONVENTIONAL SIGNS.

horizontal line, in the " grass " or " marsh " symbols, should always be **parallel to the bottom of the map.**

In executing " water-lining " the first line outside the shore line should be a full line drawn just as close to the shore line as possible, and should follow very carefully every irregularity of the shore line. The next water-line should be drawn parallel to the first but with a little more space between them than was left between the shore line and the first water-line. Then the third water-line should be spaced a little farther out, and so on; five to ten lines are sufficient to represent this symbol properly. As the successive lines are added, farther and farther from the shore line, the little irregularities of the shore gradually disappear until the outer water-line shows only a few irregularities opposite the most prominent ones of the shore.

Water-lining, as well as fresh marsh and salt marsh symbols, is often represented in Prussian blue. In fact, on some topographic maps most of the signs are represented by colors — the trees by green, the grass by a light green tint, water by a light blue tint, cultivated land by yellow ochre, and so on.

Contour lines (shown in several of the cuts in Chapter XI) are almost always drawn in burnt sienna water-color. Every fifth or tenth contour is usually represented by a line slightly heavier and also a little darker in color. Gillott's No. 303 pen will be found to give good results for this work; but a contour pen, if it can be handled well, will give very uniform lines especially where the contours have no sharp turns. In numbering the contours some prefer to break the lines and place the numbers in the spaces, while others prefer to place the numbers just above or below the contours. Frequently a number is placed on every contour, but for most plans this is entirely unnecessary. If the contours are somewhat regular it is only necessary to number, say, every fifth contour. A good general rule to follow is to number only those lines which are necessary in order that the elevation of any contour may be found without appreciable mental effort. The numbers on the contours should be small plain figures in burnt sienna.

The shape of the surface of the ground is sometimes represented by hachure lines, which are illustrated in Fig. 202. The contour lines are first sketched in pencil as a guide to the drafts-man in drawing the hachure lines, which should be drawn normal to the contours. The short lines are drawn from the summit downward in rows, each row just touching the next preceding row. The steepness of the slope is repre-sented by the weight and length of the lines — the steeper the slope the heavier and shorter the lines. The individual lines are equally spaced, but on the flat slopes where the lines are lighter they have the appearance of being spaced farther apart.

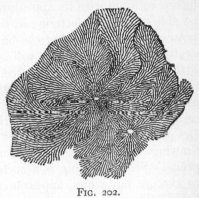

FIG. 202.

507. Such physical features as railroads, highways, buildings,

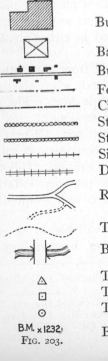

Building. (On large scale maps.)

Barn or Shed. (On large scale maps.)

Buildings. (On small scale maps.)

Fence.

City or Town Boundary.

Stone Wall.

Stone Retaining Wall.

Single Track Railroad.

Double Track Railroad.

Roads.

Trail.

Bridge.

△   Triangulation Station.
□   Transit Stadia Station.
⊙   Transit-and-Tape Traverse Point. Inter-
        section Point (In Triangulation.)
B.M. x 1232,   Bench Mark.
FIG. 203.

and boundaries are usually represented in black ink by the symbols shown in Fig. 203.

508. LETTERING.* — The lettering on a drawing probably has more to do with its appearance than any other feature. To be able to do good lettering at first is a gift which but few men possess. It is an art that can be acquired by the most awkward draftsman, however, if he will study it carefully and devote a little time to systematic practice.

Several different styles of lettering are shown in Figs. 204 and 205. The general style to use in any given case depends on the kind of drawing and on the use to which it is to be put. On plans which are to be sent from the office as completed drawings such letters as the Roman or Gothic may be appropriate. Stump writing is a style of lettering which is difficult to execute but whose appearance, when well done, is very artistic. The ornate lettering in vogue a few years ago has been superseded by simpler styles, which require much less time to produce. For construction drawings, like a plan of a bridge or a conduit, for example, the Reinhardt letters are much used. The title of such a plan looks well lettered in either erect or inclined Gothic.

All plans should be lettered so as to read from the bottom. Unless a draftsman exercises care he will find, when the plan is completed, that some of the lettering is upside down. Fig. 206 illustrates the proper lettering of lines of various slopes.

For fine lettering, No. 604 Gillott is a good pen. It may be a little too fine the first day or two but it soon wears down to about the right condition and stays in that condition. Gillott's No. 303 is a little finer pen but is adapted to the finest lettering usually required. No. 170 is still finer; it is well adapted to double stroke work, such as Roman letters.

For heavier lines, ball-point pens are available in several sizes, and are used for single stroke lettering, but one has to

---

* For a complete discussion and illustrations of lettering see any of the following publications: " Technic of Mechanical Drafting," by Charles W. Reinhardt, published by the Engineering News Publishing Company; " Technical Drawing, " by Giesecke, Mitchell and Spencer, published by The Macmillan Co.; French's " Engineering Drawing," published by McGraw-Hill Book Co.

ROMAN

ABCDEFGHIJKLMNOPQRSTU
VWXYZ&
abcdefghijklmnopqrstuvwxyz

GOTHIC

ABCDEFGHIJKLMNOPQRSTU
VWXYZ&
abcdefghijklmnopqrstuvwxyz

1234567890 $\frac{1}{2}\frac{3}{4}\frac{7}{8}$

Stump Writing

ABCDEFGHIJKLMNOPQRSTUVWXYZ
abcdefghijklmnopqrstuvwxyz

1234567890 $\frac{1}{2}\frac{3}{4}$ *1234567890 $\frac{1}{2}\frac{3}{4}\frac{7}{8}$*

Fig. 204.

(Printed by permission of Professor A. E. Burton.)

ABCDEFGHIJKLMNOPQRSTUVWXYZ
abcdefghijklmnopqrstuvwxyz
1234567890 $\frac{1}{2}$ $\frac{3}{8}$

Reinhardt's Style

ABCDEFGHIJK LMNOPQ
RSTUVWXYZ&
abcdefghijklmnopqrstuvwxyz
1234567890 $\frac{1}{2}$ $\frac{1}{4}$ $\frac{5}{32}$ $2\frac{3}{16}$ $5\frac{1}{8}$ 1234567890 $\frac{1}{8}$ $9\frac{3}{4}$ $\frac{7}{8}$

ABCDEFGHIJKLMNOPQRS
TUVWXYZ&
abcdefghijklmnopqrstuvwxyz

Fig. 391.

be expert to make such letters as *P* and *F* with a ball-point pen without blotting the upper left-hand corner of the letter.

There is a set of patent pens called Paysant pens and numbered according to their fineness; the higher the number the finer the pen. The No. 6 or No. 7 Paysant pen is about right for such lettering as appears in " Notes " on plans; No. 4 and No. 5 are adapted to lettering of titles. It requires a little knack to use a Paysant pen, but it is a knack which is readily acquired.

The appearance of freehand lettering is entirely dependent upon the skill and experience of the letterer. Many ingenious

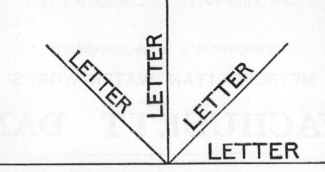

FIG. 206. LETTERING ON SLOPES.

and helpful mechanical instruments have been devised to aid in lettering; one of these is a lettering guide consisting of a strip of highly seasoned, transparent, green Pyralin, perforated with various openings which are so shaped that when the point of the lettering pen is moved in contact with the sides, the letters of the alphabet, or numerals, are formed. The center portion of the guide is grooved on the under side so as to provide ample clearance to prevent the ink from being smeared when the guide is moved from one character to another. The pens are tubular in shape, and resemble a pencil with the round points varying in five sizes. The flow of ink to the point is regulated by raising or lowering the pen plunger. Lettering guides usually come in sets of different sizes, and can be used to produce solid lettering of several weights, and also open lettering and shadow lettering. Draftsmen who cannot letter well free-hand can produce a neat

Plan of Land
belonging to

James O. Farrington

Somerville....Mass.

Scale, 1 in. = 40 ft.   January 8, 1923

COMMONWEALTH OF MASSACHUSETTS

METROPOLITAN WATER WORKS

WACHUSETT DAM

UPPER GATE-CHAMBER

JULY 9 1900

UNITED STATES
COAST AND GEODETIC SURVEY

SKETCH OF GENERAL PROGRESS

JUNE 30 1897

Eastern Sheet

Fig. 207. Titles of Plans.

TRACK ELEVATION.
C. & W. I. R. R.
Cross-Section of Bridge Showing
Floor Construction.
Scale $\frac{1}{2}$ in. = 1 ft.

HORIZONTAL SECTIONS

| THROUGH UPPER SLUICE-GATE | THROUGH LOWER SLUICE-GATE | THROUGH LOWER VALVE WELL |

0 1 2 3 4 5 6 FT.

Preliminary Profile
for a Railroad from
Redford Junction to North Liberty
Sta. 0 to Sta. 498+68.7
May 1906

FIG. 208. TITLES OF PLANS AND PROFILES.

looking plan with the aid of the guides. The disadvantage of
the guides is that the size and spacing of the letters cannot be

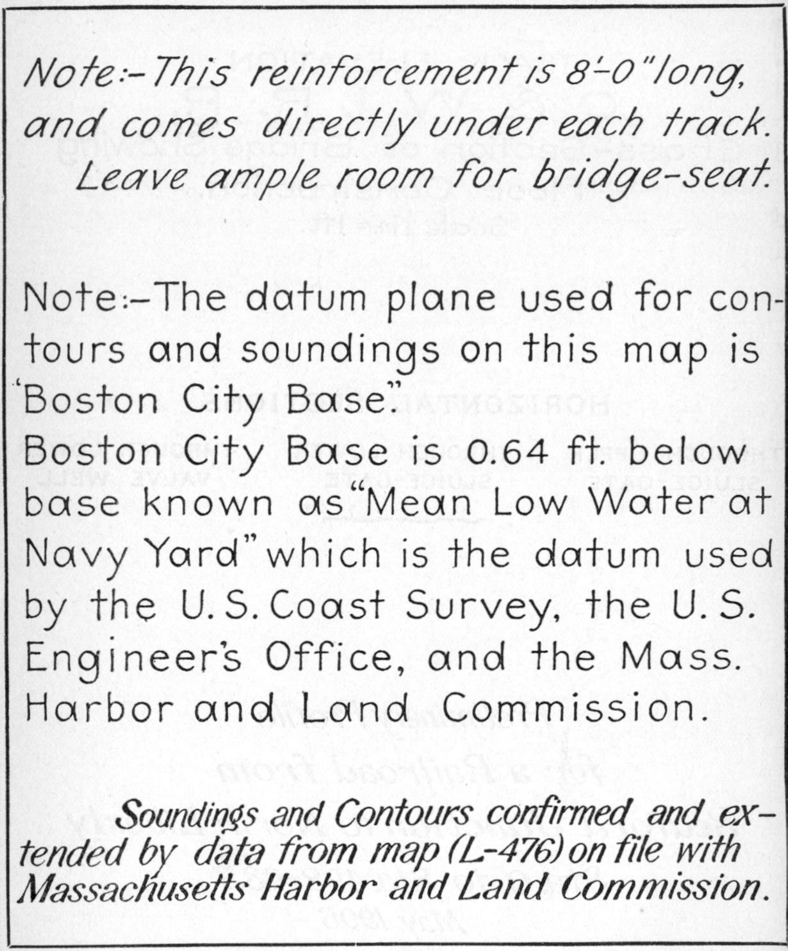

---

*Note:-This reinforcement is 8'-0" long,
and comes directly under each track.
Leave ample room for bridge-seat.*

Note:-The datum plane used for con-
tours and soundings on this map is
'Boston City Base.'
Boston City Base is 0.64 ft. below
base known as "Mean Low Water at
Navy Yard" which is the datum used
by the U. S. Coast Survey, the U. S.
Engineer's Office, and the Mass.
Harbor and Land Commission.

*Soundings and Contours confirmed and ex-
tended by data from map (L-476) on file with
Massachusetts Harbor and Land Commission.*

Fig. 209. Samples of Notes.

readily adjusted to the space available for lettering on the plan.
A good draftsman can do faster and just as presentable lettering
free-hand.

509. Titles. — The design of the title of a plan gives the draftsman an opportunity to exercise good taste. It should be so arranged and the size of the letters so chosen that the most important part of the title strikes the eye first. In general, each line of lettering should be centered, and the spacing between the lines should be so arranged that no part will either appear crowded or seem to be floating away from the rest of the title. The general outline of the title should be pleasing to the eye.

Where a number of sheets are used covering the same work, it is cheaper to have the title set up in type and stamped on. This also applies to notes on construction plans that appear on each sheet.

Fig. 207 shows a set of titles which are well balanced and complete. Fig. 208 shows the style of lettering appropriate for a profile, a cross-section, or construction details.

510. Notes. — Most drawings require notes of some sort. These are usually executed with a plain letter like the Reinhardt alphabet. In Fig. 209 are a few samples the general style of which is consistent with modern practice.

510a. Colors on Plans. — In this chapter the use of colors on plans is recommended; such as red for transit lines or grade lines on a profile, and blue for shore lines. Colors may also be used effectively on construction plans to emphasize new work, or on land taking plans to designate the parcels of land required for a project. If such plans are to be reproduced, however, it should be remembered that the colors will not be distinguishable on the prints. Red lines print as black; other colors, such as blue, print with less intensity than black. Therefore the colored lines should be of such weight or convention that they will convey their meaning on the reproduction. In some cases where the colors are essential and there are not many copies, the colors may be added to the prints in crayon or water-color.

511. Border Lines. — The border line of a drawing should consist of a heavy single line or of double lines closely spaced. It should neither be so heavy nor of such fancy design as to be conspicuous. Plain clear drawings are the practice of today, and the border line should be in keeping with the rest of the drawing. For drawings 2 ft. long, the border should be about $\frac{3}{4}''$ from the edge of the sheet: for drawings 4 ft. long, $1''$ to $1\frac{1}{4}''$ looks well.

The border line is unnecessary on office drawings; the tendency at present is toward the omission of the border line.

512. Meridians. — On all land plans it is customary to draw either the true or the magnetic meridian; often both of them are represented. To be in keeping with the rest of the drawing this should be simple in design. Too frequently, however, the draftsman attempts to "lay himself out" on the needle with the result that it is so large and ornate that it is the first thing in the drawing that strikes the eye. The simple meridians shown in Fig. 211 are suggested as suitable for ordinary land plans.

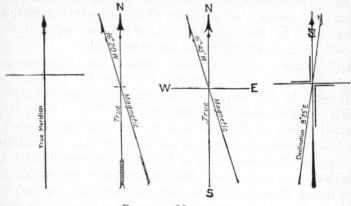

FIG. 211. MERIDIANS.

The plan should always be drawn, if possible, so that the meridian will point, in general, toward the top of the drawing rather than toward the bottom. Sometimes it is drawn with its upper part above and its tail below the drawing. The line of the meridian must never cut any of the lines of the drawings: it should be interrupted far enough from the drawing so that it cannot be mistaken for one of the property lines.

513. Scales. — On account of the shrinkage of drawing paper the scale is sometimes drawn on the plan itself **at the time that the drawing is plotted.** It is well to have it sufficiently long, say, 3 to 10 inches (depending upon the size of the drawing), so that it will be of use in detecting the amount of shrinkage. This, of course, will determine the shrinkage only in the direction of the scale. These scales are usually placed directly under the title or in one of the lower corners. Fig. 212 gives two examples of scales.

In plotting a coördinate survey, the intersections of the north and south with the east and west lines should be marked on the finished drawing, as these are of great assistance in plotting additions. Moreover the distances between these points give a reliable measure of the change in scale of the map (at that place and in that direction) due to shrinkage of paper.

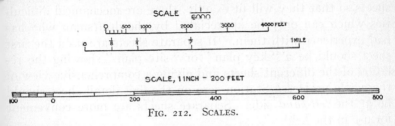

FIG. 212. SCALES.

514. SHRINKAGE OF DRAWING PAPERS. — All of the papers in use will shrink and swell more or less with variations of weather conditions. The heavy mounted papers are affected the least, but large drawings even on such paper will be found on examination to change in size perceptibly. The fact that they do not always shrink the same amount in different directions makes it difficult to estimate the amount of the change and to allow for it. This effect can be estimated quite closely, however, by testing the drawing by measuring accurately a few lines running in different directions **when it is plotted** and scaling the same lines at any other time and making allowance for the change. Scaled distances on tracing cloth are quite unreliable if it is not kept in a dry place, and blue-prints generally shrink in washing so that scale measurements taken from them usually contain large errors.

515. MAPS OF LARGE EXTENT. — Some maps, like the location map of a railroad or the map of a city, are so large that they must be made in sections. Two slightly different methods are employed for their construction. One method is to plot the several sheets so that the drawing on one will extend to but not include any of the drawing on the adjacent sheet, the limits of the drawings being defined by straight lines.   The other method is to have the drawing on each sheet lap over the drawings on the adjacent sheets a little.   Marks are made on all drawings which make it possible to fit them to the corresponding marks on the adjacent drawings when they are being assembled.

In attempting to arrange the sheets of adjacent drawings after they have been in use for a long time, it is often found that they do not fit well on account of the unequal shrinking and swelling of the paper.   Moreover, in plotting lines on separate sheets so that they will fit exactly, there are mechanical difficulties which can only be appreciated by the draftsman who has had experience with them.   If separate sheets are used the first sheet should be a " key plan " or " site plan " showing the relation of the different sheets and giving a comprehensive view of the whole project.   Station zero on the first detail sheet should be at the *left-hand* side.   Separate sheets are more convenient for use in the field.

516. INKING IN A PROFILE. — The surface line is usually shown as a full firm black line and the grade line as a full red line (Art. 478, p. 555).   The gradients are lettered in red on the grade line (Fig. 198a).   A horizontal base-line is sometimes drawn in red a short distance above the bottom of the paper and vertical red lines are drawn from this line to the grade line at every change of gradient and at both ends of the profile.   On these vertical lines are recorded the grade elevations at these points and the " plus " if the place where the gradient changes is not at a full station.   The gradients are sometimes lettered on the base-line instead of on the grade line.   The notes of alignment are recorded on the base-line, and under these the stations are marked at every heavy vertical ruling of the profile paper.

Information, such as the names of streets and brooks, is lettered vertically above the profile and at the proper station.   A title and the scale are sometimes placed on the face of the profile; sometimes these are put on the back of the profile at one end of it (or both in the case of a long profile), so that the title can be read when it is rolled up.

517. CLEANING DRAWINGS. — Every drawing, during its construction, collects more or less dirt.   Often construction lines are drawn which must be erased when the plan is completed. In cleaning a drawing an ordinary soft pencil eraser or art-gum is used for the pencil lines while a sponge eraser or stale bread crumbs will remove the dirt satisfactorily without affecting the ink lines.

To take off the pencil lines and dirt from tracing cloth, wash the drawing with a cloth saturated with gasoline or benzine. This will remove pencil lines entirely and will clean the tracing perfectly without any injurious effect on the tracing cloth. Care must be taken, if the titles or notes are stamped in printer's ink, not to rub them with gasolene or benzine, as they will be eradicated like pencil lines, leaving only the impression of the type.

518. FILING DRAWINGS. — While the particular method of filing plans varies considerably in different offices, there are a few general ideas carried out by all drafting offices in regard to the preservation as well as the systematic filing of drawings. There is no doubt that the best method of filing plans is to keep them flat, but this is not practicable with large plans, which must usually be filed rolled. In all systems of plan filing there appears to be a proper use of both flat and rolled plans.

In large offices plans are, as a rule, made in several standard sizes prescribed by the rules of the office, and are filed flat in shallow drawers built to fit the different sizes of drawings. In some offices the adherence to standard sizes is very rigid, and time is often spent to bring drawings within the limits of one of these sizes. When these sizes are exceeded the plans are either made in sections of standard size, as explained in Art. 515, or they are made as large plans which are rolled and filed away in pasteboard tubes. Sometimes very large plans are filed flat by hanging them from an overhead frame.

Plans filed flat are marked each with its proper index number in one corner, preferably the lower right-hand corner, so that as the drawer is opened the numbers can be readily examined. In some offices it is required that in returning a drawing it shall be placed in its proper order in the drawer as well as in the proper drawer, while in other offices the plan drawers are made very shallow, so as to contain only about 15 or 20 drawings, and when a plan is returned no attempt is made to put it in any particular place in the drawer, there being, at the most, only a very few drawings to handle to obtain the one desired.

Rolled drawings are marked on the side of the rolls at each end so as to be easily read by one standing in front of the shelf on which the plans are stored. Another style of roll is closed at one end with a white label on the outside of the closed end. When the plan has been put into the tube it is so placed on the shelf that the label on which the plan number is marked is at the front edge of the shelf where it can be read conveniently. When the plan is in use the empty tube is left on the shelf with its open end outward so that its number is in the back part of the shelf where it cannot be read.

Large plans which are made in sections are often filed in large folios or books in such a way that they can be taken out readily and used separately.

519. INDEXING DRAWINGS. — There are so many systems of indexing plans that no attempt will be made to explain them other than to suggest a few of the essentials of any good system. Every system of numbering the plans should be such that one can tell from its number whether the drawing is a sketch, a working drawing, a finished drawing, a tracing, or a process print. The numbering also should suggest the kind of drawing, as a land plan, or a construction plan, and the project.

For offices where few plans are on file an index book may suffice for recording the plans, but in large drafting offices the card catalogue system is used extensively. By a judicious use of " markers " a card catalogue system can be so devised that it will be necessary to examine only a few very cards to find the one corresponding to any plan. Frequently it is necessary to index a plan by two or three different cards under different general headings. Never refer back to another card when indexing plans, but give the location of drawing on every index card

520. FILING NOTE-BOOKS. — Note-books should always be filed in vaults where they will be protected against fire. Too frequently through lack of forethought note-books containing information which has cost thousands of dollars to collect are carelessly filed on a shelf in the drafting office. In some offices the rules require that every note-book and valuable plan shall be placed in the vault at the end of the day's work, and this appears to be the proper practice.

Some offices go so far as to require that all notes shall be copied in ink and the original notes kept permanently filed in the vault to guard against their loss. Whether a copy is made or not, the **original** should be preserved as it has a value, in a lawsuit for instance, which any **copy** does not possess. When copies are made of the original notes they are sometimes made by the photostat process and kept in a loose-leaf book so that if any notes are taken from the office it is not necessary to take more than a very few leaves of the copy; the original notes never go from the office except in rare cases.

521. Indexing Notes. — The notes contained in the field note-books are often indexed either in a book for this purpose or by means of a card catalogue. The method of indexing is similar to that used for plans.

522. Other Records. — Other records, such as borings, soundings, estimates, computations, etc., are carefully filed and indexed so that it will be easy to refer to them.

... the result that every ... packet and ... that one ...
... the hand of the person ... if he has a week to look ...
... things to be done properly.

... copies or go to the letter box in the hall and ... it ...
... sorted and given in such ... time permits all of it to be ...
... the result of doing this. Whether a copy is made or
not, the original should be filed; ... as it has a copy made ...
... be used for indexing, which the copy does not possess. With
... made on hand of the original notes they are continuous and ...
by the ordinary process, and kept in a box that looks so that
... one page at one time for which alike is not near any to take
... than a week in having the copy; the other may possibly be
... use in the office except in rare cases.

647. **Indexing Notes.** — The card index when the tool not
... case often indexed either in a book or the purpose of an
index. A card catalogue ... the method of indexing is useful
in the tool for pins.

648. **Other Records.** — Other records, such as bottling, coil
and estimating computations etc., are carefully filed and indexed
so that ... will be easy to refer to them.

TABLES

TABLE I.—LOGARITHMS OF NUMBERS.

N	0	1	2	3	4	5	6	7	8	9
100	00000	00043	00087	00130	00173	00217	00260	00303	00346	00389
1	0432	0475	0518	0561	0604	0647	0689	0732	0775	0817
2	0860	0903	0945	0988	1030	1072	1115	1157	1199	1242
3	1284	1326	1368	1410	1452	1494	1536	1578	1620	1662
4	1703	1745	1787	1828	1870	1912	1953	1995	2036	2078
5	2119	2160	2202	2243	2284	2325	2366	2407	2449	2490
6	2531	2572	2612	2653	2694	2735	2776	2816	2857	2898
7	2938	2979	3019	3060	3100	3141	3181	3222	3262	3302
8	3342	3383	3423	3463	3503	3543	3583	3623	3663	3703
9	3743	3782	3822	3862	3902	3941	3981	4021	4060	4100
110	04139	04179	04218	04258	04297	04336	04376	04415	04454	04493
1	4532	4571	4610	4650	4689	4727	4766	4805	4844	4883
2	4922	4961	4999	5038	5077	5115	5154	5192	5231	5269
3	5308	5346	5385	5423	5461	5500	5538	5576	5614	5652
4	5690	5729	5767	5805	5843	5881	5918	5956	5994	6032
5	6070	6108	6145	6183	6221	6258	6296	6333	6371	6408
6	6446	6483	6521	6558	6595	6633	6670	6707	6744	6781
7	6819	6856	6893	6930	6967	7004	7041	7078	7115	7151
8	7188	7225	7262	7298	7335	7372	7408	7445	7482	7518
9	7555	7591	7628	7664	7700	7737	7773	7809	7846	7882
120	07918	07954	07990	08027	08063	08099	08135	08171	08207	08243
1	8279	8314	8350	8386	8422	8458	8493	8529	8565	8600
2	8636	8672	8707	8743	8778	8814	8849	8884	8920	8955
3	8991	9026	9061	9096	9132	9167	9202	9237	9272	9307
4	9342	9377	9412	9447	9482	9517	9552	9587	9621	9656
5	9691	9726	9760	9795	9830	9864	9899	9934	9968	10003
6	10037	10072	10106	10140	10175	10209	10243	10278	10312	10346
7	0380	0415	0449	0483	0517	0551	0585	0619	0653	0687
8	0721	0755	0789	0823	0857	0890	0924	0958	0992	1025
9	1059	1093	1126	1160	1193	1227	1261	1294	1327	1361
130	11394	11428	11461	11494	11528	11561	11594	11628	11661	11694
1	1727	1760	1793	1826	1860	1893	1926	1959	1992	2024
2	2057	2090	2123	2156	2189	2222	2254	2287	2320	2352
3	2385	2418	2450	2483	2516	2548	2581	2613	2646	2678
4	2710	2743	2775	2808	2840	2872	2905	2937	2969	3001
5	3033	3066	3098	3130	3162	3194	3226	3258	3290	3322
6	3354	3386	3418	3450	3481	3513	3545	3577	3609	3640
7	3672	3704	3735	3767	3799	3830	3862	3893	3925	3956
8	3988	4019	4051	4082	4114	4145	4176	4208	4239	4270
9	4301	4333	4364	4395	4426	4457	4489	4520	4551	4582
140	14613	14644	14675	14706	14737	14768	14799	14829	14860	14891
1	4922	4953	4983	5014	5045	5076	5106	5137	5168	5198
2	5229	5259	5290	5320	5351	5381	5412	5442	5473	5503
3	5534	5564	5594	5625	5655	5685	5715	5746	5776	5806
4	5836	5866	5897	5927	5957	5987	6017	6047	6077	6107
5	6137	6167	6197	6227	6256	6286	6316	6346	6376	6406
6	6435	6465	6495	6524	6554	6584	6613	6643	6673	6702
7	6732	6761	6791	6820	6850	6879	6909	6938	6967	6997
8	7026	7056	7085	7114	7143	7173	7202	7231	7260	7289
9	7319	7348	7377	7406	7435	7464	7493	7522	7551	7580
150	17609	17638	17667	17696	17725	17754	17782	17811	17840	17869

TABLE I.—LOGARITHMS OF NUMBERS.

N	0	1	2	3	4	5	6	7	8	9
150	17609	17638	17667	17696	17725	17754	17782	17811	17840	17869
1	7898	7926	7955	7984	8013	8041	8070	8099	8127	8156
2	8184	8213	8241	8270	8298	8327	8355	8384	8412	8441
3	8469	8498	8526	8554	8583	8611	8639	8667	8696	8724
4	8752	8780	8808	8837	8865	8893	8921	8949	8977	9005
5	9033	9061	9089	9117	9145	9173	9201	9229	9257	9285
6	9312	9340	9368	9396	9424	9451	9479	9507	9535	9562
7	9590	9618	9645	9673	9700	9728	9756	9783	9811	9838
8	9866	9893	9921	9948	9976	20003	20030	20058	20085	20112
9	20140	20167	20194	20222	20249	0276	0303	0330	0358	0385
160	20412	20439	20466	20493	20520	20548	20575	20602	20629	20656
1	0683	0710	0737	0763	0790	0817	0844	0871	0898	0925
2	0952	0978	1005	1032	1059	1085	1112	1139	1165	1192
3	1219	1245	1272	1299	1325	1352	1378	1405	1431	1458
4	1484	1511	1537	1564	1590	1617	1643	1669	1696	1722
5	1748	1775	1801	1827	1854	1880	1906	1932	1958	1985
6	2011	2037	2063	2089	2115	2141	2167	2194	2220	2246
7	2272	2298	2324	2350	2376	2401	2427	2453	2479	2505
8	2531	2557	2583	2608	2634	2660	2686	2712	2737	2763
9	2789	2814	2840	2866	2891	2917	2943	2968	2994	3019
170	23045	23070	23096	23121	23147	23172	23198	23223	23240	23274
1	3300	3325	3350	3376	3401	3426	3452	3477	3502	3528
2	3553	3578	3603	3629	3654	3679	3704	3729	3754	3779
3	3805	3830	3855	3880	3905	3930	3955	3980	4005	4030
4	4055	4080	4105	4130	4155	4180	4204	4229	4254	4279
5	4304	4329	4353	4378	4403	4428	4452	4477	4502	4527
6	4551	4576	4601	4625	4650	4674	4699	4724	4748	4773
7	4797	4822	4846	4871	4895	4920	4944	4969	4993	5018
8	5042	5066	5091	5115	5139	5164	5188	5212	5237	5261
9	5285	5310	5334	5358	5382	5406	5431	5455	5479	5503
180	25527	25551	25575	25600	25624	25648	25672	25696	25720	25744
1	5768	5792	5816	5840	5864	5888	5912	5935	5959	5983
2	6007	6031	6055	6079	6102	6126	6150	6174	6198	6221
3	6245	6269	6293	6316	6340	6364	6387	6411	6435	6458
4	6482	6505	6529	6553	6576	6600	6623	6647	6670	6694
5	6717	6741	6764	6788	6811	6834	6858	6881	6905	6928
6	6951	6975	6998	7021	7045	7068	7091	7114	7138	7161
7	7184	7207	7231	7254	7277	7300	7323	7346	7370	7393
8	7416	7439	7462	7485	7508	7531	7554	7577	7600	7623
9	7646	7669	7692	7715	7738	7761	7784	7807	7830	7852
190	27875	27898	27921	27944	27967	27989	28012	28035	28058	28081
1	8103	8126	8149	8171	8194	8217	8240	8262	8285	8307
2	8330	8353	8375	8398	8421	8443	8466	8488	8511	8533
3	8556	8578	8601	8623	8646	8668	8691	8713	8735	8758
4	8780	8803	8825	8847	8870	8892	8914	8937	8959	8981
5	9003	9026	9048	9070	9092	9115	9137	9159	9181	9203
6	9226	9248	9270	9292	9314	9336	9358	9380	9403	9425
7	9447	9469	9491	9513	9535	9557	9579	9601	9623	9645
8	9667	9688	9710	9732	9754	9776	9798	9820	9842	9863
9	9885	9907	9929	9951	9973	9994	30016	30038	30060	30081
200	30103	30125	30146	30168	30190	30211	30233	30255	30276	30298

TABLE I.—LOGARITHMS OF NUMBERS.

N	0	1	2	3	4	5	6	7	8	9
200	30103	30125	30146	30168	30190	30211	30233	30255	30276	30298
1	0320	0341	0363	0384	0406	0428	0449	0471	0492	0514
2	0535	0557	0578	0600	0621	0643	0664	0685	0707	0728
3	0750	0771	0792	0814	0835	0856	0878	0899	0920	0942
4	0963	0984	1006	1027	1048	1069	1091	1112	1133	1154
5	1175	1197	1218	1239	1260	1281	1302	1323	1345	1366
6	1387	1408	1429	1450	1471	1492	1513	1534	1555	1576
7	1597	1618	1639	1660	1681	1702	1723	1744	1765	1785
8	1806	1827	1848	1869	1890	1911	1931	1952	1973	1994
9	2015	2035	2056	2077	2098	2118	2139	2160	2181	2201
210	32222	32243	32263	32284	32305	32325	32346	32366	32387	32408
1	2428	2449	2469	2490	2510	2531	2552	2572	2593	2613
2	2634	2654	2675	2695	2715	2736	2756	2777	2797	2818
3	2838	2858	2879	2899	2919	2940	2960	2980	3001	3021
4	3041	3062	3082	3102	3122	3143	3163	3183	3203	3224
5	3244	3264	3284	3304	3325	3345	3365	3385	3405	3425
6	3445	3465	3486	3506	3526	3546	3566	3586	3606	3626
7	3646	3666	3686	3706	3726	3746	3766	3786	3806	3826
8	3846	3866	3885	3905	3925	3945	3965	3985	4005	4025
9	4044	4064	4084	4104	4124	4143	4163	4183	4203	4223
220	34242	34262	34282	34301	34321	34341	34361	34380	34400	34420
1	4439	4459	4479	4498	4518	4537	4557	4577	4596	4616
2	4635	4655	4674	4694	4713	4733	4753	4772	4792	4811
3	4830	4850	4869	4889	4908	4928	4947	4967	4986	5005
4	5025	5044	5064	5083	5102	5122	5141	5160	5180	5199
5	5218	5238	5257	5276	5295	5315	5334	5353	5372	5392
6	5411	5430	5449	5468	5488	5507	5526	5545	5564	5583
7	5603	5622	5641	5660	5679	5698	5717	5736	5755	5774
8	5793	5813	5832	5851	5870	5889	5908	5927	5946	5965
9	5984	6003	6021	6040	6059	6078	6097	6116	6135	6154
230	36173	36192	36211	36229	36248	36267	36286	36305	36324	36342
1	6361	6380	6399	6418	6436	6455	6474	6493	6511	6530
2	6549	6568	6586	6605	6624	6642	6661	6680	6698	6717
3	6736	6754	6773	6791	6810	6829	6847	6866	6884	6903
4	6922	6940	6959	6977	6996	7014	7033	7051	7070	7088
5	7107	7125	7144	7162	7181	7199	7218	7236	7254	7273
6	7291	7310	7328	7346	7365	7383	7401	7420	7438	7457
7	7475	7493	7511	7530	7548	7566	7585	7603	7621	7639
8	7658	7676	7694	7712	7731	7749	7767	7785	7803	7822
9	7840	7858	7876	7894	7912	7931	7949	7967	7985	8003
240	38021	38039	38057	38075	38093	38112	38130	38148	38166	38184
1	8202	8220	8238	8256	8274	8292	8310	8328	8346	8364
2	8382	8399	8417	8435	8453	8471	8489	8507	8525	8543
3	8561	8578	8596	8614	8632	8650	8668	8686	8703	8721
4	8739	8757	8775	8792	8810	8828	8846	8863	8881	8899
5	8917	8934	8952	8970	8987	9005	9023	9041	9058	9076
6	9094	9111	9129	9146	9164	9182	9199	9217	9235	9252
7	9270	9287	9305	9322	9340	9358	9375	9393	9410	9428
8	9445	9463	9480	9498	9515	9533	9550	9568	9585	9602
9	9620	9637	9655	9672	9690	9707	9724	9742	9759	9777
250	39794	39811	39829	39846	39863	39881	39898	39915	39933	39950

TABLE I.—LOGARITHMS OF NUMBERS.

N	0	1	2	3	4	5	6	7	8	9
250	39794	39811	39829	39846	39863	39881	39898	39915	39933	39950
1	9967	9985	40002	40019	40037	40054	40071	40088	40106	40123
2	40140	40157	0175	0192	0209	0226	0243	0261	0278	0295
3	0312	0329	0346	0364	0381	0398	0415	0432	0449	0466
4	0483	0500	0518	0535	0552	0569	0586	0603	0620	0637
5	0654	0671	0688	0705	0722	0739	0756	0773	0790	0807
6	0824	0841	0858	0875	0892	0909	0926	0943	0960	0976
7	0993	1010	1027	1044	1061	1078	1095	1111	1128	1145
8	1162	1179	1196	1212	1229	1246	1263	1280	1296	1313
9	1330	1347	1363	1380	1397	1414	1430	1447	1464	1481
260	41497	41514	41531	41547	41564	41581	41597	41614	41631	41647
1	1664	1681	1697	1714	1731	1747	1764	1780	1797	1814
2	1830	1847	1863	1880	1896	1913	1929	1946	1963	1979
3	1996	2012	2029	2045	2062	2078	2095	2111	2127	2144
4	2160	2177	2193	2210	2226	2243	2259	2275	2292	2308
5	2325	2341	2357	2374	2390	2406	2423	2439	2455	2472
6	2488	2504	2521	2537	2553	2570	2586	2602	2619	2635
7	2651	2667	2684	2700	2716	2732	2749	2765	2781	2797
8	2813	2830	2846	2862	2878	2894	2911	2927	2943	2959
9	2975	2991	3008	3024	3040	3056	3072	3088	3104	3120
270	43136	43152	43169	43185	43201	43217	43233	43249	43265	43281
1	3297	3313	3329	3345	3361	3377	3393	3409	3425	3441
2	3457	3473	3489	3505	3521	3537	3553	3569	3584	3600
3	3616	3632	3648	3664	3680	3696	3712	3727	3743	3759
4	3775	3791	3807	3823	3838	3854	3870	3886	3902	3917
5	3933	3949	3965	3981	3996	4012	4028	4044	4059	4075
6	4091	4107	4122	4138	4154	4170	4185	4201	4217	4232
7	4248	4264	4279	4295	4311	4326	4342	4358	4373	4389
8	4404	4420	4436	4451	4467	4483	4498	4514	4529	4545
9	4560	4576	4592	4607	4623	4638	4654	4669	4685	4700
280	44716	44731	44747	44762	44778	44793	44809	44824	44840	44855
1	4871	4886	4902	4917	4932	4948	4963	4979	4994	5010
2	5025	5040	5056	5071	5086	5102	5117	5133	5148	5163
3	5179	5194	5209	5225	5240	5255	5271	5286	5301	5317
4	5332	5347	5362	5378	5393	5408	5423	5439	5454	5469
5	5484	5500	5515	5530	5545	5561	5576	5591	5606	5621
6	5637	5652	5667	5682	5697	5712	5728	5743	5758	5773
7	5788	5803	5818	5834	5849	5864	5879	5894	5909	5924
8	5939	5954	5969	5984	6000	6015	6030	6045	6060	6075
9	6090	6105	6120	6135	6150	6165	6180	6195	6210	6225
290	46240	46255	46270	46285	46300	46315	46330	46345	46359	46374
1	6389	6404	6419	6434	6449	6464	6479	6494	6509	6523
2	6538	6553	6568	6583	6598	6613	6627	6642	6657	6672
3	6687	6702	6716	6731	6746	6761	6776	6790	6805	6820
4	6835	6850	6864	6879	6894	6909	6923	6938	6953	6967
5	6982	6997	7012	7026	7041	7056	7070	7085	7100	7114
6	7129	7144	7159	7173	7188	7202	7217	7232	7246	7261
7	7276	7290	7305	7319	7334	7349	7363	7378	7392	7407
8	7422	7436	7451	7465	7480	7494	7509	7524	7538	7553
9	7567	7582	7596	7611	7625	7640	7654	7669	7683	7698
300	47712	47727	47741	47756	47770	47784	47799	47813	47828	47842

TABLE I.—LOGARITHMS OF NUMBERS.

N	0	1	2	3	4	5	6	7	8	9
300	47712	47727	47741	47756	47770	47784	47799	47813	47828	47842
1	7857	7871	7885	7900	7914	7929	7943	7958	7972	7986
2	8001	8015	8029	8044	8058	8073	8087	8101	8116	8130
3	8144	8159	8173	8187	8202	8216	8230	8244	8259	8273
4	8287	8302	8316	8330	8344	8359	8373	8387	8401	8416
5	8430	8444	8458	8473	8487	8501	8515	8530	8544	8558
6	8572	8586	8601	8615	8629	8643	8657	8671	8686	8700
7	8714	8728	8742	8756	8770	8785	8799	8813	8827	8841
8	8855	8869	8883	8897	8911	8926	8940	8954	8968	8982
9	8996	9010	9024	9038	9052	9066	9080	9094	9108	9122
310	49136	49150	49164	49178	49192	49206	49220	49234	49248	49262
1	9276	9290	9304	9318	9332	9346	9360	9374	9388	9402
2	9415	9429	9443	9457	9471	9485	9499	9513	9527	9541
3	9554	9568	9582	9596	9610	9624	9638	9651	9665	9679
4	9693	9707	9721	9734	9748	9762	9776	9790	9803	9817
5	9831	9845	9859	9872	9886	9900	9914	9927	9941	9955
6	9969	9982	9996	50010	50024	50037	50051	50065	50079	50092
7	50106	50120	50133	0147	0161	0174	0188	0202	0215	0229
8	0243	0256	0270	0284	0297	0311	0325	0338	0352	0365
9	0379	0393	0406	0420	0433	0447	0461	0474	0488	0501
320	50515	50529	50542	50556	50569	50583	50596	50610	50623	50637
1	0651	0664	0678	0691	0705	0718	0732	0745	0759	0772
2	0786	0799	0813	0826	0840	0853	0866	0880	0893	0907
3	0920	0934	0947	0961	0974	0987	1001	1014	1028	1041
4	1055	1068	1081	1095	1108	1121	1135	1148	1162	1175
5	1188	1202	1215	1228	1242	1255	1268	1282	1295	1308
6	1322	1335	1348	1362	1375	1388	1402	1415	1428	1441
7	1455	1468	1481	1495	1508	1521	1534	1548	1561	1574
8	1587	1601	1614	1627	1640	1654	1667	1680	1693	1706
9	1720	1733	1746	1759	1772	1786	1799	1812	1825	1838
330	51851	51865	51878	51891	51904	51917	51930	51943	51957	51970
1	1983	1996	2009	2022	2035	2048	2061	2075	2088	2101
2	2114	2127	2140	2153	2166	2179	2192	2205	2218	2231
3	2244	2257	2270	2284	2297	2310	2323	2336	2349	2362
4	2375	2388	2401	2414	2427	2440	2453	2466	2479	2492
5	2504	2517	2530	2543	2556	2569	2582	2595	2608	2621
6	2634	2647	2660	2673	2686	2699	2711	2724	2737	2750
7	2763	2776	2789	2802	2815	2827	2840	2853	2866	2879
8	2892	2905	2917	2930	2943	2956	2969	2982	2994	3007
9	3020	3033	3046	3058	3071	3084	3097	3110	3122	3135
340	53148	53161	53173	53186	53199	53212	53224	53237	53250	53263
1	3275	3288	3301	3314	3326	3339	3352	3364	3377	3390
2	3403	3415	3428	3441	3453	3466	3479	3491	3504	3517
3	3529	3542	3555	3567	3580	3593	3605	3618	3631	3643
4	3656	3668	3681	3694	3706	3719	3732	3744	3757	3769
5	3782	3794	3807	3820	3832	3845	3857	3870	3882	3895
6	3908	3920	3933	3945	3958	3970	3983	3995	4008	4020
7	4033	4045	4058	4070	4083	4095	4108	4120	4133	4145
8	4158	4170	4183	4195	4208	4220	4233	4245	4258	4270
9	4283	4295	4307	4320	4332	4345	4357	4370	4382	4394
350	54407	54419	54432	54444	54456	54469	54481	54494	54506	54518

TABLE I.—LOGARITHMS. OF NUMBERS.

N	0	1	2	3	4	5	6	7	8	9
350	54407	54419	54432	54444	54456	54469	54481	54494	54506	54518
1	4531	4543	4555	4568	4580	4593	4605	4617	4630	4642
2	4654	4667	4679	4691	4704	4716	4728	4741	4753	4765
3	4777	4790	4802	4814	4827	4839	4851	4864	4876	4888
4	4900	4913	4925	4937	4949	4962	4974	4986	4998	5011
5	5023	5035	5047	5060	5072	5084	5096	5108	5121	5133
6	5145	5157	5169	5182	5194	5206	5218	5230	5242	5255
7	5267	5279	5291	5303	5315	5328	5340	5352	5364	5376
8	5388	5400	5413	5425	5437	5449	5461	5473	5485	5497
9	5509	5522	5534	5546	5558	5570	5582	5594	5606	5618
360	55630	55642	55654	55666	55678	55691	55703	55715	55727	55739
1	5751	5763	5775	5787	5799	5811	5823	5835	5847	5859
2	5871	5883	5895	5907	5919	5931	5943	5955	5967	5979
3	5991	6003	6015	6027	6038	6050	6062	6074	6086	6098
4	6110	6122	6134	6146	6158	6170	6182	6194	6205	6217
5	6229	6241	6253	6265	6277	6289	6301	6312	6324	6336
6	6348	6360	6372	6384	6396	6407	6419	6431	6443	6455
7	6467	6478	6490	6502	6514	6526	6538	6549	6561	6573
8	6585	6597	6608	6620	6632	6644	6656	6667	6679	6691
9	6703	6714	6726	6738	6750	6761	6773	6785	6797	6808
370	56820	56832	56844	56855	56867	56879	56891	56902	56914	56926
1	6937	6949	6961	6972	6984	6996	7008	7019	7031	7043
2	7054	7066	7078	7089	7101	7113	7124	7136	7148	7159
3	7171	7183	7194	7206	7217	7229	7241	7252	7264	7276
4	7287	7299	7310	7322	7334	7345	7357	7368	7380	7392
5	7403	7415	7426	7438	7449	7461	7473	7484	7496	7507
6	7519	7530	7542	7553	7565	7576	7588	7600	7611	7623
7	7634	7646	7657	7669	7680	7692	7703	7715	7726	7738
8	7749	7761	7772	7784	7795	7807	7818	7830	7841	7852
9	7864	7875	7887	7898	7910	7921	7933	7944	7955	7967
380	57978	57990	58001	58013	58024	58035	58047	58058	58070	58081
1	8092	8104	8115	8127	8138	8149	8161	8172	8184	8195
2	8206	8218	8229	8240	8252	8263	8274	8286	8297	8309
3	8320	8331	8343	8354	8365	8377	8388	8399	8410	8422
4	8433	8444	8456	8467	8478	8490	8501	8512	8524	8535
5	8546	8557	8569	8580	8591	8602	8614	8625	8636	8647
6	8659	8670	8681	8692	8704	8715	8726	8737	8749	8760
7	8771	8782	8794	8805	8816	8827	8838	8850	8861	8872
8	8883	8894	8906	8917	8928	8939	8950	8961	8973	8984
9	8995	9006	9017	9028	9040	9051	9062	9073	9084	9095
390	59106	59118	59129	59140	59151	59162	59173	59184	59195	59207
1	9218	9229	9240	9251	9262	9273	9284	9295	9306	9318
2	9329	9340	9351	9362	9373	9384	9395	9406	9417	9428
3	9439	9450	9461	9472	9483	9494	9506	9517	9528	9539
4	9550	9561	9572	9583	9594	9605	9616	9627	9638	9649
5	9660	9671	9682	9693	9704	9715	9726	9737	9748	9759
6	9770	9780	9791	9802	9813	9824	9835	9846	9857	9868
7	9879	9890	9901	9912	9923	9934	9945	9956	9966	9977
8	9988	9999	60010	60021	60032	60043	60054	60065	60076	60086
9	60097	60108	0119	0130	0141	0152	0163	0173	0184	0195
400	60206	60217	60228	60239	60249	60260	60271	60282	60293	60304

TABLE I.—LOGARITHMS OF NUMBERS.

N	0	1	2	3	4	5	6	7	8	9
400	60206	60217	60228	60239	60249	60260	60271	60282	60293	60304
1	0314	0325	0336	0347	0358	0369	0379	0390	0401	0412
2	0423	0433	0444	0455	0466	0477	0487	0498	0509	0520
3	0531	0541	0552	0563	0574	0584	0595	0606	0617	0627
4	0638	0649	0660	0670	0681	0692	0703	0713	0724	0735
5	0746	0756	0767	0778	0788	0799	0810	0821	0831	0842
6	0853	0863	0874	0885	0895	0906	0917	0927	0938	0949
7	0959	0970	0981	0991	1002	1013	1023	1034	1045	1055
8	1066	1077	1087	1098	1109	1119	1130	1140	1151	1162
9	1172	1183	1194	1204	1215	1225	1236	1247	1257	1268
410	61278	61289	61300	61310	61321	61331	61342	61352	61363	61374
1	1384	1395	1405	1416	1426	1437	1448	1458	1469	1479
2	1490	1500	1511	1521	1532	1542	1553	1563	1574	1584
3	1595	1606	1616	1627	1637	1648	1658	1669	1679	1690
4	1700	1711	1721	1731	1742	1752	1763	1773	1784	1794
5	1805	1815	1826	1836	1847	1857	1868	1878	1888	1899
6	1909	1920	1930	1941	1951	1962	1972	1982	1993	2003
7	2014	2024	2034	2045	2055	2066	2076	2086	2097	2107
8	2118	2128	2138	2149	2159	2170	2180	2190	2201	2211
9	2221	2232	2242	2252	2263	2273	2284	2294	2304	2315
420	62325	62335	62346	62356	62366	62377	62387	62397	62408	62418
1	2428	2439	2449	2459	2469	2480	2490	2500	2511	2521
2	2531	2542	2552	2562	2572	2583	2593	2603	2613	2624
3	2634	2644	2655	2665	2675	2685	2696	2706	2716	2726
4	2737	2747	2757	2767	2778	2788	2798	2808	2818	2829
5	2839	2849	2859	2870	2880	2890	2900	2910	2921	2931
6	2941	2951	2961	2972	2982	2992	3002	3012	3022	3033
7	3043	3053	3063	3073	3083	3094	3104	3114	3124	3134
8	3144	3155	3165	3175	3185	3195	3205	3215	3225	3236
9	3246	3256	3266	3276	3286	3296	3306	3317	3327	3337
430	63347	63357	63367	63377	63387	63397	63407	63417	63428	63438
1	3448	3458	3468	3478	3488	3498	3508	3518	3528	3538
2	3548	3558	3568	3579	3589	3599	3609	3619	3629	3639
3	3649	3659	3669	3679	3689	3699	3709	3719	3729	3739
4	3749	3759	3769	3779	3789	3799	3809	3819	3829	3839
5	3849	3859	3869	3879	3889	3899	3909	3919	3929	3939
6	3949	3959	3969	3979	3988	3998	4008	4018	4028	4038
7	4048	4058	4068	4078	4088	4098	4108	4118	4128	4137
8	4147	4157	4167	4177	4187	4197	4207	4217	4227	4237
9	4246	4256	4266	4276	4286	4296	4306	4316	4326	4335
440	64345	64355	64365	64375	64385	64395	64404	64414	64424	64434
1	4444	4454	4464	4473	4483	4493	4503	4513	4523	4532
2	4542	4552	4562	4572	4582	4591	4601	4611	4621	4631
3	4640	4650	4660	4670	4680	4689	4699	4709	4719	4729
4	4738	4748	4758	4768	4777	4787	4797	4807	4816	4826
5	4836	4846	4856	4865	4875	4885	4895	4904	4914	4924
6	4933	4943	4953	4963	4972	4982	4992	5002	5011	5021
7	5031	5040	5050	5060	5070	5079	5089	5099	5108	5118
8	5128	5137	5147	5157	5167	5176	5186	5196	5205	5215
9	5225	5234	5244	5254	5263	5273	5283	5292	5302	5312
450	65321	65331	65341	65350	65360	65369	65379	65389	65398	65408

TABLE I.—LOGARITHMS OF NUMBERS.

N	0	1	2	3	4	5	6	7	8	9
450	65321	65331	65341	65350	65360	65369	65379	65389	65398	65408
1	5418	5427	5437	5447	5456	5466	5475	5485	5495	5504
2	5514	5523	5533	5543	5552	5562	5571	5581	5591	5600
3	5610	5619	5629	5639	5648	5658	5667	5677	5686	5696
4	5706	5715	5725	5734	5744	5753	5763	5772	5782	5792
5	5801	5811	5820	5830	5839	5849	5858	5868	5877	5887
6	5896	5906	5916	5925	5935	5944	5954	5963	5973	5982
7	5992	6001	6011	6020	6030	6039	6049	6058	6068	6077
8	6087	6096	6106	6115	6124	6134	6143	6153	6162	6172
9	6181	6191	6200	6210	6219	6229	6238	6247	6257	6266
460	66276	66285	66295	66304	66314	66323	66332	66342	66351	66361
1	6370	6380	6389	6398	6408	6417	6427	6436	6445	6455
2	6464	6474	6483	6492	6502	6511	6521	6530	6539	6549
3	6558	6567	6577	6586	6596	6605	6614	6624	6633	6642
4	6652	6661	6671	6680	6689	6699	6708	6717	6727	6736
5	6745	6755	6764	6773	6783	6792	6801	6811	6820	6829
6	6839	6848	6857	6867	6876	6885	6894	6904	6913	6922
7	6932	6941	6950	6960	6969	6978	6987	6997	7006	7015
8	7025	7034	7043	7052	7062	7071	7080	7089	7099	7108
9	7117	7127	7136	7145	7154	7164	7173	7182	7191	7201
470	67210	67219	67228	67237	67247	67256	67265	67274	67284	67293
1	7302	7311	7321	7330	7339	7348	7357	7367	7376	7385
2	7394	7403	7413	7422	7431	7440	7449	7459	7468	7477
3	7486	7495	7504	7514	7523	7532	7541	7550	7560	7569
4	7578	7587	7596	7605	7614	7624	7633	7642	7651	7660
5	7669	7679	7688	7697	7706	7715	7724	7733	7742	7752
6	7761	7770	7779	7788	7797	7806	7815	7825	7834	7843
7	7852	7861	7870	7879	7888	7897	7906	7916	7925	7934
8	7943	7952	7961	7970	7979	7988	7997	8006	8015	8024
9	8034	8043	8052	8061	8070	8079	8088	8097	8106	8115
480	68124	68133	68142	68151	68160	68169	68178	68187	68196	68205
1	8215	8224	8233	8242	8251	8260	8269	8278	8287	8296
2	8305	8314	8323	8332	8341	8350	8359	8368	8377	8386
3	8395	8404	8413	8422	8431	8440	8449	8458	8467	8476
4	8485	8494	8502	8511	8520	8529	8538	8547	8556	8565
5	8574	8583	8592	8601	8610	8619	8628	8637	8646	8655
6	8664	8673	8681	8690	8699	8708	8717	8726	8735	8744
7	8753	8762	8771	8780	8789	8797	8806	8815	8824	8833
8	8842	8851	8860	8869	8878	8886	8895	8904	8913	8922
9	8931	8940	8949	8958	8966	8975	8984	8993	9002	9011
490	69020	69028	69037	69046	69055	69064	69073	69082	69090	69099
1	9108	9117	9126	9135	9144	9152	9161	9170	9179	9188
2	9197	9205	9214	9223	9232	9241	9249	9258	9267	9276
3	9285	9294	9302	9311	9320	9329	9338	9346	9355	9364
4	9373	9381	9390	9399	9408	9417	9425	9434	9443	9452
5	9461	9469	9478	9487	9496	9504	9513	9522	9531	9539
6	9548	9557	9566	9574	9583	9592	9601	9609	9618	9627
7	9636	9644	9653	9662	9671	9679	9688	9697	9705	9714
8	9723	9732	9740	9749	9758	9767	9775	9784	9793	9801
9	9810	9819	9827	9836	9845	9854	9862	9871	9880	9888
500	69897	69906	69914	69923	69932	69940	69949	69958	69966	69975

TABLE I.—LOGARITHMS OF NUMBERS.

N	0	1	2	3	4	5	6	7	8	9
500	69897	69906	69914	69923	69932	69940	69949	69958	69966	69975
1	9984	9992	70001	70010	70018	70027	70036	70044	70053	70062
2	70070	70079	0088	0096	0105	0114	0122	0131	0140	0148
3	0157	0165	0174	0183	0191	0200	0209	0217	0226	0234
4	0243	0252	0260	0269	0278	0286	0295	0303	0312	0321
5	0329	0338	0346	0355	0364	0372	0381	0389	0398	0406
6	0415	0424	0432	0441	0449	0458	0467	0475	0484	0492
7	0501	0509	0518	0526	0535	0544	0552	0561	0569	0578
8	0586	0595	0603	0612	0621	0629	0638	0646	0655	0663
9	0672	0680	0689	0697	0706	0714	0723	0731	0740	0749
510	70757	70766	70774	70783	70791	70800	70808	70817	70825	70834
1	0842	0851	0859	0868	0876	0885	0893	0902	0910	0919
2	0927	0935	0944	0952	0961	0969	0978	0986	0995	1003
3	1012	1020	1029	1037	1046	1054	1063	1071	1079	1088
4	1096	1105	1113	1122	1130	1139	1147	1155	1164	1172
5	1181	1189	1198	1206	1214	1223	1231	1240	1248	1257
6	1265	1273	1282	1290	1299	1307	1315	1324	1332	1341
7	1349	1357	1366	1374	1383	1391	1399	1408	1416	1425
8	1433	1441	1450	1458	1466	1475	1483	1492	1500	1508
9	1517	1525	1533	1542	1550	1559	1567	1575	1584	1592
520	71600	71609	71617	71625	71634	71642	71650	71659	71667	71675
1	1684	1692	1700	1709	1717	1725	1734	1742	1750	1759
2	1767	1775	1784	1792	1800	1809	1817	1825	1834	1842
3	1850	1858	1867	1875	1883	1892	1900	1908	1917	1925
4	1933	1941	1950	1958	1966	1975	1983	1991	1999	2008
5	2016	2024	2032	2041	2049	2057	2066	2074	2082	2090
6	2099	2107	2115	2123	2132	2140	2148	2156	2165	2173
7	2181	2189	2198	2206	2214	2222	2230	2239	2247	2255
8	2263	2272	2280	2288	2296	2304	2313	2321	2329	2337
9	2346	2354	2362	2370	2378	2387	2395	2403	2411	2419
530	72428	72436	72444	72452	72460	72469	72477	72485	72493	72501
1	2509	2518	2526	2534	2542	2550	2558	2567	2575	2583
2	2591	2599	2607	2616	2624	2632	2640	2648	2656	2665
3	2673	2681	2689	2697	2705	2713	2722	2730	2738	2746
4	2754	2762	2770	2779	2787	2795	2803	2811	2819	2827
5	2835	2843	2852	2860	2868	2876	2884	2892	2900	2908
6	2916	2925	2933	2941	2949	2957	2965	2973	2981	2989
7	2997	3006	3014	3022	3030	3038	3046	3054	3062	3070
8	3078	3086	3094	3102	3111	3119	3127	3135	3143	3151
9	3159	3167	3175	3183	3191	3199	3207	3215	3223	3231
540	73239	73247	73255	73263	73272	73280	73288	73296	73304	73312
1	3320	3328	3336	3344	3352	3360	3368	3376	3384	3392
2	3400	3408	3416	3424	3432	3440	3448	3456	3464	3472
3	3480	3488	3496	3504	3512	3520	3528	3536	3544	3552
4	3560	3568	3576	3584	3592	3600	3608	3616	3624	3632
5	3640	3648	3656	3664	3672	3679	3687	3695	3703	3711
6	3719	3727	3735	3743	3759	3759	3767	3775	3783	3791
7	3799	3807	3815	3823	3830	3838	3846	3854	3862	3870
8	3878	3886	3894	3902	3910	3918	3926	3933	3941	3949
9	3957	3965	3973	3981	3989	3997	4005	4013	4020	4028
550	74036	74044	74052	74060	74068	74076	74084	74092	74099	74107

TABLE I.—LOGARITHMS OF NUMBERS.

N	0	1	2	3	4	5	6	7	8	9
550	74036	74044	74052	74060	74068	74076	74084	74092	74099	74107
1	4115	4123	4131	4139	4147	4155	4162	4170	4178	4186
2	4194	4202	4210	4218	4225	4233	4241	4249	4257	4265
3	4273	4280	4288	4296	4304	4312	4320	4327	4335	4343
4	4351	4359	4367	4374	4382	4390	4398	4406	4414	4421
5	4429	4437	4445	4453	4461	4468	4476	4484	4492	4500
6	4507	4515	4523	4531	4539	4547	4554	4562	4570	4578
7	4586	4593	4601	4609	4617	4624	4632	4640	4648	4656
8	4663	4671	4679	4687	4695	4702	4710	4718	4726	4733
9	4741	4749	4757	4764	4772	4780	4788	4796	4803	4811
560	74819	74827	74834	74842	74850	74858	74865	74873	74881	74889
1	4896	4904	4912	4920	4927	4935	4943	4950	4958	4966
2	4974	4981	4989	4997	5005	5012	5020	5028	5035	5043
3	5051	5059	5066	5074	5082	5089	5097	5105	5113	5120
4	5128	5136	5143	5151	5159	5166	5174	5182	5189	5197
5	5205	5213	5220	5228	5236	5243	5251	5259	5266	5274
6	5282	5289	5297	5305	5312	5320	5328	5335	5343	5351
7	5358	5366	5374	5381	5389	5397	5404	5412	5420	5427
8	5435	5442	5450	5458	5465	5473	5481	5488	5496	5504
9	5511	5519	5526	5534	5542	5549	5557	5565	5572	5580
570	75587	75595	75603	75610	75618	75626	75633	75641	75648	75656
1	5664	5671	5679	5686	5694	5702	5709	5717	5724	5732
2	5740	5747	5755	5762	5770	5778	5785	5793	5800	5808
3	5815	5823	5831	5838	5840	5858	5861	5868	5876	5884
4	5891	5899	5906	5914	5921	5929	5937	5944	5952	5959
5	5967	5974	5982	5989	5997	6005	6012	6020	6027	6035
6	6042	6050	6057	6065	6072	6080	6087	6095	6103	6110
7	6118	6125	6133	6140	6148	6155	6163	6170	6178	6185
8	6193	6200	6208	6215	6223	6230	6238	6245	6253	6260
9	6268	6275	6283	6290	6298	6305	6313	6320	6328	6335
580	76343	76350	76358	76365	76373	76380	76388	76395	76403	76410
1	6418	6425	6433	6440	6448	6455	6462	6470	6477	6485
2	6492	6500	6507	6515	6522	6530	6537	6545	6552	6559
3	6567	6574	6582	6589	6597	6604	6612	6619	6626	6634
4	6641	6649	6656	6664	6671	6678	6686	6693	6701	6708
5	6716	6723	6730	6738	6745	6753	6760	6768	6775	6782
6	6790	6797	6805	6812	6819	6827	6834	6842	6849	6856
7	6864	6871	6879	6886	6893	6901	6908	6916	6923	6930
8	6938	6945	6953	6960	6967	6975	6982	6989	6997	7004
9	7012	7019	7026	7034	7041	7048	7056	7063	7070	7078
590	77085	77093	77100	77107	77115	77122	77129	77137	77144	77151
1	7159	7166	7173	7181	7188	7195	7203	7210	7217	7225
2	7232	7240	7247	7254	7262	7269	7276	7283	7291	7298
3	7305	7313	7320	7327	7335	7342	7349	7357	7364	7371
4	7379	7386	7393	7401	7408	7415	7422	7430	7437	7444
5	7452	7459	7466	7474	7481	7488	7495	7503	7510	7517
6	7525	7532	7539	7546	7554	7561	7568	7576	7583	7590
7	7597	7605	7612	7619	7627	7634	7641	7648	7656	7663
8	7670	7677	7685	7692	7699	7706	7714	7721	7728	7735
9	7743	7750	7757	7764	7772	7779	7786	7793	7801	7808
600	77815	77822	77830	77837	77844	77851	77859	77866	77873	77880

TABLE I.—LOGARITHMS OF NUMBERS.

N	0	1	2	3	4	5	6	7	8	9
600	77815	77822	77830	77837	77844	77851	77859	77866	77873	77880
1	7887	7895	7902	7909	7916	7924	7931	7938	7945	7952
2	7960	7967	7974	7981	7988	7996	8003	8010	8017	8025
3	8032	8039	8046	8053	8061	8068	8075	8082	8089	8097
4	8104	8111	8118	8125	8132	8140	8147	8154	8161	8168
5	8176	8183	8190	8197	8204	8211	8219	8226	8233	8240
6	8247	8254	8262	8269	8276	8283	8290	8297	8305	8312
7	8319	8326	8333	8340	8347	8355	8362	8369	8376	8383
8	8390	8398	8405	8412	8419	8426	8433	8440	8447	8455
9	8462	8469	8476	8483	8490	8497	8504	8512	8519	8526
610	78533	78540	78547	78554	78561	78569	78576	78583	78590	78597
1	8604	8611	8618	8625	8633	8640	8647	8654	8661	8668
2	8675	8682	8689	8696	8704	8711	8718	8725	8732	8739
3	8746	8753	8760	8767	8774	8781	8789	8796	8803	8810
4	8817	8824	8831	8838	8845	8852	8859	8866	8873	8880
5	8888	8895	8902	8909	8916	8923	8930	8937	8944	8951
6	8958	8965	8972	8979	8986	8993	9000	9007	9014	9021
7	9029	9036	9043	9050	9057	9064	9071	9078	9085	9092
8	9099	9106	9113	9120	9127	9134	9141	9148	9155	9162
9	9169	9176	9183	9190	9197	9204	9211	9218	9225	9232
620	79239	79246	79253	79260	79267	79274	79281	79288	79295	79302
1	9309	9316	9323	9330	9337	9344	9351	9358	9365	9372
2	9379	9386	9393	9400	9407	9414	9421	9428	9435	9442
3	9449	9456	9463	9470	9477	9484	9491	9498	9505	9511
4	9518	9525	9532	9539	9546	9553	9560	9567	9574	9581
5	9588	9595	9602	9609	9616	9623	9630	9637	9644	9650
6	9657	9664	9671	9678	9685	9692	9699	9706	9713	9720
7	9727	9734	9741	9748	9754	9761	9768	9775	9782	9789
8	9796	9803	9810	9817	9824	9831	9837	9844	9851	9858
9	9865	9872	9879	9886	9893	9900	9906	9913	9920	9927
630	79934	79941	79948	79955	79962	79969	79975	79982	79989	79996
1	80003	80010	80017	80024	80030	80037	80044	80051	80058	80065
2	0072	0079	0085	0092	0099	0106	0113	0120	0127	0134
3	0140	0147	0154	0161	0168	0175	0182	0188	0195	0202
4	0209	0216	0223	0229	0236	0243	0250	0257	0264	0271
5	0277	0284	0291	0298	0305	0312	0318	0325	0332	0339
6	0346	0353	0359	0366	0373	0380	0387	0393	0400	0407
7	0414	0421	0428	0434	0441	0448	0455	0462	0468	0475
8	0482	0489	0496	0502	0509	0516	0523	0530	0536	0543
9	0550	0557	0564	0570	0577	0584	0591	0598	0604	0611
640	80618	80625	80632	80638	80645	80652	80659	80665	80672	80679
1	0686	0693	0699	0706	0713	0720	0726	0733	0740	0747
2	0754	0760	0767	0774	0781	0787	0794	0801	0808	0814
3	0821	0828	0835	0841	0848	0855	0862	0868	0875	0882
4	0889	0895	0902	0909	0916	0922	0929	0936	0943	0949
5	0956	0963	0969	0976	0983	0990	0996	1003	1010	1017
6	1023	1030	1037	1043	1050	1057	1064	1070	1077	1084
7	1090	1097	1104	1111	1117	1124	1131	1137	1144	1151
8	1158	1164	1171	1178	1184	1191	1198	1204	1211	1218
9	1224	1231	1238	1245	1251	1258	1265	1271	1278	1285
650	81291	81298	81305	81311	81318	81325	81331	81338	81345	81351

TABLE I.—LOGARITHMS OF NUMBERS.

N	0	1	2	3	4	5	6	7	8	9
650	81291	81298	81305	81311	81318	81325	81331	81338	81345	81351
1	1358	1365	1371	1378	1385	1391	1398	1405	1411	1418
2	1425	1431	1438	1445	1451	1458	1465	1471	1478	1485
3	1491	1498	1505	1511	1518	1525	1531	1538	1544	1551
4	1558	1564	1571	1578	1584	1591	1598	1604	1611	1617
5	1624	1631	1637	1644	1651	1657	1664	1671	1677	1684
6	1690	1697	1704	1710	1717	1723	1730	1737	1743	1750
7	1757	1763	1770	1776	1783	1790	1796	1803	1809	1816
8	1823	1829	1836	1842	1849	1856	1862	1869	1875	1882
9	1889	1895	1902	1908	1915	1921	1928	1935	1941	1948
660	81954	81961	81968	81974	81981	81987	81994	82000	82007	82014
1	2020	2027	2033	2040	2046	2053	2060	2066	2073	2079
2	2086	2092	2099	2105	2112	2119	2125	2132	2138	2145
3	2151	2158	2164	2171	2178	2184	2191	2197	2204	2210
4	2217	2223	2230	2236	2243	2249	2256	2263	2269	2276
5	2282	2289	2295	2302	2308	2315	2321	2328	2334	2341
6	2347	2354	2360	2367	2373	2380	2387	2393	2400	2406
7	2413	2419	2426	2432	2439	2445	2452	2458	2465	2471
8	2478	2484	2491	2497	2504	2510	2517	2523	2530	2536
9	2543	2549	2556	2562	2569	2575	2582	2588	2595	2601
670	82607	82614	82620	82627	82633	82640	82646	82653	82659	82666
1	2672	2679	2685	2692	2698	2705	2711	2718	2724	2730
2	2737	2743	2750	2756	2763	2769	2776	2782	2789	2795
3	2802	2808	2814	2821	2827	2834	2840	2847	2853	2860
4	2866	2872	2879	2885	2892	2898	2905	2911	2918	2924
5	2930	2937	2943	2950	2956	2963	2969	2975	2982	2988
6	2995	3001	3008	3014	3020	3027	3033	3040	3046	3052
7	3059	3065	3072	3078	3085	3091	3097	3104	3110	3117
8	3123	3129	3136	3142	3149	3155	3161	3168	3174	3181
9	3187	3193	3200	3206	3213	3219	3225	3232	3238	3245
680	83251	83257	83264	83270	83276	83283	83289	83296	83302	83308
1	3315	3321	3327	3334	3340	3347	3353	3359	3366	3372
2	3378	3385	3391	3398	3404	3410	3417	3423	3429	3436
3	3442	3448	3455	3461	3467	3474	3480	3487	3493	3499
4	3506	3512	3518	3525	3531	3537	3544	3550	3556	3563
5	3569	3575	3582	3588	3594	3601	3607	3613	3620	3626
6	3632	3639	3645	3651	3658	3664	3670	3677	3683	3689
7	3696	3702	3708	3715	3721	3727	3734	3740	3746	3753
8	3759	3765	3771	3778	3784	3790	3797	3803	3809	3816
9	3822	3828	3835	3841	3847	3853	3860	3866	3872	3879
690	83885	83891	83897	83904	83910	83916	83923	83929	83935	83942
1	3948	3954	3960	3967	3973	3979	3985	3992	3998	4004
2	4011	4017	4023	4029	4036	4042	4048	4055	4061	4067
3	4073	4080	4086	4092	4098	4105	4111	4117	4123	4130
4	4136	4142	4148	4155	4161	4167	4173	4180	4186	4192
5	4198	4205	4211	4217	4223	4230	4236	4242	4248	4255
6	4261	4267	4273	4280	4286	4292	4298	4305	4311	4317
7	4323	4330	4336	4342	4348	4354	4361	4367	4373	4379
8	4386	4392	4398	4404	4410	4417	4423	4429	4435	4442
9	4448	4454	4460	4466	4473	4479	4485	4491	4497	4504
700	84510	84516	84522	84528	84535	84541	84547	84553	84559	84566

TABLE I.—LOGARITHMS OF NUMBERS.

N	0	1	2	3	4	5	6	7	8	9
700	84510	84516	84522	84528	84535	84541	84547	84553	84559	84566
1	4572	4578	4584	4590	4597	4603	4609	4615	4621	4628
2	4634	4640	4646	4652	4658	4665	4671	4677	4683	4689
3	4696	4702	4708	4714	4720	4726	4733	4739	4745	4751
4	4757	4763	4770	4776	4782	4788	4794	4800	4807	4813
5	4819	4825	4831	4837	4844	4850	4856	4862	4868	4874
6	4880	4887	4893	4899	4905	4911	4917	4924	4930	4936
7	4942	4948	4954	4960	4967	4973	4979	4985	4991	4997
8	5003	5009	5016	5022	5028	5034	5040	5046	5052	5058
9	5065	5071	5077	5083	5089	5095	5101	5107	5114	5120
710	85126	85132	85138	85144	85150	85156	85163	85169	85175	85181
1	5187	5193	5199	5205	5211	5217	5224	5230	5236	5242
2	5248	5254	5260	5266	5272	5278	5285	5291	5297	5303
3	5309	5315	5321	5327	5333	5339	5345	5352	5358	5364
4	5370	5376	5382	5388	5394	5400	5406	5412	5418	5425
5	5431	5437	5443	5449	5455	5461	5467	5473	5479	5485
6	5491	5497	5503	5509	5516	5522	5528	5534	5540	5546
7	5552	5558	5564	5570	5576	5582	5588	5594	5600	5606
8	5612	5618	5625	5631	5637	5643	5649	5655	5661	5667
9	5673	5679	5685	5691	5697	5703	5709	5715	5721	5727
720	85733	85739	85745	85751	85757	85763	85769	85775	85781	85788
1	5794	5800	5806	5812	5818	5824	5830	5836	5842	5848
2	5854	5860	5866	5872	5878	5884	5890	5896	5902	5908
3	5914	5920	5926	5932	5938	5944	5950	5956	5962	5968
4	5974	5980	5986	5992	5998	6004	6010	6016	6022	6028
5	6034	6040	6046	6052	6058	6064	6070	6076	6082	6088
6	6094	6100	6106	6112	6118	6124	6130	6136	6141	6147
7	6153	6159	6165	6171	6177	6183	6189	6195	6201	6207
8	6213	6219	6225	6231	6237	6243	6249	6255	6261	6267
9	6273	6279	6285	6291	6297	6303	6308	6314	6320	6326
730	86332	86338	86344	86350	86356	86362	86368	86374	86380	86386
1	6392	6398	6404	6410	6415	6421	6427	6433	6439	6445
2	6451	6457	6463	6469	6475	6481	6487	6493	6499	6504
3	6510	6516	6522	6528	6534	6540	6546	6552	6558	6564
4	6570	6576	6581	6587	6593	6599	6605	6611	6617	6623
5	6629	6635	6641	6646	6652	6658	6664	6670	6676	6682
6	6688	6694	6700	6705	6711	6717	6723	6729	6735	6741
7	6747	6753	6759	6764	6770	6776	6782	6788	6794	6800
8	6806	6812	6817	6823	6829	6835	6841	6847	6853	6859
9	6864	6870	6876	6882	6888	6894	6900	6906	6911	6917
740	86923	86929	86935	86941	86947	86953	86958	86964	86970	86976
1	6982	6988	6994	6999	7005	7011	7017	7023	7029	7035
2	7040	7046	7052	7058	7064	7070	7075	7081	7087	7093
3	7099	7105	7111	7116	7122	7128	7134	7140	7146	7151
4	7157	7163	7169	7175	7181	7186	7192	7198	7204	7210
5	7216	7221	7227	7233	7239	7245	7251	7256	7262	7268
6	7274	7280	7286	7291	7297	7303	7309	7315	7320	7326
7	7332	7338	7344	7349	7355	7361	7367	7373	7379	7384
8	7390	7396	7402	7408	7413	7419	7425	7431	7437	7442
9	7448	7454	7460	7466	7471	7477	7483	7489	7495	7500
750	87506	87512	87518	87523	87529	87535	87541	87547	87552	87558

TABLE I.—LOGARITHMS OF NUMBERS.

N	0	1	2	3	4	5	6	7	8	9
750	87506	87512	87518	87523	87529	87535	87541	87547	87552	87558
1	7564	7570	7576	7581	7587	7593	7599	7604	7610	7616
2	7622	7628	7633	7639	7645	7651	7656	7662	7668	7674
3	7679	7685	7691	7697	7703	7708	7714	7720	7726	7731
4	7737	7743	7749	7754	7760	7766	7772	7777	7783	7789
5	7795	7800	7806	7812	7818	7823	7829	7835	7841	7846
6	7852	7858	7864	7869	7875	7881	7887	7892	7898	7904
7	7910	7915	7921	7927	7933	7938	7944	7950	7955	7961
8	7967	7973	7978	7984	7990	7996	8001	8007	8013	8018
9	8024	8030	8036	8041	8047	8053	8058	8064	8070	8076
760	88081	88087	88093	88098	88104	88110	88116	88121	88127	88133
1	8138	8144	8150	8156	8161	8167	8173	8178	8184	8190
2	8195	8201	8207	8213	8218	8224	8230	8235	8241	8247
3	8252	8258	8264	8270	8275	8281	8287	8292	8298	8304
4	8309	8315	8321	8326	8332	8338	8343	8349	8355	8360
5	8366	8372	8377	8383	8389	8395	8400	8406	8412	8417
6	8423	8429	8434	8440	8446	8451	8457	8463	8468	8474
7	8480	8485	8491	8497	8502	8508	8513	8519	8525	8530
8	8536	8542	8547	8553	8559	8564	8570	8576	8581	8587
9	8593	8598	8604	8610	8615	8621	8627	8632	8638	8643
770	88649	88655	88660	88666	88672	88677	88683	88689	88694	88700
1	8705	8711	8717	8722	8728	8734	8739	8745	8750	8756
2	8762	8767	8773	8779	8784	8790	8795	8801	8807	8812
3	8818	8824	8829	8835	8840	8846	8852	8857	8863	8868
4	8874	8880	8885	8891	8897	8902	8908	8913	8919	8925
5	8930	8936	8941	8947	8953	8958	8964	8969	8975	8981
6	8986	8992	8997	9003	9009	9014	9020	9025	9031	9037
7	9042	9048	9053	9059	9064	9070	9076	9081	9087	9092
8	9098	9104	9109	9115	9120	9126	9131	9137	9143	9148
9	9154	9159	9165	9170	9176	9182	9187	9193	9198	9204
780	89209	89215	89221	89226	89232	89237	89243	89248	89254	89260
1	9265	9271	9276	9282	9287	9293	9298	9304	9310	9315
2	9321	9326	9332	9337	9343	9348	9354	9360	9365	9371
3	9376	9382	9387	9393	9398	9404	9409	9415	9421	9426
4	9432	9437	9443	9448	9454	9459	9465	9470	9476	9481
5	9487	9492	9498	9504	9509	9515	9520	9526	9531	9537
6	9542	9548	9553	9559	9564	9570	9575	9581	9586	9592
7	9597	9603	9609	9614	9620	9625	9631	9636	9642	9647
8	9653	9658	9664	9669	9675	9680	9686	9691	9697	9702
9	9708	9713	9719	9724	9730	9735	9741	9746	9752	9757
790	89763	89768	89774	89779	89785	89790	89796	89801	89807	89812
1	9818	9823	9829	9834	9840	9845	9851	9856	9862	9867
2	9873	9878	9883	9889	9894	9900	9905	9911	9916	9922
3	9927	9933	9938	9944	9949	9955	9960	9966	9971	9977
4	9982	9988	9993	9998	90004	90009	90015	90020	90026	90031
5	90037	90042	90048	90053	0059	0064	0069	0075	0080	0086
6	0091	0097	0102	0108	0113	0119	0124	0129	0135	0140
7	0146	0151	0157	0162	0168	0173	0179	0184	0189	0195
8	0200	0206	0211	0217	0222	0227	0233	0238	0244	0249
9	0255	0260	0266	0271	0276	0282	0287	0293	0298	0304
800	90309	90314	90320	90325	90331	90336	90342	90347	90352	90358

TABLE I.—LOGARITHMS OF NUMBERS.

N	0	1	2	3	4	5	6	7	8	9
800	90309	90314	90320	90325	90331	90336	90342	90347	90352	90358
1	0363	0369	0374	0380	0385	0390	0396	0401	0407	0412
2	0417	0423	0428	0434	0439	0445	0450	0455	0461	0466
3	0472	0477	0482	0488	0493	0499	0504	0509	0515	0520
4	0526	0531	0536	0542	0547	0553	0558	0563	0569	0574
5	0580	0585	0590	0596	0601	0607	0612	0617	0623	0628
6	0634	0639	0644	0650	0655	0660	0666	0671	0677	0682
7	0687	0693	0698	0703	0709	0714	0720	0725	0730	0736
8	0741	0747	0752	0757	0763	0768	0773	0779	0784	0789
9	0795	0800	0806	0811	0816	0822	0827	0832	0838	0843
810	90849	90854	90859	90865	90870	90875	90881	90886	90891	90897
1	0902	0907	0913	0918	0924	0929	0934	0940	0945	0950
2	0956	0961	0966	0972	0977	0982	0988	0993	0998	1004
3	1009	1014	1020	1025	1030	1036	1041	1046	1052	1057
4	1062	1068	1073	1078	1084	1089	1094	1100	1105	1110
5	1116	1121	1126	1132	1137	1142	1148	1153	1158	1164
6	1169	1174	1180	1185	1190	1196	1201	1206	1212	1217
7	1222	1228	1233	1238	1243	1249	1254	1259	1265	1270
8	1275	1281	1286	1291	1297	1302	1307	1312	1318	1323
9	1328	1334	1339	1344	1350	1355	1360	1365	1371	1376
820	91381	91387	91392	91397	91403	91408	91413	91418	91424	91429
1	1434	1440	1445	1450	1455	1461	1466	1471	1477	1482
2	1487	1492	1498	1503	1508	1514	1519	1524	1529	1535
3	1540	1545	1551	1556	1561	1566	1572	1577	1582	1587
4	1593	1598	1603	1609	1614	1619	1624	1630	1635	1640
5	1645	1651	1656	1661	1666	1672	1677	1682	1687	1693
6	1698	1703	1709	1714	1719	1724	1730	1735	1740	1745
7	1751	1756	1761	1766	1772	1777	1782	1787	1793	1798
8	1803	1808	1814	1819	1824	1829	1834	1840	1845	1850
9	1855	1861	1866	1871	1876	1882	1887	1892	1897	1903
830	91908	91913	91918	91924	91929	91934	91939	91944	91950	91955
1	1960	1965	1971	1976	1981	1986	1991	1997	2002	2007
2	2012	2018	2023	2028	2033	2038	2044	2049	2054	2059
3	2065	2070	2075	2080	2085	2091	2096	2101	2106	2111
4	2117	2122	2127	2132	2137	2143	2148	2153	2158	2163
5	2169	2174	2179	2184	2189	2195	2200	2205	2210	2215
6	2221	2226	2231	2236	2241	2247	2252	2257	2262	2267
7	2273	2278	2283	2288	2293	2298	2304	2309	2314	2319
8	2324	2330	2335	2340	2345	2350	2355	2361	2366	2371
9	2376	2381	2387	2392	2397	2402	2407	2412	2418	2423
840	92428	92433	92438	92443	92449	92454	92459	92464	92469	92474
1	2480	2485	2490	2195	2500	2505	2511	2516	2521	2526
2	2531	2536	2542	2547	2552	2557	2562	2567	2572	2578
3	2583	2588	2593	2598	2603	2609	2614	2619	2624	2629
4	2634	2639	2645	2650	2655	2660	2665	2670	2675	2681
5	2686	2691	2696	2701	2706	2711	2716	2722	2727	2732
6	2737	2742	2747	2752	2758	2763	2768	2773	2778	2783
7	2788	2793	2799	2804	2809	2814	2819	2824	2829	2834
8	2840	2845	2850	2855	2860	2865	2870	2875	2881	2886
9	2891	2896	2901	2906	2911	2916	2921	2927	2932	2937
850	92942	92947	92952	92957	92962	92967	92973	92978	92983	92988

TABLE I.—LOGARITHMS OF NUMBERS.

N	0	1	2	3	4	5	6	7	8	9
850	92942	92947	92952	92957	92962	92967	92973	92978	92983	92988
1	2993	2998	3003	3008	3013	3018	3024	3029	3034	3039
2	3044	3049	3054	3059	3064	3069	3075	3080	3085	3090
3	3095	3100	3105	3110	3115	3120	3125	3131	3136	3141
4	3146	3151	3156	3161	3166	3171	3176	3181	3186	3192
5	3197	3202	3207	3212	3217	3222	3227	3232	3237	3242
6	3247	3252	3258	3263	3268	3273	3278	3283	3288	3293
7	3298	3303	3308	3313	3318	3323	3328	3334	3339	3344
8	3349	3354	3359	3364	3369	3374	3379	3384	3389	3394
9	3399	3404	3409	3414	3420	3425	3430	3435	3440	3445
860	93450	93455	93460	93465	93470	93475	93480	93485	93490	93495
1	3500	3505	3510	3515	3520	3526	3531	3536	3541	3546
2	3551	3556	3561	3566	3571	3576	3581	3586	3591	3596
3	3601	3606	3611	3616	3621	3626	3631	3636	3641	3646
4	3651	3656	3661	3666	3671	3676	3682	3687	3692	3697
5	3702	3707	3712	3717	3722	3727	3732	3737	3742	3747
6	3752	3757	3762	3767	3772	3777	3782	3787	3792	3797
7	3802	3807	3812	3817	3822	3827	3832	3837	3842	3847
8	3852	3857	3862	3867	3872	3877	3882	3887	3892	3897
9	3902	3907	3912	3917	3922	3927	3932	3937	3942	3947
870	93952	93957	93962	93967	93972	93977	93982	93987	93992	93997
1	4002	4007	4012	4017	4022	4027	4032	4037	4042	4047
2	4052	4057	4062	4067	4072	4077	4082	4086	4091	4096
3	4101	4106	4111	4116	4121	4126	4131	4136	4141	4146
4	4151	4156	4161	4166	4171	4176	4181	4186	4191	4196
5	4201	4206	4211	4216	4221	4226	4231	4236	4240	4245
6	4250	4255	4260	4265	4270	4275	4280	4285	4290	4295
7	4300	4305	4310	4315	4320	4325	4330	4335	4340	4345
8	4349	4354	4359	4364	4369	4374	4379	4384	4389	4394
9	4399	4404	4409	4414	4419	4424	4429	4433	4438	4443
880	94448	94453	94458	94463	94468	94473	94478	94483	94488	94493
1	4498	4503	4507	4512	4517	4522	4527	4532	4537	4542
2	4547	4552	4557	4562	4567	4571	4576	4581	4586	4591
3	4596	4601	4606	4611	4616	4621	4626	4630	4635	4640
4	4645	4650	4655	4660	4665	4670	4675	4680	4685	4689
5	4694	4699	4704	4709	4714	4719	4724	4729	4734	4738
6	4743	4748	4753	4758	4763	4768	4773	4778	4783	4787
7	4792	4797	4802	4807	4812	4817	4822	4827	4832	4836
8	4841	4846	4851	4856	4861	4866	4871	4876	4880	4885
9	4890	4895	4900	4905	4910	4915	4919	4924	4929	4934
890	94939	94944	94949	94954	94959	94963	94968	94973	94978	94983
1	4988	4993	4998	5002	5007	5012	5017	5022	5027	5032
2	5036	5041	5046	5051	5056	5061	5066	5071	5075	5080
3	5085	5090	5095	5100	5105	5109	5114	5119	5124	5129
4	5134	5139	5143	5148	5153	5158	5163	5168	5173	5177
5	5182	5187	5192	5197	5202	5207	5211	5216	5221	5226
6	5231	5236	5240	5245	5250	5255	5260	5265	5270	5274
7	5279	5284	5289	5294	5299	5303	5308	5313	5318	5323
8	5328	5332	5337	5342	5347	5352	5357	5361	5366	5371
9	5376	5381	5386	5390	5395	5400	5405	5410	5415	5419
900	95424	95429	95434	95439	95444	95448	95453	95458	95463	95468

TABLE I.—LOGARITHMS OF NUMBERS.

N	0	1	2	3	4	5	6	7	8	9
900	95424	95429	95434	95439	95444	95448	95453	95458	95463	95468
1	5472	5477	5482	5487	5492	5497	5501	5506	5511	5516
2	5521	5525	5530	5535	5540	5545	5550	5554	5559	5564
3	5569	5574	5578	5583	5588	5593	5598	5602	5607	5612
4	5617	5622	5626	5631	5636	5641	5646	5650	5655	5660
5	5665	5670	5674	5679	5684	5689	5694	5698	5703	5708
6	5713	5718	5722	5727	5732	5737	5742	5746	5751	5756
7	5761	5766	5770	5775	5780	5785	5789	5794	5799	5804
8	5809	5813	5818	5823	5828	5832	5837	5842	5847	5852
9	5856	5861	5866	5871	5875	5880	5885	5890	5895	5899
910	95904	95909	95914	95918	95923	95928	95933	95938	95942	95947
1	5952	5957	5961	5966	5971	5976	5980	5985	5990	5995
2	5999	6004	6009	6014	6019	6023	6028	6033	6038	6042
3	6047	6052	6057	6061	6066	6071	6076	6080	6085	6090
4	6095	6099	6104	6109	6114	6118	6123	6128	6133	6137
5	6142	6147	6152	6156	6161	6166	6171	6175	6180	6185
6	6190	6194	6199	6204	6209	6213	6218	6223	6227	6232
7	6237	6242	6246	6251	6256	6261	6265	6270	6275	6280
8	6284	6289	6294	6298	6303	6308	6313	6317	6322	6327
9	6332	6336	6341	6346	6350	6355	6360	6365	6369	6374
920	96379	96384	96388	96393	96398	96402	96407	96412	96417	96421
1	6426	6431	6435	6440	6445	6450	6454	6459	6464	6468
2	6473	6478	6483	6487	6492	6497	6501	6506	6511	6515
3	6520	6525	6530	6534	6539	6544	6548	6553	6558	6562
4	6567	6572	6577	6581	6586	6591	6595	6600	6605	6609
5	6614	6619	6624	6628	6633	6638	6642	6647	6652	6656
6	6661	6666	6670	6675	6680	6685	6689	6694	6699	6703
7	6708	6713	6717	6722	6727	6731	6736	6741	6745	6750
8	6755	6759	6764	6769	6774	6778	6783	6788	6792	6797
9	6802	6806	6811	6816	6820	6825	6830	6834	6839	6844
930	96848	96853	96858	96862	96867	96872	96876	96881	96886	96890
1	6895	6900	6904	6909	6914	6918	6923	6928	6932	6937
2	6942	6946	6951	6956	6960	6965	6970	6974	6979	6984
3	6988	6993	6997	7002	7007	7011	7016	7021	7025	7030
4	7035	7039	7044	7049	7053	7058	7063	7067	7072	7077
5	7081	7086	7090	7095	7100	7104	7109	7114	7118	7123
6	7128	7132	7137	7142	7146	7151	7155	7160	7165	7169
7	7174	7179	7183	7188	7192	7197	7202	7206	7211	7216
8	7220	7225	7230	7234	7239	7243	7248	7253	7257	7262
9	7267	7271	7276	7280	7285	7290	7294	7299	7304	7308
940	97313	97317	97322	97327	97331	97336	97340	97345	97350	97354
1	7359	7364	7368	7373	7377	7382	7387	7391	7396	7400
2	7405	7410	7414	7419	7424	7428	7433	7437	7442	7447
3	7451	7456	7460	7465	7470	7474	7479	7483	7488	7493
4	7497	7502	7506	7511	7516	7520	7525	7529	7534	7539
5	7543	7548	7552	7557	7562	7566	7571	7575	7580	7585
6	7589	7594	7598	7603	7607	7612	7617	7621	7626	7630
7	7635	7640	7644	7649	7653	7658	7663	7667	7672	7676
8	7681	7685	7690	7695	7699	7704	7708	7713	7717	7722
9	7727	7731	7736	7740	7745	7749	7754	7759	7763	7768
950	97772	97777	97782	97786	97791	97795	97800	97804	97809	97813

TABLE I.—LOGARITHMS OF NUMBERS.

N	0	1	2	3	4	5	6	7	8	9
950	97772	97777	97782	97786	97791	97795	97800	97804	97809	97813
1	7818	7823	7827	7832	7836	7841	7845	7850	7855	7859
2	7864	7868	7873	7877	7882	7886	7891	7896	7900	7905
3	7909	7914	7918	7923	7928	7932	7937	7941	7946	7950
4	7955	7959	7964	7968	7973	7978	7982	7987	7991	7996
5	8000	8005	8009	8014	8019	8023	8028	8032	8037	8041
6	8046	8050	8055	8059	8064	8068	8073	8078	8082	8087
7	8091	8096	8100	8105	8109	8114	8118	8123	8127	8132
8	8137	8141	8146	8150	8155	8159	8164	8168	8173	8177
9	8182	8186	8101	8195	8200	8204	8209	8214	8218	8223
960	98227	98232	98236	98241	98245	98250	98254	98259	98263	98268
1	8272	8277	8281	8286	8290	8295	8299	8304	8308	8313
2	8318	8322	8327	8331	8336	8340	8345	8349	8354	8358
3	8363	8367	8372	8376	8381	8385	8390	8394	8399	8403
4	8408	8412	8417	8421	8426	8430	8435	8439	8444	8448
5	8453	8457	8462	8466	8471	8475	8480	8484	8489	8493
6	8498	8502	8507	8511	8516	8520	8525	8529	8534	8538
7	8543	8547	8552	8556	8561	8565	8570	8574	8579	8583
8	8588	8592	8597	8601	8605	8610	8614	8619	8623	8628
9	8632	8637	8641	8646	8650	8655	8659	8664	8668	8673
970	98677	98682	98686	98691	98695	98700	98704	98709	98713	98717
1	8722	8726	8731	8735	8740	8744	8749	8753	8758	8762
2	8767	8771	8776	8780	8784	8789	8793	8798	8802	8807
3	8811	8816	8820	8825	8829	8834	8838	8843	8847	8851
4	8856	8860	8865	8869	8874	8878	8883	8887	8892	8896
5	8900	8905	8909	8914	8918	8923	8927	8932	8936	8941
6	8945	8949	8954	8958	8963	8967	8972	8976	8981	8985
7	8989	8994	8998	9003	9007	9012	9016	9021	9025	9029
8	9034	9038	9043	9047	9052	9056	9061	9065	9069	9074
9	9078	9083	9087	9092	9096	9100	9105	9109	9114	9118
980	99123	99127	99131	99136	99140	99145	99149	99154	99158	99162
1	9167	9171	9176	9180	9185	9189	9193	9198	9202	9207
2	9211	9216	9220	9224	9229	9233	9238	9242	9247	9251
3	9255	9260	9264	9269	9273	9277	9282	9286	9291	9295
4	9300	9304	9308	9313	9317	9322	9326	9330	9335	9339
5	9344	9348	9352	9357	9361	9366	9370	9374	9379	9383
6	9388	9392	9396	9401	9405	9410	9414	9419	9423	9427
7	9432	9436	9441	9445	9449	9454	9458	9463	9467	9471
8	9476	9480	9484	9489	9493	9498	9502	9506	9511	9515
9	9520	9524	9528	9533	9537	9542	9546	9550	9555	9559
990	99564	99568	99572	99577	99581	99585	99590	99594	99599	99603
1	9607	9612	9616	9621	9625	9629	9634	9638	9642	9647
2	9651	9656	9660	9664	9669	9673	9677	9682	9686	9691
3	9695	9699	9704	9708	9712	9717	9721	9726	9730	9734
4	9739	9743	9747	9752	9756	9760	9765	9769	9774	9778
5	9782	9787	9791	9795	9800	9804	9808	9813	9817	9822
6	9826	9830	9835	9839	9843	9848	9852	9856	9861	9865
7	9870	9874	9878	9883	9887	9891	9896	9900	9904	9909
8	9913	9917	9922	9926	9930	9935	9939	9944	9948	9952
9	9957	9961	9965	9970	9974	9978	9983	9987	9991	9996
1000	00000	00004	00009	00013	00017	00022	00026	00030	00035	00039

Logarithmic Sines and Tangents of Small Angles. — To obtain the log sin or log tan of an angle less than 1° from the 5-place tables add the log of the number of minutes and decimals to the log sin of one minute (6.463 7261) or, add the log of the number of seconds to the log sin of one second (4.685 5749).

EXAMPLE: — Required the log sin 0° 24′ 21″ (= log sin 24′.35):

$$\log \sin 1' = 6.46373$$
$$\log 24.35 = \underline{1.38650}$$
$$\log \sin 0° \ 24' \ 21'' = 7.85023$$

or, using seconds,

$$\log \sin 1'' = 4.68557$$
$$\log 1461 = \underline{3.16465}$$
$$\log \sin 0° \ 24' \ 21'' = 7.85022$$

This method is approximate but the error is only 1 or 2 units in the fifth place for an angle of 1° and is less for smaller angles. If the log sin had been obtained by direct interpolation in the 5-place table the error would be 8 or 9 in the fifth place, as shown below.

$$\log \sin 0° \ 24' = 7.84393$$
$$\log \sin 0° \ 25' = \underline{7.86166}$$
$$\text{difference} = \quad .01773$$

$$\frac{21}{60} \times 1773 = 621$$

$$\log \sin 0° \ 24' \ 21'' = 7.84393 + 621 = 7.85014$$

To obtain the angle corresponding to a log sin subtract 6.463 7261 (or 4.685 5749 for seconds) from the given log sin; the result is the log of the number of minutes (or seconds) in the angle. For example, the angle corresponding to 7.64076 is found as follows:

$$\log \sin x = 7.64076$$
$$\log \sin 1' = \underline{6.46373}$$
$$\log x' = 1.17703$$

$$x' = 15' \ .032$$
$$= 15' \ 02''$$

or, using seconds,

$$\log \sin x = 7.64076$$
$$\log \sin 1'' = \underline{4.68557}$$
$$\log x'' = 2.95519$$

$$x'' = 901''.97$$
$$= 15'\ 02''$$

The same rule applies to a log tangent.

If greater accuracy is required than can be obtained by the preceding method, or if the angle is greater than $1°$, the log sin may be found from the relation

$$n' : n = \sin n' : \sin n$$

where n is the nearest angle whose sin is given in the table and n' is the angle whose log sin is desired. The log sin is then given by

$$\log \sin n' = \log \sin n + \log n' - \log n.$$

For log sin $0°\ 24'\ 21''$ this latter method gives 7.85022.

$$\log \sin 24' = 7.84393$$
$$\log \sin 24.35 = 1.38650$$
$$\text{co-log } 24 = \underline{8.61979}$$
$$\log \sin 0°\ 24'\ 21'' = 7.85022$$

which is correct to five decimal places. For angles above $5°$ direct interpolation in the tables is sufficiently accurate.

TABLE II.—LOGARITHMIC SINES AND COSINES.

′	0°		1°		2°		′
	Sine	Cosine	Sine	Cosine	Sine	Cosine	
0	−∞	10.00000	8.24186	9.99993	8.54282	9.99974	60
1	6.46373	00000	24903	99993	54642	99973	59
2	76476	00000	25609	99993	54999	99973	58
3	94085	00000	26304	99993	55354	99972	57
4	7.06579	00000	26988	99992	55705	99972	56
5	16270	00000	27661	99992	56054	99971	55
6	24188	00000	28324	99992	56400	99971	54
7	30882	00000	28977	99992	56743	99970	53
8	36682	00000	29621	99992	57084	99970	52
9	41797	00000	30255	99991	57421	99969	51
10	7.46373	10.00000	8.30879	9.99991	8.57757	9.99969	50
11	50512	00000	31495	99991	58089	99968	49
12	54291	00000	32103	99990	58419	99968	48
13	57767	00000	32702	99990	58747	99967	47
14	60985	00000	33292	99990	59072	99967	46
15	63982	00000	33875	99990	59395	99967	45
16	66784	00000	34450	99989	59715	99966	44
17	69417	9.99999	35018	99989	60033	99966	43
18	71900	99999	35578	99989	60349	99965	42
19	74248	99999	36131	99989	60662	99964	41
20	7.76475	9.99999	8.36678	9.99988	8.60973	9.99964	40
21	78594	99999	37217	99988	61282	99963	39
22	80615	99999	37750	99988	61589	99963	38
23	82545	99999	38276	99987	61894	99962	37
24	84393	99999	38796	99987	62196	99962	36
25	86166	99999	39310	99987	62497	99961	35
26	87870	99999	39818	99986	62795	99961	34
27	89509	99999	40320	99986	63091	99960	33
28	91088	99999	40816	99986	63385	99960	32
29	92612	99998	41307	99985	63678	99959	31
30	7.94084	9.99998	8.41792	9.99985	8.63968	9.99959	30
31	95508	99998	42272	99985	64256	99958	29
32	96887	99998	42746	99984	64543	99958	28
33	98223	99998	43216	99984	64827	99957	27
34	99520	99998	43680	99984	65110	99956	26
35	8.00779	99998	44139	99983	65391	99956	25
36	02002	99998	44594	99983	65670	99955	24
37	03192	99997	45044	99983	65947	99955	23
38	04350	99997	45489	99982	66223	99954	22
39	05478	99997	45930	99982	66497	99954	21
40	8.06578	9.99997	8.46366	9.99982	8.66769	9.99953	20
41	07650	99997	46799	99981	67039	99952	19
42	08696	99997	47226	99981	67308	99952	18
43	09718	99997	47650	99981	67575	99951	17
44	10717	99996	48069	99980	67841	99951	16
45	11693	99996	48485	99980	68104	99950	15
46	12647	99996	48896	99979	68367	99949	14
47	13581	99996	49304	99979	68627	99949	13
48	14495	99996	49708	99979	68886	99948	12
49	15391	99996	50108	99978	69144	99948	11
50	8.16268	9.99995	8.50504	9.99978	8.69400	9.99947	10
51	17128	99995	50897	99977	69654	99946	9
52	17971	99995	51287	99977	69907	99946	8
53	18798	99995	51673	99977	70159	99945	7
54	19610	99995	52055	99976	70409	99944	6
55	20407	99994	52434	99976	70658	99944	5
56	21189	99994	52810	99975	70905	99943	4
57	21958	99994	53183	99975	71151	99942	3
58	22713	99994	53552	99974	71395	99942	2
59	23456	99994	53919	99974	71638	99941	1
60	24186	99993	54282	99974	71880	99940	0
′	Cosine	Sine	Cosine	Sine	Cosine	Sine	′
	89°		88°		87°		

TABLE II.—LOGARITHMIC SINES AND COSINES.

′	3° Sine	3° Cosine	4° Sine	4° Cosine	5° Sine	5° Cosine	′
0	8.71880	9.99940	8.84358	9.99894	8.94030	9.99834	60
1	72120	99940	84539	99893	94174	99833	59
2	72359	99939	84718	99892	94317	99832	58
3	72597	99938	84897	99891	94461	99831	57
4	72834	99938	85075	99891	94603	99830	56
5	73069	99937	85252	99890	94746	99829	55
6	73303	99936	85429	99889	94887	99828	54
7	73535	99936	85605	99888	95029	99827	53
8	73767	99935	85780	99887	95170	99825	52
9	73997	99934	85955	99886	95310	99824	51
10	8.74226	9.99934	8.86128	9.99885	8.95450	9.99823	50
11	74454	99933	86301	99884	95589	99822	49
12	74680	99932	86474	99883	95728	99821	48
13	74906	99932	86645	99882	95867	99820	47
14	75130	99931	86816	99881	96005	99819	46
15	75353	99930	86987	99880	96143	99817	45
16	75575	99929	87156	99879	96280	99816	44
17	75795	99929	87325	99879	96417	99815	43
18	76015	99928	87494	99878	96553	99814	42
19	76234	99927	87661	99877	96689	99813	41
20	8.76451	9.99926	8.87829	9.99876	8.96825	9.99812	40
21	76667	99926	87995	99875	96960	99810	39
22	76883	99925	88161	99874	97095	99809	38
23	77097	99924	88326	99873	97229	99808	37
24	77310	99923	88490	99872	97363	99807	36
25	77522	99923	88654	99871	97496	99806	35
26	77733	99922	88817	99870	97629	99804	34
27	77943	99921	88980	99869	97762	99803	33
28	78152	99920	89142	99868	97894	99802	32
29	78360	99920	89304	99867	98026	99801	31
30	8.78568	9.99919	8.89464	9.99866	8.98157	9.99800	30
31	78774	99918	89625	99865	98288	99798	29
32	78979	99917	89784	99864	98419	99797	28
33	79183	99917	89943	99863	98549	99796	27
34	79386	99916	90102	99862	98679	99795	26
35	79588	99915	90260	99861	98808	99793	25
36	79789	99914	90417	99860	98937	99792	24
37	79990	99913	90574	99859	99066	99791	23
38	80189	99913	90730	99858	99194	99790	22
39	80388	99912	90885	99857	99322	99788	21
40	8.80585	9.99911	8.91040	9.99856	8.99450	9.99787	20
41	80782	99910	91195	99855	99577	99786	19
42	80978	99909	91349	99854	99704	99785	18
43	81173	99909	91502	99853	99830	99783	17
44	81367	99908	91655	99852	99956	99782	16
45	81560	99907	91807	99851	9.00082	99781	15
46	81752	99906	91959	99850	00207	99780	14
47	81944	99905	92110	99848	00332	99778	13
48	82134	99904	92261	99847	00456	99777	12
49	82324	99904	92411	99846	00581	99776	11
50	8.82513	9.99903	8.92561	9.99845	9.00704	9.99775	10
51	82701	99902	92710	99844	00828	99773	9
52	82888	99901	92859	99843	00951	99772	8
53	83075	99900	93007	99842	01074	99771	7
54	83261	99899	93154	99841	01196	99769	6
55	83446	99898	93301	99840	01318	99768	5
56	83630	99898	93448	99839	01440	99767	4
57	83813	99897	93594	99838	01561	99765	3
58	83996	99896	93740	99837	01682	99764	2
59	84177	99895	93885	99836	01803	99763	1
60	84358	99894	94030	99834	01923	99761	0
′	Cosine	Sine	Cosine	Sine	Cosine	Sine	′
	86°		85°		84°		

TABLE II.—LOGARITHMIC SINES AND COSINES.

′	6° Sine	Cosine	7° Sine	Cosine	8° Sine	Cosine	′
0	9.01923	9.99761	9.08589	9.99675	9.14356	9.99575	60
1	02043	99760	08692	99674	14445	99574	59
2	02163	99759	08795	99672	14535	99572	58
3	02283	99757	08897	99670	14624	99570	57
4	02402	99756	08999	99669	14714	99568	56
5	02520	99755	09101	99667	14803	99566	55
6	02639	99753	09202	99666	14891	99565	54
7	02757	99752	09304	99664	14980	99563	53
8	02874	99751	09405	99663	15069	99561	52
9	02992	99749	09506	99661	15157	99559	51
10	9.03109	9.99748	9.09606	9.99659	9.15245	9.99557	50
11	03226	99747	09707	99658	15333	99556	49
12	03342	99745	09807	99656	15421	99554	48
13	03458	99744	09907	99655	15508	99552	47
14	03574	99742	10006	99653	15596	99550	46
15	03690	99741	10106	99651	15683	99548	45
16	03805	99740	10205	99650	15770	99546	44
17	03920	99738	10304	99648	15857	99545	43
18	04034	99737	10402	99647	15944	99543	42
19	04149	99736	10501	99645	16030	99541	41
20	9.04262	9.99734	9.10599	9.99643	9.16116	9.99539	40
21	04376	99733	10697	99642	16203	99537	39
22	04490	99731	10795	99640	16289	99535	38
23	04603	99730	10893	99638	16374	99533	37
24	04715	99728	10990	99637	16460	99532	36
25	04828	99727	11087	99635	16545	99530	35
26	04940	99726	11184	99633	16631	99528	34
27	05052	99724	11281	99632	16716	99526	33
28	05164	99723	11377	99630	16801	99524	32
29	05275	99721	11474	99629	16886	99522	31
30	9.05386	9.99720	9.11570	9.99627	9.16970	9.99520	30
31	05497	99718	11666	99625	17055	99518	29
32	05607	99717	11761	99624	17139	99517	28
33	05717	99716	11857	99622	17223	99515	27
34	05827	99714	11952	99620	17307	99513	26
35	05937	99713	12047	99618	17391	99511	25
36	06046	99711	12142	99617	17474	99509	24
37	06155	99710	12236	99615	17558	99507	23
38	06264	99708	12331	99613	17641	99505	22
39	06372	99707	12425	99612	17724	99503	21
40	9.06481	9.99705	9.12519	9.99610	9.17807	9.99501	20
41	06589	99704	12612	99608	17890	99499	19
42	06696	99702	12706	99607	17973	99497	18
43	06804	99701	12799	99605	18055	99495	17
44	06911	99699	12892	99603	18137	99494	16
45	07018	99698	12985	99601	18220	99492	15
46	07124	99696	13078	99600	18302	99490	14
47	07231	99695	13171	99598	18383	99488	13
48	07337	99693	13263	99596	18465	99486	12
49	07442	99692	13355	99595	18547	99484	11
50	9.07548	9.99690	9.13447	9.99593	9.18628	9.99482	10
51	07653	99689	13539	99591	18709	99480	9
52	07758	99687	13630	99589	18790	99478	8
53	07863	99686	13722	99588	18871	99476	7
54	07968	99684	13813	99586	18952	99474	6
55	08072	99683	13904	99584	19033	99472	5
56	08176	99681	13994	99582	19113	99470	4
57	08280	99680	14085	99581	19193	99468	3
58	08383	99678	14175	99579	19273	99466	2
59	08486	99677	14266	99577	19353	99464	1
60	08589	99675	14356	99575	19433	99462	0
′	Cosine	Sine	Cosine	Sine	Cosine	Sine	′
	83°		82°		81°		

TABLE II.—LOGARITHMIC SINES AND COSINES.

'	9°		10°		11°		'
	Sine	Cosine	Sine	Cosine	Sine	Cosine	
0	9.19433	9.99462	9.23967	9.99335	9.28060	9.99195	60
1	19513	99460	24039	99333	28125	99192	59
2	19592	99458	24110	99331	28190	99190	58
3	19672	99456	24181	99328	28254	99187	57
4	19751	99454	24253	99326	28319	99185	56
5	19830	99452	24324	99324	28384	99182	55
6	19909	99450	24395	99322	28448	99180	54
7	19988	99448	24466	99319	28512	99177	53
8	20067	99446	24536	99317	28577	99175	52
9	20145	99444	24607	99315	28641	99172	51
10	9.20223	9.99442	9.24677	9.99313	9.28705	9.99170	50
11	20302	99440	24748	99310	28769	99167	49
12	20380	99438	24818	99308	28833	99165	48
13	20458	99436	24888	99306	28896	99162	47
14	20535	99434	24958	99304	28960	99160	46
15	20613	99432	25028	99301	29024	99157	45
16	20691	99429	25098	99299	29087	99155	44
17	20768	99427	25168	99297	29150	99152	43
18	20845	99425	25237	99294	29214	99150	42
19	20922	99423	25307	99292	29277	99147	41
20	9.20999	9.99421	9.25376	9.99290	9.29340	9.99145	40
21	21076	99419	25445	99288	29403	99142	39
22	21153	99417	25514	99285	29466	99140	38
23	21229	99415	25583	99283	29529	99137	37
24	21306	99413	25652	99281	29591	99135	36
25	21382	99411	25721	99278	29654	99132	35
26	21458	99409	25790	99276	29716	99130	34
27	21634	99407	25858	99274	29779	99127	33
28	21610	99404	25927	99271	29841	99124	32
29	21685	99402	25995	99269	29903	99122	31
30	9.21761	9.99400	9.26063	9.99267	9.29966	9.99119	30
31	21836	99398	26131	99264	30028	99117	29
32	21912	99396	26199	99262	30090	99114	28
33	21987	99394	26267	99260	30151	99112	27
34	22062	99392	26335	99257	30213	99109	26
35	22137	99390	26403	99255	30275	99106	25
36	22211	99388	26470	99252	30336	99104	24
37	22286	99385	26538	99250	30398	99101	23
38	22361	99383	26605	99248	30459	99099	22
39	22435	99381	26672	99245	30521	99096	21
40	9.22509	9.99379	9.26739	9.99243	9.30582	9.99093	20
41	22583	99377	26806	99241	30643	99091	19
42	22657	99375	26873	99238	30704	99088	18
43	22731	99372	26940	99236	30765	99086	17
44	22805	99370	27007	99233	30826	99083	16
45	22878	99368	27073	99231	30887	99080	15
46	22952	99366	27140	99229	30947	99078	14
47	23025	99364	27206	99226	31008	99075	13
48	23098	99362	27273	99224	31068	99072	12
49	23171	99359	27339	99221	31129	99070	11
50	9.23244	9.99357	9.27405	9.99219	9.31189	9.99067	10
51	23317	99355	27471	99217	31250	99064	9
52	23390	99353	27537	99214	31310	99062	8
53	23462	99351	27602	99212	31370	99059	7
54	23535	99348	27668	99209	31430	99056	6
55	23607	99346	27734	99207	31490	99054	5
56	23679	99344	27799	99204	31549	99051	4
57	23752	99342	27864	99202	31609	99048	3
58	23823	99340	27930	99200	31669	99046	2
59	23895	99337	27995	99197	31728	99043	1
60	23967	99335	28060	99195	31788	99040	0
	Cosine	Sine	Cosine	Sine	Cosine	Sine	'
	80°		79°		78°		

TABLE II.—LOGARITHMIC SINES AND COSINES.

′	12°		13°		14°		′
	Sine	Cosine	Sine	Cosine	Sine	Cosine	
0	9.31788	9.99040	9.35209	9.98872	9.38368	9.98690	60
1	31847	99038	35263	98869	38418	98687	59
2	31907	99035	35318	98867	38469	98684	58
3	31966	99032	35373	98864	38519	98681	57
4	32025	99030	35427	98861	38570	98678	56
5	32084	99027	35481	98858	38620	98675	55
6	32143	99024	35536	98855	38670	98671	54
7	32202	99022	35590	98852	38721	98668	53
8	32261	99019	35644	98849	38771	98665	52
9	32319	99016	35698	98846	38821	98662	51
10	9.32378	9.99013	9.35752	9.98843	9.38871	9.98659	50
11	32437	99011	35806	98840	38921	98656	49
12	32495	99008	35860	98837	38971	98652	48
13	32553	99005	35914	98834	39021	98649	47
14	32612	99002	35968	98831	39071	98646	46
15	32670	99000	36022	98828	39121	98643	45
16	32728	98997	36075	98825	39170	98640	44
17	32786	98994	36129	98822	39220	98636	43
18	32844	98991	36182	98819	39270	98633	42
19	32902	98989	36236	98816	39319	98630	41
20	9.32960	9.98986	9.36289	9.98813	9.39369	9.98627	40
21	33018	98983	36342	98810	39418	98623	39
22	33075	98980	36395	98807	39467	98620	38
23	33133	98978	36449	98804	39517	98617	37
24	33190	98975	36502	98801	39566	98614	36
25	33248	98972	36555	98798	39615	98610	35
26	33305	98969	36608	98795	39664	98607	34
27	33362	98967	36660	98792	39713	98604	33
28	33420	98964	36713	98789	39762	98601	32
29	33477	98961	36766	98786	39811	98597	31
30	9.33534	9.98958	9.36819	9.98783	9.39860	9.98594	30
31	33591	98955	36871	98780	39909	98591	29
32	33647	98953	36924	98777	39958	98588	28
33	33704	98950	36976	98774	40006	98584	27
34	33761	98947	37028	98771	40055	98581	26
35	33818	98944	37081	98768	40103	98578	25
36	33874	98941	37133	98765	40152	98574	24
37	33931	98938	37185	98762	40200	98571	23
38	33987	98936	37237	98759	40249	98568	22
39	34043	98933	37289	98756	40297	98565	21
40	9.34100	9.98930	9.37341	9.98753	9.40346	9.98561	20
41	34156	98927	37393	98750	40394	98558	19
42	34212	98924	37445	98746	40442	98555	18
43	34268	98921	37497	98743	40490	98551	17
44	34324	98919	37549	98740	40538	98548	16
45	34380	98916	37600	98737	40586	98545	15
46	34436	98913	37652	98734	40634	98541	14
47	34491	98910	37703	98731	40682	98538	13
48	34547	98907	37755	98728	40730	98535	12
49	34602	98904	37806	98725	40778	98531	11
50	9.34658	9.98901	9.37858	9.98722	9.40825	9.98528	10
51	34713	98898	37909	98719	40873	98525	9
52	34769	98896	37960	98715	40921	98521	8
53	34824	98893	38011	98712	40968	98518	7
54	34879	98890	38062	98709	41016	98515	6
55	34934	98887	38113	98706	41063	98511	5
56	34989	98884	38164	98703	41111	98508	4
57	35044	98881	38215	98700	41158	98505	3
58	35099	98878	38266	98697	41205	98501	2
59	35154	98875	38317	98694	41252	98498	1
60	35209	98872	38368	98690	41300	98494	0
′	Cosine	Sine	Cosine	Sine	Cosine	Sine	′
	77°		76°		75°		

TABLE II.—LOGARITHMIC SINES AND COSINES.

′	15° Sine	Cosine	16° Sine	Cosine	17° Sine	Cosine	′
0	9.41300	9.98494	9.44034	9.98284	9.46594	9.98060	60
1	41347	98491	44078	98281	46635	98056	59
2	41394	98488	44122	98277	46676	98052	58
3	41441	98484	44166	98273	46717	98048	57
4	41488	98481	44210	98270	46758	98044	56
5	41535	98477	44253	98266	46800	98040	55
6	41582	98474	44297	98262	46841	98036	54
7	41628	98471	44341	98259	46882	98032	53
8	41675	98467	44385	98255	46923	98029	52
9	41722	98464	44428	98251	46964	98025	51
10	9.41768	9.98460	9.44472	9.98248	9.47005	9.98021	50
11	41815	98457	44516	98244	47045	98017	49
12	41861	98453	44559	98240	47086	98013	48
13	41908	98450	44602	98237	47127	98009	47
14	41954	98447	44646	98233	47168	98005	46
15	42001	98443	44689	98229	47209	98001	45
16	42047	98440	44733	98226	47249	97997	44
17	42093	98436	44776	98222	47290	97993	43
18	42140	98433	44819	98218	47330	97989	42
19	42186	98429	44862	98215	47371	97986	41
20	9.42232	9.98426	9.44905	9.98211	9.47411	9.97982	40
21	42278	98422	44948	98207	47452	97978	39
22	42324	98419	44992	98204	47492	97974	38
23	42370	98415	45035	98200	47533	97970	37
24	42416	98412	45077	98196	47573	97966	36
25	42461	98409	45120	98192	47613	97962	35
26	42507	98405	45163	98189	47654	97958	34
27	42553	98402	45206	98185	47694	97954	33
28	42599	98398	45249	98181	47734	97950	32
29	42644	98395	45292	98177	47774	97946	31
30	9.42690	9.98391	9.45334	9.98174	9.47814	9.97942	30
31	42735	98388	45377	98170	47864	97938	29
32	42781	98384	45419	98166	47894	97934	28
33	42826	98381	45462	98162	47934	97930	27
34	42872	98377	45504	98159	47974	97926	26
35	42917	98373	45547	98155	48014	97922	25
36	42962	98370	45589	98151	48054	97918	24
37	43008	98366	45632	98147	48094	97914	23
38	43053	98363	45674	98144	48133	97910	22
39	43098	98359	45716	98140	48173	97906	21
40	9.43143	9.98356	9.45758	9.98136	9.48213	9.97902	20
41	43188	98352	45801	98132	48252	97898	19
42	43233	98349	45843	98129	48292	97894	18
43	43278	98345	45885	98125	48332	97890	17
44	43323	98342	45927	98121	48371	97886	16
45	43367	98338	45969	98117	48411	97882	15
46	43412	98334	46011	98113	48450	97878	14
47	43457	98331	46053	98110	48490	97874	13
48	43502	98327	46095	98106	48529	97870	12
49	43546	98324	46136	98102	48568	97866	11
50	9.43591	9.98320	9.46178	9.98098	9.48607	9.97861	10
51	43635	98317	46220	98094	48647	97857	9
52	43680	98313	46262	98090	48686	97853	8
53	43724	98309	46303	98087	48725	97849	7
54	43769	98306	46345	98083	48764	97845	6
55	43813	98302	46386	98079	48803	97841	5
56	43857	98299	46428	98075	48842	97837	4
57	43901	98295	46469	98071	48881	97833	3
58	43946	98291	46511	98067	48920	97829	2
59	43990	98288	46552	98063	48959	97825	1
60	44034	98284	46594	98060	48998	97821	0
′	Cosine	Sine	Cosine	Sine	Cosine	Sine	′
	74°		73°		72°		

TABLE II.—LOGARITHMIC SINES AND COSINES.

′	18° Sine	18° Cosine	19° Sine	19° Cosine	20° Sine	20° Cosine	′
0	9.48998	9.97821	9.51264	9.97567	9.53405	9.97299	60
1	49037	97817	51301	97563	53440	97294	59
2	49076	97812	51338	97558	53475	97289	58
3	49115	97808	51374	97554	53509	97285	57
4	49153	97804	51411	97550	53544	97280	56
5	49192	97800	51447	97545	53578	97276	55
6	49231	97796	51484	97541	53613	97271	54
7	49269	97792	51520	97536	53647	97266	53
8	49308	97788	51557	97532	53682	97262	52
9	49347	97784	51593	97528	53716	97257	51
10	9.49385	9.97779	9.51629	9.97523	9.53751	9.97252	50
11	49424	97775	51666	97519	53785	97248	49
12	49462	97771	51702	97515	53819	97243	48
13	49500	97767	51738	97510	53854	97238	47
14	49539	97763	51774	97506	53888	97234	46
15	49577	97759	51811	97501	53922	97229	45
16	49615	97754	51847	97497	53957	97224	44
17	49654	97750	51883	97492	53991	97220	43
18	49692	97746	51919	97488	54025	97215	42
19	49730	97742	51955	97484	54059	97210	41
20	9.49768	9.97737	9.51991	9.97479	9.54093	9.97206	40
21	49806	97734	52027	97475	54127	97201	39
22	49844	97729	52063	97470	54161	97196	38
23	49882	97725	52099	97466	54195	97192	37
24	49920	97721	52135	97461	54229	97187	36
25	49958	97717	52171	97457	54263	97182	35
26	49996	97713	52207	97453	54297	97178	34
27	50034	97708	52242	97448	54331	97173	33
28	50072	97704	52278	97444	54365	97168	32
29	50110	97700	52314	97439	54399	97163	31
30	9.50148	9.97696	9.52350	9.97435	9.54433	9.97159	30
31	50185	97691	52385	97430	54466	97154	29
32	50223	97687	52421	97426	54500	97149	28
33	50261	97683	52456	97421	54534	97145	27
34	50298	97679	52492	97417	54567	97140	26
35	50336	97674	52527	97412	54601	97135	25
36	50374	97670	52563	97408	54635	97130	24
37	50411	97666	52598	97403	54668	97126	23
38	50449	97662	52634	97399	54702	97121	22
39	50486	97657	52669	97394	54735	97116	21
40	9.50523	9.97653	9.52705	9.97390	9.54769	9.97111	20
41	50561	97649	52740	97385	54802	97107	19
42	50598	97645	52775	97381	54836	97102	18
43	50635	97640	52811	97376	54869	97097	17
44	50673	97636	52846	97372	54903	97092	16
45	50710	97632	52881	97367	54936	97087	15
46	50747	97628	52916	97363	54969	97083	14
47	50784	97623	52951	97358	55003	97078	13
48	50821	97619	52986	97353	55036	97073	12
49	50858	97615	53021	97349	55069	97068	11
50	9.50896	9.97610	9.53056	9.97344	9.55102	9.97063	10
51	50933	97606	53092	97340	55136	97059	9
52	50970	97602	53126	97335	55169	97054	8
53	51007	97597	53161	97331	55202	97049	7
54	51043	97593	53196	97326	55235	97044	6
55	51080	97589	53231	97322	55268	97039	5
56	51117	97584	53266	97317	55301	97035	4
57	51154	97580	53301	97312	55334	97030	3
58	51191	97576	53336	97308	55367	97025	2
59	51227	97571	53370	97303	55400	97020	1
60	51264	97567	53405	97299	55433	97015	0
′	Cosine	Sine	Cosine	Sine	Cosine	Sine	′
	71°		70°		69°		

TABLE II.—LOGARITHMIC SINES AND COSINES.

′	21°		22°		23°		′
	Sine	Cosine	Sine	Cosine	Sine	Cosine	
0	9.55433	9.97015	9.57358	9.96717	9.59188	9.96403	60
1	55466	97010	57389	96711	59218	96397	59
2	55499	97005	57420	96706	59247	96392	58
3	55532	97001	57451	96701	59277	96387	57
4	55564	96996	57482	96696	59307	96381	56
5	55597	96991	57514	96691	59336	96376	55
6	55630	96986	57545	96686	59366	96370	54
7	55663	96981	57576	96681	59396	96365	53
8	55695	96976	57607	96676	59425	96360	52
9	55728	96971	57638	96670	59455	96354	51
10	9.55761	9.96966	9.57669	9.96665	9.59484	9.96349	50
11	55793	96962	57700	96660	59514	96343	49
12	55826	96957	57731	96655	59543	96338	48
13	55858	96952	57762	96650	59573	96333	47
14	55891	96947	57793	96645	59602	96327	46
15	55923	96942	57824	96640	59632	96322	45
16	55956	96937	57855	96634	59661	96316	44
17	55988	96932	57885	96629	59690	96311	43
18	56021	96927	57916	96624	59720	96305	42
19	56053	96922	57947	96619	59749	96300	41
20	9.56085	9.96917	9.57978	9.96614	9.59778	9.96294	40
21	56118	96912	58008	96608	59808	96289	39
22	56150	96907	58039	96603	59837	96284	38
23	56182	96903	58070	96598	59866	96278	37
24	56215	96898	58101	96593	59895	96273	36
25	56247	96893	58131	96588	59924	96267	35
26	56279	96888	58162	96582	59954	96262	34
27	56311	96883	58192	96577	59983	96256	33
28	56343	96878	58223	96572	60012	96251	32
29	56375	96873	58253	96567	60041	96245	31
30	9.56408	9.96868	9.58284	9.96562	9.60070	9.96240	30
31	56440	96863	58314	96556	60099	96234	29
32	56472	96868	58345	96551	60128	96229	28
33	56504	96853	58375	96546	60157	96223	27
34	56536	96848	58406	96541	60186	96218	26
35	56568	96843	58436	96535	60215	96212	25
36	56599	96838	58467	96530	60244	96207	24
37	56631	96833	58497	96525	60273	96201	23
38	56663	96828	58527	96520	60302	96196	22
39	56695	96823	58557	96514	60331	96190	21
40	9.56727	9.96818	9.58588	9.96509	9.60359	9.96185	20
41	56759	96813	58618	96504	60388	96179	19
42	56790	96808	58648	96498	60417	96174	18
43	56822	96803	58678	96493	60446	96168	17
44	56854	96798	58709	96488	60474	96162	16
45	56886	96793	58739	96483	60503	96157	15
46	56917	96788	58769	96477	60532	96151	14
47	56949	96783	58799	96472	60561	96146	13
48	56980	96778	58829	96467	60589	96140	12
49	57012	96772	58859	96461	60618	96135	11
50	9.57044	9.96767	9.58889	9.96456	9.60646	9.96129	10
51	57075	96762	58919	96451	60675	96123	9
52	57107	96757	58949	96445	60704	96118	8
53	57138	96752	58979	96440	60732	96112	7
54	57169	96747	59009	96435	60761	96107	6
55	57201	96742	59039	96429	60789	96101	5
56	57232	96737	59069	96424	60818	96095	4
57	57264	96732	59098	96419	60846	96090	3
58	57295	96727	59128	96413	60875	96084	2
59	57326	96722	59158	96408	60903	96079	1
60	57358	96717	59188	96403	60931	96073	0
′	Cosine	Sine	Cosine	Sine	Cosine	Sine	′
	68°		67°		66°		

TABLE II.—LOGARITHMIC SINES AND COSINES.

′	24°		25°		26°		′
	Sine	Cosine	Sine	Cosine	Sine	Cosine	
0	9.60931	9.96073	9.62595	9.95728	9.64184	9.95366	60
1	60960	96067	62622	95722	64210	95360	59
2	60988	96062	62649	95716	64236	95354	58
3	61016	96056	62676	95710	64262	95348	57
4	61045	96050	62703	95704	64288	95341	56
5	61073	96045	62730	95698	64313	95335	55
6	61101	96039	62757	95692	64339	95329	54
7	61129	96034	62784	95686	64365	95323	53
8	61158	96028	62811	95680	64391	95317	52
9	61186	96022	62838	95674	64417	95310	51
10	9.61214	9.96017	9.62865	9.95668	9.64442	9.95304	50
11	61242	96011	62892	95663	64468	95298	49
12	61270	96005	62918	95657	64494	95292	48
13	61298	96000	62945	95651	64519	95286	47
14	61326	95994	62972	95645	64545	95279	46
15	61354	95988	62999	95639	64571	95273	45
16	61382	95982	63026	95633	64596	95267	44
17	61411	95977	63052	95627	64622	95261	43
18	61438	95971	63079	95621	64647	95254	42
19	61466	95965	63106	95615	64673	95248	41
20	9.61494	9.95960	9.63133	9.95609	9.64698	9.95242	40
21	61522	95954	63159	95603	64724	95236	39
22	61550	95948	63186	95597	64749	95229	38
23	61578	95942	63213	95591	64775	95223	37
24	61606	95937	63239	95585	64800	95217	36
25	61634	95931	63266	95579	64826	95211	35
26	61662	95925	63292	95573	64851	95204	34
27	61689	95920	63319	95567	64877	95198	33
28	61717	95914	63345	95561	64902	95192	32
29	61745	95908	63372	95555	64927	95185	31
30	9.61773	9.95902	9.63398	9.95549	9.64953	9.95179	30
31	61800	95897	63425	95543	64978	95173	29
32	61828	95891	63451	95537	65003	95167	28
33	61856	95885	63478	95531	65029	95160	27
34	61883	95879	63504	95525	65054	95154	26
35	61911	95873	63531	95519	65079	95148	25
36	61939	95868	63557	95513	65104	95141	24
37	61966	95862	63583	95507	65130	95135	23
38	61994	95856	63610	95500	65155	95129	22
39	62021	95850	63636	95494	65180	95122	21
40	9.62049	9.95844	9.63662	9.95488	9.65205	9.95116	20
41	62076	95839	63689	95482	65230	95110	19
42	62104	95833	63715	95476	65255	95103	18
43	62131	95827	63741	95470	65281	95097	17
44	62159	95821	63767	95464	65306	95090	16
45	62186	95815	63794	95458	65331	95084	15
46	62214	95810	63820	95452	65356	95078	14
47	62241	95804	63846	95446	65381	95071	13
48	62268	95798	63872	95440	65406	95065	12
49	62296	95792	63898	95434	65431	95059	11
50	9.62323	9.95786	9.63924	9.95427	9.65456	9.95052	10
51	62350	95780	63950	95421	65481	95046	9
52	62377	95775	63976	95415	65506	95039	8
53	62405	95769	64002	95409	65531	95033	7
54	62432	95763	64028	95403	65556	95027	6
55	62459	95757	64054	95397	65580	95020	5
56	62486	95751	64080	95391	65605	95014	4
57	62513	95745	64106	95384	65630	95007	3
58	62541	95739	64132	95378	65655	95001	2
59	62568	95733	64158	95372	65680	94995	1
60	62595	95728	64184	95366	65705	94988	0
′	Cosine	Sine	Cosine	Sine	Cosine	Sine	′
	65°		64°		63°		

TABLE II.—LOGARITHMIC SINES AND COSINES.

′	27°		28°		29°		′
	Sine	Cosine	Sine	Cosine	Sine	Cosine	
0	9.65705	9.94988	9.67161	9.94593	9.68557	9.94182	60
1	65729	94982	67185	94587	68580	94175	59
2	65754	94975	67208	94580	68603	94168	58
3	65779	94969	67232	94573	68625	94161	57
4	65804	94962	67256	94567	68648	94154	56
5	65828	94956	67280	94560	68671	94147	55
6	65853	94949	67303	94553	68694	94140	54
7	65878	94943	67327	94546	68716	94133	53
8	65902	94936	67350	94540	68739	94126	52
9	65927	94930	67374	94533	68762	94119	51
10	9.65952	9.94923	9.67398	9.94526	9.68784	9.94112	50
11	65976	94917	67421	94519	68807	94105	49
12	66001	94911	67445	94513	68829	94098	48
13	66025	94904	67468	94506	68852	94090	47
14	66050	94898	67492	94499	68875	94083	46
15	66075	94891	67515	94492	68897	94076	45
16	66099	94885	67539	94485	68920	94069	44
17	66124	94878	67562	94479	68942	94062	43
18	66148	94871	67586	94472	68965	94055	42
19	66173	94865	67609	94465	68987	94048	41
20	9.66197	9.94858	9.67633	9.94458	9.69010	9.94041	40
21	66221	94852	67656	94451	69032	94034	39
22	66246	94845	67680	94445	69055	94027	38
23	66270	94839	67703	94438	69077	94020	37
24	66295	94832	67726	94431	69100	94012	36
25	66319	94826	67750	94424	69122	94005	35
26	66343	94819	67773	94417	69144	93998	34
27	66368	94813	67796	94410	69167	93991	33
28	66392	94806	67820	94404	69189	93984	32
29	66416	94799	67843	94397	69212	93977	31
30	9.66441	9.94793	9.67866	9.94390	9.69234	9.93970	30
31	66465	94786	67890	94383	69256	93963	29
32	66489	94780	67913	94376	69279	93955	28
33	66513	94773	67936	94369	69301	93948	27
34	66537	94767	67959	94362	69323	93941	26
35	66562	94760	67982	94355	69345	93934	25
36	66586	94753	68006	94349	69368	93927	24
37	66610	94747	68029	94342	69390	93920	23
38	66634	94740	68052	94335	69412	93912	22
39	66658	94734	68075	94328	69434	93905	21
40	9.66682	9.94727	9.68098	9.94321	9.69456	9.93898	20
41	66706	94720	68121	94314	69479	93891	19
42	66731	94714	68144	94307	69501	93884	18
43	66755	94707	68167	94300	69523	93876	17
44	66779	94700	68190	94293	69545	93869	16
45	66803	94694	68213	94286	69567	93862	15
46	66827	94687	68237	94279	69589	93855	14
47	66851	94680	68260	94273	69611	93847	13
48	66875	94674	68283	94266	69633	93840	12
49	66899	94667	68305	94259	69655	93833	11
50	9.66922	9.94660	9.68328	9.94252	9.69677	9.93826	10
51	66946	94654	68351	94245	69699	93819	9
52	66970	94647	68374	94238	69721	93811	8
53	66994	94640	68397	94231	69743	93804	7
54	67018	94634	68420	94224	69765	93797	6
55	67042	94627	68443	94217	69787	93789	5
56	67066	94620	68466	94210	69809	93782	4
57	67090	94614	68489	94203	69831	93775	3
58	67113	94607	68512	94196	69853	93768	2
59	67137	94600	68534	94189	69875	93760	1
60	67161	94593	68557	94182	69897	93753	0
′	Cosine	Sine	Cosine	Sine	Cosine	Sine	′
	62°		61°		60°		

TABLE II.—LOGARITHMIC SINES AND COSINES.

′	30°		31°		32°		′
	Sine	Cosine	Sine	Cosine	Sine	Cosine	
0	9.69897	9.93753	9.71184	9.93307	9.72421	9.92842	60
1	69919	93746	71205	93299	72441	92834	59
2	69941	93738	71226	93291	72461	92826	58
3	69963	93731	71247	93284	72482	92818	57
4	69984	93724	71268	93276	72502	92810	56
5	70006	93717	71289	93269	72522	92803	55
6	70028	93709	71310	93261	72542	92795	54
7	70050	93702	71331	93253	72562	92787	53
8	70072	93695	71352	93246	72582	92779	52
9	70093	93687	71373	93238	72602	92771	51
10	9.70115	9.93680	9.71393	9.93230	9.72622	9.92763	50
11	70137	93673	71414	93223	72643	92755	49
12	70159	93665	71435	93215	72663	92747	48
13	70180	93658	71456	93207	72683	92739	47
14	70202	93650	71477	93200	72703	92731	46
15	70224	93643	71498	93192	72723	92723	45
16	70245	93636	71519	93184	72743	92715	44
17	70267	93628	71539	93177	72763	92707	43
18	70288	93621	71560	93169	72783	92699	42
19	70310	93614	71581	93161	72803	92691	41
20	9.70332	9.93606	9.71602	9.93154	9.72823	9.92683	40
21	70353	93599	71622	93146	72843	92675	39
22	70375	93591	71643	93138	72863	92667	38
23	70396	93584	71664	93131	72883	92659	37
24	70418	93577	71685	93123	72902	92651	36
25	70439	93569	71705	93115	72922	92643	35
26	70461	93562	71726	93108	72942	92635	34
27	70482	93554	71747	93100	72962	92627	33
28	70504	93547	71767	93092	72982	92619	32
29	70525	93539	71788	93084	73002	92611	31
30	9.70547	9.93532	9.71809	9.93077	9.73022	9.92603	30
31	70568	93525	71829	93069	73041	92595	29
32	70590	93517	71850	93061	73061	92587	28
33	70611	93510	71870	93053	73081	92579	27
34	70633	93502	71891	93046	73101	92571	26
35	70654	93495	71911	93038	73121	92563	25
36	70675	93487	71932	93030	73140	92555	24
37	70697	93480	71952	93022	73160	92546	23
38	70718	93472	71973	93014	73180	92538	22
39	70739	93465	71994	93007	73200	92530	21
40	9.70761	9.93457	9.72014	9.92999	9.73219	9.92522	20
41	70782	93450	72034	92991	73239	92514	19
42	70803	93442	72055	92983	73259	92506	18
43	70824	93435	72075	92976	73278	92498	17
44	70846	93427	72096	92968	73298	92490	16
45	70867	93420	72116	92960	73318	92482	15
46	70888	93412	72137	92952	73337	92473	14
47	70909	93405	72157	92944	73357	92465	13
48	70931	93397	72177	92936	73377	92457	12
49	70952	93390	72198	92929	73396	92449	11
50	9.70973	9.93382	9.72218	9.92921	9.73416	9.92441	10
51	70994	93375	72238	92913	73435	92433	9
52	71015	93367	72259	92905	73455	92425	8
53	71036	93360	72279	92897	73474	92416	7
54	71058	93352	72299	92889	73494	92408	6
55	71079	93344	72320	92881	73513	92400	5
56	71100	93337	72340	92874	73533	92392	4
57	71121	93329	72360	92866	73552	92384	3
58	71142	93322	72381	92858	73572	92376	2
59	71163	93314	72401	92850	73591	92367	1
60	71184	93307	72421	92842	73611	92359	0
′	Cosine	Sine	Cosine	Sine	Cosine	Sine	′
	59°		58°		57°		

TABLE II.—LOGARITHMIC SINES AND COSINES.

′	33°		34°		35°		′
	Sine	Cosine	Sine	Cosine	Sine	Cosine	
0	9.73611	9.92359	9.74756	9.91857	9.75859	9.91336	60
1	73630	92351	74775	91849	75877	91328	59
2	73650	92343	74794	91840	75895	91319	58
3	73669	92335	74812	91832	75913	91310	57
4	73689	92326	74831	91823	75931	91301	56
5	73708	92318	74850	91815	75949	91292	55
6	73727	92310	74868	91806	75967	91283	54
7	73747	92302	74887	91798	75985	91274	53
8	73766	92293	74906	91789	76003	91266	52
9	73785	92285	74924	91781	76021	91257	51
10	9.73805	9.92277	9.74943	9.91772	9.76039	9.91248	50
11	73824	92269	74961	91763	76057	91239	49
12	73843	92260	74980	91755	76075	91230	48
13	73863	92252	74999	91746	76093	91221	47
14	73882	92244	75017	91738	76111	91212	46
15	73901	92235	75036	91729	76129	91203	45
16	73921	92227	75054	91720	76146	91194	44
17	73940	92219	75073	91712	76164	91185	43
18	73959	92211	75091	91703	76182	91176	42
19	73978	92202	75110	91695	76200	91167	41
20	9.73997	9.92194	9.75128	9.91686	9.76218	9.91158	40
21	74017	92186	75147	91677	76236	91149	39
22	74036	92177	75165	91669	76253	91141	38
23	74055	92169	75184	91660	76271	91132	37
24	74074	92161	75202	91651	76289	91123	36
25	74093	92152	75221	91643	76307	91114	35
26	74113	92144	75239	91634	76324	91105	34
27	74132	92136	75258	91625	76342	91096	33
28	74151	92127	75276	91617	76360	91087	32
29	74170	92119	75294	91608	76378	91078	31
30	9.74189	9.92111	9.75313	9.91599	9.76395	9.91069	30
31	74208	92102	75331	91591	76413	91060	29
32	74227	92094	75350	91582	76431	91051	28
33	74246	92086	75368	91573	76448	91042	27
34	74265	92077	75386	91565	76466	91033	26
35	74284	92069	75405	91556	76484	91023	25
36	74303	92060	75423	91547	76501	91014	24
37	74322	92052	75441	91538	76519	91005	23
38	74341	92044	75459	91530	76537	90996	22
39	74360	92035	75478	91521	76554	90987	21
40	9.74379	9.92027	9.75496	9.91512	9.76572	9.90978	20
41	74398	92018	75514	91504	76590	90969	19
42	74417	92010	75533	91495	76607	90960	18
43	74436	92002	75551	91486	76625	90951	17
44	74455	91993	75569	91477	76642	90942	16
45	74474	91985	75587	91469	76660	90933	15
46	74493	91976	75605	91460	76677	90924	14
47	74512	91968	75624	91451	76695	90915	13
48	74531	91959	75642	91442	76712	90906	12
49	74549	91951	75660	91433	76730	90896	11
50	9.74568	9.91942	9.75678	9.91425	9.76747	9.90887	10
51	74587	91934	75696	91416	76765	90878	9
52	74606	91925	75714	91407	76782	90869	8
53	74625	91917	75733	91398	76800	90860	7
54	74644	91908	75751	91389	76817	90851	6
55	74662	91900	75769	91381	76835	90842	5
56	74681	91891	75787	91372	76852	90832	4
57	74700	91883	75805	91363	76870	90823	3
58	74719	91874	75823	91354	76887	90814	2
59	74737	91866	75841	91345	76904	90805	1
60	74756	91857	75859	91336	76922	90796	0
′	Cosine	Sine	Cosine	Sine	Cosine	Sine	′
	56°		55°		54°		

TABLE II.—LOGARITHMIC SINES AND COSINES.

′	36°		37°		38°		′
	Sine	Cosine	Sine	Cosine	Sine	Cosine	
0	9.76922	9.90796	9.77946	9.90235	9.78934	9.89653	60
1	76939	90787	77963	90225	78950	89643	59
2	76957	90777	77980	90216	78967	89633	58
3	76974	90768	77997	90206	78983	89624	57
4	76991	90759	78013	90197	78999	89614	56
5	77009	90750	78030	90187	79015	89604	55
6	77026	90741	78047	90178	79031	89594	54
7	77043	90731	78063	90168	79047	89584	53
8	77061	90722	78080	90159	79063	89574	52
9	77078	90713	78097	90149	79079	89564	51
10	9.77095	9.90704	9.78113	9.90139	9.79095	9.89554	50
11	77112	90694	78130	90130	79111	89544	49
12	77130	90685	78147	90120	79128	89534	48
13	77147	90676	78163	90111	79144	89524	47
14	77164	90667	78180	90101	79160	89514	46
15	77181	90657	78197	90091	79176	89504	45
16	77199	90648	78213	90082	79192	89495	44
17	77216	90639	78230	90072	79208	89485	43
18	77233	90630	78246	90063	79224	89475	42
19	77250	90620	78263	90053	79240	89465	41
20	9.77268	9.90611	9.78280	9.90043	9.79256	9.89455	40
21	77285	90602	78296	90034	79272	89445	39
22	77302	90592	78313	90024	79288	89435	38
23	77319	90583	78329	90014	79304	89425	37
24	77336	90574	78346	90005	79319	89415	36
25	77353	90565	78362	89995	79335	89405	35
26	77370	90555	78379	89985	79351	89395	34
27	77387	90546	78395	89976	79367	89385	33
28	77405	90537	78412	89966	79383	89375	32
29	77422	90527	78428	89956	79399	89364	31
30	9.77439	9.90518	9.78445	9.89947	9.79415	9.89354	30
31	77456	90509	78461	89937	79431	89344	29
32	77473	90499	78478	89927	79447	89334	28
33	77490	90490	78494	89918	79463	89324	27
34	77507	90480	78510	89908	79478	89314	26
35	77524	90471	78527	89898	79494	89304	25
36	77541	90462	78543	89888	79510	89294	24
37	77558	90452	78560	89879	79526	89284	23
38	77575	90443	78576	89869	79542	89274	22
39	77592	90434	78592	89859	79558	89264	21
40	9.77609	9.90424	9.78609	9.89849	9.79573	9.89254	20
41	77626	90415	78625	89840	79589	89244	19
42	77643	90405	78642	89830	79605	89233	18
43	77660	90396	78658	89820	79621	89223	17
44	77677	90386	78674	89810	79636	89213	16
45	77694	90377	78691	89801	79652	89203	15
46	77711	90368	78707	89791	79668	89193	14
47	77728	90358	78723	89781	79684	89183	13
48	77744	90349	78739	89771	79699	89173	12
49	77761	90339	78756	89761	79715	89162	11
50	9.77778	9.90330	9.78772	9.89752	9.79731	9.89152	10
51	77795	90320	78788	89742	79746	89142	9
52	77812	90311	78805	89732	79762	89132	8
53	77829	90301	78821	89722	79778	89122	7
54	77846	90292	78837	89712	79793	89112	6
55	77862	90282	78853	89702	79809	89101	5
56	77879	90273	78869	89693	79825	89091	4
57	77896	90263	78886	89683	79840	89081	3
58	77913	90254	78902	89673	79856	89071	2
59	77930	90244	78918	89663	79872	89060	1
60	77946	90235	78934	89663	79887	89050	0
′	Cosine	Sine	Cosine	Sine	Cosine	Sine	′
	53°		52°		51°		

TABLE II.—LOGARITHMIC SINES AND COSINES.

′	39°		40°		41°		′
	Sine	Cosine	Sine	Cosine	Sine	Cosine	
0	9.79887	9.89050	9.80807	9.88425	9.81694	9.87778	60
1	79903	89040	80822	88415	81709	87767	59
2	79918	89030	80837	88404	81723	87756	58
3	79934	89020	80852	88394	81738	87745	57
4	79950	89009	80867	88383	81752	87734	56
5	79965	88999	80882	88372	81767	87723	55
6	79981	88989	80897	88362	81781	87712	54
7	79996	88978	80912	88351	81796	87701	53
8	80012	88968	80927	88340	81810	87690	52
9	80027	88958	80942	88330	81825	87679	51
10	9.80043	9.88948	9.80957	9.88319	9.81839	9.87668	50
11	80058	88937	80972	88308	81854	87657	49
12	80074	88927	80987	88298	81868	87646	48
13	80089	88917	81002	88287	81882	87635	47
14	80105	88906	81017	88276	81897	87624	46
15	80120	88896	81032	88266	81911	87613	45
16	80136	88886	81047	88255	81926	87601	44
17	80151	88875	81061	88244	81940	87590	43
18	80166	88865	81076	88234	81955	87579	42
19	80182	88855	81091	88223	81969	87568	41
20	9.80197	9.88844	9.81106	9.88212	9.81983	9.87557	40
21	80213	88834	81121	88201	81998	87546	39
22	80228	88824	81136	88191	82012	87535	38
23	80244	88813	81151	88180	82026	87524	37
24	80259	88803	81166	88169	82041	87513	36
25	80274	88793	81180	88158	82055	87501	35
26	80290	88782	81195	88148	82069	87490	34
27	80305	88772	81210	88137	82084	87479	33
28	80320	88761	81225	88126	82098	87468	32
29	80336	88751	81240	88115	82112	87457	31
30	9.80351	9.88741	9.81254	9.88105	9.82126	9.87446	30
31	80366	88730	81269	88094	82141	87434	29
32	80382	88720	81284	88083	82155	87423	28
33	80397	88709	81299	88072	82169	87412	27
34	80412	88699	81314	88061	82184	87401	26
35	80428	88688	81328	88051	82198	87390	25
36	80443	88678	81343	88040	82212	87378	24
37	80458	88668	81358	88029	82226	87367	23
38	80473	88657	81372	88018	82240	87356	22
39	80489	88647	81387	88007	82255	87345	21
40	9.80504	9.88636	9.81402	9.87996	9.82269	9.87334	20
41	80519	88626	81417	87985	82283	87322	19
42	80534	88615	81431	87975	82297	87311	18
43	80550	88605	81446	87964	82311	87300	17
44	80565	88594	81461	87953	82326	87288	16
45	80580	88584	81475	87942	82340	87277	15
46	80595	88573	81490	87931	82354	87266	14
47	80610	88563	81505	87920	82368	87255	13
48	80625	88552	81519	87909	82382	87243	12
49	80641	88542	81534	87898	82396	87232	11
50	9.80656	9.88531	9.81549	9.87887	9.82410	9.87221	10
51	80671	88521	81563	87877	82424	87209	9
52	80686	88510	81578	87866	82439	87198	8
53	80701	88499	81592	87855	82453	87187	7
54	80716	88489	81607	87844	82467	87175	6
55	80731	88478	81622	87833	82481	87164	5
56	80746	88468	81636	87822	82495	87153	4
57	80762	88457	81651	87811	82509	87141	3
58	80777	88447	81665	87800	82523	87130	2
59	80792	88436	81680	87789	82537	87119	1
60	80807	88425	81694	87778	82551	87107	0
′	Cosine	Sine	Cosine	Sine	Cosine	Sine	′
	50°		49°		48°		

TABLE II.—LOGARITHMIC SINES AND COSINES.

′	42° Sine	42° Cosine	43° Sine	43° Cosine	44° Sine	44° Cosine	′
0	9.82551	9.87107	9.83378	9.86413	9.84177	9.85693	60
1	82565	87096	83392	86401	84190	85681	59
2	82579	87085	83405	86389	84203	85669	58
3	82593	87073	83419	86377	84216	85657	57
4	82607	87062	83432	86366	84229	85645	56
5	82621	87050	83446	86354	84242	85632	55
6	82635	87039	83459	86342	84255	85620	54
7	82649	87028	83473	86330	84269	85608	53
8	82663	87016	83486	86318	84282	85596	52
9	82677	87005	83500	86306	84295	85583	51
10	9.82691	9.86993	9.83513	9.86295	9.84308	9.85571	50
11	82705	86982	83527	86283	84321	85559	49
12	82719	86970	83540	86271	84334	85547	48
13	82733	86959	83554	86259	84347	85534	47
14	82747	86947	83567	86247	84360	85522	46
15	82761	86936	83581	86235	84373	85510	45
16	82775	86924	83594	86223	84385	85497	44
17	82788	86913	83608	86211	84398	85485	43
18	82802	86902	83621	86200	84411	85473	42
19	82816	86890	83634	86188	84424	85460	41
20	9.82830	9.86879	9.83648	9.86176	9.84437	9.85448	40
21	82844	86867	83661	86164	84450	85436	39
22	82858	86855	83674	86152	84463	85423	38
23	82872	86844	83688	86140	84476	85411	37
24	82885	86832	83701	86128	84489	85399	36
25	82899	86821	83715	86116	84502	85386	35
26	82913	86809	83728	86104	84515	85374	34
27	82927	86798	83741	86092	84528	85361	33
28	82941	86786	83755	86080	84540	85349	32
29	82955	86775	83768	86068	84553	85337	31
30	9.82968	9.86763	9.83781	9.86056	9.84566	9.85324	30
31	82982	86752	83795	86044	84579	85312	29
32	82996	86740	83808	86032	84592	85299	28
33	83010	86728	83821	86020	84605	85287	27
34	83023	86717	83834	86008	84618	85274	26
35	83037	86705	83848	85996	84630	85262	25
36	83051	86694	83861	85984	84643	85250	24
37	83065	86682	83874	85972	84656	85237	23
38	83078	86670	83887	85960	84669	85225	22
39	83092	86659	83901	85948	84682	85212	21
40	9.83106	9.86647	9.83914	9.85936	9.84694	9.85200	20
41	83120	86635	83927	85924	84707	85187	19
42	83133	86624	83940	85912	84720	85175	18
43	83147	86612	83954	85900	84733	85162	17
44	83161	86600	83967	85888	84745	85150	16
45	83174	86589	83980	85876	84758	85137	15
46	83188	86577	83993	85864	84771	85125	14
47	83202	86565	84006	85851	84784	85112	13
48	83215	86554	84020	85839	84796	85100	12
49	83229	86542	84033	85827	84809	85087	11
50	9.83242	9.86530	9.84046	9.85815	9.84822	9.85074	10
51	83256	86518	84059	85803	84835	85062	9
52	83270	86507	84072	85791	84847	85049	8
53	83283	86495	84085	85779	84860	85037	7
54	83297	86483	84098	85766	84873	85024	6
55	83310	86472	84112	85754	84885	85012	5
56	83324	86460	84125	85742	84898	84999	4
57	83338	86448	84138	85730	84911	84986	3
58	83351	86436	84151	85718	84923	84974	2
59	83365	86425	84164	85706	84936	84961	1
60	83378	86413	84177	85693	84949	84949	0

′	Cosine	Sine	Cosine	Sine	Cosine	Sine	′
	47°		46°		45°		

TABLE III.—LOG. TANGENTS AND COTANGENTS.

′	0° Tan	0° Cotan	1° Tan	1° Cotan	2° Tan	2° Cotan	′
0	−∞	∞	8.24192	11.75808	8.54308	11.45692	60
1	6.46373	13.53627	24910	75090	54669	45331	59
2	76476	23524	25616	74384	55027	44973	58
3	94085	05915	26312	73688	55382	44618	57
4	7.06579	12.93421	26996	73004	55734	44266	56
5	16270	83730	27669	72331	56083	43917	55
6	24188	75812	28332	71668	56429	43571	54
7	30882	69118	28986	71014	56773	43227	53
8	36682	63318	29629	70371	57114	42886	52
9	41797	58203	30263	69737	57452	42548	51
10	7.46373	12.53627	8.30888	11.69112	8.57788	11.42212	50
11	50512	49488	31505	68495	58121	41879	49
12	54291	45709	32112	67888	58451	41549	48
13	57767	42233	32711	67289	58779	41221	47
14	60986	39014	33302	66698	59105	40895	46
15	63982	36018	33886	66114	59428	40572	45
16	66785	33215	34461	65539	59749	40251	44
17	69418	30582	35029	64971	60068	39932	43
18	71900	28100	35590	64410	60384	39616	42
19	74248	25752	36143	63857	60698	39302	41
20	7.76476	12.23524	8.36689	11.63311	8.61009	11.38991	40
21	78595	21405	37229	62771	61319	38681	39
22	80615	19385	37762	62238	61626	38374	38
23	82546	17454	38289	61711	61931	38069	37
24	84394	15606	38809	61191	62234	37766	36
25	86167	13833	39323	60677	62535	37465	35
26	87871	12129	39832	60168	62834	37166	34
27	89510	10490	40334	59666	63131	36869	33
28	91089	08911	40830	59170	63426	36574	32
29	92613	07387	41321	58679	63718	36282	31
30	7.94086	12.05914	8.41807	11.58193	8.64009	11.35991	30
31	95510	04490	42287	57713	64298	35702	29
32	96889	03111	42762	57238	64585	35415	28
33	98225	01775	43232	56768	64870	35130	27
34	99522	00478	43696	56304	65154	34846	26
35	8.00781	11.99219	44156	55844	65435	34565	25
36	02004	97996	44611	55389	65715	34285	24
37	03194	96806	45061	54939	65993	34007	23
38	04353	95647	45507	54493	66269	33731	22
39	05481	94519	45948	54052	66543	33457	21
40	8.06581	11.93419	8.46385	11.53615	8.66816	11.33184	20
41	07653	92347	46817	53183	67087	32913	19
42	08700	91300	47245	52755	67356	32644	18
43	09722	90278	47669	52331	67624	32376	17
44	10720	89280	48089	51911	67890	32110	16
45	11696	88304	48505	51495	68154	31846	15
46	12651	87349	48917	51083	68417	31583	14
47	13585	86415	49325	50675	68678	31322	13
48	14500	85500	49729	50271	68938	31062	12
49	15395	84605	50130	49870	69196	30804	11
50	8.16273	11.83727	8.50527	11.49473	8.69453	11.30547	10
51	17133	82867	50920	49080	69708	30292	9
52	17976	82024	51310	48690	69962	30038	8
53	18804	81196	51696	48304	70214	29786	7
54	19616	80384	52079	47921	70465	29535	6
55	20413	79587	52459	47541	70714	29286	5
56	21195	78805	52835	47165	70962	29038	4
57	21964	78036	53208	46792	71208	28792	3
58	22720	77280	53578	46422	71453	28547	2
59	23462	76538	53945	46055	71697	28303	1
60	24192	75808	54308	45692	71940	28060	0
′	Cotan	Tan	Cotan	Tan	Cotan	Tan	′
	89°		88°		87°		

TABLE III.—LOG. TANGENTS AND COTANGENTS.

′	3° Tan	Cotan	4° Tan	Cotan	5° Tan	Cotan	′
0	8.71940	11.28060	8.84464	11.15536	8.94195	11.05805	60
1	72181	27819	84646	15354	94340	05660	59
2	72420	27580	84826	15174	94485	05515	58
3	72659	27341	85006	14994	94630	05370	57
4	72896	27104	85185	14815	94773	05227	56
5	73132	26868	85363	14637	94917	05083	55
6	73366	26634	85540	14460	95060	04940	54
7	73600	26400	85717	14283	95202	04798	53
8	73832	26168	85893	14107	95344	04656	52
9	74063	25937	86069	13931	95486	04514	51
10	8.74292	11.25708	8.86243	11.13757	8.95627	11.04373	50
11	74521	25479	86417	13583	95767	04233	49
12	74748	25252	86591	13409	95908	04092	48
13	74974	25026	86763	13237	96047	03953	47
14	75199	24801	86935	13065	96187	03813	46
15	75423	24577	87106	12894	96325	03675	45
16	75645	24355	87277	12723	96464	03536	44
17	75867	24133	87447	12553	96602	03398	43
18	76087	23913	87616	12384	96739	03261	42
19	76306	23694	87785	12215	96877	03123	41
20	8.76525	11.23475	8.87953	11.12047	8.97013	11.02987	40
21	76742	23258	88120	11880	97150	02850	39
22	76958	23042	88287	11713	97285	02715	38
23	77173	22827	88453	11547	97421	02579	37
24	77387	22613	88618	11382	97556	02444	36
25	77600	22400	88783	11217	97691	02309	35
26	77811	22189	88948	11052	97825	02175	34
27	78022	21978	89111	10889	97959	02041	33
28	78232	21768	89274	10726	98092	01908	32
29	78441	21559	89437	10563	98225	01775	31
30	8.78649	11.21351	8.89598	11.10402	8.98358	11.01642	30
31	78855	21145	89760	10240	98490	01510	29
32	79061	20939	89920	10080	98622	01378	28
33	79266	20734	90080	09920	98753	01247	27
34	79470	20530	90240	09760	98884	01116	26
35	79673	20327	90399	09601	99015	00985	25
36	79875	20125	90557	09443	99145	00855	24
37	80076	19924	90715	09285	99275	00725	23
38	80277	19723	90872	09128	99405	00595	22
39	80476	19524	91029	08971	99534	00466	21
40	8.80674	11.19326	8.91185	11.08815	8.99662	11.00338	20
41	80872	19128	91340	08660	99791	00209	19
42	81068	18932	91495	08505	99919	00081	18
43	81264	18736	91650	08350	9.00046	10.99954	17
44	81459	18541	91803	08197	00174	99826	16
45	81653	18347	91957	08043	00301	99699	15
46	81846	18154	92110	07890	00427	99573	14
47	82038	17962	92262	07738	00553	99447	13
48	82230	17770	92414	07586	00679	99321	12
49	82420	17580	92565	07435	00805	99195	11
50	8.82610	11.17390	8.92716	11.07284	9.00930	10.99070	10
51	82799	17201	92866	07134	01055	98945	9
52	82987	17013	93016	06984	01179	98821	8
53	83175	16825	93165	06835	01303	98697	7
54	83361	16639	93313	06687	01427	98573	6
55	83547	16453	93462	06538	01550	98450	5
56	83732	16268	93609	06391	01673	98327	4
57	83916	16084	93756	06244	01796	98204	3
58	84100	15900	93903	06097	01918	98082	2
59	84282	15718	94049	05951	02040	97960	1
60	84464	15536	94195	05805	02162	97838	0
′	Cotan	Tan	Cotan	Tan	Cotan	Tan	′
	86°		85°		84°		

TABLE III.—LOG. TANGENTS AND COTANGENTS.

′	6°		7°		8°		′
	Tan	Cotan	Tan	Cotan	Tan	Cotan	
0	9.02162	10.97838	9.08914	10.91086	9.14780	10.85220	60
1	02283	97717	09019	90981	14872	85128	59
2	02404	97596	09123	90877	14963	85037	58
3	02525	97475	09227	90773	15054	84946	57
4	02645	97355	09330	90670	15145	84855	56
5	02766	97234	09434	90566	15236	84764	55
6	02885	97115	09537	90463	15327	84673	54
7	03005	96995	09640	90360	15417	84583	53
8	03124	96876	09742	90258	15508	84492	52
9	03242	96758	09845	90155	15598	84402	51
10	9.03361	10.96639	9.09947	10.90053	9.15688	10.84312	50
11	03479	96521	10049	89951	15777	84223	49
12	03597	96403	10150	89850	15867	84133	48
13	03714	96286	10252	89748	15956	84044	47
14	03832	96168	10353	89647	16046	83954	46
15	03948	96052	10454	89546	16135	83865	45
16	04065	95935	10555	89445	16224	83776	44
17	04181	95819	10656	89344	16312	83688	43
18	04297	95703	10756	89244	16401	83599	42
19	04413	95587	10856	89144	16489	83511	41
20	9.04528	10.95472	9.10956	10.89044	9.16577	10.83423	40
21	04643	95357	11056	88944	16665	83335	39
22	04758	95242	11155	88845	16753	83247	38
23	04873	95127	11254	88746	16841	83159	37
24	04987	95013	11353	88647	16928	83072	36
25	05101	94899	11452	88548	17016	82984	35
26	05214	94786	11551	88449	17103	82897	34
27	05328	94672	11649	88351	17190	82810	33
28	05441	94559	11747	88253	17277	82723	32
29	05553	94447	11845	88155	17363	82637	31
30	9.05666	10.94334	9.11943	10.88057	9.17450	10.82550	30
31	05778	94222	12040	87960	17536	82464	29
32	05890	94110	12138	87862	17622	82378	28
33	06002	93998	12235	87765	17708	82292	27
34	06113	93887	12332	87668	17794	82206	26
35	06224	93776	12428	87572	17880	82120	25
36	06335	93665	12525	87475	17965	82035	24
37	06445	93555	12621	87379	18051	81949	23
38	06556	93444	12717	87283	18136	81864	22
39	06666	93334	12813	87187	18221	81779	21
40	9.06775	10.93225	9.12909	10.87091	9.18306	10.81694	20
41	06885	93115	13004	86996	18391	81609	19
42	06994	93006	13099	86901	18475	81525	18
43	07103	92897	13194	86806	18560	81440	17
44	07211	92789	13289	86711	18644	81356	16
45	07320	92680	13384	86616	18728	81272	15
46	07428	92572	13478	86522	18812	81188	14
47	07536	92464	13573	86427	18896	81104	13
48	07643	92357	13667	86333	18979	81021	12
49	07751	92249	13761	86239	19063	80937	11
50	9.07858	10.92142	9.13854	10.86146	9.19146	10.80854	10
51	07964	92036	13948	86052	19229	80771	9
52	08071	91929	14041	85959	19312	80688	8
53	08177	91823	14134	85866	19395	80605	7
54	08283	91717	14227	85773	19478	80522	6
55	08389	91611	14320	85680	19561	80439	5
56	08495	91505	14412	85588	19643	80357	4
57	08600	91400	14504	85496	19725	80275	3
58	08705	91295	14597	85403	19807	80193	2
59	08810	91190	14688	85312	19889	80111	1
60	08914	91086	14780	85220	19971	80029	0
′	Cotan	Tan	Cotan	Tan	Cotan	Tan	′
	83°		82°		81°		

TABLE III.—LOG. TANGENTS AND COTANGENTS.

′	9° Tan	9° Cotan	10° Tan	10° Cotan	11° Tan	11° Cotan	′
0	9.19971	10.80029	9.24632	10.75368	9.28865	10.71135	60
1	20053	79947	24706	75294	28933	71067	59
2	20134	79866	24779	75221	29000	71000	58
3	20216	79784	24853	75147	29067	70933	57
4	20297	79703	24926	75074	29134	70866	56
5	20378	79622	25000	75000	29201	70799	55
6	20459	79541	25073	74927	29268	70732	54
7	20540	79460	25146	74854	29335	70665	53
8	20621	79379	25219	74781	29402	70598	52
9	20701	79299	25292	74708	29468	70532	51
10	9.20782	10.79218	9.25365	10.74635	9.29535	10.70465	50
11	20862	79138	25437	74563	29601	70399	49
12	20942	79058	25510	74490	29668	70332	48
13	21022	78978	25582	74418	29734	70266	47
14	21102	78898	25655	74345	29800	70200	46
15	21182	78818	25727	74273	29866	70134	45
16	21261	78739	25799	74201	29932	70068	44
17	21341	78659	25871	74129	29998	70002	43
18	21420	78580	25943	74057	30064	69936	42
19	21499	78501	26015	73985	30130	69870	41
20	9.21578	10.78422	9.26086	10.73914	9.30195	10.69805	40
21	21657	78343	26158	73842	30261	69739	39
22	21736	78264	26229	73771	30326	69674	38
23	21814	78186	26301	73699	30391	69609	37
24	21893	78107	26372	73628	30457	69543	36
25	21971	78029	26443	73557	30522	69478	35
26	22049	77951	26514	73486	30587	69413	34
27	22127	77873	26585	73415	30652	69348	33
28	22205	77795	26655	73345	30717	69283	32
29	22283	77717	26726	73274	30782	69218	31
30	9.22361	10.77639	9.26797	10.73203	9.30846	10.69154	30
31	22438	77562	26867	73133	30911	69089	29
32	22516	77484	26937	73063	30975	69025	28
33	22593	77407	27008	72992	31040	68960	27
34	22670	77330	27078	72922	31104	68896	26
35	22747	77253	27148	72852	31168	68832	25
36	22824	77176	27218	72782	31233	68767	24
37	22901	77099	27288	72712	31297	68703	23
38	22977	77023	27357	72643	31361	68639	22
39	23054	76946	27427	72573	31425	68575	21
40	9.23130	10.76870	9.27496	10.72504	9.31489	10.68511	20
41	23206	76794	27566	72434	31552	68448	19
42	23283	76717	27635	72365	31616	68384	18
43	23359	76641	27704	72296	31679	68321	17
44	23435	76565	27773	72227	31743	68257	16
45	23510	76490	27842	72158	31806	68194	15
46	23586	76414	27911	72089	31870	68130	14
47	23661	76339	27980	72020	31933	68067	13
48	23737	76263	28049	71951	31996	68004	12
49	23812	76188	28117	71883	32059	67941	11
50	9.23887	10.76113	9.28186	10.71814	9.32122	10.67878	10
51	23962	76038	28254	71746	32185	67815	9
52	24037	75963	28323	71677	32248	67752	8
53	24112	75888	28391	71609	32311	67689	7
54	24186	75814	28459	71541	32373	67627	6
55	24261	75739	28527	71473	32436	67564	5
56	24335	75665	28595	71405	32498	67502	4
57	24410	75590	28662	71338	32561	67439	3
58	24484	75516	28730	71270	32623	67377	2
59	24558	75442	28798	71202	32685	67315	1
60	24632	75368	28865	71135	32747	67253	0
′	Cotan	Tan	Cotan	Tan	Cotan	Tan	′
	80°		79°		78°		

TABLE III.—LOG. TANGENTS AND COTANGENTS.

′	12° Tan	12° Cotan	13° Tan	13° Cotan	14° Tan	14° Cotan	′
0	9.32747	10.67253	9.36336	10.63664	9.39677	10.60323	60
1	32810	67190	36394	63606	39731	60269	59
2	32872	67128	36452	63548	39785	60215	58
3	32933	67067	36509	63491	39838	60162	57
4	32995	67005	36566	63434	39892	60108	56
5	33057	66943	36624	63376	39945	60055	55
6	33119	66881	36681	63319	39999	60001	54
7	33180	66820	36738	63262	40052	59948	53
8	33242	66758	36795	63205	40106	59894	52
9	33303	66697	36852	63148	40159	59841	51
10	9.33365	10.66635	9.36909	10.63091	9.40212	10.59788	50
11	33426	66574	36966	63034	40266	59734	49
12	33487	66513	37023	62977	40319	59681	48
13	33548	66452	37080	62920	40372	59628	47
14	33609	66391	37137	62863	40425	59575	46
15	33670	66330	37193	62807	40478	59522	45
16	33731	66269	37250	62750	40531	59469	44
17	33792	66208	37306	62694	40584	59416	43
18	33853	66147	37363	62637	40636	59364	42
19	33913	66087	37419	62581	40689	59311	41
20	9.33974	10.66026	9.37476	10.62524	9.40742	10.59258	40
21	34034	65966	37532	62468	40795	59205	39
22	34095	65905	37588	62412	40847	59153	38
23	34155	65845	37644	62356	40900	59100	37
24	34215	65785	37700	62300	40952	59048	36
25	34276	65724	37756	62244	41005	58995	35
26	34336	65664	37812	62188	41057	58943	34
27	34396	65604	37868	62132	41109	58891	33
28	34456	65544	37924	62076	41161	58839	32
29	34516	65484	37980	62020	41214	58786	31
30	9.34576	10.65424	9.38035	10.61965	9.41266	10.58734	30
31	34635	65365	38091	61909	41318	58682	29
32	34695	65305	38147	61853	41370	58630	28
33	34755	65245	38202	61798	41422	58578	27
34	34814	65186	38257	61743	41474	58526	26
35	34874	65126	38313	61687	41526	58474	25
36	34933	65067	38368	61632	41578	58422	24
37	34992	65008	38423	61577	41629	58371	23
38	35051	64949	38479	61521	41681	58319	22
39	35111	64889	38534	61466	41733	58267	21
40	9.35170	10.64830	9.38589	10.61411	9.41784	10.58216	20
41	35229	64771	38644	61356	41836	58164	19
42	35288	64712	38699	61301	41887	58113	18
43	35347	64653	38754	61246	41939	58061	17
44	35405	64595	38808	61192	41990	58010	16
45	35464	64536	38863	61137	42041	57959	15
46	35523	64477	38918	61082	42093	57907	14
47	35581	64419	38972	61028	42144	57856	13
48	35640	64360	39027	60973	42195	57805	12
49	35698	64302	39082	60918	42246	57754	11
50	9.35757	10.64243	9.39136	10.60864	9.42297	10.57703	10
51	35815	64185	39190	60810	42348	57652	9
52	35873	64127	39245	60755	42399	57601	8
53	35931	64069	39299	60701	42450	57550	7
54	35989	64011	39353	60647	42501	57499	6
55	36047	63953	39407	60593	42552	57448	5
56	36105	63895	39461	60539	42603	57397	4
57	36163	63837	39515	60485	42653	57347	3
58	36221	63779	39569	60431	42704	57296	2
59	36279	63721	39623	60377	42755	57245	1
60	36336	63664	39677	60323	42805	57195	0
′	Cotan	Tan	Cotan	Tan	Cotan	Tan	′
	77°		76°		75°		

TABLE III.—LOG. TANGENTS AND COTANGENTS.

′	15°		16°		17°		′
	Tan	Cotan	Tan	Cotan	Tan	Cotan	
0	9.42805	10.57195	9.45750	10.54250	9.48534	10.51466	60
1	42856	57144	45797	54203	48579	51421	59
2	42906	57094	45845	54155	48624	51376	58
3	42957	57043	45892	54108	48669	51331	57
4	43007	56993	45940	54060	48714	51286	56
5	43057	56943	45987	54013	48759	51241	55
6	43108	56892	46035	53965	48804	51196	54
7	43158	56842	46082	53918	48849	51151	53
8	43208	56792	46130	53870	48894	51106	52
9	43258	56742	46177	53823	48939	51061	51
10	9.43308	10.56692	9.46224	10.53776	9.48984	10.51016	50
11	43358	56642	46271	53729	49029	50971	49
12	43408	56592	46319	53681	49073	50927	48
13	43458	56542	46366	53634	49118	50882	47
14	43508	56492	46413	53587	49163	50837	46
15	43558	56442	46460	53540	49207	50793	45
16	43607	56393	46507	53493	49252	50748	44
17	43657	56343	46554	53446	49296	50704	43
18	43707	56293	46601	53399	49341	50659	42
19	43756	56244	46648	53352	49385	50615	41
20	9.43806	10.56194	9.46694	10.53306	9.49430	10.50570	40
21	43855	56145	46741	53259	49474	50526	39
22	43905	56095	46788	53212	49519	50481	38
23	43954	56046	46835	53165	49563	50437	37
24	44004	55996	46881	53119	49607	50393	36
25	44053	55947	46928	53072	49652	50348	35
26	44102	55898	46975	53025	49696	50304	34
27	44151	55849	47021	52979	49740	50260	33
28	44201	55799	47068	52932	49784	50216	32
29	44250	55750	47114	52886	49828	50172	31
30	9.44299	10.55701	9.47160	10.52840	9.49872	10.50128	30
31	44348	55652	47207	52793	49916	50084	29
32	44397	55603	47253	52747	49960	50040	28
33	44446	55554	47299	52701	50004	49996	27
34	44495	55505	47346	52654	50048	49952	26
35	44544	55456	47392	52608	50092	49908	25
36	44592	55408	47438	52562	50136	49864	24
37	44641	55359	47484	52516	50180	49820	23
38	44690	55310	47530	52470	50223	49777	22
39	44738	55262	47576	52424	50267	49733	21
40	9.44787	10.55213	9.47622	10.52378	9.50311	10.49689	20
41	44836	55164	47668	52332	50355	49645	19
42	44884	55116	47714	52286	50398	49602	18
43	44933	55067	47760	52240	50442	49558	17
44	44981	55019	47806	52194	50485	49515	16
45	45029	54971	47852	52148	50529	49471	15
46	45078	54922	47897	52103	50572	49428	14
47	45126	54874	47943	52057	50616	49384	13
48	45174	54826	47989	52011	50659	49341	12
49	45222	54778	48035	51965	50703	49297	11
50	9.45271	10.54729	9.48080	10.51920	9.50746	10.49254	10
51	45319	54681	48126	51874	50789	49211	9
52	45367	54633	48171	51829	50833	49167	8
53	45415	54585	48217	51783	50876	49124	7
54	45463	54537	48262	51738	50919	49081	6
55	45511	54489	48307	51693	50962	49038	5
56	45559	54441	48353	51647	51005	48995	4
57	45606	54394	48398	51602	51048	48952	3
58	45654	54346	48443	51557	51092	48908	2
59	45702	54298	48489	51511	51135	48865	1
60	45750	54250	48534	51466	51178	48822	0
′	Cotan	Tan	Cotan	Tan	Cotan	Tan	′
	74°		73°		72°		

TABLE III.—LOG. TANGENTS AND COTANGENTS.

′	18°		19°		20°		′
	Tan	Cotan	Tan	Cotan	Tan	Cotan	
0	9.51178	10.48822	9.53697	10.46303	9.56107	10.43893	60
1	51221	48779	53738	46262	56146	43854	59
2	51264	48736	53779	46221	56185	43815	58
3	51306	48694	53820	46180	56224	43776	57
4	51349	48651	53861	46139	56264	43736	56
5	51392	48608	53902	46098	56303	43697	55
6	51435	48565	53943	46057	56342	43658	54
7	51478	48522	53984	46016	56381	43619	53
8	51520	48480	54025	45975	56420	43580	52
9	51563	48437	54065	45935	56459	43541	51
10	9.51606	10.48394	9.54106	10.45894	9.56498	10.43502	50
11	51648	48352	54147	45853	56537	43463	49
12	51691	48309	54187	45813	56576	43424	48
13	51734	48266	54228	45772	56615	43385	47
14	51776	48224	54269	45731	56654	43346	46
15	51819	48181	54309	45691	56693	43307	45
16	51861	48139	54350	45650	56732	43268	44
17	51903	48097	54390	45610	56771	43229	43
18	51946	48054	54431	45569	56810	43190	42
19	51988	48012	54471	45529	56849	43151	41
20	9.52031	10.47969	9.54512	10.45488	9.56887	10.43113	40
21	52073	47927	54552	45448	56926	43074	39
22	52115	47885	54593	45407	56965	43035	38
23	52157	47843	54633	45367	57004	42996	37
24	52200	47800	54673	45327	57042	42958	36
25	52242	47758	54714	45286	57081	42919	35
26	52284	47716	54754	45246	57120	42880	34
27	52326	47674	54794	45206	57158	42842	33
28	52368	47632	54835	45165	57197	42803	32
29	52410	47590	54875	45125	57235	42765	31
30	9.52452	10.47548	9.54915	10.45085	9.57274	10.42726	30
31	52494	47506	54955	45045	57312	42688	29
32	52536	47464	54995	45005	57351	42649	28
33	52578	47422	55035	44965	57389	42611	27
34	52620	47380	55075	44925	57428	42572	26
35	52661	47339	55115	44885	57466	42534	25
36	52703	47297	55155	44845	57504	42496	24
37	52745	47255	55195	44805	57543	42457	23
38	52787	47213	55235	44765	57581	42419	22
39	52829	47171	55275	44725	57619	42381	21
40	9.52870	10.47130	9.55315	10.44685	9.57658	10.42342	20
41	52912	47088	55355	44645	57696	42304	19
42	52953	47047	55395	44605	57734	42266	18
43	52995	47005	55434	44566	57772	42228	17
44	53037	46963	55474	44526	57810	42190	16
45	53078	46922	55514	44486	57849	42151	15
46	53120	46880	55554	44446	57887	42113	14
47	53161	46839	55593	44407	57925	42075	13
48	53202	46798	55633	44367	57963	42037	12
49	53244	46756	55673	44327	58001	41999	11
50	9.53285	10.46715	9.55712	10.44288	9.58039	10.41961	10
51	53327	46673	55752	44248	58077	41923	9
52	53368	46632	55791	44209	58115	41885	8
53	53409	46591	55831	44169	58153	41847	7
54	53450	46550	55870	44130	58191	41809	6
55	53492	46508	55910	44090	58229	41771	5
56	53533	46467	55949	44051	58267	41733	4
57	53574	46426	55989	44011	58304	41696	3
58	53615	46385	56028	43972	58342	41658	2
59	53656	46344	56067	43933	58380	41620	1
60	53697	46303	56107	43893	58418	41582	0
	Cotan	Tan	Cotan	Tan	Cotan	Tan	
′	71°		70°		69°		′

TABLE III.—LOG. TANGENTS AND COTANGENTS.

′	21°		22°		23°		′
	Tan	Cotan	Tan	Cotan	Tan	Cotan	
0	9.58418	10.41582	9.60641	10.39359	9.62785	10.37215	60
1	58455	41545	60677	39323	62820	37180	59
2	58493	41507	60714	39286	62855	37145	58
3	58531	41469	60750	39250	62890	37110	57
4	58569	41431	60786	39214	62926	37074	56
5	58606	41394	60823	39177	62961	37039	55
6	58644	41356	60859	39141	62996	37004	54
7	58681	41319	60895	39105	63031	36969	53
8	58719	41281	60931	39069	63066	36934	52
9	58757	41243	60967	39033	63101	36899	51
10	9.58794	10.41206	9.61004	10.38996	9.63135	10.36865	50
11	58832	41168	61040	38960	63170	36830	49
12	58869	41131	61076	38924	63205	36795	48
13	58907	41093	61112	38888	63240	36760	47
14	58944	41056	61148	38852	63275	36725	46
15	58981	41019	61184	38816	63310	36690	45
16	59019	40981	61220	38780	63345	36655	44
17	59056	40944	61256	38744	63379	36621	43
18	59094	40906	61292	38708	63414	36586	42
19	59131	40869	61328	38672	63449	36551	41
20	9.59168	10.40832	9.61364	10.38636	9.63484	10.36516	40
21	59205	40795	61400	38600	63519	36481	39
22	59243	40757	61436	38564	63553	36447	38
23	59280	40720	61472	38528	63588	36412	37
24	59317	40683	61508	38492	63623	36377	36
25	59354	40646	61544	38456	63657	36343	35
26	59391	40609	61579	38421	63692	36308	34
27	59429	40571	61615	38385	63726	36274	33
28	59466	40534	61651	38349	63761	36239	32
29	59503	40497	61687	38313	63796	36204	31
30	9.59540	10.40460	9.61722	10.38278	9.63830	10.36170	30
31	59577	40423	61758	38242	63865	36135	29
32	59614	40386	61794	38206	63899	36101	28
33	59651	40349	61830	38170	63934	36066	27
34	59688	40312	61865	38135	63968	36032	26
35	59725	40275	61901	38099	64003	35997	25
36	59762	40238	61936	38064	64037	35963	24
37	59799	40201	61972	38028	64072	35928	23
38	59835	40165	62008	37992	64106	35894	22
39	59872	40128	62043	37957	64140	35860	21
40	9.59909	10.40091	9.62079	10.37921	9.64175	10.35825	20
41	59946	40054	62114	37886	64209	35791	19
42	59983	40017	62150	37850	64243	35757	18
43	60019	39981	62185	37815	64278	35722	17
44	60056	39944	62221	37779	64312	35688	16
45	60093	39907	62256	37744	64346	35654	15
46	60130	39870	62292	37708	64381	35619	14
47	60166	39834	62327	37673	64415	35585	13
48	60203	39797	62362	37638	64449	35551	12
49	60240	39760	62398	37602	64483	35517	11
50	9.60276	10.39724	9.62433	10.37567	9.64517	10.35483	10
51	60313	39687	62468	37532	64552	35448	9
52	60349	39651	62504	37496	64586	35414	8
53	60386	39614	62539	37461	64620	35380	7
54	60422	39578	62574	37426	64654	35346	6
55	60459	39541	62609	37391	64688	35312	5
56	60495	39505	62645	37355	64722	35278	4
57	60532	39468	62680	37320	64756	35244	3
58	60568	39432	62715	37285	64790	35210	2
59	60605	39395	62750	37250	64824	35176	1
60	60641	39359	62785	37215	64858	35142	0
′	Cotan	Tan	Cotan	Tan	Cotan	Tan	′
	68°		67°		66°		

TABLE III.—LOG. TANGENTS AND COTANGENTS.

′	24°		25°		26°		′
	Tan	Cotan	Tan	Cotan	Tan	Cotan	
0	9.64858	10.35142	9.66867	10.33133	9.68818	10.31182	60
1	64892	35108	66900	33100	68850	31150	59
2	64926	35074	66933	33067	68882	31118	58
3	64960	35040	66966	33034	68914	31086	57
4	64994	35006	66999	33001	68946	31054	56
5	65028	34972	67032	32968	68978	31022	55
6	65062	34938	67065	32935	69010	30990	54
7	65096	34904	67098	32902	69042	30958	53
8	65130	34870	67131	32869	69074	30926	52
9	65164	34836	67163	32837	69106	30894	51
10	9.65197	10.34803	9.67196	10.32804	9.69138	10.30862	50
11	65231	34769	67229	32771	69170	30830	49
12	65265	34735	67262	32738	69202	30798	48
13	65299	34701	67295	32705	69234	30766	47
14	65333	34667	67327	32673	69266	30734	46
15	65366	34634	67360	32640	69298	30702	45
16	65400	34600	67393	32607	69329	30671	44
17	65434	34566	67426	32574	69361	30639	43
18	65467	34533	67458	32542	69393	30607	42
19	65501	34499	67491	32509	69425	30575	41
20	9.65535	10.34465	9.67524	10.32476	9.69457	10.30543	40
21	65568	34432	67556	32444	69488	30512	39
22	65602	34398	67589	32411	69520	30480	38
23	65636	34364	67622	32378	69552	30448	37
24	65669	34331	67654	32346	69584	30416	36
25	65703	34297	67687	32313	69615	30385	35
26	65736	34264	67719	32281	69647	30353	34
27	65770	34230	67752	32248	69679	30321	33
28	65803	34197	67785	32215	69710	30290	32
29	65837	34163	67817	32183	69742	30258	31
30	9.65870	10.34130	9.67850	10.32150	9.69774	10.30226	30
31	65904	34096	67882	32118	69805	30195	29
32	65937	34063	67915	32085	69837	30163	28
33	65971	34029	67947	32053	69868	30132	27
34	66004	33996	67980	32020	69900	30100	26
35	66038	33962	68012	31988	69932	30068	25
36	66071	33929	68044	31956	69963	30037	24
37	66104	33896	68077	31923	69995	30005	23
38	66138	33862	68109	31891	70026	29974	22
39	66171	33829	68142	31858	70058	29942	21
40	9.66204	10.33796	9.68174	10.31826	9.70089	10.29911	20
41	66238	33762	68206	31794	70121	29879	19
42	66271	33729	68239	31761	70152	29848	18
43	66304	33696	68271	31729	70184	29816	17
44	66337	33663	68303	31697	70215	29785	16
45	66371	33629	68336	31664	70247	29753	15
46	66404	33596	68368	31632	70278	29722	14
47	66437	33563	68400	31600	70309	29691	13
48	66470	33530	68432	31568	70341	29659	12
49	66503	33497	68465	31535	70372	29628	11
50	9.66537	10.33463	9.68497	10.31503	9.70404	10.29596	10
51	66570	33430	68529	31471	70435	29565	9
52	66603	33397	68561	31439	70466	29534	8
53	66636	33364	68593	31407	70498	29502	7
54	66669	33331	68626	31374	70529	29471	6
55	66702	33298	68658	31342	70560	29440	5
56	66735	33265	68690	31310	70592	29408	4
57	66768	33232	68722	31278	70623	29377	3
58	66801	33199	68754	31246	70654	29346	2
59	66834	33166	68786	31214	70685	29315	1
60	66867	33133	68818	31182	70717	29283	0
	Cotan	Tan	Cotan	Tan	Cotan	Tan	
′	65°		64°		63°		′

TABLE III.—LOG. TANGENTS AND COTANGENTS.

′	27°		28°		29°		′
	Tan	Cotan	Tan	Cotan	Tan	Cotan	
0	9.70717	10.29283	9.72567	10.27433	9.74375	10.25625	60
1	70748	29252	72598	27402	74405	25595	59
2	70779	29221	72628	27372	74435	25565	58
3	70810	29190	72659	27341	74465	25535	57
4	70841	29159	72689	27311	74494	25506	66
5	70873	29127	72720	27280	74524	25476	55
6	70904	29096	72750	27250	74554	25446	54
7	70935	29065	72780	27220	74583	25417	53
8	70966	29034	72811	27189	74613	25387	52
9	70997	29003	72841	27159	74643	25357	51
10	9.71028	10.28972	9.72872	10.27128	9.74673	10.25327	50
11	71059	28941	72902	27098	74702	25298	49
12	71090	28910	72932	27068	74732	25268	48
13	71121	28879	72963	27037	74762	25238	47
14	71153	28847	72993	27007	74791	25209	46
15	71184	28816	73023	26977	74821	25179	45
16	71215	28785	73054	26946	74851	25149	44
17	71246	28754	73084	26916	74880	25120	43
18	71277	28723	73114	26886	74910	25090	42
19	71308	28692	73144	26856	74939	25061	41
20	9.71339	10.28661	9.73175	10.26825	9.74969	10.25031	40
21	71370	28630	73205	26795	74998	25002	39
22	71401	28599	73235	26765	75028	24972	38
23	71431	28569	73265	26735	75058	24942	37
24	71462	28538	73295	26705	75087	24913	36
25	71493	28507	73326	26674	75117	24883	35
26	71524	28476	73356	26644	75146	24854	34
27	71555	28445	73386	26614	75176	24824	33
28	71586	28414	73416	26584	75205	24795	32
29	71617	28383	73446	26554	75235	24765	31
30	9.71648	10.28352	9.73476	10.26524	9.75264	10.24736	30
31	71679	28321	73507	26493	75294	24706	29
32	71709	28291	73537	26463	75323	24677	28
33	71740	28260	73567	26433	75353	24647	27
34	71771	28229	73597	26403	75382	24618	26
35	71802	28198	73627	26373	75411	24589	25
36	71833	28167	73657	26343	75441	24559	24
37	71863	28137	73687	26313	75470	24530	23
38	71894	28106	73717	26283	75500	24500	22
39	71925	28075	73747	26253	75529	24471	21
40	9.71955	10.28045	9.73777	10.26223	9.75558	10.24442	20
41	71986	28014	73807	26193	75588	24412	19
42	72017	27983	73837	26163	75617	24383	18
43	72048	27952	73867	26133	75647	24353	17
44	72078	27922	73897	26103	75676	24324	16
45	72109	27891	73927	26073	75705	24295	15
46	72140	27860	73957	26043	75735	24265	14
47	72170	27830	73987	26013	75764	24236	13
48	72201	27799	74017	25983	75793	24207	12
49	72231	27769	74047	25953	75822	24178	11
50	9.72262	10.27738	9.74077	10.25923	9.75852	10.24148	10
51	72293	27707	74107	25893	75881	24119	9
52	72323	27677	74137	25863	75910	24090	8
53	72354	27646	74166	25834	75939	24061	7
54	72384	27616	74196	25804	75969	24031	6
55	72415	27585	74226	25774	75998	24002	5
56	72445	27555	74256	25744	76027	23973	4
57	72476	27524	74286	25714	76056	23944	3
58	72506	27494	74316	25684	76086	23914	2
59	72537	27463	74345	25655	76115	23885	1
60	72567	27433	74375	25625	76144	23856	0
′	Cotan	Tan	Cotan	Tan	Cotan	Tan	′
	62°		61°		60°		

TABLE III.—LOG. TANGENTS AND COTANGENTS.

′	30° Tan	30° Cotan	31° Tan	31° Cotan	32° Tan	32° Cotan	′
0	9.76144	10.23856	9.77877	10.22123	9.79579	10.20421	60
1	76173	23827	77906	22094	79607	20393	59
2	76202	23798	77935	22065	79635	20365	58
3	76231	23769	77963	22037	79663	20337	57
4	76261	23739	77992	22008	79691	20309	56
5	76290	23710	78020	21980	79719	20281	55
6	76319	23681	78049	21951	79747	20253	54
7	76348	23652	78077	21923	79776	20224	53
8	76377	23623	78106	21894	79804	20196	52
9	76406	23594	78135	21865	79832	20168	51
10	9.76435	10.23565	9.78163	10.21837	9.79860	10.20140	50
11	76464	23536	78192	21808	79888	20112	49
12	76493	23507	78220	21780	79916	20084	48
13	76522	23478	78249	21751	79944	20056	47
14	76551	23449	78277	21723	79972	20028	46
15	76580	23420	78306	21694	80000	20000	45
16	76609	23391	78334	21666	80028	19972	44
17	76639	23361	78363	21637	80056	19944	43
18	76668	23332	78391	21609	80084	19916	42
19	76697	23303	78419	21581	80112	19888	41
20	9.76725	10.23275	9.78448	10.21552	9.80140	10.19860	40
21	76754	23246	78476	21524	80168	19832	39
22	76783	23217	78505	21495	80195	19805	38
23	76812	23188	78533	21467	80223	19777	37
24	76841	23159	78562	21438	80251	19749	36
25	76870	23130	78590	21410	80279	19721	35
26	76899	23101	78618	21382	80307	19693	34
27	76928	23072	78647	21353	80335	19665	33
28	76957	23043	78675	21325	80363	19637	32
29	76986	23014	78704	21296	80391	19609	31
30	9.77015	10.22985	9.78732	10.21268	9.80419	10.19581	30
31	77044	22956	78760	21240	80447	19553	29
32	77073	22927	78789	21211	80474	19526	28
33	77101	22899	78817	21183	80502	19498	27
34	77130	22870	78845	21155	80530	19470	26
35	77159	22841	78874	21126	80558	19442	25
36	77188	22812	78902	21098	80586	19414	24
37	77217	22783	78930	21070	80614	19386	23
38	77246	22754	78959	21041	80642	19358	22
39	77274	22726	78987	21013	80669	19331	21
40	9.77303	10.22697	9.79015	10.20985	9.80697	10.19303	20
41	77332	22668	79043	20957	80725	19275	19
42	77361	22639	79072	20928	80753	19247	18
43	77390	22610	79100	20900	80781	19219	17
44	77418	22582	79128	20872	80808	19192	16
45	77447	22553	79156	20844	80836	19164	15
46	77476	22524	79185	20815	80864	19136	14
47	77505	22495	79213	20787	80892	19108	13
48	77533	22467	79241	20759	80919	19081	12
49	77562	22438	79269	20731	80947	19053	11
50	9.77591	10.22409	9.79297	10.20703	9.80975	10.19025	10
51	77619	22381	79326	20674	81003	18997	9
52	77648	22352	79354	20646	81030	18970	8
53	77677	22323	79382	20618	81058	18942	7
54	77706	22294	79410	20590	81086	18914	6
55	77734	22266	79438	20562	81113	18887	5
56	77763	22237	79466	20534	81141	18859	4
57	77791	22209	79495	20505	81169	18831	3
58	77820	22180	79523	20477	81196	18804	2
59	77849	22151	79551	20449	81224	18776	1
60	77877	22123	79579	20421	81252	18748	0
′	Cotan	Tan	Cotan	Tan	Cotan	Tan	′
	59°		58°		57°		

TABLE III.—LOG. TANGENTS AND COTANGENTS.

′	33°		34°		35°		′
	Tan	Cotan	Tan	Cotan	Tan	Cotan	
0	9.81252	10.18748	9.82899	10.17101	9.84523	10.15477	60
1	81279	18721	82926	17074	84550	15450	59
2	81307	18693	82953	17047	84576	15424	58
3	81335	18665	82980	17020	84603	15397	57
4	81362	18638	83008	16992	84630	15370	56
5	81390	18610	83035	16965	84657	15343	55
6	81418	18582	83062	16938	84684	15316	54
7	81445	18555	83089	16911	84711	15289	53
8	81473	18527	83117	16883	84738	15262	52
9	81500	18500	83144	16856	84764	15236	51
10	9.81528	10.18472	9.83171	10.16829	9.84791	10.15209	50
11	81556	18444	83198	16802	84818	15182	49
12	81583	18417	83225	16775	84845	15155	48
13	81611	18389	83252	16748	84872	15128	47
14	81638	18362	83280	16720	84899	15101	46
15	81666	18334	83307	16693	84925	15075	45
16	81693	18307	83334	16666	84952	15048	44
17	81721	18279	83361	16639	84979	15021	43
18	81748	18252	83388	16612	85006	14994	42
19	81776	18224	83415	16585	85033	14967	41
20	9.81803	10.18197	9.83442	10.16558	9.85059	10.14941	40
21	81831	18169	83470	16530	85086	14914	39
22	81858	18142	83497	16503	85113	14887	38
23	81886	18114	83524	16476	85140	14860	37
24	81913	18087	83551	16449	85166	14834	36
25	81941	18059	83578	16422	85193	14807	35
26	81968	18032	83605	16395	85220	14780	34
27	81996	18004	83632	16368	85247	14753	33
28	82023	17977	83659	16341	85273	14727	32
29	82051	17949	83686	16314	85300	14700	31
30	9.82078	10.17922	9.83713	10.16287	9.85327	10.14673	30
31	82106	17894	83740	16260	85354	14646	29
32	82133	17867	83768	16232	85380	14620	28
33	82161	17839	83795	16205	85407	14593	27
34	82188	17812	83822	16178	85434	14566	26
35	82215	17785	83849	16151	85460	14540	25
36	82243	17757	83876	16124	85487	14513	24
37	82270	17730	83903	16097	85514	14486	23
38	82298	17702	83930	16070	85540	14460	22
39	82325	17675	83957	16043	85567	14433	21
40	9.82352	10.17648	9.83984	10.16016	9.85594	10.14406	20
41	82380	17620	84011	15989	85620	14380	19
42	82407	17593	84038	15962	85647	14353	18
43	82435	17565	84065	15935	85674	14326	17
44	82462	17538	84092	15908	85700	14300	16
45	82489	17511	84119	15881	85727	14273	15
46	82517	17483	84146	15854	85754	14246	14
47	82544	17456	84173	15827	85780	14220	13
48	82571	17429	84200	15800	85807	14193	12
49	82599	17401	84227	15773	85834	14166	11
50	9.82626	10.17374	9.84254	10.15746	9.85860	10.14140	10
51	82653	17347	84280	15720	85887	14113	9
52	82681	17319	84307	15693	85913	14087	8
53	82708	17292	84334	15666	85940	14060	7
54	82735	17265	84361	15639	85967	14033	6
55	82762	17238	84388	15612	85993	14007	5
56	82790	17210	84415	15585	86020	13980	4
57	82817	17183	84442	15558	86046	13954	3
58	82844	17156	84469	15531	86073	13927	2
59	82871	17129	84496	15504	86100	13900	1
60	82899	17101	84523	15477	86126	13874	0
′	Cotan	Tan	Cotan	Tan	Cotan	Tan	′
	56°		55°		54°		

TABLE III.—LOG. TANGENTS AND COTANGENTS.

′	36°		37°		38°		′
	Tan	Cotan	Tan	Cotan	Tan	Cotan	
0	9.86126	10.13874	9.87711	10.12289	9.89281	10.10719	60
1	86153	13847	87738	12262	89307	10693	59
2	86179	13821	87764	12236	89333	10667	58
3	86206	13794	87790	12210	89359	10641	57
4	86232	13768	87817	12183	89385	10615	56
5	86259	13741	87843	12157	89411	10589	55
6	86285	13715	87869	12131	89437	10563	54
7	86312	13688	87895	12105	89463	10537	53
8	86338	13662	87922	12078	89489	10511	52
9	86365	13635	87948	12052	89515	10485	51
10	9.86392	10.13608	9.87974	10.12026	9.89541	10.10459	50
11	86418	13582	88000	12000	89567	10433	49
12	86445	13555	88027	11973	89593	10407	48
13	86471	13529	88053	11947	89619	10381	47
14	86498	13502	88079	11921	89645	10355	46
15	86524	13476	88105	11895	89671	10329	45
16	86551	13449	88131	11869	89697	10303	44
17	86577	13423	88158	11842	89723	10277	43
18	86603	13397	88184	11816	89749	10251	42
19	86630	13370	88210	11790	89775	10225	41
20	9.86656	10.13344	9.88236	10.11764	9.89801	10.10199	40
21	86683	13317	88262	11738	89827	10173	39
22	86709	13291	88289	11711	89853	10147	38
23	86736	13264	88315	11685	89879	10121	37
24	86762	13238	88341	11659	89905	10095	36
25	86789	13211	88367	11633	89931	10069	35
26	86815	13185	88393	11607	89957	10043	34
27	86842	13158	88420	11580	89983	10017	33
28	86868	13132	88446	11554	90009	09991	32
29	86894	13106	88472	11528	90035	09965	31
30	9.86921	10.13079	9.88498	10.11502	9.90061	10.09939	30
31	86947	13053	88524	11476	90086	09914	29
32	86974	13026	88550	11450	90112	09888	28
33	87000	13000	88577	11423	90138	09862	27
34	87027	12973	88603	11397	90164	09836	26
35	87053	12947	88629	11371	90190	09810	25
36	87079	12921	88655	11345	90216	09784	24
37	87106	12894	88681	11319	90242	09758	23
38	87132	12868	88707	11293	90268	09732	22
39	87158	12842	88733	11267	90294	09706	21
40	9.87185	10.12815	9.88759	10.11241	9.90320	10.09680	20
41	87211	12789	88786	11214	90346	09654	19
42	87238	12762	88812	11188	90371	09629	18
43	87264	12736	88838	11162	90397	09603	17
44	87290	12710	88864	11136	90423	09577	16
45	87317	12683	88890	11110	90449	09551	15
46	87343	12657	88916	11084	90475	09525	14
47	87369	12631	88942	11058	90501	09499	13
48	87396	12604	88968	11032	90527	09473	12
49	87422	12578	88994	11006	90553	09447	11
50	9.87448	10.12552	9.89020	10.10980	9.90578	10.09422	10
51	87475	12525	89046	10954	90604	09396	9
52	87501	12499	89073	10927	90630	09370	8
53	87527	12473	89099	10901	90656	09344	7
54	87554	12446	89125	10875	90682	09318	6
55	87580	12420	89151	10849	90708	09292	5
56	87606	12394	89177	10823	90734	09266	4
57	87633	12367	89203	10797	90759	09241	3
58	87659	12341	89229	10771	90785	09215	2
59	87685	12315	89255	10745	90811	09189	1
60	87711	12289	89281	10719	90837	09163	0
′	Cotan	Tan	Cotan	Tan	Cotan	Tan	′
	53°		52°		51°		

648

TABLE III.—LOG. TANGENTS AND COTANGENTS.

′	39°		40°		41°		′
	Tan	Cotan	Tan	Cotan	Tan	Cotan	
0	9.90837	10.09163	9.92381	10.07619	9.93916	10.06084	60
1	90863	09137	92407	07593	93942	06058	59
2	90889	09111	92433	07567	93967	06033	58
3	90914	09086	92458	07542	93993	06007	57
4	90940	09060	92484	07516	94018	05982	56
5	90966	09034	92510	07490	94044	05956	55
6	90992	09008	92535	07465	94069	05931	54
7	91018	08982	92561	07439	94095	05905	53
8	91043	08957	92587	07413	94120	05880	52
9	91069	08931	92612	07388	94146	05854	51
10	9.91095	10.08905	9.92638	10.07362	9.94171	10.05829	50
11	91121	08879	92663	07337	94197	05803	49
12	91147	08853	92689	07311	94222	05778	48
13	91172	08828	92715	07285	94248	05752	47
14	91198	08802	92740	07260	94273	05727	46
15	91224	08776	92766	07234	94299	05701	45
16	91250	08750	92792	07208	94324	05676	44
17	91276	08724	92817	07183	94350	05650	43
18	91301	08699	92843	07157	94375	05625	42
19	91327	08673	92868	07132	94401	05599	41
20	9.91353	10.08647	9.92894	10.07106	9.94426	10.05574	40
21	91379	08621	92920	07080	94452	05548	39
22	91404	08596	92945	07055	94477	05523	38
23	91430	08570	92971	07029	94503	05497	37
24	91456	08544	92996	07004	94528	05472	36
25	91482	08518	93022	06978	94554	05446	35
26	91507	08493	93048	06952	94579	05421	34
27	91533	08467	93073	06927	94604	05396	33
28	91559	08441	93099	06901	94630	05370	32
29	91585	08415	93124	06876	94655	05345	31
30	9.91610	10.08390	9.93150	10.06850	9.94681	10.05319	30
31	91636	08364	93175	06825	94706	05294	29
32	91662	08338	93201	06799	94732	05268	28
33	91688	08312	93227	06773	94757	05243	27
34	91713	08287	93252	06748	94783	05217	26
35	91739	08261	93278	06722	94808	05192	25
36	91765	08235	93303	06697	94834	05166	24
37	91791	08209	93329	06671	94859	05141	23
38	91816	08184	93354	06646	94884	05116	22
39	91842	08158	93380	06620	94910	05090	21
40	9.91868	10.08132	9.93406	10.06594	9.94935	10.05065	20
41	91893	08107	93431	06569	94961	05039	19
42	91919	08081	93457	06543	94986	05014	18
43	91945	08055	93482	06518	95012	04988	17
44	91971	08029	93508	06492	95037	04963	16
45	91996	08004	93533	06467	95062	04938	15
46	92022	07978	93559	06441	95088	04912	14
47	92048	07952	93584	06416	95113	04887	13
48	92073	07927	93610	06390	95139	04861	12
49	92099	07901	93636	06364	95164	04836	11
50	9.92125	10.07875	9.93661	10.06339	9.95190	10.04810	10
51	92150	07850	93687	06313	95215	04785	9
52	92176	07824	93712	06288	95240	04760	8
53	92202	07798	93738	06262	95266	04734	7
54	92227	07773	93763	06237	95291	04709	6
55	92253	07747	93789	06211	95317	04683	5
56	92279	07721	93814	06186	95342	04658	4
57	92304	07696	93840	06160	95368	04632	3
58	92330	07670	93865	06135	95393	04607	2
59	92356	07644	93891	06109	95418	04582	1
60	92381	07619	93916	06084	95444	04556	0
′	Cotan	Tan	Cotan	Tan	Cotan	Tan	′
	50°		49°		48°		

TABLE III.—LOG. TANGENTS AND COTANGENTS.

′	42° Tan	42° Cotan	43° Tan	43° Cotan	44° Tan	44° Cotan	′
0	9.95444	10.04556	9.96966	10.03034	9.98484	10.01516	60
1	95469	04531	96991	03009	98509	01491	59
2	95495	04505	97016	02984	98534	01466	58
3	95520	04480	97042	02958	98560	01440	57
4	95545	04455	97067	02933	98585	01415	56
5	95571	04429	97092	02908	98610	01390	55
6	95596	04404	97118	02882	98635	01365	54
7	95622	04378	97143	02857	98661	01339	53
8	95647	04353	97168	02832	98686	01314	52
9	95672	04328	97193	02807	98711	01289	51
10	9.95698	10.04302	9.97219	10.02781	9.98737	10.01263	50
11	95723	04277	97244	02756	98762	01238	49
12	95748	04252	97269	02731	98787	01213	48
13	95774	04226	97295	02705	98812	01188	47
14	95799	04201	97320	02680	98838	01162	46
15	95825	04175	97345	02655	98863	01137	45
16	95850	04150	97371	02629	98888	01112	44
17	95875	04125	97396	02604	98913	01087	43
18	95901	04099	97421	02579	98939	01061	42
19	95926	04074	97447	02553	98964	01036	41
20	9.95952	10.04048	9.97472	10.02528	9.98989	10.01011	40
21	95977	04023	97497	02503	99015	00985	39
22	96002	03998	97523	02477	99040	00960	38
23	96028	03972	97548	02452	99065	00935	37
24	96053	03947	97573	02427	99090	00910	36
25	96078	03922	97598	02402	99116	00884	35
26	96104	03896	97624	02376	99141	00859	34
27	96129	03871	97649	02351	99166	00834	33
28	96155	03845	97674	02326	99191	00809	32
29	96180	03820	97700	02300	99217	00783	31
30	9.96205	10.03795	9.97725	10.02275	9.99242	10.00758	30
31	96231	03769	97750	02250	99267	00733	29
32	96256	03744	97776	02224	99293	00707	28
33	96281	03719	97801	02199	99318	00682	27
34	96307	03693	97826	02174	99343	00657	26
35	96332	03668	97851	02149	99368	00632	25
36	96357	03643	97877	02123	99394	00606	24
37	96383	03617	97902	02098	99419	00581	23
38	96408	03592	97927	02073	99444	00556	22
39	96433	03567	97953	02047	99469	00531	21
40	9.96459	10.03541	9.97978	10.02022	9.99495	10.00505	20
41	96484	03516	98003	01997	99520	00480	19
42	96510	03490	98029	01971	99545	00455	18
43	96535	03465	98054	01946	99570	00430	17
44	96560	03440	98079	01921	99596	00404	16
45	96586	03414	98104	01896	99621	00379	15
46	96611	03389	98130	01870	99646	00354	14
47	96636	03364	98155	01845	99672	00328	13
48	96662	03338	98180	01820	99697	00303	12
49	96687	03313	98206	01794	99722	00278	11
50	9.96712	10.03288	9.98231	10.01769	9.99747	10.00253	10
51	96738	03262	98256	01744	99773	00227	9
52	96763	03237	98281	01719	99798	00202	8
53	96788	03212	98307	01693	99823	00177	7
54	96814	03186	98332	01668	99848	00152	6
55	96839	03161	98357	01643	99874	00126	5
56	96864	03136	98383	01617	99899	00101	4
57	96890	03110	98408	01592	99924	00076	3
58	96915	03085	98433	01567	99949	00051	2
59	96940	03060	98458	01542	99975	00025	1
60	96966	03034	98484	01516	10.00000	00000	0
′	Cotan	Tan	Cotan	Tan	Cotan	Tan	′
	47°		46°		45°		

TABLE IV.—NATURAL SINES AND COSINES.

′	0°		1°		2°		3°		4°		′
	Sine	Cosin	Sine	Cosin	Sine	Cosin	Sine	Cosin	Sine	Cosin	
0	.00000	One.	.01745	.99985	.03490	.99939	.05234	.99863	.06976	.99756	60
1	.00029	One.	.01774	.99984	.03519	.99938	.05263	.99861	.07005	.99754	59
2	.00058	One.	.01803	.99984	.03548	.99937	.05292	.99860	.07034	.99752	58
3	.00087	One.	.01832	.99983	.03577	.99936	.05321	.99858	.07063	.99750	57
4	.00116	One.	.01862	.99983	.03606	.99935	.05350	.99857	.07092	.99748	56
5	.00145	One.	.01891	.99982	.03635	.99934	.05379	.99855	.07121	.99746	55
6	.00175	One.	.01920	.99982	.03664	.99933	.05408	.99854	.07150	.99744	54
7	.00204	One.	.01949	.99981	.03693	.99932	.05437	.99852	.07179	.99742	53
8	.00233	One.	.01978	.99980	.03723	.99931	.05466	.99851	.07208	.99740	52
9	.00262	One.	.02007	.99980	.03752	.99930	.05495	.99849	.07237	.99738	51
10	.00291	One.	.02036	.99979	.03781	.99929	.05524	.99847	.07266	.99736	50
11	.00320	.99999	.02065	.99979	.03810	.99927	.05553	.99846	.07295	.99734	49
12	.00349	.99999	.02094	.99978	.03839	.99926	.05582	.99844	.07324	.99731	48
13	.00378	.99999	.02123	.99977	.03868	.99925	.05611	.99842	.07353	.99729	47
14	.00407	.99999	.02152	.99977	.03897	.99924	.05640	.99841	.07382	.99727	46
15	.00436	.99999	.02181	.99976	.03926	.99923	.05669	.99839	.07411	.99725	45
16	.00465	.99999	.02211	.99976	.03955	.99922	.05698	.99838	.07440	.99723	44
17	.00495	.99999	.02240	.99975	.03984	.99921	.05727	.99836	.07469	.99721	43
18	.00524	.99999	.02269	.99974	.04013	.99919	.05756	.99834	.07498	.99719	42
19	.00553	.99998	.02298	.99974	.04042	.99918	.05785	.99833	.07527	.99716	41
20	.00582	.99998	.02327	.99973	.04071	.99917	.05814	.99831	.07556	.99714	40
21	.00611	.99998	.02356	.99972	.04100	.99916	.05844	.99829	.07585	.99712	39
22	.00640	.99998	.02385	.99972	.04129	.99915	.05873	.99827	.07614	.99710	38
23	.00669	.99998	.02414	.99971	.04159	.99913	.05902	.99826	.07643	.99708	37
24	.00698	.99998	.02443	.99970	.04188	.99912	.05931	.99824	.07672	.99705	36
25	.00727	.99997	.02472	.99969	.04217	.99911	.05960	.99822	.07701	.99703	35
26	.00756	.99997	.02501	.99969	.04246	.99910	.05989	.99821	.07730	.99701	34
27	.00785	.99997	.02530	.99968	.04275	.99909	.06018	.99819	.07759	.99699	33
28	.00814	.99997	.02560	.99967	.04304	.99907	.06047	.99817	.07788	.99696	32
29	.00844	.99996	.02589	.99966	.04333	.99906	.06076	.99815	.07817	.99694	31
30	.00873	.99996	.02618	.99966	.04362	.99905	.06105	.99813	.07846	.99692	30
31	.00902	.99996	.02647	.99965	.04391	.99904	.06134	.99812	.07875	.99689	29
32	.00931	.99996	.02676	.99964	.04420	.99902	.06163	.99810	.07904	.99687	28
33	.00960	.99995	.02705	.99963	.04449	.99901	.06192	.99808	.07933	.99685	27
34	.00989	.99995	.02734	.99963	.04478	.99900	.06221	.99806	.07962	.99683	26
35	.01018	.99995	.02763	.99962	.04507	.99898	.06250	.99804	.07991	.99680	25
36	.01047	.99995	.02792	.99961	.04536	.99897	.06279	.99803	.08020	.99678	24
37	.01076	.99994	.02821	.99960	.04565	.99896	.06308	.99801	.08049	.99676	23
38	.01105	.99994	.02850	.99959	.04594	.99894	.06337	.99799	.08078	.99673	22
39	.01134	.99994	.02879	.99959	.04623	.99893	.06366	.99797	.08107	.99671	21
40	.01164	.99993	.02908	.99958	.04653	.99892	.06395	.99795	.08136	.99668	20
41	.01193	.99993	.02938	.99957	.04682	.99890	.06424	.99793	.08165	.99666	19
42	.01222	.99993	.02967	.99956	.04711	.99889	.06453	.99792	.08194	.99664	18
43	.01251	.99992	.02996	.99955	.04740	.99888	.06482	.99790	.08223	.99661	17
44	.01280	.99992	.03025	.99954	.04769	.99886	.06511	.99788	.08252	.99659	16
45	.01309	.99991	.03054	.99953	.04798	.99885	.06540	.99786	.08281	.99657	15
46	.01338	.99991	.03083	.99952	.04827	.99883	.06569	.99784	.08310	.99654	14
47	.01367	.99991	.03112	.99952	.04856	.99882	.06598	.99782	.08339	.99652	13
48	.01396	.99990	.03141	.99951	.04885	.99881	.06627	.99780	.08368	.99649	12
49	.01425	.99990	.03170	.99950	.04914	.99879	.06656	.99778	.08397	.99647	11
50	.01454	.99989	.03199	.99949	.04943	.99878	.06685	.99776	.08426	99644	10
51	.01483	.99989	.03228	.99948	.04972	.99876	.06714	.99774	.08455	.99642	9
52	.01513	.99989	.03257	.99947	.05001	.99875	.06743	.99772	.08484	.99639	8
53	.01542	.99988	.03286	.99946	.05030	.99873	.06773	.99770	.08513	.99637	7
54	.01571	.99988	.03316	.99945	.05059	.99872	.06802	.99768	.08542	.99635	6
55	.01600	.99987	.03345	.99944	.05088	.99870	.06831	.99766	.08571	.99632	5
56	.01629	.99987	.03374	.99943	.05117	.99869	.06860	.99764	.08600	.99630	4
57	.01658	.99986	.03403	.99942	.05146	.99867	.06889	.99762	.08629	.99627	3
58	.01687	.99986	.03432	.99941	.05175	.99866	.06918	.99760	.08658	.99625	2
59	.01716	.99985	.03461	.99940	.05205	.99864	.06947	.99758	.08687	.99622	1
60	.01745	.99985	.03490	.99939	.05234	.99863	.06976	.99756	.08716	.99619	0
′	Cosin	Sine	Cosin	Sine	Cosin	Sine	Cosin	Sine	Cosin	Sine	′
	89°		88°		87°		86°		85°		

TABLE IV.—NATURAL SINES AND COSINES.

′	5° Sine	5° Cosin	6° Sine	6° Cosin	7° Sine	7° Cosin	8° Sine	8° Cosin	9° Sine	9° Cosin	′
0	.08716	.99619	.10453	.99452	.12187	.99255	.13917	.99027	.15643	.98769	60
1	.08745	.99617	.10482	.99449	.12216	.99251	.13946	.99023	.15672	.98764	59
2	.08774	.99614	.10511	.99446	.12245	.99248	.13975	.99019	.15701	.98760	58
3	.08803	.99612	.10540	.99443	.12274	.99244	.14004	.99015	.15730	.98755	57
4	.08831	.99609	.10569	.99440	.12302	.99240	.14033	.99011	.15758	.98751	56
5	.08860	.99607	.10597	.99437	.12331	.99237	.14061	.99006	.15787	.98746	55
6	.08889	.99604	.10626	.99434	.12360	.99233	.14090	.99002	.15816	.98741	54
7	.08918	.99602	.10655	.99431	.12389	.99230	.14119	.98998	.15845	.98737	53
8	.08947	.99599	.10684	.99428	.12418	.99226	.14148	.98994	.15873	.98732	52
9	.08976	.99596	.10713	.99424	.12447	.99222	.14177	.98990	.15902	.98728	51
10	.09005	.99594	.10742	.99421	.12476	.99219	.14205	.98986	.15931	.98723	50
11	.09034	.99591	.10771	.99418	.12504	.99215	.14234	.98982	.15959	.98718	49
12	.09063	.99588	.10800	.99415	.12533	.99211	.14263	.98978	.15988	.98714	48
13	.09092	.99586	.10829	.99412	.12562	.99208	.14292	.98973	.16017	.98709	47
14	.09121	.99583	.10858	.99409	.12591	.99204	.14320	.98969	.16046	.98704	46
15	.09150	.99580	.10887	.99406	.12620	.99200	.14349	.98965	.16074	.98700	45
16	.09179	.99578	.10916	.99402	.12649	.99197	.14378	.98961	.16103	.98695	44
17	.09208	.99575	.10945	.99399	.12678	.99193	.14407	.98957	.16132	.98690	43
18	.09237	.99572	.10973	.99396	.12706	.99189	.14436	.98953	.16160	.98686	42
19	.09266	.99570	.11002	.99393	.12735	.99186	.14464	.98948	.16189	.98681	41
20	.09295	.99567	.11031	.99390	.12764	.99182	.14493	.98944	.16218	.98676	40
21	.09324	.99564	.11060	.99386	.12793	.99178	.14522	.98940	.16246	.98671	39
22	.09353	.99562	.11089	.99383	.12822	.99175	.14551	.98936	.16275	.98667	38
23	.09382	.99559	.11118	.99380	.12851	.99171	.14580	.98931	.16304	.98662	37
24	.09411	.99556	.11147	.99377	.12880	.99167	.14608	.98927	.16333	.98657	36
25	.09440	.99553	.11176	.99374	.12908	.99163	.14637	.98923	.16361	.98652	35
26	.09469	.99551	.11205	.99370	.12937	.99160	.14666	.98919	.16390	.98648	34
27	.09498	.99548	.11234	.99367	.12966	.99156	.14695	.98914	.16419	.98643	33
28	.09527	.99545	.11263	.99364	.12995	.99152	.14723	.98910	.16447	.98638	32
29	.09556	.99542	.11291	.99360	.13024	.99148	.14752	.98906	.16476	.98633	31
30	.09585	.99540	.11320	.99357	.13053	.99144	.14781	.98902	.16505	.98629	30
31	.09614	.99537	.11349	.99354	.13081	.99141	.14810	.98897	.16533	.98624	29
32	.09642	.99534	.11378	.99351	.13110	.99137	.14838	.98893	.16562	.98619	28
33	.09671	.99531	.11407	.99347	.13139	.99133	.14867	.98889	.16591	.98614	27
34	.09700	.99528	.11436	.99344	.13168	.99129	.14896	.98884	.16620	.98609	26
35	.09729	.99526	.11465	.99341	.13197	.99125	.14925	.98880	.16648	.98604	25
36	.09758	.99523	.11494	.99337	.13226	.99122	.14954	.98876	.16677	.98600	24
37	.09787	.99520	.11523	.99334	.13254	.99118	.14982	.98871	.16706	.98595	23
38	.09816	.99517	.11552	.99331	.13283	.99114	.15011	.98867	.16734	.98590	22
39	.09845	.99514	.11580	.99327	.13312	.99110	.15040	.98863	.16763	.98585	21
40	.09874	.99511	.11609	.99324	.13341	.99106	.15069	.98858	.16792	.98580	20
41	.09903	.99508	.11638	.99320	.13370	.99102	.15097	.98854	.16820	.98575	19
42	.09932	.99506	.11667	.99317	.13399	.99098	.15126	.98849	.16849	.98570	18
43	.09961	.99503	.11696	.99314	.13427	.99094	.15155	.98845	.16878	.98565	17
44	.09990	.99500	.11725	.99310	.13456	.99091	.15184	.98841	.16906	.98561	16
45	.10019	.99497	.11754	.99307	.13485	.99087	.15212	.98836	.16935	.98556	15
46	.10048	.99494	.11783	.99303	.13514	.99083	.15241	.98832	.16964	.98551	14
47	.10077	.99491	.11812	.99300	.13543	.99079	.15270	.98827	.16992	.98546	13
48	.10106	.99488	.11840	.99297	.13572	.99075	.15299	.98823	.17021	.98541	12
49	.10135	.99485	.11869	.99293	.13600	.99071	.15327	.98818	.17050	.98536	11
50	.10164	.99482	.11898	.99290	.13629	.99067	.15356	.98814	.17078	.98531	10
51	.10192	.99479	.11927	.99286	.13658	.99063	.15385	.98809	.17107	.98526	9
52	.10221	.99476	.11956	.99283	.13687	.99059	.15414	.98805	.17136	.98521	8
53	.10250	.99473	.11985	.99279	.13716	.99055	.15442	.98800	.17164	.98516	7
54	.10279	.99470	.12014	.99276	.13744	.99051	.15471	.98796	.17193	.98511	6
55	.10308	.99467	.12043	.99272	.13773	.99047	.15500	.98791	.17222	.98506	5
56	.10337	.99464	.12071	.99269	.13802	.99043	.15529	.98787	.17250	.98501	4
57	.10366	.99461	.12100	.99265	.13831	.99039	.15557	.98782	.17279	.98496	3
58	.10395	.99458	.12129	.99262	.13860	.99035	.15586	.98778	.17308	.98491	2
59	.10424	.99455	.12158	.99258	.13889	.99031	.15615	.98773	.17336	.98486	1
60	.10453	.99452	.12187	.99255	.13917	.99027	.15643	.98769	.17365	.98481	0
′	Cosin	Sine	Cosin	Sine	Cosin	Sine	Cosin	Sine	Cosin	Sine	′
	84°		83°		82°		81°		80°		

TABLE IV.—NATURAL SINES AND COSINES.

′	10° Sine	10° Cosin	11° Sine	11° Cosin	12° Sine	12° Cosin	13° Sine	13° Cosin	14° Sine	14° Cosin	′
0	.17365	.98481	.19081	.98163	.20791	.97815	.22495	.97437	.24192	.97030	60
1	.17393	.98476	.19109	.98157	.20820	.97809	.22523	.97430	.24220	.97023	59
2	.17422	.98471	.19138	.98152	.20848	.97803	.22552	.97424	.24249	.97015	58
3	.17451	.98466	.19167	.98146	.20877	.97797	.22580	.97417	.24277	.97008	57
4	.17479	.98461	.19195	.98140	.20905	.97791	.22608	.97411	.24305	.97001	56
5	.17508	.98455	.19224	.98135	.20933	.97784	.22637	.97404	.24333	.96994	55
6	.17537	.98450	.19252	.98129	.20962	.97778	.22665	.97398	.24362	.96987	54
7	.17565	.98445	.19281	.98124	.20990	.97772	.22693	.97391	.24390	.96980	53
8	.17594	.98440	.19309	.98118	.21019	.97766	.22722	.97384	.24418	.96973	52
9	.17623	.98435	.19338	.98112	.21047	.97760	.22750	.97378	.24446	.96966	51
10	.17651	.98430	.19366	.98107	.21076	.97754	.22778	.97371	.24474	.96959	50
11	.17680	.98425	.19395	.98101	.21104	.97748	.22807	.97365	.24503	.96953	49
12	.17708	.98420	.19423	.98096	.21132	.97742	.22835	.97358	.24531	.96945	48
13	.17737	.98414	.19452	.98090	.21161	.97735	.22863	.97351	.24559	.96937	47
14	.17766	.98409	.19481	.98084	.21189	.97729	.22892	.97345	.24587	.96930	46
15	.17794	.98404	.19509	.98079	.21218	.97723	.22920	.97338	.24615	.96923	45
16	.17823	.98399	.19538	.98073	.21246	.97717	.22948	.97331	.24644	.96916	44
17	.17852	.98394	.19566	.98067	.21275	.97711	.22977	.97325	.24672	.96909	43
18	.17880	.98389	.19595	.98061	.21303	.97705	.23005	.97318	.24700	.96902	42
19	.17909	.98383	.19623	.98056	.21331	.97698	.23033	.97311	.24728	.96894	41
20	.17937	.98378	.19652	.98050	.21360	.97692	.23062	.97304	.24756	.96887	40
21	.17966	.98373	.19680	.98044	.21388	.97686	.23090	.97298	.24784	.96880	39
22	.17995	.98368	.19709	.98039	.21417	.97680	.23118	.97291	.24813	.96873	38
23	.18023	.98362	.19737	.98033	.21445	.97673	.23146	.97284	.24841	.96866	37
24	.18052	.98357	.19766	.98027	.21474	.97667	.23175	.97278	.24869	.96858	36
25	.18081	.98352	.19794	.98021	.21502	.97661	.23203	.97271	.24897	.96851	35
26	.18109	.98347	.19823	.98016	.21530	.97655	.23231	.97264	.24925	.96844	34
27	.18138	.98341	.19851	.98010	.21559	.97648	.23260	.97257	.24954	.96837	33
28	.18166	.98336	.19880	.98004	.21587	.97642	.23288	.97251	.24982	.96829	32
29	.18195	.98331	.19908	.97998	.21616	.97636	.23316	.97244	.25010	.96822	31
30	.18224	.98325	.19937	.97992	.21644	.97630	.23345	.97237	.25038	.96815	30
31	.18252	.98320	.19965	.97987	.21672	.97623	.23373	.97230	.25066	.96807	29
32	.18281	.98315	.19994	.97981	.21701	.97617	.23401	.97223	.25094	.96800	28
33	.18309	.98310	.20022	.97975	.21729	.97611	.23429	.97217	.25122	.96793	27
34	.18338	.98304	.20051	.97969	.21758	.97604	.23458	.97210	.25151	.96786	26
35	.18367	.98299	.20079	.97963	.21786	.97598	.23486	.97203	.25179	.96778	25
36	.18395	.98294	.20108	.97958	.21814	.97592	.23514	.97196	.25207	.96771	24
37	.18424	.98288	.20136	.97952	.21843	.97585	.23542	.97189	.25235	.96764	23
38	.18452	.98283	.20165	.97946	.21871	.97579	.23571	.97182	.25263	.96756	22
39	.18481	.98277	.20193	.97940	.21899	.97573	.23599	.97176	.25291	.96749	21
40	.18509	.98272	.20222	.97934	.21928	.97566	.23627	.97169	.25320	.96742	20
41	.18538	.98267	.20250	.97928	.21956	.97560	.23656	.97162	.25348	.96734	19
42	.18567	.98261	.20279	.97922	.21985	.97553	.23684	.97155	.25376	.96727	18
43	.18595	.98256	.20307	.97916	.22013	.97547	.23712	.97148	.25404	.96719	17
44	.18624	.98250	.20336	.97910	.22041	.97541	.23740	.97141	.25432	.96712	16
45	.18652	.98245	.20364	.97905	.22070	.97534	.23769	.97134	.25460	.96705	15
46	.18681	.98240	.20393	.97899	.22098	.97528	.23797	.97127	.25488	.96697	14
47	.18710	.98234	.20421	.97893	.22126	.97521	.23825	.97120	.25516	.96690	13
48	.18738	.98229	.20450	.97887	.22155	.97515	.23853	.97113	.25545	.96682	12
49	.18767	.98223	.20478	.97881	.22183	.97508	.23882	.97106	.25573	.96675	11
50	.18795	.98218	.20507	.97875	.22212	.97502	.23910	.97100	.25601	.96667	10
51	.18824	.98212	.20535	.97869	.22240	.97496	.23938	.97093	.25629	.96660	9
52	.18852	.98207	.20563	.97863	.22268	.97489	.23966	.97086	.25657	.96653	8
53	.18881	.98201	.20592	.97857	.22297	.97483	.23995	.97079	.25685	.96645	7
54	.18910	.98196	.20620	.97851	.22325	.97476	.24023	.97072	.25713	.96638	6
55	.18938	.98190	.20649	.97845	.22353	.97470	.24051	.97065	.25741	.96630	5
56	.18967	.98185	.20677	.97839	.22382	.97463	.24079	.97058	.25769	.96623	4
57	.18995	.98179	.20706	.97833	.22410	.97457	.24108	.97051	.25798	.96615	3
58	.19024	.98174	.20734	.97827	.22438	.97450	.24136	.97044	.25826	.96608	2
59	.19052	.98168	.20763	.97821	.22467	.97444	.24164	.97037	.25854	.96600	1
60	.19081	.98163	.20791	.97815	.22495	.97437	.24192	.97030	.25882	.96593	0
′	Cosin	Sine	Cosin	Sine	Cosin	Sine	Cosin	Sine	Cosin	Sine	′
	79°		78°		77°		76°		75°		

TABLE IV.—NATURAL SINES AND COSINES.

′	15° Sine	Cosin	16° Sine	Cosin	17° Sine	Cosin	18° Sine	Cosin	19° Sine	Cosin	′
0	.25882	.96593	.27564	.96126	.29237	.95630	.30902	.95106	.32557	.94552	60
1	.25910	.96585	.27592	.96118	.29265	.95622	.30929	.95097	.32584	.94542	59
2	.25938	.96578	.27620	.96110	.29293	.95613	.30957	.95088	.32612	.94533	58
3	.25966	.96570	.27648	.96102	.29321	.95605	.30985	.95079	.32639	.94523	57
4	.25994	.96562	.27676	.96094	.29348	.95596	.31012	.95070	.32667	.94514	56
5	.26022	.96555	.27704	.96086	.29376	.95588	.31040	.95061	.32694	.94504	55
6	.26050	.96547	.27731	.96078	.29404	.95579	.31068	.95052	.32722	.94495	54
7	.26079	.96540	.27759	.96070	.29432	.95571	.31095	.95043	.32749	.94485	53
8	.26107	.96532	.27787	.96062	.29460	.95562	.31123	.95033	.32777	.94476	52
9	.26135	.96524	.27815	.96054	.29487	.95554	.31151	.95024	.32804	.94466	51
10	.26163	.96517	.27843	.96046	.29515	.95545	.31178	.95015	.32832	.94457	50
11	.26191	.96509	.27871	.96037	.29543	.95536	.31206	.95006	.32859	.94447	49
12	.26219	.96502	.27899	.96029	.29571	.95528	.31233	.94997	.32887	.94438	48
13	.26247	.96494	.27927	.96021	.29599	.95519	.31261	.94988	.32914	.94428	47
14	.26275	.96486	.27955	.96013	.29626	.95511	.31289	.94979	.32942	.94418	46
15	.26303	.96479	.27983	.96005	.29654	.95502	.31316	.94970	.32969	.94409	45
16	.26331	.96471	.28011	.95997	.29682	.95493	.31344	.94961	.32997	.94399	44
17	.26359	.96463	.28039	.95989	.29710	.95485	.31372	.94952	.33024	.94390	43
18	.26387	.96456	.28067	.95981	.29737	.95476	.31399	.94943	.33051	.94380	42
19	.26415	.96448	.28095	.95972	.29765	.95467	.31427	.94933	.33079	.94370	41
20	.26443	.96440	.28123	.95964	.29793	.95459	.31454	.94924	.33106	.94361	40
21	.26471	.96433	.28150	.95956	.29821	.95450	.31482	.94915	.33134	.94351	39
22	.26500	.96425	.28178	.95948	.29849	.95441	.31510	.94906	.33161	.94342	38
23	.26528	.96417	.28206	.95940	.29876	.95433	.31537	.94897	.33189	.94332	37
24	.26556	.96410	.28234	.95931	.29904	.95424	.31565	.94888	.33216	.94322	36
25	.26584	.96402	.28262	.95923	.29932	.95415	.31593	.94878	.33244	.94313	35
26	.26612	.96394	.28290	.95915	.29960	.95407	.31620	.94869	.33271	.94303	34
27	.26640	.96386	.28318	.95907	.29987	.95398	.31648	.94860	.33298	.94293	33
28	.26668	.96379	.28346	.95898	.30015	.95389	.31675	.94851	.33326	.94284	32
29	.26696	.96371	.28374	.95890	.30043	.95380	.31703	.94842	.33353	.94274	31
30	.26724	.96363	.28402	.95882	.30071	.95372	.31730	.94832	.33381	.94264	30
31	.26752	.96355	.28429	.95874	.30098	.95363	.31758	.94823	.33408	.94254	29
32	.26780	.96347	.28457	.95865	.30126	.95354	.31786	.94814	.33436	.94245	28
33	.26808	.96340	.28485	.95857	.30154	.95345	.31813	.94805	.33463	.94235	27
34	.26836	.96332	.28513	.95849	.30182	.95337	.31841	.94795	.33490	.94225	26
35	.26864	.96324	.28541	.95841	.30209	.95328	.31868	.94786	.33518	.94215	25
36	.26892	.96316	.28569	.95832	.30237	.95319	.31896	.94777	.33545	.94206	24
37	.26920	.96308	.28597	.95824	.30265	.95310	.31923	.94768	.33573	.94196	23
38	.26948	.96301	.28625	.95816	.30292	.95301	.31951	.94758	.33600	.94186	22
39	.26976	.96293	.28652	.95807	.30320	.95293	.31979	.94749	.33627	.94176	21
40	.27004	.96285	.28680	.95799	.30348	.95284	.32006	.94740	.33655	.94167	20
41	.27032	.96277	.28708	.95791	.30376	.95275	.32034	.94730	.33682	.94157	19
42	.27060	.96269	.28736	.95782	.30403	.95266	.32061	.94721	.33710	.94147	18
43	.27088	.96261	.28764	.95774	.30431	.95257	.32089	.94712	.33737	.94137	17
44	.27116	.96253	.28792	.95766	.30459	.95248	.32116	.94702	.33764	.94127	16
45	.27144	.96246	.28820	.95757	.30486	.95240	.32144	.94693	.33792	.94118	15
46	.27172	.96238	.28847	.95749	.30514	.95231	.32171	.94684	.33819	.94108	14
47	.27200	.96230	.28875	.95740	.30542	.95222	.32199	.94674	.33846	.94098	13
48	.27228	.96222	.28903	.95732	.30570	.95213	.32227	.94665	.33874	.94088	12
49	.27256	.96214	.28931	.95724	.30597	.95204	.32254	.94656	.33901	.94078	11
50	.27284	.96206	.28959	.95715	.30625	.95195	.32282	.94646	.33929	.94068	10
51	.27312	.96198	.28987	.95707	.30653	.95186	.32309	.94637	.33956	.94058	9
52	.27340	.96190	.29015	.95698	.30680	.95177	.32337	.94627	.33983	.94049	8
53	.27368	.96182	.29042	.95690	.30708	.95168	.32364	.94618	.34011	.94039	7
54	.27396	.96174	.29070	.95681	.30736	.95159	.32392	.94609	.34038	.94029	6
55	.27424	.96166	.29098	.95673	.30763	.95150	.32419	.94599	.34065	.94019	5
56	.27452	.96158	.29126	.95664	.30791	.95142	.32447	.94590	.34093	.94009	4
57	.27480	.96150	.29154	.95656	.30819	.95133	.32474	.94580	.34120	.93999	3
58	.27508	.96142	.29182	.95647	.30846	.95124	.32502	.94571	.34147	.93989	2
59	.27536	.96134	.29209	.95639	.30874	.95115	.32529	.94561	.34175	.93979	1
60	.27564	.96126	.29237	.95630	.30902	.95106	.32557	.94552	.34202	.93969	0
′	Cosin	Sine	Cosin	Sine	Cosin	Sine	Cosin	Sine	Cosin	Sine	′
	74°		73°		72°		71°		70°		

TABLE IV.—NATURAL SINES AND COSINES.

′	20° Sine	20° Cosin	21° Sine	21° Cosin	22° Sine	22° Cosin	23° Sine	23° Cosin	24° Sine	24° Cosin	′
0	.34202	.93969	.35837	.93358	.37461	.92718	.39073	.92050	.40674	.91355	60
1	.34229	.93959	.35864	.93348	.37488	.92707	.39100	.92039	.40700	.91343	59
2	.34257	.93949	.35891	.93337	.37515	.92697	.39127	.92028	.40727	.91331	58
3	.34284	.93939	.35918	.93327	.37542	.92686	.39153	.92016	.40753	.91319	57
4	.34311	.93929	.35945	.93316	.37569	.92675	.39180	.92005	.40780	.91307	56
5	.34339	.93919	.35973	.93306	.37595	.92664	.39207	.91994	.40806	.91295	55
6	.34366	.93909	.36000	.93295	.37622	.92653	.39234	.91982	.40833	.91283	54
7	.34393	.93899	.36027	.93285	.37649	.92642	.39260	.91971	.40860	.91272	53
8	.34421	.93889	.36054	.93274	.37676	.92631	.39287	.91959	.40886	.91260	52
9	.34448	.93879	.36081	.93264	.37703	.92620	.39314	.91948	.40913	.91248	51
10	.34475	.93869	.36108	.93253	.37730	.92609	.39341	.91936	.40939	.91236	50
11	.34503	.93859	.36135	.93243	.37757	.92598	.39367	.91925	.40966	.91224	49
12	.34530	.93849	.36162	.93232	.37784	.92587	.39394	.91914	.40992	.91212	48
13	.34557	.93839	.36190	.93222	.37811	.92576	.39421	.91902	.41019	.91200	47
14	.34584	.93829	.36217	.93211	.37838	.92565	.39448	.91891	.41045	.91188	46
15	.34612	.93819	.36244	.93201	.37865	.92554	.39474	.91879	.41072	.91176	45
16	.34639	.93809	.36271	.93190	.37892	.92543	.39501	.91868	.41098	.91164	44
17	.34666	.93799	.36298	.93180	.37919	.92532	.39528	.91856	.41125	.91152	43
18	.34694	.93789	.36325	.93169	.37946	.92521	.39555	.91845	.41151	.91140	42
19	.34721	.93779	.36352	.93159	.37973	.92510	.39581	.91833	.41178	.91128	41
20	.34748	.93769	.36379	.93148	.37999	.92499	.39608	.91822	.41204	.91116	40
21	.34775	.93759	.36406	.93137	.38026	.92488	.39635	.91810	.41231	.91104	39
22	.34803	.93748	.36434	.93127	.38053	.92477	.39661	.91799	.41257	.91092	38
23	.34830	.93738	.36461	.93116	.38080	.92466	.39688	.91787	.41284	.91080	37
24	.34857	.93728	.36488	.93106	.38107	.92455	.39715	.91775	.41310	.91068	36
25	.34884	.93718	.36515	.93095	.38134	.92444	.39741	.91764	.41337	.91056	35
26	.34912	.93708	.36542	.93084	.38161	.92432	.39768	.91752	.41363	.91044	34
27	.34939	.93698	.36569	.93074	.38188	.92421	.39795	.91741	.41390	.91032	33
28	.34966	.93688	.36596	.93063	.38215	.92410	.39822	.91729	.41416	.91020	32
29	.34993	.93677	.36623	.93052	.38241	.92399	.39848	.91718	.41443	.91008	31
30	.35021	.93667	.36650	.93042	.38268	.92388	.39875	.91706	.41469	.90996	30
31	.35048	.93657	.36677	.93031	.38295	.92377	.39902	.91694	.41496	.90984	29
32	.35075	.93647	.36704	.93020	.38322	.92366	.39928	.91683	.41522	.90972	28
33	.35102	.93637	.36731	.93010	.38349	.92355	.39955	.91671	.41549	.90960	27
34	.35130	.93626	.36758	.92999	.38376	.92343	.39982	.91660	.41575	.90948	26
35	.35157	.93616	.36785	.92988	.38403	.92332	.40008	.91648	.41602	.90936	25
36	.35184	.93606	.36812	.92978	.38430	.92321	.40035	.91636	.41628	.90924	24
37	.35211	.93596	.36839	.92967	.38456	.92310	.40062	.91625	.41655	.90911	23
38	.35239	.93585	.36867	.92956	.38483	.92299	.40088	.91613	.41681	.90899	22
39	.35266	.93575	.36894	.92945	.38510	.92287	.40115	.91601	.41707	.90887	21
40	.35293	.93565	.36921	.92935	.38537	.92276	.40141	.91590	.41734	.90875	20
41	.35320	.93555	.36948	.92924	.38564	.92265	.40168	.91578	.41760	.90863	19
42	.35347	.93544	.36975	.92913	.38591	.92254	.40195	.91566	.41787	.90851	18
43	.35375	.93534	.37002	.92902	.38617	.92243	.40221	.91555	.41813	.90839	17
44	.35402	.93524	.37029	.92892	.38644	.92231	.40248	.91543	.41840	.90826	16
45	.35429	.93514	.37056	.92881	.38671	.92220	.40275	.91531	.41866	.90814	15
46	.35456	.93503	.37083	.92870	.38698	.92209	.40301	.91519	.41892	.90802	14
47	.35484	.93493	.37110	.92859	.38725	.92198	.40328	.91508	.41919	.90790	13
48	.35511	.93483	.37137	.92849	.38752	.92186	.40355	.91496	.41945	.90778	12
49	.35538	.93472	.37164	.92838	.38778	.92175	.40381	.91484	.41972	.90766	11
50	.35565	.93462	.37191	.92827	.38805	.92164	.40408	.91472	.41998	.90753	10
51	.35592	.93452	.37218	.92816	.38832	.92152	.40434	.91461	.42024	.90741	9
52	.35619	.93441	.37245	.92805	.38859	.92141	.40461	.91449	.42051	.90729	8
53	.35647	.93431	.37272	.92794	.38886	.92130	.40488	.91437	.42077	.90717	7
54	.35674	.93420	.37299	.92784	.38912	.92119	.40514	.91425	.42104	.90704	6
55	.35701	.93410	.37326	.92773	.38939	.92107	.40541	.91414	.42130	.90692	5
56	.35728	.93400	.37353	.92762	.38966	.92096	.40567	.91402	.42156	.90680	4
57	.35755	.93389	.37380	.92751	.38993	.92085	.40594	.91390	.42183	.90668	3
58	.35782	.93379	.37407	.92740	.39020	.92073	.40621	.91378	.42209	.90655	2
59	.35810	.93368	.37434	.92729	.39046	.92062	.40647	.91366	.42235	.90643	1
60	.35837	.93358	.37461	.92718	.39073	.92050	.40674	.91355	.42262	.90631	0
′	Cosin	Sine	Cosin	Sine	Cosin	Sine	Cosin	Sine	Cosin	Sine	′
	69°		68°		67°		66°		65°		

TABLE IV.—NATURAL SINES AND COSINES.

′	25°		26°		27°		28°		29°		′
	Sine	Cosin	Sine	Cosin	Sine	Cosin	Sine	Cosin	Sine	Cosin	
0	.42262	.90631	.43837	.89879	.45399	.89101	.46947	.88295	.48481	.87462	60
1	.42288	.90618	.43863	.89867	.45425	.89087	.46973	.88281	.48506	.87448	59
2	.42315	.90606	.43889	.89854	.45451	.89074	.46999	.88267	.48532	.87434	58
3	.42341	.90594	.43916	.89841	.45477	.89061	.47024	.88254	.48557	.87420	57
4	.42367	.90582	.43942	.89828	.45503	.89048	.47050	.88240	.48583	.87406	56
5	.42394	.90569	.43968	.89816	.45529	.89035	.47076	.88226	.48608	.87391	55
6	.42420	.90557	.43994	.89803	.45554	.89021	.47101	.88213	.48634	.87377	54
7	.42446	.90545	.44020	.89790	.45580	.89008	.47127	.88199	.48659	.87363	53
8	.42473	.90532	.44046	.89777	.45606	.88995	.47153	.88186	.48684	.87349	52
9	.42499	.90520	.44072	.89764	.45632	.88981	.47178	.88172	.48710	.87335	51
10	.42525	.90507	.44098	.89752	.45658	.88968	.47204	.88158	.48735	.87321	50
11	.42552	.90495	.44124	.89739	.45684	.88955	.47229	.88144	.48761	.87306	49
12	.42578	.90483	.44151	.89726	.45710	.88942	.47255	.88130	.48786	.07292	48
13	.42604	.90470	.44177	.89713	.45736	.88928	.47281	.88117	.48811	.87278	47
14	.42631	.90458	.44203	.89700	.45762	.88915	.47306	.88103	.48837	.87264	46
15	.42657	.90446	.44229	.89687	.45787	.88902	.47332	.88089	.48862	.87250	45
16	.42683	.90433	.44255	.89674	.45813	.88888	.47358	.88075	.48888	.87235	44
17	.42709	.90421	.44281	.89662	.45839	.88875	.47383	.88062	.48913	.87221	43
18	.42736	.90408	.44307	.89649	.45865	.88862	.47409	.88048	.48938	.87207	42
19	.42762	.90396	.44333	.89636	.45891	.88848	.47434	.88034	.48964	.87193	41
20	.42788	.90383	.44359	.89623	.45917	.88835	.47460	.88020	.48989	.87178	40
21	.42815	.90371	.44385	.89610	.45942	.88822	.47486	.88006	.49014	.87164	39
22	.42841	.90358	.44411	.89597	.45968	.88808	.47511	.87993	.49040	.87150	38
23	.42867	.90346	.44437	.89584	.45994	.88795	.47537	.87979	.49065	.87136	37
24	.42894	.90334	.44464	.89571	.46020	.88782	.47562	.87965	.49090	.87121	36
25	.42920	.90321	.44490	.89558	.46046	.88768	.47588	.87951	.49116	.87107	35
26	.42946	.90309	.44516	.89545	.46072	.88755	.47614	.87937	.49141	.87093	34
27	.42972	.90296	.44542	.89532	.46097	.88741	.47639	.87923	.49166	.87079	33
28	.42999	.90284	.44568	.89519	.46123	.88728	.47665	.87909	.49192	.87064	32
29	.43025	.90271	.44594	.89506	.46149	.88715	.47690	.87896	.49217	.87050	31
30	.43051	.90259	.44620	.89493	.46175	.88701	.47716	.87882	.49242	.87036	30
31	.43077	.90246	.44646	.89480	.46201	.88688	.47741	.87868	.49268	.87021	29
32	.43104	.90233	.44672	.89467	.46226	.88674	.47767	.87854	.49293	.87007	28
33	.43130	.90221	.44698	.89454	.46252	.88661	.47793	.87840	.49318	.86993	27
34	.43156	.90208	.44724	.89441	.46278	.88647	.47818	.87826	.49344	.86978	26
35	.43182	.90196	.44750	.89428	.46304	.88634	.47844	.87812	.49369	.86964	25
36	.43209	.90183	.44776	.89415	.46330	.88620	.47869	.87798	.49394	.86949	24
37	.43235	.90171	.44802	.89402	.46355	.88607	.47895	.87784	.49419	.86935	23
38	.43261	.90158	.44828	.89389	.46381	.88593	.47920	.87770	.49445	.86921	22
39	.43287	.90146	.44854	.89376	.46407	.88580	.47946	.87756	.49470	.86906	21
40	.43313	.90133	.44880	.89363	.46433	.88566	.47971	.87743	.49495	.86892	20
41	.43340	.90120	.44906	.89350	.46458	.88553	.47997	.87729	.49521	.86878	19
42	.43366	.90108	.44932	.89337	.46484	.88539	.48022	.87715	.49546	.86863	18
43	.43392	.90095	.44958	.89324	.46510	.88526	.48048	.87701	.49571	.86849	17
44	.43418	.90082	.44984	.89311	.46536	.88512	.48073	.87687	.49596	.86834	16
45	.43445	.90070	.45010	.89298	.46561	.88499	.48099	.87673	.49622	.86820	15
46	.43471	.90057	.45036	.89285	.46587	.88485	.48124	.87659	.49647	.86805	14
47	.43497	.90045	.45062	.89272	.46613	.88472	.48150	.87645	.49672	.86791	13
48	.43523	.90032	.45088	.89259	.46639	.88458	.48175	.87631	.49697	.86777	12
49	.43549	.90019	.45114	.89245	.46664	.88445	.48201	.87617	.49723	.86762	11
50	.43575	.90007	.45140	.89232	.46690	.88431	.48226	.87603	.49748	.86748	10
51	.43602	.89994	.45166	.89219	.46716	.88417	.48252	.87589	.49773	.86733	9
52	.43628	.89981	.45192	.89206	.46742	.88404	.48277	.87575	.49798	.86719	8
53	.43654	.89968	.45218	.89193	.46767	.88390	.48303	.87561	.49824	.86704	7
54	.43680	.89956	.45243	.89180	.46793	.88377	.48328	.87546	.49849	.86690	6
55	.43706	.89943	.45269	.89167	.46819	.88363	.48354	.87532	.49874	.86675	5
56	.43733	.89930	.45295	.89153	.46844	.88349	.48379	.87518	.49899	.86661	4
57	.43759	.89918	.45321	.89140	.46870	.88336	.48405	.87504	.49924	.86646	3
58	.43785	.89905	.45347	.89127	.46896	.88322	.48430	.87490	.49950	.86632	2
59	.43811	.89892	.45373	.89114	.46921	.88308	.48456	.87476	.49975	.86617	1
60	.43837	.89879	.45399	.89101	.46947	.88295	.48481	.87462	.50000	.86603	0
′	Cosin	Sine	Cosin	Sine	Cosin	Sine	Cosin	Sine	Cosin	Sine	′
	64°		63°		62°		61°		60°		

656

TABLE IV.—NATURAL SINES AND COSINES.

′	30° Sine	30° Cosin	31° Sine	31° Cosin	32° Sine	32° Cosin	33° Sine	33° Cosin	34° Sine	34° Cosin	′
0	.50000	.86603	.51504	.85717	.52992	.84805	.54464	.83867	.55919	.82904	60
1	.50025	.86588	.51529	.85702	.53017	.84789	.54488	.83851	.55943	.82887	59
2	.50050	.86573	.51554	.85687	.53041	.84774	.54513	.83835	.55968	.82871	58
3	.50076	.86559	.51579	.85672	.53066	.84759	.54537	.83819	.55992	.82855	57
4	.50101	.86544	.51604	.85657	.53091	.84743	.54561	.83804	.56016	.82839	56
5	.50126	.86530	.51628	.85642	.53115	.84728	.54586	.83788	.56040	.82822	55
6	.50151	.86515	.51653	.85627	.53140	.84712	.54610	.83772	.56064	.82806	54
7	.50176	.86501	.51678	.85612	.53164	.84697	.54635	.83756	.56088	.82790	53
8	.50201	.86486	.51703	.85597	.53189	.84681	.54659	.83740	.56112	.82773	52
9	.50227	.86471	.51728	.85582	.53214	.84666	.54683	.83724	.56136	.82757	51
10	.50252	.86457	.51753	.85567	.53238	.84650	.54708	.83708	.56160	.82741	50
11	.50277	.86442	.51778	.85551	.53263	.84635	.54732	.83692	.56184	.82724	49
12	.50302	.86427	.51803	.85536	.53288	.84619	.54756	.83676	.56208	.82708	48
13	.50327	.86413	.51828	.85521	.53312	.84604	.54781	.83660	.56232	.82692	47
14	.50352	.86398	.51852	.85506	.53337	.84588	.54805	.83645	.56256	.82675	46
15	.50377	.86384	.51877	.85491	.53361	.84573	.54829	.83629	.56280	.82659	45
16	.50403	.86369	.51902	.85476	.53386	.84557	.54854	.83613	.56305	.82643	44
17	.50428	.86354	.51927	.85461	.53411	.84542	.54878	.83597	.56329	.82626	43
18	.50453	.86340	.51952	.85446	.53435	.84526	.54902	.83581	.56353	.82610	42
19	.50478	.86325	.51977	.85431	.53460	.84511	.54927	.83565	.56377	.82593	41
20	.50503	.86310	.52002	.85416	.53484	.84495	.54951	.83549	.56401	.82577	40
21	.50528	.86295	.52026	.85401	.53509	.84480	.54975	.83533	.56425	.82561	39
22	.50553	.86281	.52051	.85385	.53534	.84464	.54999	.83517	.56449	.82544	38
23	.50578	.86266	.52076	.85370	.53558	.84448	.55024	.83501	.56473	.82528	37
24	.50603	.86251	.52101	.85355	.53583	.84433	.55048	.83485	.56497	.82511	36
25	.50628	.86237	.52126	.85340	.53607	.84417	.55072	.83469	.56521	.82495	35
26	.50654	.86222	.52151	.85325	.53632	.84402	.55097	.83453	.56545	.82478	34
27	.50679	.86207	.52175	.85310	.53656	.84386	.55121	.83437	.56569	.82462	33
28	.50704	.86192	.52200	.85294	.53681	.84370	.55145	.83421	.56593	.82446	32
29	.50729	.86178	.52225	.85279	.53705	.84355	.55169	.83405	.56617	.82429	31
30	.50754	.86163	.52250	.85264	.53730	.84339	.55194	.83389	.56641	.82413	30
31	.50779	.86148	.52275	.85249	.53754	.84324	.55218	.83373	.56665	.82396	29
32	.50804	.86133	.52299	.85234	.53779	.84308	.55242	.83356	.56689	.82380	28
33	.50829	.86119	.52324	.85218	.53804	.84292	.55266	.83340	.56713	.82363	27
34	.50854	.86104	.52349	.85203	.53828	.84277	.55291	.83324	.56736	.82347	26
35	.50879	.86089	.52374	.85188	.53853	.84261	.55315	.83308	.56760	.82330	25
36	.50904	.86074	.52399	.85173	.53877	.84245	.55339	.83292	.56784	.82314	24
37	.50929	.86059	.52423	.85157	.53902	.84230	.55363	.83276	.56808	.82297	23
38	.50954	.86045	.52448	.85142	.53926	.84214	.55388	.83260	.56832	.82281	22
39	.50979	.86030	.52473	.85127	.53951	.84198	.55412	.83244	.56856	.82264	21
40	.51004	.86015	.52498	.85112	.53975	.84182	.55436	.83228	.56880	.82248	20
41	.51029	.86000	.52522	.85096	.54000	.84167	.55460	.83212	.56904	.82231	19
42	.51054	.85985	.52547	.85081	.54024	.84151	.55484	.83195	.56928	.82214	18
43	.51079	.85970	.52572	.85066	.54049	.84135	.55509	.83179	.56952	.82198	17
44	.51104	.85956	.52597	.85051	.54073	.84120	.55533	.83163	.56976	.82181	16
45	.51129	.85941	.52621	.85035	.54097	.84104	.55557	.83147	.57000	.82165	15
46	.51154	.85926	.52646	.85020	.54122	.84088	.55581	.83131	.57024	.82148	14
47	.51179	.85911	.52671	.85005	.54146	.84072	.55605	.83115	.57047	.82132	13
48	.51204	.85896	.52696	.84989	.54171	.84057	.55630	.83098	.57071	.82115	12
49	.51229	.85881	.52720	.84974	.54195	.84041	.55654	.83082	.57095	.82098	11
50	.51254	.85866	.52745	.84959	.54220	.84025	.55678	.83066	.57119	.82082	10
51	.51279	.85851	.52770	.84943	.54244	.84009	.55702	.83050	.57143	.82065	9
52	.51304	.85836	.52794	.84928	.54269	.83994	.55726	.83034	.57167	.82048	8
53	.51329	.85821	.52819	.84913	.54293	.83978	.55750	.83017	.57191	.82032	7
54	.51354	.85806	.52844	.84897	.54317	.83962	.55775	.83001	.57215	.82015	6
55	.51379	.85792	.52869	.84882	.54342	.83946	.55799	.82985	.57238	.81999	5
56	.51404	.85777	.52893	.84866	.54366	.83930	.55823	.82969	.57262	.81982	4
57	.51429	.85762	.52918	.84851	.54391	.83915	.55847	.82953	.57286	.81965	3
58	.51454	.85747	.52943	.84836	.54415	.83899	.55871	.82936	.57310	.81949	2
59	.51479	.85732	.52967	.84820	.54440	.83883	.55895	.82920	.57334	.81932	1
60	.51504	.85717	.52992	.84805	.54464	.83867	.55919	.82904	.57358	.81915	0

′	Cosin	Sine	Cosin	Sine	Cosin	Sine	Cosin	Sine	Cosin	Sine	′
	59°		58°		57°		56°		55°		

TABLE IV.—NATURAL SINES AND COSINES.

′	35° Sine	35° Cosin	36° Sine	36° Cosin	37° Sine	37° Cosin	38° Sine	38° Cosin	39° Sine	39° Cosin	′
0	.57358	.81915	.58779	.80902	.60182	.79864	.61566	.78801	.62932	.77715	60
1	.57381	.81899	.58802	.80885	.60205	.79846	.61589	.78783	.62955	.77696	59
2	.57405	.81882	.58826	.80867	.60228	.79829	.61612	.78765	.62977	.77678	58
3	.57429	.81865	.58849	.80850	.60251	.79811	.61635	.78747	.63000	.77660	57
4	.57453	.81848	.58873	.80833	.60274	.79793	.61658	.78729	.63022	.77641	56
5	.57477	.81832	.58896	.80816	.60298	.79776	.61681	.78711	.63045	.77623	55
6	.57501	.81815	.58920	.80799	.60321	.79758	.61704	.78694	.63068	.77605	54
7	.57524	.81798	.58943	.80782	.60344	.79741	.61726	.78676	.63090	.77586	53
8	.57548	.81782	.58967	.80765	.60367	.79723	.61749	.78658	.63113	.77568	52
9	.57572	.81765	.58990	.80748	.60390	.79706	.61772	.78640	.63135	.77550	51
10	.57596	.81748	.59014	.80730	.60414	.79688	.61795	.78622	.63158	.77531	50
11	.57619	.81731	.59037	.80713	.60437	.79671	.61818	.78604	.63180	.77513	49
12	.57643	.81714	.59061	.80696	.60460	.79653	.61841	.78586	.63203	.77494	48
13	.57667	.81698	.59084	.80679	.60483	.79635	.61864	.78568	.63225	.77476	47
14	.57691	.81681	.59108	.80662	.60506	.79618	.61887	.78550	.63248	.77458	46
15	.57715	.81664	.59131	.80644	.60529	.79600	.61909	.78532	.63271	.77439	45
16	.57738	.81647	.59154	.80627	.60553	.79583	.61932	.78514	.63293	.77421	44
17	.57762	.81631	.59178	.80610	.60576	.79565	.61955	.78496	.63316	.77402	43
18	.57786	.81614	.59201	.80593	.60599	.79547	.61978	.78478	.63338	.77384	42
19	.57810	.81597	.59225	.80576	.60622	.79530	.62001	.78460	.63361	.77366	41
20	.57833	.81580	.59248	.80558	.60645	.79512	.62024	.78442	.63383	.77347	40
21	.57857	.81563	.59272	.80541	.60668	.79494	.62046	.78424	.63406	.77329	39
22	.57881	.81546	.59295	.80524	.60691	.79477	.62069	.78405	.63428	.77310	38
23	.57904	.81530	.59318	.80507	.60714	.79459	.62092	.78387	.63451	.77292	37
24	.57928	.81513	.59342	.80489	.60738	.79441	.62115	.78369	.63473	.77273	36
25	.57952	.81496	.59365	.80472	.60761	.79424	.62138	.78351	.63496	.77255	35
26	.57976	.81479	.59389	.80455	.60784	.79406	.62160	.78333	.63518	.77236	34
27	.57999	.81462	.59412	.80438	.60807	.79388	.62183	.78315	.63540	.77218	33
28	.58023	.81445	.59436	.80420	.60830	.79371	.62206	.78297	.63563	.77199	32
29	.58047	.81428	.59459	.80403	.60853	.79353	.62229	.78279	.63585	.77181	31
30	.58070	.81412	.59482	.80386	.60876	.79335	.62251	.78261	.63608	.77162	30
31	.58094	.81395	.59506	.80368	.60899	.79318	.62274	.78243	.63630	.77144	29
32	.58118	.81378	.59529	.80351	.60922	.79300	.62297	.78225	.63653	.77125	28
33	.58141	.81361	.59552	.80334	.60945	.79282	.62320	.78206	.63675	.77107	27
34	.58165	.81344	.59576	.80316	.60968	.79264	.62342	.78188	.63698	.77088	26
35	.58189	.81327	.59599	.80299	.60991	.79247	.62365	.78170	.63720	.77070	25
36	.58212	.81310	.59622	.80282	.61015	.79229	.62388	.78152	.63742	.77051	24
37	.58236	.81293	.59646	.80264	.61038	.79211	.62411	.78134	.63765	.77033	23
38	.58260	.81276	.59669	.80247	.61061	.79193	.62433	.78116	.63787	.77014	22
39	.58283	.81259	.59693	.80230	.61084	.79176	.62456	.78098	.63810	.76996	21
40	.58307	.81242	.59716	.80212	.61107	.79158	.62479	.78079	.63832	.76977	20
41	.58330	.81225	.59739	.80195	.61130	.79140	.62502	.78061	.63854	.76959	19
42	.58354	.81208	.59763	.80178	.61153	.79122	.62524	.78043	.63877	.76940	18
43	.58378	.81191	.59786	.80160	.61176	.79105	.62547	.78025	.63899	.76921	17
44	.58401	.81174	.59809	.80143	.61199	.79087	.62570	.78007	.63922	.76903	16
45	.58425	.81157	.59832	.80125	.61222	.79069	.62592	.77988	.63944	.76884	15
46	.58449	.81140	.59856	.80108	.61245	.79051	.62615	.77970	.63966	.76866	14
47	.58472	.81123	.59879	.80091	.61268	.79033	.62638	.77952	.63989	.76847	13
48	.58496	.81106	.59902	.80073	.61291	.79016	.62660	.77934	.64011	.76828	12
49	.58519	.81089	.59926	.80056	.61314	.78998	.62683	.77916	.64033	.76810	11
50	.58543	.81072	.59949	.80038	.61337	.78980	.62706	.77897	.64056	.76791	10
51	.58567	.81055	.59972	.80021	.61360	.78962	.62728	.77879	.64078	.76772	9
52	.58590	.81038	.59995	.80003	.61383	.78944	.62751	.77861	.64100	.76754	8
53	.58614	.81021	.60019	.79986	.61406	.78926	.62774	.77843	.64123	.76735	7
54	.58637	.81004	.60042	.79968	.61429	.78908	.62796	.77824	.64145	.76717	6
55	.58661	.80987	.60065	.79951	.61451	.78891	.62819	.77806	.64167	.76698	5
56	.58684	.80970	.60089	.79934	.61474	.78873	.62842	.77788	.64190	.76679	4
57	.58708	.80953	.60112	.79916	.61497	.78855	.62864	.77769	.64212	.76661	3
58	.58731	.80936	.60135	.79899	.61520	.78837	.62887	.77751	.64234	.76642	2
59	.58755	.80919	.60158	.79881	.61543	.78819	.62909	.77733	.64256	.76623	1
60	.58779	.80902	.60182	.79864	.61566	.78801	.62932	.77715	.64279	.76604	0
′	Cosin	Sine	Cosin	Sine	Cosin	Sine	Cosin	Sine	Cosin	Sine	′
	54°		53°		52°		51°		50°		

TABLE IV.—NATURAL SINES AND COSINES.

′	40° Sine	40° Cosin	41° Sine	41° Cosin	42° Sine	42° Cosin	43° Sine	43° Cosin	44° Sine	44° Cosin	′
0	.64279	.76604	.65606	.75471	.66913	.74314	.68200	.73135	.69466	.71934	60
1	.64301	.76586	.65628	.75452	.66935	.74295	.68221	.73116	.69487	.71914	59
2	.64323	.76567	.65650	.75433	.66956	.74276	.68242	.73096	.69508	.71894	58
3	.64346	.76548	.65672	.75414	.66978	.74256	.68264	.73076	.69529	.71873	57
4	.64368	.76530	.65694	.75395	.66999	.74237	.68285	.73056	.69549	.71853	56
5	.64390	.76511	.65716	.75375	.67021	.74217	.68306	.73036	.69570	.71833	55
6	.64412	.76492	.65738	.75356	.67043	.74198	.68327	.73016	.69591	.71813	54
7	.64435	.76473	.65759	.75337	.67064	.74178	.68349	.72996	.69612	.71792	53
8	.64457	.76455	.65781	.75318	.67086	.74159	.68370	.72976	.69633	.71772	52
9	.64479	.76436	.65803	.75299	.67107	.74139	.68391	.72957	.69654	.71752	51
10	.64501	.76417	.65825	.75280	.67129	.74120	.68412	.72937	.69675	.71732	50
11	.64524	.76398	.65847	.75261	.67151	.74100	.68434	.72917	.69696	.71711	49
12	.64546	.76380	.65869	.75241	.67172	.74080	.68455	.72897	.69717	.71691	48
13	.64568	.76361	.65891	.75222	.67194	.74061	.68476	.72877	.69737	.71671	47
14	.64590	.76342	.65913	.75203	.67215	.74041	.68497	.72857	.69758	.71650	46
15	.64612	.76323	.65935	.75184	.67237	.74022	.68518	.72837	.69779	.71630	45
16	.64635	.76304	.65956	.75165	.67258	.74002	.68539	.72817	.69800	.71610	44
17	.64657	.76286	.65978	.75146	.67280	.73983	.68561	.72797	.69821	.71590	43
18	.64679	.76267	.66000	.75126	.67301	.73963	.68582	.72777	.69842	.71569	42
19	.64701	.76248	.66022	.75107	.67323	.73944	.68603	.72757	.69862	.71549	41
20	.64723	.76229	.66044	.75088	.67344	.73924	.68624	.72737	.69883	.71529	40
21	.64746	.76210	.66066	.75069	.67366	.73904	.68645	.72717	.69904	.71508	39
22	.64768	.76192	.66088	.75050	.67387	.73885	.68666	.72697	.69925	.71488	38
23	.64790	.76173	.66109	.75030	.67409	.73865	.68688	.72677	.69946	.71468	37
24	.64812	.76154	.66131	.75011	.67430	.73846	.68709	.72657	.69966	.71447	36
25	.64834	.76135	.66153	.74992	.67452	.73826	.68730	.72637	.69987	.71427	35
26	.64856	.76116	.66175	.74973	.67473	.73806	.68751	.72617	.70008	.71407	34
27	.64878	.76097	.66197	.74953	.67495	.73787	.68772	.72597	.70029	.71386	33
28	.64901	.76078	.66218	.74934	.67516	.73767	.68793	.72577	.70049	.71366	32
29	.64923	.76059	.66240	.74915	.67538	.73747	.68814	.72557	.70070	.71345	31
30	.64945	.76041	.66262	.74896	.67559	.73728	.68835	.72537	.70091	.71325	30
31	.64967	.76022	.66284	.74876	.67580	.73708	.68857	.72517	.70112	.71305	29
32	.64989	.76003	.66306	.74857	.67602	.73688	.68878	.72497	.70132	.71284	28
33	.65011	.75984	.66327	.74838	.67623	.73669	.68899	.72477	.70153	.71264	27
34	.65033	.75965	.66349	.74818	.67645	.73649	.68920	.72457	.70174	.71243	26
35	.65055	.75946	.66371	.74799	.67666	.73629	.68941	.72437	.70195	.71223	25
36	.65077	.75927	.66393	.74780	.67688	.73610	.68962	.72417	.70215	.71203	24
37	.65100	.75908	.66414	.74760	.67709	.73590	.68983	.72397	.70236	.71182	23
38	.65122	.75889	.66436	.74741	.67730	.73570	.69004	.72377	.70257	.71162	22
39	.65144	.75870	.66458	.74722	.67752	.73551	.69025	.72357	.70277	.71141	21
40	.65166	.75851	.66480	.74703	.67773	.73531	.69046	.72337	.70298	.71121	20
41	.65188	.75832	.66501	.74683	.67795	.73511	.69067	.72317	.70319	.71100	19
42	.65210	.75813	.66523	.74664	.67816	.73491	.69088	.72297	.70339	.71080	18
43	.65232	.75794	.66545	.74644	.67837	.73472	.69109	.72277	.70360	.71059	17
44	.65254	.75775	.66566	.74625	.67859	.73452	.69130	.72257	.70381	.71039	16
45	.65276	.75756	.66588	.74606	.67880	.73432	.69151	.72236	.70401	.71019	15
46	.65298	.75738	.66610	.74586	.67901	.73413	.69172	.72216	.70422	.70998	14
47	.65320	.75719	.66632	.74567	.67923	.73393	.69193	.72196	.70443	.70978	13
48	.65342	.75700	.66653	.74548	.67944	.73373	.69214	.72176	.70463	.70957	12
49	.65364	.75680	.66675	.74528	.67965	.73353	.69235	.72156	.70484	.70937	11
50	.65386	.75661	.66697	.74509	.67987	.73333	.69256	.72136	.70505	.70916	10
51	.65408	.75642	.66718	.74489	.68008	.73314	.69277	.72116	.70525	.70896	9
52	.65430	.75623	.66740	.74470	.68029	.73294	.69298	.72095	.70546	.70875	8
53	.65452	.75604	.66762	.74451	.68051	.73274	.69319	.72075	.70567	.70855	7
54	.65474	.75585	.66783	.74431	.68072	.73254	.69340	.72055	.70587	.70834	6
55	.65496	.75566	.66805	.74412	.68093	.73234	.69361	.72035	.70608	.70813	5
56	.65518	.75547	.66827	.74392	.68115	.73215	.69382	.72015	.70628	.70793	4
57	.65540	.75528	.66848	.74373	.68136	.73195	.69403	.71995	.70649	.70772	3
58	.65562	.75509	.66870	.74353	.68157	.73175	.69424	.71974	.70670	.70752	2
59	.65584	.75490	.66891	.74334	.68179	.73155	.69445	.71954	.70690	.70731	1
60	.65606	.75471	.66913	.74314	.68200	.73135	.69466	.71934	.70711	.70711	0
′	Cosin	Sine	Cosin	Sine	Cosin	Sine	Cosin	Sine	Cosin	Sine	′
	49°		48°		47°		46°		45°		

TABLE V.—NATURAL TANGENTS AND COTANGENTS.

′	0°		1°		2°		3°		′
	Tang	Cotang	Tang	Cotang	Tang	Cotang	Tang	Cotang	
0	.00000	Infinite.	.01746	57.2900	.03492	28.6363	.05241	19.0811	60
1	.00029	3437.75	.01775	56.3506	.03521	28.3994	.05270	18.9755	59
2	.00058	1718.87	.01804	55.4415	.03550	28.1664	.05299	18.8711	58
3	.00087	1145.92	.01833	54.5613	.03579	27.9372	.05328	18.7678	57
4	.00116	859.436	.01862	53.7086	.03609	27.7117	.05357	18.6656	56
5	.00145	687.549	.01891	52.8821	.03638	27.4899	.05387	18.5645	55
6	.00175	572.957	.01920	52.0807	.03667	27.2715	.05416	18.4645	54
7	.00204	491.106	.01949	51.3032	.03696	27.0566	.05445	18.3655	53
8	.00233	429.718	.01978	50.5485	.03725	26.8450	.05474	18.2677	52
9	.00262	381.971	.02007	49.8157	.03754	26.6367	.05503	18.1708	51
10	.00291	343.774	.02036	49.1039	.03783	26.4316	.05533	18.0750	50
11	.00320	312.521	.02066	48.4121	.03812	26.2296	.05562	17.9802	49
12	.00349	286.478	.02095	47.7395	.03842	26.0307	.05591	17.8863	48
13	.00378	264.441	.02124	47.0853	.03871	25.8348	.05620	17.7934	47
14	.00407	245.552	.02153	46.4489	.03900	25.6418	.05649	17.7015	46
15	.00436	229.182	.02182	45.8294	.03929	25.4517	.05678	17.6106	45
16	.00465	214.858	.02211	45.2261	.03958	25.2644	.05708	17.5205	44
17	.00495	202.219	.02240	44.6386	.03987	25.0798	.05737	17.4314	43
18	.00524	190.984	.02269	44.0661	.04016	24.8978	.05766	17.3432	42
19	.00553	180.932	.02298	43.5081	.04046	24.7185	.05795	17.2558	41
20	.00582	171.885	.02328	42.9641	.04075	24.5418	.05824	17.1693	40
21	.00611	163.700	.02357	42.4335	.04104	24.3675	.05854	17.0837	39
22	.00640	156.259	.02386	41.9158	.04133	24.1957	.05883	16.9990	38
23	.00669	149.465	.02415	41.4106	.04162	24.0263	.05912	16.9150	37
24	.00698	143.237	.02444	40.9174	.04191	23.8593	.05941	16.8319	36
25	.00727	137.507	.02473	40.4358	.04220	23.6945	.05970	16.7496	35
26	.00756	132.219	.02502	39.9655	.04250	23.5321	.05999	16.6681	34
27	.00785	127.321	.02531	39.5059	.04279	23.3718	.06029	16.5874	33
28	.00815	122.774	.02560	39.0568	.04308	23.2137	.06058	16.5075	32
29	.00844	118.540	.02589	38.6177	.04337	23.0577	.06087	16.4283	31
30	.00873	114.589	.02619	38.1885	.04366	22.9038	.06116	16.3499	30
31	.00902	110.892	.02648	37.7686	.04395	22.7519	.06145	16.2722	29
32	.00931	107.426	.02677	37.3579	.04424	22.6020	.06175	16.1952	28
33	.00960	104.171	.02706	36.9560	.04454	22.4541	.06204	16.1190	27
34	.00989	101.107	.02735	36.5627	.04483	22.3081	.06233	16.0435	26
35	.01018	98.2179	.02764	36.1776	.04512	22.1640	.06262	15.9687	25
36	.01047	95.4895	.02793	35.8006	.04541	22.0217	.06291	15.8945	24
37	.01076	92.9085	.02822	35.4313	.04570	21.8813	.06321	15.8211	23
38	.01105	90.4633	.02851	35.0695	.04599	21.7426	.06350	15.7483	22
39	.01135	88.1436	.02881	34.7151	.04628	21.6056	.06379	15.6762	21
40	.01164	85.9398	.02910	34.3678	.04658	21.4704	.06408	15.6048	20
41	.01193	83.8435	.02939	34.0273	.04687	21.3369	.06437	15.5340	19
42	.01222	81.8470	.02968	33.6935	.04716	21.2049	.06467	15.4638	18
43	.01251	79.9434	.02997	33.3662	.04745	21.0747	.06496	15.3943	17
44	.01280	78.1263	.03026	33.0452	.04774	20.9460	.06525	15.3254	16
45	.01309	76.3900	.03055	32.7303	.04803	20.8188	.06554	15.2571	15
46	.01338	74.7292	.03084	32.4213	.04833	20.6932	.06584	15.1893	14
47	.01367	73.1390	.03114	32.1181	.04862	20.5691	.06613	15.1222	13
48	.01396	71.6151	.03143	31.8205	.04891	20.4465	.06642	15.0557	12
49	.01425	70.1533	.03172	31.5284	.04920	20.3253	.06671	14.9898	11
50	.01455	68.7501	.03201	31.2416	.04949	20.2056	.06700	14.9244	10
51	.01484	67.4019	.03230	30.9599	.04978	20.0872	.06730	14.8596	9
52	.01513	66.1055	.03259	30.6833	.05007	19.9702	.06759	14.7954	8
53	.01542	64.8580	.03288	30.4116	.05037	19.8546	.06788	14.7317	7
54	.01571	63.6567	.03317	30.1446	.05066	19.7403	.06817	14.6685	6
55	.01600	62.4992	.03346	29.8823	.05095	19.6273	.06847	14.6059	5
56	.01629	61.3829	.03376	29.6245	.05124	19.5156	.06876	14.5438	4
57	.01658	60.3058	.03405	29.3711	.05153	19.4051	.06905	14.4823	3
58	.01687	59.2659	.03434	29.1220	.05182	19.2959	.06934	14.4212	2
59	.01716	58.2612	.03463	28.8771	.05212	19.1879	.06963	14.3607	1
60	.01746	57.2900	.03492	28.6363	.05241	19.0811	.06993	14.3007	0
′	Cotang	Tang	Cotang	Tang	Cotang	Tang	Cotang	Tang	′
	89°		88°		87°		86°		

TABLE V.—NATURAL TANGENTS AND COTANGENTS.

′	4° Tang	Cotang	5° Tang	Cotang	6° Tang	Cotang	7° Tang	Cotang	′
0	.06993	14.3007	.08749	11.4301	.10510	9.51436	.12278	8.14435	60
1	.07022	14.2411	.08778	11.3919	.10540	9.48781	.12308	8.12481	59
2	.07051	14.1821	.08807	11.3540	.10569	9.46141	.12338	8.10536	58
3	.07080	14.1235	.08837	11.3163	.10599	9.43515	.12367	8.08600	57
4	.07110	14.0655	.08866	11.2789	.10628	9.40904	.12397	8.06674	56
5	.07139	14.0079	.08895	11.2417	.10657	9.38307	.12426	8.04756	55
6	.07168	13.9507	.08925	11.2048	.10687	9.35724	.12456	8.02848	54
7	.07197	13.8940	.08954	11.1681	.10716	9.33155	.12485	8.00948	53
8	.07227	13.8378	.08983	11.1316	.10746	9.30599	.12515	7.99058	52
9	.07256	13.7821	.09013	11.0954	.10775	9.28058	.12544	7.97176	51
10	.07285	13.7267	.09042	11.0594	.10805	9.25530	.12574	7.95302	50
11	.07314	13.6719	.09071	11.0237	.10834	9.23016	.12603	7.93438	49
12	.07344	13.6174	.09101	10.9882	.10863	9.20516	.12633	7.91582	48
13	.07373	13.5634	.09130	10.9529	.10893	9.18028	.12662	7.89734	47
14	.07402	13.5098	.09159	10.9178	.10922	9.15554	.12692	7.87895	46
15	.07431	13.4566	.09189	10.8829	.10952	9.13093	.12722	7.86064	45
16	.07461	13.4039	.09218	10.8483	.10981	9.10646	.12751	7.84242	44
17	.07490	13.3515	.09247	10.8139	.11011	9.08211	.12781	7.82428	43
18	.07519	13.2996	.09277	10.7797	.11040	9.05789	.12810	7.80622	42
19	.07548	13.2480	.09306	10.7457	.11070	9.03379	.12840	7.78825	41
20	.07578	13.1969	.09335	10.7119	.11099	9.00983	.12869	7.77035	40
21	.07607	13.1461	.09365	10.6783	.11128	8.98598	.12899	7.75254	39
22	.07636	13.0958	.09394	10.6450	.11158	8.96227	.12929	7.73480	38
23	.07665	13.0458	.09423	10.6118	.11187	8.93867	.12958	7.71715	37
24	.07695	12.9962	.09453	10.5789	.11217	8.91520	.12988	7.69957	36
25	.07724	12.9469	.09482	10.5462	.11246	8.89185	.13017	7.68208	35
26	.07753	12.8981	.09511	10.5136	.11276	8.86862	.13047	7.66466	34
27	.07782	12.8496	.09541	10.4813	.11305	8.84551	.13076	7.64732	33
28	.07812	12.8014	.09570	10.4491	.11335	8.82252	.13106	7.63005	32
29	.07841	12.7536	.09600	10.4172	.11364	8.79964	.13136	7.61287	31
30	.07870	12.7062	.09629	10.3854	.11394	8.77689	.13165	7.59575	30
31	.07899	12.6591	.09658	10.3538	.11423	8.75425	.13195	7.57872	29
32	.07929	12.6124	.09688	10.3224	.11452	8.73172	.13224	7.56176	28
33	.07958	12.5660	.09717	10.2913	.11482	8.70931	.13254	7.54487	27
34	.07987	12.5199	.09746	10.2602	.11511	8.68701	.13284	7.52806	26
35	.08017	12.4742	.09776	10.2294	.11541	8.66482	.13313	7.51132	25
36	.08046	12.4288	.09805	10.1988	.11570	8.64275	.13343	7.49465	24
37	.08075	12.3838	.09834	10.1683	.11600	8.62078	.13372	7.47806	23
38	.08104	12.3390	.09864	10.1381	.11629	8.59893	.13402	7.46154	22
39	.08134	12.2946	.09893	10.1080	.11659	8.57718	.13432	7.44509	21
40	.08163	12.2505	.09923	10.0780	.11688	8.55555	.13461	7.42871	20
41	.08192	12.2067	.09952	10.0483	.11718	8.53402	.13491	7.41240	19
42	.08221	12.1632	.09981	10.0187	.11747	8.51259	.13521	7.39616	18
43	.08251	12.1201	.10011	9.98931	.11777	8.49128	.13550	7.37999	17
44	.08280	12.0772	.10040	9.96007	.11806	8.47007	.13580	7.36389	16
45	.08309	12.0346	.10069	9.93101	.11836	8.44896	.13609	7.34786	15
46	.08339	11.9923	.10099	9.90211	.11865	8.42795	.13639	7.33190	14
47	.08368	11.9504	.10128	9.87338	.11895	8.40705	.13669	7.31600	13
48	.08397	11.9087	.10158	9.84482	.11924	8.38625	.13698	7.30018	12
49	.08427	11.8673	.10187	9.81641	.11954	8.36555	.13728	7.28442	11
50	.08456	11.8262	.10216	9.78817	.11983	8.34496	.13758	7.26873	10
51	.08485	11.7853	.10246	9.76009	.12013	8.32446	.13787	7.25310	9
52	.08514	11.7448	.10275	9.73217	.12042	8.30406	.13817	7.23754	8
53	.08544	11.7045	.10305	9.70441	.12072	8.28376	.13846	7.22204	7
54	.08573	11.6645	.10334	9.67680	.12101	8.26355	.13876	7.20661	6
55	.08602	11.6248	.10363	9.64935	.12131	8.24345	.13906	7.19125	5
56	.08632	11.5853	.10393	9.62205	.12160	8.22344	.13935	7.17594	4
57	.08661	11.5461	.10422	9.59490	.12190	8.20352	.13965	7.16071	3
58	.08690	11.5072	.10452	9.56791	.12219	8.18370	.13995	7.14553	2
59	.08720	11.4685	.10481	9.54106	.12249	8.16398	.14024	7.13042	1
60	.08749	11.4301	.10510	9.51436	.12278	8.14435	.14054	7.11537	0
′	Cotang	Tang	Cotang	Tang	Cotang	Tang	Cotang	Tang	′
	85°		84°		83°		82°		

TABLE V.—NATURAL TANGENTS AND COTANGENTS.

′	8°		9°		10°		11°		′
	Tang	Cotang	Tang	Cotang	Tang	Cotang	Tang	Cotang	
0	.14054	7.11537	.15838	6.31375	.17633	5.67128	.19438	5.14455	60
1	.14084	7.10038	.15868	6.30189	.17663	5.66165	.19468	5.13658	59
2	.14113	7.08546	.15898	6.29007	.17693	5.65205	.19498	5.12862	58
3	.14143	7.07059	.15928	6.27829	.17723	5.64248	.19529	5.12069	57
4	.14173	7.05579	.15958	6.26655	.17753	5.63295	.19559	5.11279	56
5	.14202	7.04105	.15988	6.25486	.17783	5.62344	.19589	5.10490	55
6	.14232	7.02637	.16017	6.24321	.17813	5.61397	.19619	5.09704	54
7	.14262	7.01174	.16047	6.23160	.17843	5.60452	.19649	5.08921	53
8	.14291	6.99718	.16077	6.22003	.17873	5.59511	.19680	5.08139	52
9	.14321	6.98268	.16107	6.20851	.17903	5.58573	.19710	5.07360	51
10	.14351	6.96823	.16137	6.19703	.17933	5.57638	.19740	5.06584	50
11	.14381	6.95385	.16167	6.18559	.17963	5.56706	.19770	5.05809	49
12	.14410	6.93952	.16196	6.17419	.17993	5.55777	.19801	5.05037	48
13	.14440	6.92525	.16226	6.16283	.18023	5.54851	.19831	5.04267	47
14	.14470	6.91104	.16256	6.15151	.18053	5.53927	.19861	5.03499	46
15	.14499	6.89688	.16286	6.14023	.18083	5.53007	.19891	5.02734	45
16	.14529	6.88278	.16316	6.12899	.18113	5.52090	.19921	5.01971	44
17	.14559	6.86874	.16346	6.11779	.18143	5.51176	.19952	5.01210	43
18	.14588	6.85475	.16376	6.10664	.18173	5.50264	.19982	5.00451	42
19	.14618	6.84082	.16405	6.09552	.18203	5.49356	.20012	4.99695	41
20	.14648	6.82694	.16435	6.08444	.18233	5.48451	.20042	4.98940	40
21	.14678	6.81312	.16465	6.07340	.18263	5.47548	.20073	4.98188	39
22	.14707	6.79936	.16495	6.06240	.18293	5.46648	.20103	4.97438	38
23	.14737	6.78564	.16525	6.05143	.18323	5.45751	.20133	4.96690	37
24	.14767	6.77199	.16555	6.04051	.18353	5.44857	.20164	4.95945	36
25	.14796	6.75838	.16585	6.02962	.18384	5.43966	.20194	4.95201	35
26	.14826	6.74483	.16615	6.01878	.18414	5.43077	.20224	4.94460	34
27	.14856	6.73133	.16645	6.00797	.18444	5.42192	.20254	4.93721	33
28	.14886	6.71789	.16674	5.99720	.18474	5.41309	.20285	4.92984	32
29	.14915	6.70450	.16704	5.98646	.18504	5.40429	.20315	4.92249	31
30	.14945	6.69116	.16734	5.97576	.18534	5.39552	.20345	4.91516	30
31	.14975	6.67787	.16764	5.96510	.18564	5.38677	.20376	4.90785	29
32	.15005	6.66463	.16794	5.95448	.18594	5.37805	.20406	4.90056	28
33	.15034	6.65144	.16824	5.94390	.18624	5.36936	.20436	4.89330	27
34	.15064	6.63831	.16854	5.93335	.18654	5.36070	.20466	4.88605	26
35	.15094	6.62523	.16884	5.92283	.18684	5.35206	.20497	4.87882	25
36	.15124	6.61219	.16914	5.91236	.18714	5.34345	.20527	4.87162	24
37	.15153	6.59921	.16944	5.90191	.18745	5.33487	.20557	4.86444	23
38	.15183	6.58627	.16974	5.89151	.18775	5.32631	.20588	4.85727	22
39	.15213	6.57339	.17004	5.88114	.18805	5.31778	.20618	4.85013	21
40	.15243	6.56055	.17033	5.87080	.18835	5.30928	.20648	4.84300	20
41	.15272	6.54777	.17063	5.86051	.18865	5.30080	.20679	4.83590	19
42	.15302	6.53503	.17093	5.85024	.18895	5.29235	.20709	4.82882	18
43	.15332	6.52234	.17123	5.84001	.18925	5.28393	.20739	4.82175	17
44	.15362	6.50970	.17153	5.82982	.18955	5.27553	.20770	4.81471	16
45	.15391	6.49710	.17183	5.81966	.18986	5.26715	.20800	4.80769	15
46	.15421	6.48456	.17213	5.80953	.19016	5.25880	.20830	4.80068	14
47	.15451	6.47206	.17243	5.79944	.19046	5.25048	.20861	4.79370	13
48	.15481	6.45961	.17273	5.78938	.19076	5.24218	.20891	4.78673	12
49	.15511	6.44720	.17303	5.77936	.19106	5.23391	.20921	4.77978	11
50	.15540	6.43484	.17333	5.76937	.19136	5.22566	.20952	4.77286	10
51	.15570	6.42253	.17363	5.75941	.19166	5.21744	.20982	4.76595	9
52	.15600	6.41026	.17393	5.74949	.19197	5.20925	.21013	4.75906	8
53	.15630	6.39804	.17423	5.73960	.19227	5.20107	.21043	4.75219	7
54	.15660	6.38587	.17453	5.72974	.19257	5.19293	.21073	4.74534	6
55	.15689	6.37374	.17483	5.71992	.19287	5.18480	.21104	4.73851	5
56	.15719	6.36165	.17513	5.71013	.19317	5.17671	.21134	4.73170	4
57	.15749	6.34961	.17543	5.70037	.19347	5.16863	.21164	4.72490	3
58	.15779	6.33761	.17573	5.69064	.19378	5.16058	.21195	4.71813	2
59	.15809	6.32566	.17603	5.68094	.19408	5.15256	.21225	4.71137	1
60	.15838	6.31375	.17633	5.67128	.19438	5.14455	.21256	4.70463	0
′	Cotang	Tang	Cotang	Tang	Cotang	Tang	Cotang	Tang	′
	81°		80°		79°		78°		

TABLE V.—NATURAL TANGENTS AND COTANGENTS.

′	12°		13°		14°		15°		′
	Tang	Cotang	Tang	Cotang	Tang	Cotang	Tang	Cotang	
0	.21256	4.70463	.23087	4.33148	.24933	4.01078	.26795	3.73205	60
1	.21286	4.69791	.23117	4.32573	.24964	4.00582	.26826	3.72771	59
2	.21316	4.69121	.23148	4.32001	.24995	4.00086	.26857	3.72338	58
3	.21347	4.68452	.23179	4.31430	.25026	3.99592	.26888	3.71907	57
4	.21377	4.67786	.23209	4.30860	.25056	3.99099	.26920	3.71476	56
5	.21408	4.67121	.23240	4.30291	.25087	3.98607	.26951	3.71046	55
6	.21438	4.66458	.23271	4.29724	.25118	3.98117	.26982	3.70616	54
7	.21469	4.65797	.23301	4.29159	.25149	3.97627	.27013	3.70188	53
8	.21499	4.65138	.23332	4.28595	.25180	3.97139	.27044	3.69761	52
9	.21529	4.64480	.23363	4.28032	.25211	3.96651	.27076	3.69335	51
10	.21560	4.63825	.23393	4.27471	.25242	3.96165	.27107	3.68909	50
11	.21590	4.63171	.23424	4.26911	.25273	3.95680	.27138	3.68485	49
12	.21621	4.62518	.23455	4.26352	.25304	3.95196	.27169	3.68061	48
13	.21651	4.61868	.23485	4.25795	.25335	3.94713	.27201	3.67638	47
14	.21682	4.61219	.23516	4.25239	.25366	3.94232	.27232	3.67217	46
15	.21712	4.60572	.23547	4.24685	.25397	3.93751	.27263	3.66796	45
16	.21743	4.59927	.23578	4.24132	.25428	3.93271	.27294	3.66376	44
17	.21773	4.59283	.23608	4.23580	.25459	3.92793	.27326	3.65957	43
18	.21804	4.58641	.23639	4.23030	.25490	3.92316	.27357	3.65538	42
19	.21834	4.58001	.23670	4.22481	.25521	3.91839	.27388	3.65121	41
20	.21864	4.57363	.23700	4.21933	.25552	3.91364	.27419	3.64705	40
21	.21895	4.56726	.23731	4.21387	.25583	3.90890	.27451	3.64289	39
22	.21925	4.56091	.23762	4.20842	.25614	3.90417	.27482	3.63874	38
23	.21956	4.55458	.23793	4.20298	.25645	3.89945	.27513	3.63461	37
24	.21986	4.54826	.23823	4.19756	.25676	3.89474	.27545	3.63048	36
25	.22017	4.54196	.23854	4.19215	.25707	3.89004	.27576	3.62636	35
26	.22047	4.53568	.23885	4.18675	.25738	3.88536	.27607	3.62224	34
27	.22078	4.52941	.23916	4.18137	.25769	3.88068	.27638	3.61814	33
28	.22108	4.52316	.23946	4.17600	.25800	3.87601	.27670	3.61405	32
29	.22139	4.51693	.23977	4.17064	.25831	3.87136	.27701	3.60996	31
30	.22169	4.51071	.24008	4.16530	.25862	3.86671	.27732	3.60588	30
31	.22200	4.50451	.24039	4.15997	.25893	3.86208	.27764	3.60181	29
32	.22231	4.49832	.24069	4.15465	.25924	3.85745	.27795	3.59775	28
33	.22261	4.49215	.24100	4.14934	.25955	3.85284	.27826	3.59370	27
34	.22292	4.48600	.24131	4.14405	.25986	3.84824	.27858	3.58966	26
35	.22322	4.47986	.24162	4.13877	.26017	3.84364	.27889	3.58562	25
36	.22353	4.47374	.24193	4.13350	.26048	3.83906	.27921	3.58160	24
37	.22383	4.46764	.24223	4.12825	.26079	3.83449	.27952	3.57758	23
38	.22414	4.46155	.24254	4.12301	.26110	3.82992	.27983	3.57357	22
39	.22444	4.45548	.24285	4.11778	.26141	3.82537	.28015	3.56957	21
40	.22475	4.44942	.24316	4.11256	.26172	3.82083	.28046	3.56557	20
41	.22505	4.44338	.24347	4.10736	.26203	3.81630	.28077	3.56159	19
42	.22536	4.43735	.24377	4.10216	.26235	3.81177	.28109	3.55761	18
43	.22567	4.43134	.24408	4.09699	.26266	3.80726	.28140	3.55364	17
44	.22597	4.42534	.24439	4.09182	.26297	3.80276	.28172	3.54968	16
45	.22628	4.41936	.24470	4.08666	.26328	3.79827	.28203	3.54573	15
46	.22658	4.41340	.24501	4.08152	.26359	3.79378	.28234	3.54179	14
47	.22689	4.40745	.24532	4.07639	.26390	3.78931	.28266	3.53785	13
48	.22719	4.40152	.24562	4.07127	.26421	3.78485	.28297	3.53393	12
49	.22750	4.39560	.24593	4.06616	.26452	3.78040	.28329	3.53001	11
50	.22781	4.38969	.24624	4.06107	.26483	3.77595	.28360	3.52609	10
51	.22811	4.38381	.24655	4.05599	.26515	3.77152	.28391	3.52219	9
52	.22842	4.37793	.24686	4.05092	.26546	3.76709	.28423	3.51829	8
53	.22872	4.37207	.24717	4.04586	.26577	3.76268	.28454	3.51441	7
54	.22903	4.36623	.24747	4.04081	.26608	3.75828	.28486	3.51053	6
55	.22934	4.36040	.24778	4.03578	.26639	3.75388	.28517	3.50666	5
56	.22964	4.35459	.24809	4.03076	.26670	3.74950	.28549	3.50279	4
57	.22995	4.34879	.24840	4.02574	.26701	3.74512	.28580	3.49894	3
58	.23026	4.34300	.24871	4.02074	.26733	3.74075	.28612	3.49509	2
59	.23056	4.33723	.24902	4.01576	.26764	3.73640	28643	3.49125	1
60	.23087	4.33148	.24933	4.01078	26795	3.73205	.28675	3.48741	0
	Cotang	Tang	Cotang	Tang	Cotang	Tang	Cotang	Tang	
′	77°		76°		75°		74°		′

TABLE V.—NATURAL TANGENTS AND COTANGENTS.

′	16°		17°		18°		19°		′
	Tang	Cotang	Tang	Cotang	Tang	Cotang	Tang	Cotang	
0	.28675	3.48741	.30573	3.27085	.32492	3.07768	.34433	2.90421	60
1	.28706	3.48359	.30605	3.26745	.32524	3.07464	.34465	2.90147	59
2	.28738	3.47977	.30637	3.26406	.32556	3.07160	.34498	2.89873	58
3	.28769	3.47596	.30669	3.26067	.32588	3.06857	.34530	2.89600	57
4	.28800	3.47216	.30700	3.25729	.32621	3.06554	.34563	2.89327	56
5	.28832	3.46837	.30732	3.25392	.32653	3.06252	.34596	2.89055	55
6	.28864	3.46458	.30764	3.25055	.32685	3.05950	.34628	2.88783	54
7	.28895	3.46080	.30796	3.24719	.32717	3.05649	.34661	2.88511	53
8	.28927	3.45703	.30828	3.24383	.32749	3.05349	.34693	2.88240	52
9	.28958	3.45327	.30860	3.24049	.32782	3.05049	.34726	2.87970	51
10	.28990	3.44951	.30891	3.23714	.32814	3.04749	.34758	2.87700	50
11	.29021	3.44576	.30923	3.23381	.32846	3.04450	.34791	2.87430	49
12	.29053	3.44202	.30955	3.23048	.32878	3.04152	.34824	2.87161	48
13	.29084	3.43829	.30987	3.22715	.32911	3.03854	.34856	2.86892	47
14	.29116	3.43456	.31019	3.22384	.32943	3.03556	.34889	2.86624	46
15	.29147	3.43084	.31051	3.22053	.32975	3.03260	.34922	2.86356	45
16	.29179	3.42713	.31083	3.21722	.33007	3.02963	.34954	2.86089	44
17	.29210	3.42343	.31115	3.21392	.33040	3.02667	.34987	2.85822	43
18	.29242	3.41973	.31147	3.21063	.33072	3.02372	.35020	2.85555	42
19	.29274	3.41604	.31178	3.20734	.33104	3.02077	.35052	2.85289	41
20	.29305	3.41236	.31210	3.20406	.33136	3.01783	.35085	2.85023	40
21	.29337	3.40869	.31242	3.20079	.33169	3.01489	.35118	2.84758	39
22	.29368	3.40502	.31274	3.19752	.33201	3.01196	.35150	2.84494	38
23	.29400	3.40136	.31306	3.19426	.33233	3.00903	.35183	2.84229	37
24	.29432	3.39771	.31338	3.19100	.33266	3.00611	.35216	2.83965	36
25	.29463	3.39406	.31370	3.18775	.33298	3.00319	.35248	2.83702	35
26	.29495	3.39042	.31402	3.18451	.33330	3.00028	.35281	2.83439	34
27	.29526	3.38679	.31434	3.18127	.33363	2.99738	.35314	2.83176	33
28	.29558	3.38317	.31466	3.17804	.33395	2.99447	.35346	2.82914	32
29	.29590	3.37955	.31498	3.17481	.33427	2.99158	.35379	2.82653	31
30	.29621	3.37594	.31530	3.17159	.33460	2.98868	.35412	2.82391	30
31	.29653	3.37234	.31562	3.16838	.33492	2.98580	.35445	2.82130	29
32	.29685	3.36875	.31594	3.16517	.33524	2.98292	.35477	2.81870	28
33	.29716	3.36516	.31626	3.16197	.33557	2.98004	.35510	2.81610	27
34	.29748	3.36158	.31658	3.15877	.33589	2.97717	.35543	2.81350	26
35	.29780	3.35800	.31690	3.15558	.33621	2.97430	.35576	2.81091	25
36	.29811	3.35443	.31722	3.15240	.33654	2.97144	.35608	2.80833	24
37	.29843	3.35087	.31754	3.14922	.33686	2.96858	.35641	2.80574	23
38	.29875	3.34732	.31786	3.14605	.33718	2.96573	.35674	2.80316	22
39	.29906	3.34377	.31818	3.14288	.33751	2.96288	.35707	2.80059	21
40	.29938	3.34023	.31850	3.13972	.33783	2.96004	.35740	2.79802	20
41	.29970	3.33670	.31882	3.13656	.33816	2.95721	.35772	2.79545	19
42	.30001	3.33317	.31914	3.13341	.33848	2.95437	.35805	2.79289	18
43	.30033	3.32965	.31946	3.13027	.33881	2.95155	.35838	2.79033	17
44	.30065	3.32614	.31978	3.12713	.33913	2.94872	.35871	2.78778	16
45	.30097	3.32264	.32010	3.12400	.33945	2.94591	.35904	2.78523	15
46	.30128	3.31914	.32042	3.12087	.33978	2.94309	.35937	2.78269	14
47	.30160	3.31565	.32074	3.11775	.34010	2.94028	.35969	2.78014	13
48	.30192	3.31216	.32106	3.11464	.34043	2.93748	.36002	2.77761	12
49	.30224	3.30868	.32139	3.11153	.34075	2.93468	.36035	2.77507	11
50	.30255	3.30521	.32171	3.10842	.34108	2.93189	.36068	2.77254	10
51	.30287	3.30174	.32203	3.10532	.34140	2.92910	.36101	2.77002	9
52	.30319	3.29829	.32235	3.10223	.34173	2.92632	.36134	2.76750	8
53	.30351	3.29483	.32267	3.09914	.34205	2.92354	.36167	2.76498	7
54	.30382	3.29139	.32299	3.09606	.34238	2.92076	.36199	2.76247	6
55	.30414	3.28795	.32331	3.09298	.34270	2.91799	.36232	2.75996	5
56	.30446	3.28452	.32363	3.08991	.34303	2.91523	.36265	2.75746	4
57	.30478	3.28109	.32396	3.08685	.34335	2.91246	.36298	2.75496	3
58	.30509	3.27767	.32428	3.08379	.34368	2.90971	.36331	2.75246	2
59	.30541	3.27426	.32460	3.08073	.34400	2.90696	.36364	2.74997	1
60	.30573	3.27085	.32492	3.07768	.34433	2.90421	.36397	2.74748	0
	Cotang	Tang	Cotang	Tang	Cotang	Tang	Cotang	Tang	
′	73°		72°		71°		70°		′

TABLE V.—NATURAL TANGENTS AND COTANGENTS.

′	20°		21°		22°		23°		′
	Tang	Cotang	Tang	Cotang	Tang	Cotang	Tang	Cotang	
0	.36397	2.74748	.38386	2.60509	.40403	2.47509	.42447	2.35585	60
1	.36430	2.74499	.38420	2.60283	.40436	2.47302	.42482	2.35395	59
2	.36463	2.74251	.38453	2.60057	.40470	2.47095	.42516	2.35205	58
3	.36496	2.74004	.38487	2.59831	.40504	2.46888	.42551	2.35015	57
4	.36529	2.73756	.38520	2.59606	.40538	2.46682	.42585	2.34825	56
5	.36562	2.73509	.38553	2.59381	.40572	2.46476	.42619	2.34636	55
6	.36595	2.73263	.38587	2.59156	.40606	2.46270	.42654	2.34447	54
7	.36628	2.73017	.38620	2.58932	.40640	2.46065	.42688	2.34258	53
8	.36661	2.72771	.38654	2.58708	.40674	2.45860	.42722	2.34069	52
9	.36694	2.72526	.38687	2.58484	.40707	2.45655	.42757	2.33881	51
10	.36727	2.72281	.38721	2.58261	.40741	2.45451	.42791	2.33693	50
11	.36760	2.72036	.38754	2.58038	.40775	2.45246	.42826	2.33505	49
12	.36793	2.71792	.38787	2.57815	.40809	2.45043	.42860	2.33317	48
13	.36826	2.71548	.38821	2.57593	.40843	2.44839	.42894	2.33130	47
14	.36859	2.71305	.38854	2.57371	.40877	2.44636	.42929	2.32943	46
15	.36892	2.71062	.38888	2.57150	.40911	2.44433	.42963	2.32756	45
16	.36925	2.70819	.38921	2.56928	.40945	2.44230	.42998	2.32570	44
17	.36958	2.70577	.38955	2.56707	.40979	2.44027	.43032	2.32383	43
18	.36991	2.70335	.38988	2.56487	.41013	2.43825	.43067	2.32197	42
19	.37024	2.70094	.39022	2.56266	.41047	2.43623	.43101	2.32012	41
20	.37057	2.69853	.39055	2.56046	.41081	2.43422	.43136	2.31826	40
21	.37090	2.69612	.39089	2.55827	.41115	2.43220	.43170	2.31641	39
22	.37123	2.69371	.39122	2.55608	.41149	2.43019	.43205	2.31456	38
23	.37157	2.69131	.39156	2.55389	.41183	2.42819	.43239	2.31271	37
24	.37190	2.68892	.39190	2.55170	.41217	2.42618	.43274	2.31086	36
25	.37223	2.68653	.39223	2.54952	.41251	2.42418	.43308	2.30902	35
26	.37256	2.68414	.39257	2.54734	.41285	2.42218	.43343	2.30718	34
27	.37289	2.68175	.39290	2.54516	.41319	2.42019	.43378	2.30534	33
28	.37322	2.67937	.39324	2.54299	.41353	2.41819	.43412	2.30351	32
29	.37355	2.67700	.39357	2.54082	.41387	2.41620	.43447	2.30167	31
30	.37388	2.67462	.39391	2.53865	.41421	2.41421	.43481	2.29984	30
31	.37422	2.67225	.39425	2.53648	.41455	2.41223	.43516	2.29801	29
32	.37455	2.66989	.39458	2.53432	.41490	2.41025	.43550	2.29619	28
33	.37488	2.66752	.39492	2.53217	.41524	2.40827	.43585	2.29437	27
34	.37521	2.66516	.39526	2.53001	.41558	2.40629	.43620	2.29254	26
35	.37554	2.66281	.39559	2.52786	.41592	2.40432	.43654	2.29073	25
36	.37588	2.66046	.39593	2.52571	.41626	2.40235	.43689	2.28891	24
37	.37621	2.65811	.39626	2.52357	.41660	2.40038	.43724	2.28710	23
38	.37654	2.65576	.39660	2.52142	.41694	2.39841	.43758	2.28528	22
39	.37687	2.65342	.39694	2.51929	.41728	2.39645	.43793	2.28348	21
40	.37720	2.65109	.39727	2.51715	.41763	2.39449	.43828	2.28167	20
41	.37754	2.64875	.39761	2.51502	.41797	2.39253	.43862	2.27987	19
42	.37787	2.64642	.39795	2.51289	.41831	2.39058	.43897	2.27806	18
43	.37820	2.64410	.39829	2.51076	.41865	2.38863	.43932	2.27626	17
44	.37853	2.64177	.39862	2.50864	.41899	2.38668	.43966	2.27447	16
45	.37887	2.63945	.39896	2.50652	.41933	2.38473	.44001	2.27267	15
46	.37920	2.63714	.39930	2.50440	.41968	2.38279	.44036	2.27088	14
47	.37953	2.63483	.39963	2.50229	.42002	2.38084	.44071	2.26909	13
48	.37986	2.63252	.39997	2.50018	.42036	2.37891	.44105	2.26730	12
49	.38020	2.63021	.40031	2.49807	.42070	2.37697	.44140	2.26552	11
50	.38053	2.62791	.40065	2.49597	.42105	2.37504	.44175	2.26374	10
51	.38086	2.62561	.40098	2.49386	.42139	2.37311	.44210	2.26196	9
52	.38120	2.62332	.40132	2.49177	.42173	2.37118	.44244	2.26018	8
53	.38153	2.62103	.40166	2.48967	.42207	2.36925	.44279	2.25840	7
54	.38186	2.61874	.40200	2.48758	.42242	2.36733	.44314	2.25663	6
55	.38220	2.61646	.40234	2.48549	.42276	2.36541	.44349	2.25486	5
56	.38253	2.61418	.40267	2.48340	.42310	2.36349	.44384	2.25309	4
57	.38286	2.61190	.40301	2.48132	.42345	2.36158	.44418	2.25132	3
58	.38320	2.60963	.40335	2.47924	.42379	2.35967	.44453	2.24956	2
59	.38353	2.60736	.40369	2.47716	.42413	2.35776	.44488	2.24780	1
60	.38386	2.60509	.40403	2.47509	.42447	2.35585	.44523	2.24604	0
′	Cotang	Tang	Cotang	Tang	Cotang	Tang	Cotang	Tang	′
	69°		68°		67°		66°		

TABLE V.—NATURAL TANGENTS AND COTANGENTS.

′	24° Tang	24° Cotang	25° Tang	25° Cotang	26° Tang	26° Cotang	27° Tang	27° Cotang	′
0	.44523	2.24604	.46631	2.14451	.48773	2.05030	.50953	1.96261	60
1	.44558	2.24428	.46666	2.14288	.48809	2.04879	.50989	1.96120	59
2	.44593	2.24252	.46702	2.14125	.48845	2.04728	.51026	1.95979	58
3	.44627	2.24077	.46737	2.13963	.48881	2.04577	.51063	1.95838	57
4	.44662	2.23902	.46772	2.13801	.48917	2.04426	.51099	1.95698	56
5	.44697	2.23727	.46808	2.13639	.48953	2.04276	.51136	1.95557	55
6	.44732	2.23553	.46843	2.13477	.48989	2.04125	.51173	1.95417	54
7	.44767	2.23378	.46879	2.13316	.49026	2.03975	.51209	1.95277	53
8	.44802	2.23204	.46914	2.13154	.49062	2.03825	.51246	1.95137	52
9	.44837	2.23030	.46950	2.12993	.49098	2.03675	.51283	1.94997	51
10	.44872	2.22857	.46985	2.12832	.49134	2.03526	.51319	1.94858	50
11	.44907	2.22683	.47021	2.12671	.49170	2.03376	.51356	1.94718	49
12	.44942	2.22510	.47056	2.12511	.49206	2.03227	.51393	1.94579	48
13	.44977	2.22337	.47092	2.12350	.49242	2.03078	.51430	1.94440	47
14	.45012	2.22164	.47128	2.12190	.49278	2.02929	.51467	1.94301	46
15	.45047	2.21992	.47163	2.12030	.49315	2.02780	.51503	1.94162	45
16	.45082	2.21819	.47199	2.11871	.49351	2.02631	.51540	1.94023	44
17	.45117	2.21647	.47234	2.11711	.49387	2.02483	.51577	1.93885	43
18	.45152	2.21475	.47270	2.11552	.49423	2.02335	.51614	1.93746	42
19	.45187	2.21304	.47305	2.11392	.49459	2.02187	.51651	1.93608	41
20	.45222	2.21132	.47341	2.11233	.49495	2.02039	.51688	1.93470	40
21	.45257	2.20961	.47377	2.11075	.49532	2.01891	.51724	1.93332	39
22	.45292	2.20790	.47412	2.10916	.49568	2.01743	.51761	1.93195	38
23	.45327	2.20619	.47448	2.10758	.49604	2.01596	.51798	1.93057	37
24	.45362	2.20449	.47483	2.10600	.49640	2.01449	.51835	1.92920	36
25	.45397	2.20278	.47519	2.10442	.49677	2.01302	.51872	1.92782	35
26	.45432	2.20108	.47555	2.10284	.49713	2.01155	.51909	1.92645	34
27	.45467	2.19938	.47590	2.10126	.49749	2.01008	.51946	1.92508	33
28	.45502	2.19769	.47626	2.09969	.49786	2.00862	.51983	1.92371	32
29	.45538	2.19599	.47662	2.09811	.49822	2.00715	.52020	1.92235	31
30	.45573	2.19430	.47698	2.09654	.49858	2.00569	.52057	1.92098	30
31	.45608	2.19261	.47733	2.09498	.49894	2.00423	.52094	1.91962	29
32	.45643	2.19092	.47769	2.09341	.49931	2.00277	.52131	1.91826	28
33	.45678	2.18923	.47805	2.09184	.49967	2.00131	.52168	1.91690	27
34	.45713	2.18755	.47840	2.09028	.50004	1.99986	.52205	1.91554	26
35	.45748	2.18587	.47876	2.08872	.50040	1.99841	.52242	1.91418	25
36	.45784	2.18419	.47912	2.08716	.50076	1.99695	.52279	1.91282	24
37	.45819	2.18251	.47948	2.08560	.50113	1.99550	.52316	1.91147	23
38	.45854	2.18084	.47984	2.08405	.50149	1.99406	.52353	1.91012	22
39	.45889	2.17916	.48019	2.08250	.50185	1.99261	.52390	1.90876	21
40	.45924	2.17749	.48055	2.08094	.50222	1.99116	.52427	1.90741	20
41	.45960	2.17582	.48091	2.07939	.50258	1.98972	.52464	1.90607	19
42	.45995	2.17416	.48127	2.07785	.50295	1.98828	.52501	1.90472	18
43	.46030	2.17249	.48163	2.07630	.50331	1.98684	.52538	1.90337	17
44	.46065	2.17083	.48198	2.07476	.50368	1.98540	.52575	1.90203	16
45	.46101	2.16917	.48234	2.07321	.50404	1.98396	.52613	1.90069	15
46	.46136	2.16751	.48270	2.07167	.50441	1.98253	.52650	1.89935	14
47	.46171	2.16585	.48306	2.07014	.50477	1.98110	.52687	1.89801	13
48	.46206	2.16420	.48342	2.06860	.50514	1.97966	.52724	1.89667	12
49	.46242	2.16255	.48378	2.06706	.50550	1.97823	.52761	1.89533	11
50	.46277	2.16090	.48414	2.06553	.50587	1.97681	.52798	1.89400	10
51	.46312	2.15925	.48450	2.06400	.50623	1.97538	.52836	1.89266	9
52	.46348	2.15760	.48486	2.06247	.50660	1.97395	.52873	1.89133	8
53	.46383	2.15596	.48521	2.06094	.50696	1.97253	.52910	1.89000	7
54	.46418	2.15432	.48557	2.05942	.50733	1.97111	.52947	1.88867	6
55	.46454	2.15268	.48593	2.05790	.50769	1.96969	.52985	1.88734	5
56	.46489	2.15104	.48629	2.05637	.50806	1.96827	.53022	1.88602	4
57	.46525	2.14940	.48665	2.05485	.50843	1.96685	.53059	1.88469	3
58	.46560	2.14777	.48701	2.05333	.50879	1.96544	.53096	1.88337	2
59	.46595	2.14614	.48737	2.05182	.50916	1.96402	.53134	1.88205	1
60	.46631	2.14451	.48773	2.05030	.50953	1.96261	.53171	1.88073	0
′	Cotang	Tang	Cotang	Tang	Cotang	Tang	Cotang	Tang	′
	65°		64°		63°		62°		

TABLE V.—NATURAL TANGENTS AND COTANGENTS.

′	28°		29°		30°		31°		′
	Tang	Cotang	Tang	Cotang	Tang	Cotang	Tang	Cotang	
0	.53171	1.88073	.55431	1.80405	.57735	1.73205	.60086	1.66428	60
1	.53208	1.87941	.55469	1.80281	.57774	1.73089	.60126	1.66318	59
2	.53246	1.87809	.55507	1.80158	.57813	1.72973	.60165	1.66209	58
3	.53283	1.87677	.55545	1.80034	.57851	1.72857	.60205	1.66099	57
4	.53320	1.87546	.55583	1.79911	.57890	1.72741	.60245	1.65990	56
5	.53358	1.87415	.55621	1.79788	.57929	1.72625	.60284	1.65881	55
6	.53395	1.87283	.55659	1.79665	.57968	1.72509	.60324	1.65772	54
7	53432	1.87152	.55697	1.79542	.58007	1.72393	.60364	1.65663	53
8	.53470	1.87021	.55736	1.79419	.58046	1.72278	.60403	1.65554	52
9	.53507	1.86891	.55774	1.79296	.58085	1.72163	.60443	1.65445	51
10	.53545	1.86760	.55812	1.79174	.58124	1.72047	.60483	1.65337	50
11	.53582	1.86630	.55850	1.79051	.58162	1.71932	.60522	1.65228	49
12	.53620	1.86499	.55888	1.78929	.58201	1.71817	.60562	1.65120	48
13	.53657	1.86369	.55926	1.78807	.58240	1.71702	.60602	1.65011	47
14	.53694	1.86239	.55964	1.78685	.58279	1.71588	.60642	1.64903	46
15	.53732	1.86109	.56003	1.78563	.58318	1.71473	.60681	1.64795	45
16	.53769	1.85979	.56041	1.78441	.58357	1.71358	.60721	1.64687	44
17	.53807	1.85850	.56079	1.78319	.58396	1.71244	.60761	1.64579	43
18	.53844	1.85720	.56117	1.78198	.58435	1.71129	.60801	1.64471	42
19	.53882	1.85591	.56156	1.78077	.58474	1.71015	.60841	1.64363	41
20	.53920	1.85462	.56194	1.77955	.58513	1.70901	.60881	1.64256	40
21	.53957	1.85333	.56232	1.77834	.58552	1.70787	.60921	1.64148	39
22	.53995	1.85204	.56270	1.77713	.58591	1.70673	.60960	1.64041	38
23	.54032	1.85075	.56309	1.77592	.58631	1.70560	.61000	1.63934	37
24	.54070	1.84946	.56347	1.77471	.58670	1.70446	.61040	1.63826	36
25	.54107	1.84818	.56385	1.77351	.58709	1.70332	.61080	1.63719	35
26	.54145	1.84689	.56424	1.77230	.58748	1.70219	.61120	1.63612	34
27	.54183	1.84561	.56462	1.77110	.58787	1.70106	.61160	1.63505	33
28	.54220	1.84433	.56501	1.76990	.58826	1.69992	.61200	1.63398	32
29	.54258	1.84305	.56539	1.76869	.58865	1.69879	.61240	1.63292	31
30	.54296	1.84177	.56577	1.76749	.58905	1.69766	.61280	1.63185	30
31	.54333	1.84049	.56616	1.76629	.58944	1.69653	.61320	1.63079	29
32	.54371	1.83922	.56654	1.76510	.58983	1.69541	.61360	1.62972	28
33	.54409	1.83794	.56693	1.76390	.59022	1.69428	.61400	1.62866	27
34	.54446	1.83667	.56731	1.76271	.59061	1.69316	.61440	1.62760	26
35	.54484	1.83540	.56769	1.76151	.59101	1.69203	.61480	1.62654	25
36	.54522	1.83413	.56808	1.76032	.59140	1.69091	.61520	1.62548	24
37	.54560	1.83286	.56846	1.75913	.59179	1.68979	.61561	1.62442	23
38	.54597	1.83159	.56885	1.75794	.59218	1.68866	.61601	1.62336	22
39	.54635	1.83033	.56923	1.75675	.59258	1.68754	.61641	1.62230	21
40	.54673	1.82906	.56962	1.75556	.59297	1.68643	.61681	1.62125	20
41	.54711	1.82780	.57000	1.75437	.59336	1.68531	.61721	1.62019	19
42	.54748	1.82654	.57039	1.75319	.59376	1.68419	.61761	1.61914	18
43	.54786	1.82528	.57078	1.75200	.59415	1.68308	.61801	1.61808	17
44	.54824	1.82402	.57116	1.75082	.59454	1.68196	.61842	1.61703	16
45	.54862	1.82276	.57155	1.74964	.59494	1.68085	.61882	1.61598	15
46	.54900	1.82150	.57193	1.74846	.59533	1.67974	.61922	1.61493	14
47	.54938	1.82025	.57232	1.74728	.59573	1.67863	.61962	1.61388	13
48	.54975	1.81899	.57271	1.74610	.59612	1.67752	.62003	1.61283	12
49	.55013	1.81774	.57309	1.74492	.59651	1.67641	.62043	1.61179	11
50	.55051	1.81649	.57348	1.74375	.59691	1.67530	.62083	1.61074	10
51	.55089	1.81524	.57386	1.74257	.59730	1.67419	.62124	1.60970	9
52	.55127	1.81399	.57425	1.74140	.59770	1.67309	.62164	1.60865	8
53	.55165	1.81274	.57464	1.74022	.59809	1.67198	.62204	1.60761	7
54	.55203	1.81150	.57503	1.73905	.59849	1.67088	.62245	1.60657	6
55	.55241	1.81025	.57541	1.73788	.59888	1.66978	.62285	1.60553	5
56	.55279	1.80901	.57580	1.73671	.59928	1.66867	.62325	1.60449	4
57	.55317	1.80777	.57619	1.73555	.59967	1.66757	.62366	1.60345	3
58	.55355	1.80653	.57657	1.73438	.60007	1.66647	.62406	1.60241	2
59	.55393	1.80529	.57696	1.73321	.60046	1.66538	.62446	1.60137	1
60	.55431	1.80405	.57735	1.73205	.60086	1.66428	.62487	1.60033	0
	Cotang	Tang	Cotang	Tang	Cotang	Tang	Cotang	Tang	
′	61°		60°		59°		58°		′

TABLE V.—NATURAL TANGENTS AND COTANGENTS.

′	32° Tang	Cotang	33° Tang	Cotang	34° Tang	Cotang	35° Tang	Cotang	′
0	.62487	1.60033	.64941	1.53986	.67451	1.48256	.70021	1.42815	60
1	.62527	1.59930	.64982	1.53888	.67493	1.48163	.70064	1.42726	59
2	.62568	1.59826	.65024	1.53791	.67536	1.48070	.70107	1.42638	58
3	.62608	1.59723	.65065	1.53693	.67578	1.47977	.70151	1.42550	57
4	.62649	1.59620	.65106	1.53595	.67620	1.47885	.70194	1.42462	56
5	.62689	1.59517	.65148	1.53497	.67663	1.47792	.70238	1.42374	55
6	.62730	1.59414	.65189	1.53400	.67705	1.47699	.70281	1.42286	54
7	.62770	1.59311	.65231	1.53302	.67748	1.47607	.70325	1.42198	53
8	.62811	1.59208	.65272	1.53205	.67790	1.47514	.70368	1.42110	52
9	.62852	1.59105	.65314	1.53107	.67832	1.47422	.70412	1.42022	51
10	.62892	1.59002	.65355	1.53010	.67875	1.47330	.70455	1.41934	50
11	.62933	1.58900	.65397	1.52913	.67917	1.47238	.70499	1.41847	49
12	.62973	1.58797	.65438	1.52816	.67960	1.47146	.70542	1.41759	48
13	.63014	1.58695	.65480	1.52719	.68002	1.47053	.70586	1.41672	47
14	.63055	1.58593	.65521	1.52622	.68045	1.46962	.70629	1.41584	46
15	.63095	1.58490	.65563	1.52525	.68088	1.46870	.70673	1.41497	45
16	.63136	1.58388	.65604	1.52429	.68130	1.46778	.70717	1.41409	44
17	.63177	1.58286	.65646	1.52332	.68173	1.46686	.70760	1.41322	43
18	.63217	1.58184	.65688	1.52235	.68215	1.46595	.70804	1.41235	42
19	.63258	1.58083	.65729	1.52139	.68258	1.46503	.70848	1.41148	41
20	.63299	1.57981	.65771	1.52043	.68301	1.46411	.70891	1.41061	40
21	.63340	1.57879	.65813	1.51946	.68343	1.46320	.70935	1.40974	39
22	.63380	1.57778	.65854	1.51850	.68386	1.46229	.70979	1.40887	38
23	.63421	1.57676	.65896	1.51754	.68429	1.46137	.71023	1.40800	37
24	.63462	1.57575	.65938	1.51658	.68471	1.46046	.71066	1.40714	36
25	.63503	1.57474	.65980	1.51562	.68514	1.45955	.71110	1.40627	35
26	.63544	1.57372	.66021	1.51466	.68557	1.45864	.71154	1.40540	34
27	.63584	1.57271	.66063	1.51370	.68600	1.45773	.71198	1.40454	33
28	.63625	1.57170	.66105	1.51275	.68642	1.45682	.71242	1.40367	32
29	.63666	1.57069	.66147	1.51179	.68685	1.45592	.71285	1.40281	31
30	.63707	1.56969	.66189	1.51084	.68728	1.45501	.71329	1.40195	30
31	.63748	1.56868	.66230	1.50988	.68771	1.45410	.71373	1.40109	29
32	.63789	1.56767	.66272	1.50893	.68814	1.45320	.71417	1.40022	28
33	.63830	1.56667	.66314	1.50797	.68857	1.45229	.71461	1.39936	27
34	.63871	1.56566	.66356	1.50702	.68900	1.45139	.71505	1.39850	26
35	.63912	1.56466	.66398	1.50607	.68942	1.45049	.71549	1.39764	25
36	.63953	1.56366	.66440	1.50512	.68985	1.44958	.71593	1.39679	24
37	.63994	1.56265	.66482	1.50417	.69028	1.44868	.71637	1.39593	23
38	.64035	1.56165	.66524	1.50322	.69071	1.44778	.71681	1.39507	22
39	.64076	1.56065	.66566	1.50228	.69114	1.44688	.71725	1.39421	21
40	.64117	1.55966	.66608	1.50133	.69157	1.44598	.71769	1.39336	20
41	.64158	1.55866	.66650	1.50038	.69200	1.44508	.71813	1.39250	19
42	.64199	1.55766	.66692	1.49944	.69243	1.44418	.71857	1.39165	18
43	.64240	1.55666	.66734	1.49849	.69286	1.44329	.71901	1.39079	17
44	.64281	1.55567	.66776	1.49755	.69329	1.44239	.71946	1.38994	16
45	.64322	1.55467	.66818	1.49661	.69372	1.44149	.71990	1.38909	15
46	.64363	1.55368	.66860	1.49566	.69416	1.44060	.72034	1.38824	14
47	.64404	1.55269	.66902	1.49472	.69459	1.43970	.72078	1.38738	13
48	.64446	1.55170	.66944	1.49378	.69502	1.43881	.72122	1.38653	12
49	.64487	1.55071	.66986	1.49284	.69545	1.43792	.72167	1.38568	11
50	.64528	1.54972	.67028	1.49190	.69588	1.43703	.72211	1.38484	10
51	.64569	1.54873	.67071	1.49097	.69631	1.43614	.72255	1.38399	9
52	.64610	1.54774	.67113	1.49003	.69675	1.43525	.72299	1.38314	8
53	.64652	1.54675	.67155	1.48909	.69718	1.43436	.72344	1.38229	7
54	.64693	1.54576	.67197	1.48816	.69761	1.43347	.72388	1.38145	6
55	.64734	1.54478	.67239	1.48722	.69804	1.43258	.72432	1.38060	5
56	.64775	1.54379	.67282	1.48629	.69847	1.43169	.72477	1.37976	4
57	.64817	1.54281	.67324	1.48536	.69891	1.43080	.72521	1.37891	3
58	.64858	1.54183	.67366	1.48442	.69934	1.42992	.72565	1.37807	2
59	.64899	1.54085	.67409	1.48349	.69977	1.42903	.72610	1.37722	1
60	.64941	1.53986	.67451	1.48256	.70021	1.42815	.72654	1.37638	0
′	Cotang	Tang	Cotang	Tang	Cotang	Tang	Cotang	Tang	′
	57°		56°		55°		54°		

TABLE V.—NATURAL TANGENTS AND COTANGENTS.

′	36° Tang	36° Cotang	37° Tang	37° Cotang	38° Tang	38° Cotang	39° Tang	39° Cotang	′
0	.72654	1.37638	.75355	1.32704	.78129	1.27994	.80978	1.23490	60
1	.72699	1.37554	.75401	1.32624	.78175	1.27917	.81027	1.23416	59
2	.72743	1.37470	.75447	1.32544	.78222	1.27841	.81075	1.23343	58
3	.72788	1.37386	.75492	1.32464	.78269	1.27764	.81123	1.23270	57
4	.72832	1.37302	.75538	1.32384	.78316	1.27688	.81171	1.23196	56
5	.72877	1.37218	.75584	1.32304	.78363	1.27611	.81220	1.23123	55
6	.72921	1.37134	.75629	1.32224	.78410	1.27535	.81268	1.23050	54
7	.72966	1.37050	.75675	1.32144	.78457	1.27458	.81316	1.22977	53
8	.73010	1.36967	.75721	1.32064	.78504	1.27382	.81364	1.22904	52
9	.73055	1.36883	.75767	1.31984	.78551	1.27306	.81413	1.22831	51
10	.73100	1.36800	.75812	1.31904	.78598	1.27230	.81461	1.22758	50
11	.73144	1.36716	.75858	1.31825	.78645	1.27153	.81510	1.22685	49
12	.73189	1.36633	.75904	1.31745	.78692	1.27077	.81558	1.22612	48
13	.73234	1.36549	.75950	1.31666	.78739	1.27001	.81606	1.22539	47
14	.73278	1.36466	.75996	1.31586	.78786	1.26925	.81655	1.22467	46
15	.73323	1.36383	.76042	1.31507	.78834	1.26849	.81703	1.22394	45
16	.73368	1.36300	.76088	1.31427	.78881	1.26774	.81752	1.22321	44
17	.73413	1.36217	.76134	1.31348	.78928	1.26698	.81800	1.22249	43
18	.73457	1.36134	.76180	1.31269	.78975	1.26622	.81849	1.22176	42
19	.73502	1.36051	.76226	1.31190	.79022	1.26546	.81898	1.22104	41
20	.73547	1.35968	.76272	1.31110	.79070	1.26471	.81946	1.22031	40
21	.73592	1.35885	.76318	1.31031	.79117	1.26395	.81995	1.21959	39
22	.73637	1.35802	.76364	1.30952	.79164	1.26319	.82044	1.21886	38
23	.73681	1.35719	.76410	1.30873	.79212	1.26244	.82092	1.21814	37
24	.73726	1.35637	.76456	1.30795	.79259	1.26169	.82141	1.21742	36
25	.73771	1.35554	.76502	1.30716	.79306	1.26093	.82190	1.21670	35
26	.73816	1.35472	.76548	1.30637	.79354	1.26018	.82238	1.21598	34
27	.73861	1.35389	.76594	1.30558	.79401	1.25943	.82287	1.21526	33
28	.73906	1.35307	.76640	1.30480	.79449	1.25867	.82336	1.21454	32
29	.73951	1.35224	.76686	1.30401	.79496	1.25792	.82385	1.21382	31
30	.73996	1.35142	.76733	1.30323	.79544	1.25717	.82434	1.21310	30
31	.74041	1.35060	.76779	1.30244	.79591	1.25642	.82483	1.21238	29
32	.74086	1.34978	.76825	1.30166	.79639	1.25567	.82531	1.21166	28
33	.74131	1.34896	.76871	1.30087	.79686	1.25492	.82580	1.21094	27
34	.74176	1.34814	.76918	1.30009	.79734	1.25417	.82629	1.21023	26
35	.74221	1.34732	.76964	1.29931	.79781	1.25343	.82678	1.20951	25
36	.74267	1.34650	.77010	1.29853	.79829	1.25268	.82727	1.20879	24
37	.74312	1.34568	.77057	1.29775	.79877	1.25193	.82776	1.20808	23
38	.74357	1.34487	.77103	1.29696	.79924	1.25118	.82825	1.20736	22
39	.74402	1.34405	.77149	1.29618	.79972	1.25044	.82874	1.20665	21
40	.74447	1.34323	.77196	1.29541	.80020	1.24969	.82923	1.20593	20
41	.74492	1.34242	.77242	1.29463	.80067	1.24895	.82972	1.20522	19
42	.74538	1.34160	.77289	1.29385	.80115	1.24820	.83022	1.20451	18
43	.74583	1.34079	.77335	1.29307	.80163	1.24746	.83071	1.20379	17
44	.74628	1.33998	.77382	1.29229	.80211	1.24672	.83120	1.20308	16
45	.74674	1.33916	.77428	1.29152	.80258	1.24597	.83169	1.20237	15
46	.74719	1.33835	.77475	1.29074	.80306	1.24523	.83218	1.20166	14
47	.74764	1.33754	.77521	1.28997	.80354	1.24449	.83268	1.20095	13
48	.74810	1.33673	.77568	1.28919	.80402	1.24375	.83317	1.20024	12
49	.74855	1.33592	.77615	1.28842	.80450	1.24301	.83366	1.19953	11
50	.74900	1.33511	.77661	1.28764	.80498	1.24227	.83415	1.19882	10
51	.74946	1.33430	.77708	1.28687	.80546	1.24153	.83465	1.19811	9
52	.74991	1.33349	.77754	1.28610	.80594	1.24079	.83514	1.19740	8
53	.75037	1.33268	.77801	1.28533	.80642	1.24005	.83564	1.19669	7
54	.75082	1.33187	.77848	1.28456	.80690	1.23931	.83613	1.19599	6
55	.75128	1.33107	.77895	1.28379	.80738	1.23858	.83662	1.19528	5
56	.75173	1.33026	.77941	1.28302	.80786	1.23784	.83712	1.19457	4
57	.75219	1.32946	.77988	1.28225	.80834	1.23710	.83761	1.19387	3
58	.75264	1.32865	.78035	1.28148	.80882	1.23637	.83811	1.19316	2
59	.75310	1.32785	.78082	1.28071	.80930	1.23563	.83860	1.19246	1
60	.75355	1.32704	.78129	1.27994	.80978	1.23490	.83910	1.19175	0
′	Cotang	Tang	Cotang	Tang	Cotang	Tang	Cotang	Tang	′
	53°		52°		51°		50°		

TABLE V.—NATURAL TANGENTS AND COTANGENTS.

′	40° Tang	40° Cotang	41° Tang	41° Cotang	42° Tang	42° Cotang	43° Tang	43° Cotang	′
0	.83910	1.19175	.86929	1.15037	.90040	1.11061	.93252	1.07237	60
1	.83960	1.19105	.86980	1.14969	.90093	1.10996	.93306	1.07174	59
2	.84009	1.19035	.87031	1.14902	.90146	1.10931	.93360	1.07112	58
3	.84059	1.18964	.87082	1.14834	.90199	1.10867	.93415	1.07049	57
4	.84108	1.18894	.87133	1.14767	.90251	1.10802	.93469	1.06987	56
5	.84158	1.18824	.87184	1.14699	.90304	1.10737	.93524	1.06925	55
6	.84208	1.18754	.87236	1.14632	.90357	1.10672	.93578	1.06862	54
7	.84258	1.18684	.87287	1.14565	.90410	1.10607	.93633	1.06800	53
8	.84307	1.18614	.87338	1.14498	.90463	1.10543	.93688	1.06738	52
9	.84357	1.18544	.87389	1.14430	.90516	1.10478	.93742	1.06676	51
10	.84407	1.18474	.87441	1.14363	.90569	1.10414	.93797	1.06613	50
11	.84457	1.18404	.87492	1.14296	.90621	1.10349	.93852	1.06551	49
12	.84507	1.18334	.87543	1.14229	.90674	1.10285	.93906	1.06489	48
13	.84556	1.18264	.87595	1.14162	.90727	1.10220	.93961	1.06427	47
14	.84606	1.18194	.87646	1.14095	.90781	1.10156	.94016	1.06365	46
15	.84656	1.18125	.87698	1.14028	.90834	1.10091	.94071	1.06303	45
16	.84706	1.18055	.87749	1.13961	.90887	1.10027	.94125	1.06241	44
17	.84756	1.17986	.87801	1.13894	.90940	1.09963	.94180	1.06179	43
18	.84806	1.17916	.87852	1.13828	.90993	1.09899	.94235	1.06117	42
19	.84856	1.17846	.87904	1.13761	.91046	1.09834	.94290	1.06056	41
20	.84906	1.17777	.87955	1.13694	.91099	1.09770	.94345	1.05994	40
21	.84956	1.17708	.88007	1.13627	.91153	1.09706	.94400	1.05932	39
22	.85006	1.17638	.88059	1.13561	.91206	1.09642	.94455	1.05870	38
23	.85057	1.17569	.88110	1.13494	.91259	1.09578	.94510	1.05809	37
24	.85107	1.17500	.88162	1.13428	.91313	1.09514	.94565	1.05747	36
25	.85157	1.17430	.88214	1.13361	.91366	1.09450	.94620	1.05685	35
26	.85207	1.17361	.88265	1.13295	.91419	1.09386	.94676	1.05624	34
27	.85257	1.17292	.88317	1.13228	.91473	1.09322	.94731	1.05562	33
28	.85308	1.17223	.88369	1.13162	.91526	1.09258	.94786	1.05501	32
29	.85358	1.17154	.88421	1.13096	.91580	1.09195	.94841	1.05439	31
30	.85408	1.17085	.88473	1.13029	.91633	1.09131	.94896	1.05378	30
31	.85458	1.17016	.88524	1.12963	.91687	1.09067	.94952	1.05317	29
32	.85509	1.16947	.88576	1.12897	.91740	1.09003	.95007	1.05255	28
33	.85559	1.16878	.88628	1.12831	.91794	1.08940	.95062	1.05194	27
34	.85609	1.16809	.88680	1.12765	.91847	1.08876	.95118	1.05133	26
35	.85660	1.16741	.88732	1.12699	.91901	1.08813	.95173	1.05072	25
36	.85710	1.16672	.88784	1.12633	.91955	1.08749	.95229	1.05010	24
37	.85761	1.16603	.88836	1.12567	.92008	1.08686	.95284	1.04949	23
38	.85811	1.16535	.88888	1.12501	.92062	1.08622	.95340	1.04888	22
39	.85862	1.16466	.88940	1.12435	.92116	1.08559	.95395	1.04827	21
40	.85912	1.16398	.88992	1.12369	.92170	1.08496	.95451	1.04766	20
41	.85963	1.16329	.89045	1.12303	.92224	1.08432	.95506	1.04705	19
42	.86014	1.16261	.89097	1.12238	.92277	1.08369	.95562	1.04644	18
43	.86064	1.16192	.89149	1.12172	.92331	1.08306	.95618	1.04583	17
44	.86115	1.16124	.89201	1.12106	.92385	1.08243	.95673	1.04522	16
45	.86166	1.16056	.89253	1.12041	.92439	1.08179	.95729	1.04461	15
46	.86216	1.15987	.89306	1.11975	.92493	1.08116	.95785	1.04401	14
47	.86267	1.15919	.89358	1.11909	.92547	1.08053	.95841	1.04340	13
48	.86318	1.15851	.89410	1.11844	.92601	1.07990	.95897	1.04279	12
49	.86368	1.15783	.89463	1.11778	.92655	1.07927	.95952	1.04218	11
50	.86419	1.15715	.89515	1.11713	.92709	1.07864	.96008	1.04158	10
51	.86470	1.15647	.89567	1.11648	.92763	1.07801	.96064	1.04097	9
52	.86521	1.15579	.89620	1.11582	.92817	1.07738	.96120	1.04036	8
53	.86572	1.15511	.89672	1.11517	.92872	1.07676	.96176	1.03976	7
54	.86623	1.15443	.89725	1.11452	.92926	1.07613	.96232	1.03915	6
55	.86674	1.15375	.89777	1.11387	.92980	1.07550	.96288	1.03855	5
56	.86725	1.15308	.89830	1.11321	.93034	1.07487	.96344	1.03794	4
57	.86776	1.15240	.89883	1.11256	.93088	1.07425	.96400	1.03734	3
58	.86827	1.15172	.89935	1.11191	.93143	1.07362	.96457	1.03674	2
59	.86878	1.15104	.89988	1.11126	.93197	1.07299	.96513	1.03613	1
60	.86929	1.15037	.90040	1.11061	.93252	1.07237	.96569	1.03553	0
′	Cotang	Tang	Cotang	Tang	Cotang	Tang	Cotang	Tang	′
	49°		48°		47°		46°		

TABLE V.—NATURAL TANGENTS AND COTANGENTS.

′	44°		′	′	44°		′	′	44°		′
	Tang	Cotang			Tang	Cotang			Tang	Cotang	
0	.96569	1.03553	60	20	.97700	1.02355	40	40	.98843	1.01170	20
1	.96625	1.03493	59	21	.97756	1.02295	39	41	.98901	1.01112	19
2	.96681	1.03433	58	22	.97813	1.02236	38	42	.98958	1.01053	18
3	.96738	1.03372	57	23	.97870	1.02176	37	43	.99016	1.00994	17
4	.96794	1.03312	56	24	.97927	1.02117	36	44	.99073	1.00935	16
5	.96850	1.03252	55	25	.97984	1.02057	35	45	.99131	1.00876	15
6	.96907	1.03192	54	26	.98041	1.01998	34	46	.99189	1.00818	14
7	.96963	1.03132	53	27	.98098	1.01939	33	47	.99247	1.00759	13
8	.97020	1.03072	52	28	.98155	1.01879	32	48	.99304	1.00701	12
9	.97076	1.03012	51	29	.98213	1.01820	31	49	.99362	1.00642	11
10	.97133	1.02952	50	30	.98270	1.01761	30	50	.99420	1.00583	10
11	.97189	1.02892	49	31	.98327	1.01702	29	51	.99478	1.00525	9
12	.97246	1.02832	48	32	.98384	1.01642	28	52	.99536	1.00467	8
13	.97302	1.02772	47	33	.98441	1.01583	27	53	.99594	1.00408	7
14	.97359	1.02713	46	34	.98499	1.01524	26	54	.99652	1.00350	6
15	.97416	1.02653	45	35	.98556	1.01465	25	55	.99710	1.00291	5
16	.97472	1.02593	44	36	.98613	1.01406	24	56	.99768	1.00233	4
17	.97529	1.02533	43	37	.98671	1.01347	23	57	.99826	1.00175	3
18	.97586	1.02474	42	38	.98728	1.01288	22	58	.99884	1.00116	2
19	.97643	1.02414	41	39	.98786	1.01229	21	59	.99942	1.00058	1
20	.97700	1.02355	40	40	.98843	1.01170	20	60	1.00000	1.00000	0
′	Cotang	Tang	′	′	Cotang	Tang	′	′	Cotang	Tang	′
	45°				45°				45°		

Table VI. — Natural Versed Sines.

			3°	4°	5°	6°	7°	8°	9°
0° 00'	.00000	00'	.00137	.00244	.00381	.00548	.00745	.00973	.01231
05	000	01	139	246	383	551	749	977	236
10	000	02	140	248	386	554	752	981	240
15	001	03	142	250	388	557	756	985	245
20	002	04	143	252	391	560	760	989	249
25	003	05	.00145	.00254	.00393	.00563	.00763	.00994	.01254
30	.00004	06	146	256	396	566	767	998	259
35	005	07	148	258	398	569	770	.01002	263
40	007	08	149	260	401	572	774	006	268
45	009	09	151	262	404	576	778	010	272
50	011	10	.00153	.00264	.00406	.00579	.00781	.01014	.01177
55	013	11	154	266	409	582	785	018	282
1°00'	.00015	12	156	269	412	585	789	022	286
05	018	13	158	271	414	588	792	027	291
10	021	14	159	273	417	591	796	031	296
15	024	15	.00161	.00275	.00420	.00594	.00800	.01035	.01300
20	027	16	162	277	422	598	803	039	305
25	031	17	164	279	425	601	807	043	310
30	.00034	18	166	281	428	604	811	047	314
35	038	19	167	284	430	607	814	052	319
40	042	20	.00169	.00286	.00433	.00610	.00818	.01056	.01324
45	047	21	171	288	436	614	822	060	329
50	051	22	173	290	438	617	825	064	333
55	056	23	174	292	441	620	829	069	338
4° 00'	.00061	24	176	295	444	623	833	073	343
		25	.00178	.00297	.00447	.00626	.00837	.01077	.01348
		26	179	299	449	630	840	081	352
		27	181	301	452	633	844	086	357
		28	183	304	455	636	848	090	362
		29	185	306	458	640	852	094	367
2° 00'	.00061	30	.00187	.00308	.00460	.00643	.00856	.01098	.01371
02	063	31	188	311	463	646	859	103	376
04	065	32	190	313	466	649	863	107	381
06	067	33	192	315	469	653	867	111	386
08	069	34	194	317	472	656	871	116	391
10	.00071	35	.00196	.00320	.00474	.00659	.00875	.01120	.01396
12	074	36	197	322	477	663	878	124	400
14	076	37	199	324	480	666	882	129	405
16	078	38	201	327	483	669	886	133	410
18	081	39	203	329	486	673	890	137	415
20	.00083	40	.00205	.00332	.00489	.00676	.00894	.01142	.01420
22	085	41	207	334	492	680	898	146	425
24	088	42	208	336	494	683	902	151	430
26	090	43	210	339	497	686	906	155	435
28	093	44	212	341	500	690	909	159	439
30	.00095	45	.00214	.00343	.00503	.00693	.00913	.01164	.01444
32	098	46	216	346	506	697	917	168	449
34	100	47	218	348	509	700	921	173	454
36	103	48	220	351	512	703	925	177	459
38	106	49	222	353	515	707	929	182	464
40	.00108	50	.00224	.00356	.00518	.00710	.00933	.01186	.01469
42	111	51	226	358	521	714	937	191	474
44	114	52	228	361	524	717	941	195	479
46	117	53	230	363	527	721	945	200	484
48	120	54	232	365	530	724	949	204	489
50	.00122	55	.00234	.00368	.00533	.00728	.00953	.01209	.01494
52	125	56	236	370	536	731	957	213	499
54	128	57	238	373	539	735	961	218	504
56	131	58	240	375	542	738	965	222	509
58	134	59	0242	378	545	742	969	227	514
3° 00'	.00137	60	.0244	.00381	.00548	.00745	.00973	.01231	.01519

Table VI. — Natural Versed Sines.

	10°	11°	12°	13°	14°	15°	16°	17°
00'	.01519	.01837	.02185	.02563	.02970	.03407	.03874	.04370
01	524	843	191	570	977	415	882	378
02	529	848	197	576	985	422	890	387
03	534	854	203	583	992	430	898	395
04	539	860	209	589	999	438	906	404
05	.01545	.01865	.02216	.02596	.03006	.03445	.03914	.04412
06	550	871	222	602	013	453	922	421
07	555	876	228	609	020	460	930	429
08	560	882	234	616	027	468	938	438
09	565	888	240	622	034	476	946	446
10	.01570	.01893	.02246	.02629	.03041	.03483	.03954	.04455
11	575	899	252	635	048	491	963	464
12	580	904	258	642	055	498	971	472
13	586	910	265	649	063	506	979	481
14	591	916	271	655	070	514	987	489
15	.01596	.01921	.02277	.02662	.03077	.03521	.03995	.04498
16	601	927	283	669	084	529	.04003	507
17	606	933	289	675	091	537	011	515
18	611	939	295	682	098	544	019	524
19	617	944	302	689	106	552	028	533
20	.01622	.01950	.02308	.02696	.03113	.03560	.04036	.04541
21	627	956	314	702	120	567	044	550
22	632	961	320	709	127	575	052	559
23	638	967	327	716	134	583	060	567
24	643	973	333	722	142	590	069	576
25	.01648	.01979	.02339	.02729	.03149	.03598	.04077	.04585
26	653	984	345	736	156	606	085	593
27	659	990	352	743	163	614	093	602
28	664	996	358	749	171	621	102	611
29	669	.02002	364	756	178	629	110	620
30	.01675	.02008	.02370	.02763	.03185	.03637	.04118	.04628
31	680	013	377	770	193	645	126	637
32	685	019	383	777	200	653	135	646
33	690	025	389	783	207	660	143	655
34	696	031	396	790	214	668	151	663
35	.01701	.02037	.02402	.02797	.03222	.03676	.04159	.04672
36	706	042	408	804	229	684	168	681
37	712	048	415	811	236	692	176	690
38	717	054	421	818	244	699	184	699
39	723	060	427	824	251	707	193	707
40	.01728	.02066	.02434	.02831	.03258	.03715	.04201	.04716
41	733	072	440	838	266	723	209	725
42	739	078	447	845	273	731	218	734
43	744	084	453	852	281	739	226	743
44	750	090	459	859	288	747	234	752
45	.01755	.02095	.02466	.02866	.03295	.03754	.04243	.04760
46	760	101	472	873	303	762	251	769
47	766	107	479	880	310	770	260	778
48	771	113	485	887	318	778	268	787
49	777	119	492	894	325	786	276	796
50	.01782	.02125	.02498	.02900	.03333	.03794	.04285	.04805
51	788	131	504	907	340	802	293	814
52	793	137	511	914	347	810	302	823
53	799	143	517	921	355	818	310	832
54	804	149	524	928	362	826	319	841
55	.01810	.02155	.02530	.02935	.03370	.03834	.04327	.04850
56	815	161	537	942	377	842	336	858
57	821	167	543	949	385	850	344	867
58	826	173	550	956	392	858	353	876
59	832	179	556	963	400	866	361	885
60	.01837	.02185	.02563	.02970	.03407	.03874	.04370	.04894

TABLE VII. — LENGTHS OF CIRCULAR ARCS: RADIUS = 1.

Sec.	Length.	Min.	Length.	Deg.	Length.	Deg.	Length.
1	.0000048	1	.0002909	1	.0174533	61	1.0646508
2	.0000097	2	.0005818	2	.0349066	62	1.0821041
3	.0000145	3	.0008727	3	.0523599	63	1.0995574
4	.0000194	4	.0011636	4	.0698132	64	1.1170107
5	.0000242	5	.0014544	5	.0872665	65	1.1344640
6	.0000291	6	.0017453	6	.1047198	66	1.1519173
7	.0000339	7	.0020362	7	.1221730	67	1.1693706
8	.0000388	8	.0023271	8	.1396263	68	1.1868239
9	.0000436	9	.0026180	9	.1570796	69	1.2042772
10	.0000485	10	.0029089	10	.1745329	70	1.2217305
11	.0000533	11	.0031998	11	.1919862	71	1.2391838
12	.0000582	12	.0034907	12	.2094395	72	1.2566371
13	.0000630	13	.0037815	13	.2268928	73	1.2740904
14	.0000679	14	.0040724	14	.2443461	74	1.2915436
15	.0000727	15	.0043633	15	.2617994	75	1.3089969
16	.0000776	16	.0046542	16	.2792527	76	1.3264502
17	.0000824	17	.0049451	17	.2967060	77	1.3439035
18	.0000873	18	.0052360	18	.3141593	78	1.3613568
19	.0000921	19	.0055269	19	.3316126	79	1.3788101
20	.0000970	20	.0058178	20	.3490659	80	1.3962634
21	.0001018	21	.0061087	21	.3665191	81	1.4137167
22	.0001067	22	.0063995	22	.3839724	82	1.4311700
23	.0001115	23	.0066904	23	.4014257	83	1.4486233
24	.0001164	24	.0069813	24	.4188790	84	1.4660766
25	.0001212	25	.0072722	25	.4363323	85	1.4835299
26	.0001261	26	.0075631	26	.4537856	86	1.5009832
27	.0001309	27	.0078540	27	.4712389	87	1.5184364
28	.0001357	28	.0081449	28	.4886922	88	1.5358897
29	.0001406	29	.0084358	29	.5061455	89	1.5533430
30	.0001454	30	.0087266	30	.5235988	90	1.5707963
31	.0001503	31	.0090175	31	.5410521	91	1.5882496
32	.0001551	32	.0093084	32	.5585054	92	1.6057029
33	.0001600	33	.0095993	33	.5759587	93	1.6231562
34	.0001648	34	.0098902	34	.5934119	94	1.6406095
35	.0001697	35	.0101811	35	.6108652	95	1.6580628
36	.0001745	36	.0104720	36	.6283185	96	1.6755161
37	.0001794	37	.0107629	37	.6457718	97	1.6929694
38	.0001842	38	.0110538	38	.6632251	98	1.7104227
39	.0001891	39	.0113446	39	.6806784	99	1.7278760
40	.0001939	40	.0116355	40	.6981317	100	1.7453293
41	.0001988	41	.0119264	41	.7155050	101	1.7627826
42	.0002036	42	.0122173	42	.7330383	102	1.7802358
43	.0002085	43	.0125082	43	.7504916	103	1.7976891
44	.0002133	44	.0127991	44	.7679449	104	1.8151424
45	.0002182	45	.0130900	45	.7853982	105	1.8325957
46	.0002230	46	.0133809	46	.8028515	106	1.8500490
47	.0002279	47	.0136717	47	.8203047	107	1.8675023
48	.0002327	48	.0139626	48	.8377580	108	1.8849556
49	.0002376	49	.0142535	49	.8552113	109	1.9024089
50	.0002424	50	.0145444	50	.8726646	110	1.9198622
51	.0002473	51	.0148353	51	.8901179	111	1.9373155
52	.0002521	52	.0151262	52	.9075712	112	1.9547688
53	.0002570	53	.0154171	53	.9250245	113	1.9722221
54	.0002618	54	.0157080	54	.9424778	114	1.9896753
55	.0002666	55	.0159989	55	.9599311	115	2.0071286
56	.0002715	56	.0162897	56	.9773844	116	2.0245819
57	.0002763	57	.0165806	57	.9948377	117	2.0420352
58	.0002812	58	.0168715	58	1.0122910	118	2.0594885
59	.0002860	59	.0171624	59	1.0297443	119	2.0769418
60	.0002909	60	.0174533	60	1.0471976	120	2.0943951

VERTICAL HEIGHTS

Min-utes	0°	1°	2°	3°	4°	5°	6°	7°	8°	9°
0...	0.00	1.74	3.49	5.23	6.96	8.68	10.40	12.10	13.78	15.45
2...	0.06	1.80	3.55	5.28	7.02	8.74	10.45	12.15	13.84	15.51
4...	0.12	1.86	3.60	5.34	7.07	8.80	10.51	12.21	13.89	15.56
6...	0.17	1.92	3.66	5.40	7.13	8.85	10.57	12.26	13.95	15.62
8...	0.23	1.98	3.72	5.46	7.19	8.91	10.62	12.32	14.01	15.67
10...	0.29	2.04	3.78	5.52	7.25	8.97	10.68	12.38	14.06	15.73
12...	0.35	2.09	3.84	5.57	7.30	9.03	10.74	12.43	14.12	15.78
14...	0.41	2.15	3.90	5.63	7.36	9.08	10.79	12.49	14.17	15.84
16...	0.47	2.21	3.95	5.69	7.42	9.14	10.85	12.55	14.23	15.89
18...	0.52	2.27	4.01	5.75	7.48	9.20	10.91	12.60	14.28	15.95
20...	0.58	2.33	4.07	5.80	7.53	9.25	10.96	12.66	14.34	16.00
22...	0.64	2.38	4.13	5.86	7.59	9.31	11.02	12.72	14.40	16.06
24...	0.70	2.44	4.18	5.92	7.65	9.37	11.08	12.77	14.45	16.11
26...	0.76	2.50	4.24	5.98	7.71	9.43	11.13	12.83	14.51	16.17
28...	0.81	2.56	4.30	6.04	7.76	9.48	11.19	12.88	14.56	16.22
30...	0.87	2.62	4.36	6.09	7.82	9.54	11.25	12.94	14.62	16.28
32...	0.93	2.67	4.42	6.15	7.88	9.60	11.30	13.00	14.67	16.33
34...	0.99	2.73	4.48	6.21	7.94	9.65	11.36	13.05	14.73	16.39
36...	1.05	2.79	4.53	6.27	7.99	9.71	11.42	13.11	14.79	16.44
38...	1.11	2.85	4.59	6.33	8.05	9.77	11.47	13.17	14.84	16.50
40...	1.16	2.91	4.65	6.38	8.11	9.83	11.53	13.22	14.90	16.55
42...	1.22	2.97	4.71	6.44	8.17	9.88	11.59	13.28	14.95	16.61
44...	1.28	3.02	4.76	6.50	8.22	9.94	11.64	13.33	15.01	16.66
46...	1.34	3.08	4.82	6.56	8.28	10.00	11.70	13.39	15.06	16.72
48...	1.40	3.14	4.88	6.61	8.34	10.05	11.76	13.45	15.12	16.77
50...	1.45	3.20	4.94	6.67	8.40	10.11	11.81	13.50	15.17	16.83
52...	1.51	3.26	4.99	6.73	8.45	10.17	11.87	13.56	15.23	16.88
54...	1.57	3.31	5.05	6.79	8.51	10.22	11.93	13.61	15.28	16.94
56...	1.63	3.37	5.11	6.84	8.57	10.28	11.98	13.67	15.34	16.99
58...	1.69	3.43	5.17	6.90	8.63	10.34	12.04	13.73	15.40	17.05
60...	1.74	3.49	5.23	6.96	8.68	10.40	12.10	13.78	15.45	17.10

HORIZONTAL CORRECTIONS

Dist.	0°	1°	2°	3°	4°	5°	6°	7°	8°	9°
100..	0.0	0.0	0.1	0.3	0.5	0.8	1.1	1.5	1.9	2.5
200..	0.0	0.1	0.2	0.5	1.0	1.5	2.2	3.0	3.9	4.9
300..	0.0	0.1	0.4	0.8	1.5	2.3	3.3	4.5	5.8	7.4
400..	0.0	0.1	0.5	1.1	2.0	3.0	4.4	6.0	7.8	9.8
500..	0.0	0.2	0.6	1.4	2.5	3.8	5.5	7.5	9.7	12.3
600..	0.0	0.2	0.7	1.6	2.9	4.6	6.5	8.9	11.6	14.7
700..	0.0	0.2	0.8	1.9	3.4	5.3	7.6	10.4	13.6	17.2
800..	0.0	0.2	1.0	2.2	3.9	6.1	8.7	11.9	15.5	19.6
900..	0.0	0.3	1.1	2.4	4.4	6.8	9.8	13.4	17.5	22.1
1000..	0.0	0.3	1.2	2.7	4.9	7.6	10.9	14.9	19.4	24.5

TABLE VIII.—STADIA REDUCTIONS 675

VERTICAL HEIGHTS

Min-utes	10°	11°	12°	13°	14°	15°	16°	17°	18°	19°
0...	17.10	18.73	20.34	21.92	23.47	25.00	26.50	27.96	29.39	30.78
2...	17.16	18.78	20.39	21.97	23.52	25.05	26.55	28.01	29.44	30.83
4...	17.21	18.84	20.44	22.02	23.58	25.10	26.59	28.06	29.48	30.87
6...	17.26	18.89	20.50	22.08	23.63	25.15	26.64	28.10	29.53	30.92
8...	17.32	18.95	20.55	22.13	23.68	25.20	26.69	28.15	29.58	30.97
10...	17.37	19.00	20.60	22.18	23.73	25.25	26.74	28.20	29.62	31.01
12...	17.43	19.05	20.66	22.23	23.78	25.30	26.79	28.25	29.67	31.06
14...	17.48	19.11	20.71	22.28	23.83	25.35	26.84	28.30	29.72	31.10
16...	17.54	19.16	20.76	22.34	23.88	25.40	26.89	28.34	29.76	31.15
18...	17.59	19.21	20.81	22.39	23.93	25.45	26.94	28.39	29.81	31.19
20...	17.65	19.27	20.87	22.44	23.99	25.50	26.99	28.44	29.86	31.24
22...	17.70	19.32	20.92	22.49	24.04	25.55	27.04	28.49	29.90	31.28
24...	17.76	19.38	20.97	22.54	24.09	25.60	27.09	28.54	29.95	31.33
26...	17.81	19.43	21.03	22.60	24.14	25.65	27.13	28.58	30.00	31.38
28...	17.86	19.48	21.08	22.65	24.19	25.70	27.18	28.63	30.04	31.42
30...	17.92	19.54	21.13	22.70	24.24	25.75	27.23	28.68	30.09	31.47
32...	17.97	19.59	21.18	22.75	24.29	25.80	27.28	28.73	30.14	31.51
34...	18.03	19.64	21.24	22.80	24.34	25.85	27.33	28.77	30.19	31.56
36...	18.08	19.70	21.29	22.85	24.39	25.90	27.38	28.82	30.23	31.60
38...	18.14	19.75	21.34	22.91	24.44	25.95	27.43	28.87	30.28	31.65
40...	18.19	19.80	21.39	22.96	24.49	26.00	27.48	28.92	30.32	31.69
42...	18.24	19.86	21.45	23.01	24.55	26.05	27.52	28.96	30.37	31.74
44...	18.30	19.91	21.50	23.06	24.60	26.10	27.57	29.01	30.41	31.78
46...	18.35	19.96	21.55	23.11	24.65	26.15	27.62	29.06	30.46	31.83
48...	18.41	20.02	21.60	23.16	24.70	26.20	27.67	29.11	30.51	31.87
50...	18.46	20.07	21.66	23.22	24.75	26.25	27.72	29.15	30.55	31.92
52...	18.51	20.12	21.71	23.27	24.80	26.30	27.77	29.20	30.60	31.96
54...	18.57	20.18	21.76	23.32	24.85	26.35	27.81	29.25	30.65	32.01
56...	18.62	20.23	21.81	23.37	24.90	26.40	27.86	29.30	30.69	32.05
58...	18.68	20.28	21.87	23.42	24.95	26.45	27.91	29.34	30.74	32.09
60...	18.73	20.34	21.92	23.47	25.00	26.50	27.96	29.39	30.78	32.14

HORIZONTAL CORRECTIONS

Dist.	10°	11°	12°	13°	14°	15°	16°	17°	18°	19°
100..	3.0	3.6	4.3	5.1	5.9	6.7	7.6	8.5	9.5	10.6
200..	6.0	7.3	8.6	10.1	11.7	13.4	15.2	17.1	19.1	21.2
300..	9.1	10.9	13.0	15.2	17.6	20.1	22.8	25.6	28.6	31.8
400..	12.1	14.6	17.3	20.2	23.4	26.8	30.4	34.2	38.2	42.4
500..	15.1	18.2	21.6	25.3	29.3	33.5	38.0	42.7	47.7	53.0
600..	18.1	21.8	25.9	30.4	35.1	40.2	45.6	51.3	57.3	63.6
700..	21.1	25.5	30.2	35.4	41.0	46.9	53.2	59.8	66.8	74.2
800..	24.2	29.1	34.6	40.5	46.8	53.6	60.8	68.4	76.4	84.8
900..	27.2	32.8	38.9	45.5	52.7	60.3	68.4	76.9	85.9	95.4
1000..	30.2	36.4	43.2	50.6	58.5	67.0	76.0	85.5	95.5	106.0

VERTICAL HEIGHTS

Min-utes	20°	21°	22°	23°	24°	25°	26°	27°	28°	29°
0...	32.14	33.46	34.73	35.97	37.16	38.30	39.40	40.45	41.45	42.40
2...	32.18	33.50	34.77	36.01	37.20	38.34	39.44	40.49	41.48	42.43
4...	32.23	33.54	34.82	36.05	37.23	38.38	39.47	40.52	41.52	42.46
6...	32.27	33.59	34.86	36.09	37.27	38.41	39.51	40.55	41.55	42.49
8...	32.32	33.63	34.90	36.13	37.31	38.45	39.54	40.59	41.58	42.53
10...	32.36	33.67	34.94	36.17	37.35	38.49	39.58	40.62	41.61	42.56
12...	32.41	33.72	34.98	36.21	37.39	38.53	39.61	40.66	41.65	42.59
14...	32.45	33.76	35.02	36.25	37.43	38.56	39.65	40.69	41.68	42.62
16...	32.49	33.80	35.07	36.29	37.47	38.60	39.69	40.72	41.71	42.65
18...	32.54	33.84	35.11	36.33	37.51	38.64	39.72	40.76	41.74	42.68
20...	32.58	33.89	35.15	36.37	37.54	38.67	39.76	40.79	41.77	42.71
22...	32.63	33.93	35.19	36.41	37.58	38.71	39.79	40.82	41.81	42.74
24...	32.67	33.97	35.23	36.45	37.62	38.75	39.83	40.86	41.84	42.77
26...	32.72	34.01	35.27	36.49	37.66	38.78	39.86	40.89	41.87	42.80
28...	32.76	34.06	35.31	36.53	37.70	38.82	39.90	40.92	41.90	42.83
30...	32.80	34.10	35.36	36.57	37.74	38.86	39.93	40.96	41.93	42.86
32...	32.85	34.14	35.40	36.61	37.77	38.89	39.97	40.99	41.97	42.89
34...	32.89	34.18	35.44	36.65	37.81	38.93	40.00	41.02	42.00	42.92
36...	32.93	34.23	35.48	36.69	37.85	38.97	40.04	41.06	42.03	42.95
38...	32.98	34.27	35.52	36.73	37.89	39.00	40.07	41.09	42.06	42.98
40...	33.02	34.31	35.56	36.77	37.93	39.04	40.11	41.12	42.09	43.01
42...	33.07	34.35	35.60	36.80	37.96	39.08	40.14	41.16	42.12	43.04
44...	33.11	34.40	35.64	36.84	38.00	39.11	40.18	41.19	42.15	43.07
46...	33.15	34.44	35.68	36.88	38.04	39.15	40.21	41.22	42.19	43.10
48...	33.20	34.48	35.72	36.92	38.08	39.18	40.24	41.26	42.22	43.13
50...	33.24	34.52	35.76	36.96	38.11	39.22	40.28	41.29	42.25	43.16
52...	33.28	34.57	35.80	37.00	38.15	39.26	40.31	41.32	42.28	43.18
54...	33.33	34.61	35.85	37.04	38.19	39.29	40.35	41.35	42.31	43.21
56...	33.37	34.65	35.89	37.08	38.23	39.33	40.38	41.39	42.34	43.24
58...	33.41	34.69	35.93	37.12	38.26	39.36	40.42	41.42	42.37	43.27
60...	33.46	34.73	35.97	37.16	38.30	39.40	40.45	41.45	42.40	43.30

HORIZONTAL CORRECTIONS

Dist.	20°	21°	22°	23°	24°	25°	26°	27°	28°	29°
100..	11.7	12.8	14.0	15.3	16.5	17.9	19.2	20.6	22.0	23.5
200..	23.4	25.7	28.1	30.5	33.1	35.7	38.4	41.2	44.1	47.0
300..	35.1	38.5	42.1	45.8	49.6	53.6	57.7	61.8	66.1	70.5
400..	46.8	51.4	56.1	61.1	66.2	71.4	76.9	82.4	88.2	94.0
500..	58.5	64.2	70.2	76.4	82.7	89.3	96.1	103.1	110.2	117.5
600..	70.2	77.0	84.2	91.6	99.2	107.2	115.3	123.7	132.2	141.0
700..	81.9	89.9	98.2	106.9	115.8	125.0	134.5	144.3	154.3	164.5
800..	93.6	102.7	112.2	122.2	132.3	142.9	153.8	164.9	176.3	188.0
900..	105.3	115.6	126.3	137.4	148.9	160.7	173.0	185.5	198.4	211.5
1000..	117.0	128.4	140.3	152.7	165.4	178.6	192.2	206.1	220.4	235.0

TABLE VIII. — STADIA REDUCTIONS   677

VERTICAL HEIGHTS.

Min-utes	30°	31°	32°	33°	34°	35°	36°	37°	38°	39°
0....	43.30	44.15	44.94	45.68	46.36	46.98	47.55	48.06	48.52	48.91
2....	43.33	44.17	44.97	45.70	46.38	47.00	47.57	48.08	48.53	48.92
4....	43.36	44.20	44.99	45.72	46.40	47.02	47.59	48.10	48.54	48.93
6....	43.39	44.23	45.02	45.75	46.42	47.04	47.61	48.11	48.56	48.94
8....	43.42	44.26	45.04	45.77	46.45	47.06	47.62	48.13	48.57	48.96
10....	43.45	44.28	45.07	45.80	46.47	47.08	47.64	48.14	48.58	48.97
12....	43.47	44.31	45.09	45.82	46.49	47.10	47.66	48.16	48.60	48.98
14....	43.50	44.34	45.12	45.84	46.51	47.12	47.68	48.17	48.61	48.99
16....	43.52	44.36	45.14	45.86	46.53	47.14	47.69	48.19	48.63	49.00
18....	43.56	44.39	45.17	45.89	46.55	47.16	47.71	48.21	48.64	49.01
20....	43.59	44.42	45.19	45.91	46.57	47.18	47.73	48.22	48.65	49.03
22....	43.62	44.44	45.22	45.93	46.60	47.20	47.75	48.24	48.67	49.04
24....	43.65	44.47	45.24	45.96	46.62	47.22	47.76	48.25	48.68	49.05
26....	43.67	44.50	45.27	45.98	46.64	47.24	47.78	48.27	48.69	49.06
28....	43.70	44.52	45.29	46.00	46.66	47.26	47.80	48.28	48.71	49.07
30....	43.73	44.55	45.32	46.03	46.68	47.28	47.82	48.30	48.72	49.08
32....	43.76	44.58	45.34	46.05	46.70	47.30	47.83	48.31	48.73	49.09
34....	43.79	44.60	45.36	46.07	46.72	47.31	47.85	48.33	48.74	49.10
36....	43.82	44.63	45.39	46.09	46.74	47.33	47.87	48.34	48.76	49.11
38....	43.84	44.66	45.41	46.12	46.76	47.35	47.88	48.36	48.77	49.13
40....	43.87	44.68	45.44	46.14	46.78	47.37	47.90	48.37	48.78	49.14
42....	43.90	44.71	45.46	46.16	46.80	47.39	47.92	48.39	48.80	49.15
44....	43.93	44.74	45.49	46.18	46.82	47.41	47.93	48.40	48.81	49.16
46....	43.95	44.76	45.51	46.21	46.84	47.43	47.95	48.41	48.82	49.17
48....	43.98	44.79	45.53	46.23	46.86	47.44	47.97	48.43	48.83	49.18
50....	44.01	44.81	45.56	46.25	46.88	47.46	47.98	48.44	48.85	49.19
52....	44.04	44.84	45.58	46.27	46.90	47.48	48.00	48.46	48.86	49.20
54....	44.07	44.86	45.61	46.29	46.92	47.50	48.01	48.47	48.87	49.21
56....	44.09	44.89	45.63	46.32	46.94	47.52	48.03	48.49	48.88	49.22
58....	44.12	44.91	45.65	46.34	46.96	47.54	48.05	48.50	48.90	49.23
60....	44.15	44.94	45.68	46.36	46.98	47.55	48.06	48.52	48.91	49.24

HORIZONTAL CORRECTIONS.

Dist.	30° 00′	30° 30′	31° 00′	31° 30′	32° 00′	32° 30′	33° 00′	33° 30′	34° 00′	34° 30′
100....	25.0	25.8	26.5	27.3	28.1	28.9	29.7	30.5	31.3	32.1
200....	50.0	51.5	53.1	54.6	56.2	57.7	59.3	60.9	62.5	64.2
300....	75.0	77.3	79.6	81.9	84.2	86.6	89.0	91.4	93.8	96.2
400....	100.0	103.0	106.1	109.2	112.3	115.5	118.6	121.8	125.1	128.3
500....	125.0	128.8	132.6	136.5	140.4	144.3	148.3	152.3	156.3	160.4

Dist.	35° 00′	35° 30′	36° 00′	36° 30′	37° 00′	37° 30′	38° 00′	38° 30′	39° 00′	39° 30′
100....	32.9	33.7	34.6	35.4	36.2	37.1	37.9	38.7	39.6	40.5
200....	65.8	67.4	69.1	70.8	72.4	74.1	75.8	77.5	79.2	80.9
300....	98.7	101.2	103.7	106.1	108.7	111.2	113.7	116.2	118.8	121.4
400....	131.6	134.9	138.2	141.5	144.9	148.2	151.6	155.0	158.4	161.8
500....	164.5	168.6	172.8	176.9	181.1	185.3	189.5	193.7	198.0	202.3

TABLE IX.

MEAN REFRACTIONS IN DECLINATION.*

TO BE USED WITH THE SOLAR ATTACHMENT.

Computed by Edward W. Arms, C. E., for W. & L. E. Gurley, Troy, N. Y.)

Hour Angle.	DECLINATIONS.								
	For Latitude 2° 30'.								
	+20°	+15°	+10°	+5°	0°	−5°	−10°	−15°	−20°
† 0 h.	−18″	−12″	−07″	−02″	+02″	07″	12″	18″	23″
2	−18	−12	−07	−02	+02	07	12	18	23
3	−17	−11	−06	−01	+03	08	13	19	25
4	−15	−10	−05	0	+05	10	15	21	27
5	−10	−05	0	+05	10	15	20	26	32
	For Latitude 5°.								
0 h.	−15″	−10″	−05″	0″	+05″	10″	15″	20″	27″
2	−15	−10	−05	0	+05	10	15	20	27
3	−13	−08	−03	+02	07	12	17	23	29
4	−10	−05	0	+05	10	15	20	27	32
5	−05	0	+05	10	15	20	27	32	40
	For Latitude 7° 30'.								
0 h.	−13″	−08′	−02″	+02″	08″	13″	18″	24″	29″
2	−12	−07	−01	+03	09	14	19	25	31
3	−10	−05	0	+05	10	15	20	26	32
4	−05	0	+05	10	15	20	26	32	39
5	+07	12	17	23	29	36	43	51	1′01
	For Latitude 10°.								
0 h.	−10″	−05″	0″	+05″	10″	15″	20″	26″	32″
2	−07	−03	+02	07	12	17	22	28	34
3	−05	0	+03	08	13	19	25	31	38
4	0	05	10	15	20	26	32	39	46
5	+15	20	26	32	39	46	55	1′06	1′19
	For Latitude 12° 30'.								
0 h.	−08″	−02″	+02″	8″	13″	18″	24″	30″	36″
2	−06	00	+05	10	17	20	26	32	39
3	+02	07	12	17	23	29	36	43	51
4	04	09	14	20	25	31	40	48	55
5	21	27	33	40	48	57	1′08	1′23	1′41
	For Latitude 15°.								
0 h.	−05″	0″	+05″	10″	15″	21″	27″	33″	40″
2	−03	+02	07	12	18	23	29	36	43
3	+01	05	11	16	22	28	34	41	49
4	08	12	19	24	30	37	44	53	1′04
5	29	34	41	49	59	1′10	1′24	1′43	2 08

* Printed by permission of W. & L. E. Gurley.

† Hour angles are reckoned either way from local noon.

Hour Angle.	DECLINATIONS.								
	For Latitude 17° 30'.								
	+20°	+15°	+10°	+5°	0°	−5°	−10°	−15°	−20°
0 h.	−02″	+02″	08″	13″	18″	24″	30″	36″	44″
2	0	05	10	15	21	27	33	40	48
3	+02	10	15	21	27	33	40	48	57
4	13	18	23	29	35	43	51	1′01	1′13
5	34	41	49	58	1′10	1′23	1′41	2 06	2 42
	For Latitude 20°.								
0 h.	0″	05″	10″	15″	21″	27″	33″	40″	48″
2	03	07	13	18	24	30	36	44	52
3	06	13	18	24	30	36	44	52	1′02
4	17	22	28	35	42	50	1′00	1′11	1 26
5	39	47	57	1′07	1′20	1′37	2 00	2 32	3 25
	For Latitude 22° 30'.								
0 h.	02″	08″	13″	18″	24″	30″	36″	44″	52″
2	06	11	15	21	27	33	40	48	57
3	11	15	21	27	33	40	48	57	1′08
4	20	26	32	39	46	56	1′07	1′19	1 37
5	45	53	1′03	1′16	1′31	1′52	2 21	3 07	4 28
	For Latitude 25°.								
0 h.	05″	10″	15″	21″	27″	33″	40″	48″	57″
2	08	14	19	25	31	38	46	54	1′05
3	12	18	24	30	37	44	53	1′04	1 18
4	23	29	35	45	53	1′03	1′16	1 31	1 52
5	49	59	1′10	1′24	1′52	2 07	2 44	3 46	5 43
	For Latitude 27° 30'.								
0 h.	08″	13″	18″	24″	30″	36″	44″	52″	1′02″
2	11	16	22	28	34	41	49	1′00	1 10
3	17	22	28	35	42	50	1′00	1 11	1 26
4	28	35	42	50	1′00	1′11	1 26	1 43	2 09
5	54	1′05	1′18	1′34	1 54	2 24	3 11	4 38	8 15
	For Latitude 30°.								
0 h.	10″	15″	21″	27″	33″	40″	48″	57″	1′08″
2	14	19	25	31	38	46	54	1 18	1 18
3	20	26	32	39	47	55	1′06	1 19	1 36
4	32	39	46	52	1′06	1′19	1 35	1 57	2 29
5	1′00	1′10	1′24	1′42	2 07	2 44	3 46	5 43	13 06
	For Latitude 32° 30'.								
0 h.	13″	18″	24″	30″	36″	44″	52″	1′02″	1′14″
2	17	22	28	35	42	50	1′00	1 11	1 26
3	23	29	35	43	51	1′01	1 13	1 28	1 47
4	35	43	51	1′01	1′13	1 27	1 46	2 13	2 54
5	1′03	1′15	1′31	1 53	2 20	3 05	4 25	7 36	

Hour Angle	DECLINATIONS.								
	For Latitude 35°.								
	+20°	+15°	+10°	+5°	0°	—5°	—10°	—15°	—20°
0 h.	15″	21″	27″	33″	40″	48″	57″	1′08″	1′21″
2	20	25	32	38	46	55	1′05	1 18	1 35
3	26	33	39	47	56	1′07	1 21	1 38	2 00
4	39	47	56	1′07	1′20	1 36	1 59	2 32	3 25
5	1′07	1′20	1′38	2 00	2 34	3 29	5 14	10 16	
	For Latitude 37° 30′.								
0 h.	18″	24″	30″	36″	44″	52″	1′02″	1′14″	1′29″
2	22	28	35	42	50	1′00	1 12	1 26	1 45
3	29	36	43	52	1′02	1 14	1 29	1 49	2 16
4	43	51	1′01	1′13	1 27	1 49	2 14	2 54	4 05
5	1′11	1′26	1 54	2 10	2 49	3 55	6 15	14 58	
	For Latitude 40°.								
0 h.	21″	27″	33″	40″	48″	57″	1′08″	1′21″	1′39″
2	25	32	39	46	52	1′06	1 19	1 35	1 57
3	33	40	48	57	1′08	1 21	1 38	2 02	2 36
4	47	55	1′06	1′19	1 36	1 58	2 30	3 21	4 59
5	1′15	1′31	1 51	2 20	3 05	4 25	7 34	25 18	
	For Latitude 42° 30′.								
0 h.	24″	30″	36″	44″	52″	1′02″	1′14″	1′29″	1′49″
2	28	35	39	50	1′00	1 12	1 26	1 45	2 11
3	36	43	52	1′02	1 13	1 29	1 49	2 17	2 59
4	50	1′00	1′11	1 26	1 44	2 10	2 49	3 55	6 16
5	1′19	1 36	1 58	2 30	3 22	5 00	9 24		
	For Latitude 45°.								
0 h.	27″	33″	40″	48″	57″	1′08″	1′21″	1′39″	2′02″
2	32	39	46	52	1′06	1 19	1 35	1 57	2 29
3	40	47	56	1′07	1 21	1 38	2 00	2 34	3 29
4	54	1′04	1′16	1 33	1 54	2 24	3 11	4 38	8 15
5	1′23	1 41	2 05	2 41	3 40	5 40	12 02		
	For Latitude 47° 30′.								
0 h.	30″	36″	44″	52″	1′02″	1′14″	1′29″	1′49″	2′18″
2	35	42	50	1′00	1 12	1 26	1 45	2 01	2 51
3	43	51	1′01	1 13	1 28	1 47	2 15	2 56	4 08
4	56	1′09	1 23	1 40	2 05	2 40	3 39	5 37	11 18
5	1′27	1 46	2 12	2 52	4 01	6 30	16 19		
	For Latitude 50°.								
0 h.	33″	40″	48″	57″	1′08″	1′21″	1′39″	2′02″	2′36″
2	38	46	55	1′06	1 18	1 35	1 57	2 28	3 19
3	47	56	1′06	1 19	1 36	2 29	2 31	3 23	5 02
4	1′02	1′14	1 29	1 48	2 16	2 58	4 18	6 59	19 47
5	1 30	1 51	2 19	3 04	4 22	7 28	24 10		

H UR ANGLE.	DECLINATIONS.								
	+20°	+15°	+10°	+5°	0°	−5°	−10°	−15°	−20°
For Latitude 52° 30′.									
0 h.	36″	44″	52″	1′02″	1′14″	1′29″	1′49″	2′18″	3′05″
2	43	50	59	1 11	1 26	1 42	2 23	2 49	3 55
3	50	1′00	1′11	1 26	1 45	2 11	2 51	2 58	6 22
4	1′05	1 18	1 35	2 10	2 28	3 19	4 53	8 42	
5	1 34	1 56	2 27	3 16	4 47	8 52			
For Latitude 55°.									
0 h.	40″	48″	57″	1′08″	1′21″	1′39″	2′02″	2′36″	3′33″
2	46	55	1′05	1 18	1 34	1 56	2 30	3 15	4 47
3	55	1′06	1 19	1 35	1 58	2 30	3 21	4 58	9 19
4	1′10	1 23	1 42	2 06	2 43	3 44	5 49	12 41	
5	1 37	2 01	2 34	3 28	5 15	10 18			
For Latitude 57° 30′.									
0 h.	44″	52″	1′02″	1′14″	1′29″	1′49″	2′18″	3′05″	4′37″
2	50	59	1 11	1 25	1 40	2 00	2 47	0 51	6 04
3	58	1′10	1 24	1 42	2 07	2 43	3 45	5 50	12 47
4	1′11	1 25	1 43	2 10	2 50	3 55	6 14	14 49	
5	1 41	2 06	2 42	3 42	5 46	12 26			
For Latitude 60°.									
0 h.	48″	57″	1′08″	1′21″	1′39″	2′02″	2′36″	3′33″	5′23″
2	54	1′04	1 17	1 33	1 54	2 24	3 12	4 38	8 15
3	1′03	1 15	1 30	1 51	2 20	3 04	4 24	7 31	24 44
4	1 18	1 34	1 56	2 28	3 18	4 50	8 53		
5	1 45	2 11	2 50	3 57	6 21	15 32			
For Latitude 62° 30′.									
0 h.	52″	1′02″	1′14″	1′29″	1′56″	2′18″	3′00″	4′17″	7′13″
2	58	1′09	1 23	1 41	2 06	2 43	3 44	5 50	12 44
3	1′07″	1 23	1 58	2 01	2 35	3 30	5 16	10 24	
4	1 23	1 40	2 05	2 40	3 40	5 37	11 50		
5	1 48	2 17	2 59	4 14	7 03				
For Latitude 65°.									
0 h.	57″	1′08″	1′21″	1′39″	2′02″	2′36″	3′33″	5′23″	10′51″
2	1′03″	1 16	1 31	1 52	2 21	3 07	4 28	7 44	
3	1 12	1 27	1 46	2 12	2 52	4 02	6 33		
4	1 27	1 47	2 13	2 54	4 05	6 40			
5	1 52	2 22	3 08	4 30	7 52				
For Latitude 67° 30′.									
0 h.	1′02″	1′14″	1′29″	1′50″	2′18″	3′00″	4′17″	7′13″	
2	1 08	1 22	1 40	2 03	2 39	3 37	5 32	11 28	
3	1 17	1 34	1 55	2 26	3 14	4 44	8 34		
4	1 32	1 53	2 23	3 14	4 35	8 05			
5	1 56	2 28	3 17	4 40	8 51				
For Latitude 70°.									
0 h.	1′08″	1′21″	1′39″	2′02″	2′36″	3′33″	5′23″	10′51″	
2	1 14	1 29	1 50	2 18	3 00	4 17	7 13		
3	1 23	1 43	2 05	2 41	3 41	5 59	12 15		
4	1 37	2 00	2 34	3 28	5 20	10 12			
5	2 02	2 33	3 27	5 11	10 05				

TABLE X. TRIGONOMETRIC AND MISCELLANEOUS FORMULAS.

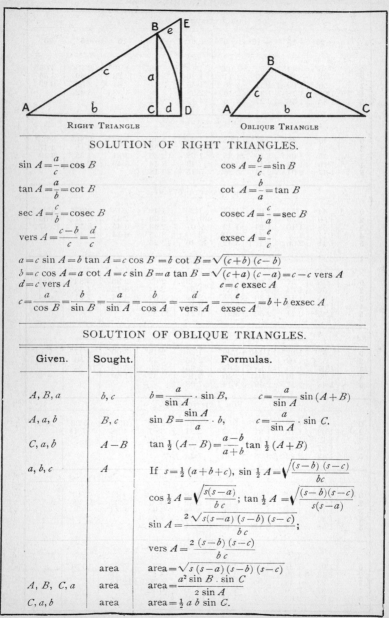

RIGHT TRIANGLE   OBLIQUE TRIANGLE

SOLUTION OF RIGHT TRIANGLES.

$\sin A = \dfrac{a}{c} = \cos B$ $\qquad\qquad$ $\cos A = \dfrac{b}{c} = \sin B$

$\tan A = \dfrac{a}{b} = \cot B$ $\qquad\qquad$ $\cot A = \dfrac{b}{a} = \tan B$

$\sec A = \dfrac{c}{b} = \operatorname{cosec} B$ $\qquad\qquad$ $\operatorname{cosec} A = \dfrac{c}{a} = \sec B$

$\text{vers } A = \dfrac{c-b}{c} = \dfrac{d}{c}$ $\qquad\qquad$ $\text{exsec } A = \dfrac{e}{c}$

$a = c \sin A = b \tan A = c \cos B = b \cot B = \sqrt{(c+b)(c-b)}$

$b = c \cos A = a \cot A = c \sin B = a \tan B = \sqrt{(c+a)(c-a)} = c - c \text{ vers } A$

$d = c \text{ vers } A \qquad\qquad\qquad e = c \text{ exsec } A$

$c = \dfrac{a}{\cos B} = \dfrac{b}{\sin B} = \dfrac{a}{\sin A} = \dfrac{b}{\cos A} = \dfrac{d}{\text{vers } A} = \dfrac{e}{\text{exsec } A} = b + b \text{ exsec } A$

SOLUTION OF OBLIQUE TRIANGLES.

Given.	Sought.	Formulas.
A, B, a	b, c	$b = \dfrac{a}{\sin A} \cdot \sin B, \qquad c = \dfrac{a}{\sin A} \sin (A + B)$
A, a, b	B, c	$\sin B = \dfrac{\sin A}{a} \cdot b, \qquad c = \dfrac{a}{\sin A} \cdot \sin C.$
C, a, b	$A - B$	$\tan \tfrac{1}{2}(A - B) = \dfrac{a - b}{a + b} \tan \tfrac{1}{2}(A + B)$
a, b, c	A	If $s = \tfrac{1}{2}(a + b + c)$, $\sin \tfrac{1}{2} A = \sqrt{\dfrac{(s-b)(s-c)}{bc}}$
		$\cos \tfrac{1}{2} A = \sqrt{\dfrac{s(s-a)}{bc}}$; $\tan \tfrac{1}{2} A = \sqrt{\dfrac{(s-b)(s-c)}{s(s-a)}}$
		$\sin A = \dfrac{2\sqrt{s(s-a)(s-b)(s-c)}}{bc};$
		$\text{vers } A = \dfrac{2(s-b)(s-c)}{bc}$
	area	$\text{area} = \sqrt{s(s-a)(s-b)(s-c)}$
A, B, C, a	area	$\text{area} = \dfrac{a^2 \sin B \cdot \sin C}{2 \sin A}$
C, a, b	area	$\text{area} = \tfrac{1}{2} a b \sin C.$

TABLE X. TRIGONOMETRIC AND MISCELLANEOUS FORMULAS.

GENERAL TRIGONOMETRIC FORMULAS.

$$\sin A = 2 \sin \tfrac{1}{2} A \cos \tfrac{1}{2} A = \sqrt{1 - \cos^2 A} = \tan A \cos A = \sqrt{\tfrac{1}{2}(1 - \cos 2A)}$$

$$\cos A = 2 \cos^2 \tfrac{1}{2} A - 1 = 1 - 2 \sin^2 \tfrac{1}{2} A = \cos^2 \tfrac{1}{2} A - \sin^2 \tfrac{1}{2} A = 1 - \text{vers } A$$

$$\tan A = \frac{\sin A}{\cos A} = \frac{\sqrt{1 - \cos^2 A}}{\cos A} = \frac{\sin 2A}{1 + \cos 2A}$$

$$\cot A = \frac{\cos A}{\sin A} = \frac{\sin 2A}{1 - \cos 2A} = \frac{\sin 2A}{\text{vers } 2A}$$

$$\text{vers } A = 1 - \cos A = \sin A \tan \tfrac{1}{2} A = 2 \sin^2 \tfrac{1}{2} A$$

$$\text{exsec } A = \sec A - 1 = \tan A \tan \tfrac{1}{2} A = \frac{\text{vers } A}{\cos A}$$

$$\sin 2A = 2 \sin A \cos A$$

$$\cos 2A = 2 \cos^2 A - 1 = \cos^2 A - \sin^2 A = 1 - 2 \sin^2 A$$

$$\tan 2A = \frac{2 \tan A}{1 - \tan^2 A}$$

$$\cot 2A = \frac{\cot^2 A - 1}{2 \cot A}$$

$$\text{vers } 2A = 2 \sin^2 A = 2 \sin A \cos A \tan A$$

$$\text{exsec } 2A = \frac{2 \tan^2 A}{1 - \tan^2 A}$$

$$\sin^2 A + \cos^2 A = 1$$

$$\sin (A \pm B) = \sin A \cos B \pm \sin B \cos A$$

$$\cos (A \pm B) = \cos A \cos B \mp \sin A \sin B$$

$$\sin A + \sin B = 2 \sin \tfrac{1}{2} (A + B) \cos \tfrac{1}{2} (A - B)$$

$$\sin A - \sin B = 2 \cos \tfrac{1}{2} (A + B) \sin \tfrac{1}{2} (A - B)$$

$$\cos A + \cos B = 2 \cos \tfrac{1}{2} (A + B) \cos \tfrac{1}{2} (A - B)$$

$$\cos B - \cos A = 2 \sin \tfrac{1}{2} (A + B) \sin \tfrac{1}{2} (A - B)$$

$$\sin^2 A - \sin^2 B = \cos^2 B - \cos^2 A = \sin (A + B) \sin (A - B)$$

$$\cos^2 A - \sin^2 B = \cos (A + B) \cos (A - B)$$

$$\tan A + \tan B = \frac{\sin (A + B)}{\cos A \cos B}$$

$$\tan A - \tan B = \frac{\sin (A - B)}{\cos A \cos B}$$

TABLE XI. CIRCULAR CURVE FORMULAS.

R = Radius	M = Middle Ordinate
I = Central Angle	L_c = Length of Arc
T = Tangent Distance	C = Chord
E = External Distance	t = Tangent Offset

$T = R \tan \tfrac{1}{2} I$

$E = R \operatorname{exsec} \tfrac{1}{2} I$

$M = R \operatorname{vers} \tfrac{1}{2} I$

$C = 2 R \sin \tfrac{1}{2} I$

$L_c = R \times \text{Circular Measure } I$

$L_c - C = \dfrac{C^3}{24 R^2}$ (Approximate)

$M = R - \sqrt{R^2 - \left(\dfrac{C}{2}\right)^2}$

$M = \dfrac{C^2}{8R}$ (Approximate)

$t = \dfrac{C^2}{2R}$

TABLE XII. GEOMETRIC FORMULAS.

Required.	Given.	Formulas.
Area of		
Circle	Radius $= r$	πr^2
Sector of Circle	Radius $= r$, Arc $= L_c$	$\dfrac{r L_c}{2}$
Segment of Circle	Chord $= C$, Middle Ordinate $= M$	$\tfrac{2}{3} CM$ (Approximate)
Ellipse	Semi-axes $= a$ and b	πab
Surface of		
Cone	Radius of Base $= r$; Slant Height $= s$	πrs
Cylinder	Radius $= r$, Height $= h$	$2\pi rh$
Sphere	Radius $= r$	$4\pi r^2$
Zone	Radius of Sphere $= r$, Height of Zone $= h$	$2\pi rh$
Volume of		
Prism or Cylinder	Area of Base $= b$; Height $= h$	bh
Pyramid or Cone	Area of Base $= b$; Height $= h$	$\dfrac{bh}{3}$
Frustum of Pyramid or Cone	Area of bases $= b$ and b'; Height $= h$	$\dfrac{h}{3}(b + b' + \sqrt{bb'})$
Sphere	Radius $= r$	$\tfrac{4}{3}\pi r^3$

TABLE XIII. LINEAR MEASURE.

1 foot = 12 inches

1 yard = 3 feet

1 rod = $5\frac{1}{2}$ yards = $16\frac{1}{2}$ feet

1 mile = 320 rods = 1760 yards = 5280 feet

TABLE XIV. SQUARE MEASURE.

1 sq. foot = 144 sq. inches

1 sq. yard = 9 sq. feet = 1296 sq. inches

1 sq. rod = $30\frac{1}{4}$ sq. yards = $272\frac{1}{4}$ sq. feet

1 acre = 160 sq. rods = 4840 sq. yards = 43,560 sq. feet

1 sq. mile = 640 acres = 102,400 sq. rods = 27,878,400 sq. feet

---

TABLE XV. LINEAR MEASURE — METRIC SYSTEM.

1 myriameter = 10 kilometers

1 kilometer = 10 hectometers

1 hectometer = 10 decameters

1 decameter = 10 meters

1 meter = 10 decimeters

1 decimeter = 10 centimeters

1 centimeter = 10 millimeters

TABLE XVI. SQUARE MEASURE — METRIC SYSTEM.

1 centare = 1 sq. meter

1 are = 100 sq. meters

1 hectare = 100 ares = 10,000 sq. meters

CONSTANTS

TABLE XVII. CONSTANTS.

	Number.	Logarithm.
Ratio of circumference to diameter	3.14159	0.49715
Base of hyperbolic logarithms	2.71828	0.43429
Modulus of common system of logs	0.43429	9.63778−10
Length of seconds pendulum at N. Y. (inches)	39.1017	1.59220
Acceleration due to gravity at N. Y.	32.15949	1.50731
Cubic inches in 1 U. S. gallon	231	2.36361
Cubic feet in 1 U. S. gallon	0.1337	9.12613−10
U. S. gallons in 1 cubic foot	7.4805	0.87393
Pounds of water in 1 cubic foot	62.5	1.79588
Pounds of water in 1 U. S. gallon	8.355	0.92195
Pounds per square inch due to 1 atmosphere	14.7	1.16732
Pounds per square inch due to 1 foot head of water	0.434	9.63749−10
Feet of head for pressure of 1 pound per square inch	2.304	0.36248
Inches in 1 centimeter	0.3937	9.59517−10
Centimeters in 1 inch	2.5400	0.40483
Feet in 1 meter	3.2808	0.51598
Meters in 1 foot	0.3048	9.48402−10
Miles in 1 kilometer	0.62137	9.79335−10
Kilometers in 1 mile	1.60935	0.20665
Square inches in 1 square centimeter	0.1550	9.19033−10
Square centimeters in 1 square inch	6.4520	0.80969
Square feet in 1 square meter	10.764	1.03197
Square meters in 1 square foot	0.09290	8.96802−10
Cubic feet in 1 cubic meter	35.3156	1.54797
Pounds (av.) in 1 kilogram	2.2046	0.34333
Kilograms in 1 pound (av.)	0.4536	9.65667−10
Ft.-lbs. in 1 kilogram-meter	7.23308	0.85932

APPROXIMATE VALUES OF SINES.

Natural sine of $1° = \dfrac{1.75 \text{ ft.}}{100 \text{ ft.}} = \dfrac{1}{6c}$ (roughly)

Natural sine of $0° 1' = \dfrac{0.03 \text{ ft.}}{100 \text{ ft.}}$

Natural sine of $0° 00' 01'' = \dfrac{0.3 \text{ inch}}{1 \text{ mile}}$

GREEK ALPHABET.

LETTERS	NAME
A, α,	Alpha
B, β,	Beta
Γ, γ,	Gamma
Δ, δ,	Delta
E, ε,	Epsilon
Z, ζ,	Zeta
H, η,	Eta
Θ, θ,	Theta
Ι, ι,	Iota
K, κ,	Kappa
Λ, λ,	Lambda
M, μ,	Mu
N, ν,	Nu
Ξ, ξ,	Xi
O, ο,	Omicron
Π, π,	Pi
P, ρ,	Rho
Σ, σ, ς,	Sigma
T, τ,	Tau
Υ, υ,	Upsilon
Φ, φ,	Phi
X, χ,	Chi
Ψ, ψ,	Psi
Ω, ω,	Omega

APPENDICES

APPENDIX A.

THE PLANIMETER.

The planimeter is an instrument used to determine the area of a figure by moving the tracing point of the instrument around the perimeter of the plotted area. When the figure has a regular shape its area can be easily computed from its dimensions, but when the boundaries are crooked, such as river boundaries, the planimeter is most useful, and with careful manipulation results can be obtained which are accurate enough for many engineering purposes.

The Amsler Polar Planimeter. — The most common planimeter is the *Amsler Polar Planimeter* (Fig. 213). This instrument

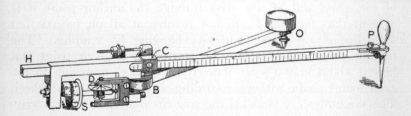

FIG. 213.

has two arms, *BO* and *HP*. The arm *BO* is of fixed length; it is anchored at *O* by a needle point which sticks into the paper and is held in position by a small weight which is detachable. At *B* it is connected by a pivot to a collar, *C*, through which the tracing arm *HP* can slide. At *P* is a tracing point which is moved along the outline of the area to be measured; the distance *CP* being adjusted to conform to the scale of the map. The graduated wheel *S*, whose axis is parallel to *HP*, records the area in units dependent upon the length of the arm *CP*.

The planimeter rests then on three points, the anchor, the tracing point, and the periphery of the wheel. As the tracing point is moved around the given area, the wheel drags along, sometimes slipping and sometimes rolling, and the difference between the reading of the scale on the wheel at the beginning and end of the circuit represents the area of the figure. Besides the scale on the wheel there is a small disk D which records the number of full revolutions of the wheel. The result of reading the disk, the wheel, and its vernier will usually give four figures.

Since the length of the anchor arm is fixed and the point O stationary, the pivot B moves on the circular arc whose center is O and whose radius (R) is the distance OB. The wheel, however, does not follow the arc of a circle, but the instrument must be so constructed that the wheel will always lie somewhere on the line dC or on dC produced (Fig. 214).

If in moving the tracing point its arm be maintained in such a position with reference to the anchor arm that the plane of the wheel will always pass through the anchor point, it is evident that the wheel will not revolve at all on its axis but will slip on the paper without changing its reading. The tracing point can therefore be started at a given point and moved about in the path of a circumference, returning to the same point again without recording any reading of the wheel. This circumference is called the *zero circumference*, or the *correction circle*.

Theory of the Amsler Polar Planimeter. — The following proof has been taken from Cours de Mécanique, by Édouard Collignon.

Let A (Fig. 214) be the area to be measured. Conceive cd (corresponding to the tracing arm) to be a straight line of constant length moving so that one end d is always upon the outline of A and the other end c is always upon a given curve cc' (in general a circle described from O).

Let cd and $c'd'$ be consecutive positions of the moving line, and let an expression be obtained for the elementary area $cdd'c'$ generated by the line in moving from the first position to the second. This movement may be considered as composed of two parts; a translation from cd to a parallel position $c'e$, and a rotation from $c'e$ to $c'd'$, the first generating a parallelogram $cdec'$, and the second a sector $c'ed'$.

Let dA' = the elementary area $cdd'c'$
         L = the length of cd
         dh = the width of the parallelogram
         $d\alpha$ = the elementary angle of rotation

Then $dA' = L \cdot dh + \tfrac{1}{2}L^2 \cdot d\alpha$ [1]

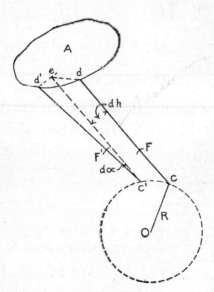

Fig. 214.

Now suppose a wheel F fixed upon cd, its plane perpendicular to that line, so that in the displacement of cd the wheel rolls when the point F moves perpendicularly to cd, and glides without turning when F is displaced in the direction of cd. Let $d\theta$ be the angle through which the wheel turns upon its axis in passing from F to F'. If r is the radius of the wheel, $rd\theta$ is the length of arc applied to the paper. This length is equal to dh (the rotation of the wheel in the translation from cd to $c'e$ corresponding to the normal displacement only) + the arc $L'd\alpha$ (letting $cF = L' = c'F'$).

$$\therefore r \cdot d\theta = dh + L'd\alpha \qquad [2]$$

With the wheel beyond c on dc produced, $r \cdot d\theta = dh - L'd\alpha$
Eliminating dh from equations [1] and [2]

$$dA' = r \cdot L \cdot d\theta + \left(\frac{L^2}{2} - LL'\right)d\alpha \qquad [3]$$

$$\int dA' = \int r \cdot L \cdot d\theta + \int\left(\frac{L^2}{2} - LL'\right)d\alpha \qquad [4]$$

Conceive now the point d to traverse the entire outline of A, the elements dA' being reckoned positively or negatively according to the direction in which they are generated. Two cases are to be noticed:

(a) When the directing curve cc' is exterior to (but not including) the area A (Fig. 214). The algebraic sum, $\int dA'$, will be the difference between the sum of the positive and the sum of the negative elementary areas, and will equal the area A.

$$\int r \cdot L \cdot d\theta = rL\theta$$

$= Lu$ (where $u = r\theta =$ algebraic sum of arcs applied to paper by wheel).

$\int d\alpha = 0$, since cd returns to its original position without having made a circuit about O.

$\therefore$ Integrating expression [4], $A' = A = Lu$.

(b) When the directing curve cc' is within the area A (Fig. 215). The line cd now makes an entire revolution in order to return to its primitive position, and $\int d\alpha = 2\pi$. Also the area

$$A = \int dA' + \text{area of circle described by } Oc.$$

By integrating expression [4]

$$A' = Lu + 2\pi \left(\frac{L^2}{2} - LL' \right)$$

$$A = A' + \pi R^2$$
$$= Lu + \pi (L^2 - 2 LL' + R^2)$$
$$= Lu + \text{the area of a circle of radius } \sqrt{L^2 - 2 LL' + R^2}.$$

The sign of $2 LL'$ is $-$ if the wheel be between tracing point and pivot point; otherwise it is $+$.

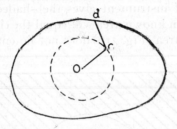

Fig. 215.

This circle is called the "circle of correction" and its value may be found by measuring with the planimeter a circle or other figure of known area inclosing the directing curve cc'.

It will be seen that the radius $\sqrt{L^2 \pm 2 LL' + R^2}$ is the distance from anchor point to tracing point, when the plane of the wheel passes through the anchor point; in other words, is the radius of the zero circle.

If $C =$ circumference of wheel

and $n =$ number of revolutions made in a given measurement
$$Lu = LnC$$

If L and C be given in inches A will be found in square inches. By varying L the area A corresponding to one revolution of the wheel ($n = 1$) may be varied at pleasure. Commonly, if the area is sought in square inches the length L is made such, by adjustment on the tracing arm, that one complete revolution of the wheel corresponds to 10 square inches of area.

Since, for the anchor point **outside** the area to be measured, $A = LnC$, it appears that for any setting of L, A is directly proportional to n. So that L may be set at random and n' determined for a known area A' (say a circle or rectangle) in whatever unit the area is desired, then $\dfrac{A}{A'} = \dfrac{n}{n'}$. But this process evidently does not apply to the case of anchor point **inside** the area to be measured.

In finding the area of the circle of correction, the instrument gives directly only the **difference** between circle and known area.

If the perimeter lies entirely outside of circle (Fig. 216), then the record of instrument gives the shaded area only, and this **subtracted** from known area will equal the circle of correction.

If the known area (Fig. 216) does not lie entirely without the

FIG. 216.

circle then record of instrument must be **added** to the known area if the circle of correction is the larger, otherwise **subtracted**.

Use of Polar Planimeter. — In measuring a closed area the anchor point is pressed into the paper at a position **outside** of the area of the figure, if it is not too large, and the tracing point is started from a definite point on the periphery of the area, preferably such as will bring the two arms approximately at right angles to each other. The wheel is then read. The tracing point is then moved around the outline of the area, being careful to follow the line accurately, until the starting point is reached again. The wheel is again read and the difference between the two wheel readings gives the area in the unit depending upon the setting of the arm. The disk should also be read when the wheel is read if the area is large enough to require a full revolution of the wheel. Care must be taken to bring the tracing point **exactly** back to the point from which it was started.

While some instruments have a tracing arm of fixed length, so that all areas recorded by the wheel are in the same unit, square inches for example, many planimeters have adjustable tracing arms which can be set by means of a clamp and slow-motion screw at whatever reading of the scale on the tracing arm is desired. Usually it will be necessary to use a reading glass to make this setting accurately. The arm is sometimes marked by vertical lines and beside these lines are letters and figures indicating the unit of area to which the setting corresponds. In some instances, however, the scale is marked as a continuous scale and the proper settings for given area units are supplied by the instrument maker.

A way of avoiding the use of the correction circle in measuring large areas is to divide the area into smaller ones by light pencil lines and to determine each fractional area separately. If, however, the anchor point is placed inside the area the value of the correction circle must be applied to the reading of the wheel as explained in the previous article.

A planimeter can be readily used even though the setting of the arm is not known. A square, say four inches on a side, can be accurately drawn on the map and its area determined with the planimeter in the usual manner, making several independent determinations with the anchor point in different positions so that if there are any irregularities in the paper over which the wheel passes which are affecting one result, this error will not enter into the other determinations. The mean of these results divided by the number of square inches in the given area will be the wheel reading for one square inch. This being determined the area in square inches of any given figure can be obtained by the planimeter and this can be easily converted into the desired units by using the scale of the map.

It is well before beginning to trace out the figure to run the tracing point around the figure, keeping approximately on the line so as to be sure that the anchor point has been placed in a satisfactory position. To insure accuracy the area should always be measured by at least two independent determinations with a different position of the anchor for each measurement for the reason explained above. Furthermore, it is of extreme importance to check the area roughly by observation or by scaling and rough calculations. If the paper has shrunk since the drawing was made the amount of this change should be determined and allowed for in arriving at a correct value for the area. By the use of a polar planimeter a result which is not in error more than one per cent is easily obtained, except in the case of very small areas.

The Rolling Planimeter. — The rolling planimeter, unlike the polar planimeter, is not anchored to the drawing. It has a tracing point at the end of an adjustable pivoted arm which is fastened to a frame which is supported on two rollers. In using this planimeter the whole instrument moves forward or backward in a straight line while the tracing point traverses the outline of the area to be measured.

With the rolling planimeter it is possible to obtain a remarkable degree of accuracy, results correct to a tenth of a per cent being easily reached.

APPENDIX B.

Arc — Chord Formula. — Following is the proof of formula expressing approximately the difference between the lengths of the arc of a circle and the subtending chord, used in Art. 284, p. 337.

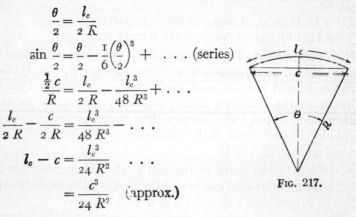

$$\frac{\theta}{2} = \frac{l_c}{2\,R}$$

$$\sin\frac{\theta}{2} = \frac{\theta}{2} - \frac{1}{6}\left(\frac{\theta}{2}\right)^3 + \ldots \text{ (series)}$$

$$\frac{\frac{1}{2}c}{R} = \frac{l_c}{2\,R} - \frac{l_c^3}{48\,R^3} + \ldots$$

$$\frac{l_c}{2\,R} - \frac{c}{2\,R} = \frac{l_c^3}{48\,R^3} - \ldots$$

$$l_c - c = \frac{l_c^3}{24\,R^2} \quad \ldots$$

$$= \frac{c^3}{24\,R^2} \quad \text{(approx.)}$$

Fig. 217.

APPENDIX C

COPY

Party-Wall Agreement — 37–39 Hammond St., Lawton, Mass.

October 28, 1927

AGREEMENT 3085–231.

Ellen C. Hart et al party of the first part;

John H. Elliot et al party of the second part;

WITNESSETH, That Whereas the party of the First Part is the owner of the premises situate and now numbered 37 on Hammond Street in said Lawton, and the party of the Second Part is the owner of the premises situate and now numbered 39 on said Hammond Street, the division line between said two estates running in part through the middle of an existing brick partition wall, and

WHEREAS the party of the first part is about to erect a new building upon its said estate and the party of the second part may in the future desire to erect a new building upon its said estate and both parties desire to provide for the use of the said existing brick partition wall and for any extension of and additions thereto,

NOW THERFORE, it is mutually agreed as follows:

(1). The division line between said two estates and the location of said existing brick partition wall is as shown on a plan by Hartwell & Johnson, Civil Engineers, dated Oct. 18, 1927, and recorded herewith.

(2). Subject to the rights of the parties hereto as hereinafter set forth, said existing brick partition wall shall be and remain a common party wall and either party may add to said wall in height, depth, length or thickness, and in case of damage, may repair, or in case of destruction or decay, may rebuild the same or any part thereof and any addition thereto or extension thereof. No extension of or addition to said wall shall be placed by either on land of the other, unless said land of the other is vacant, without the assent in writing of the owners and all tenants or occupants of said land of the other, and in no event so as to cause more than the present thickness of wall, and a portion as hereinafter provided for, of the necessary foundations, to be upon the land of the other.

(3). Whenever either party uses any additions to or extensions of the existing brick partition wall as such made by the other party, or any wall or part thereof rebuilt or reconstructed in accordance with the provisions of the preceding paragraph by the other party, the said party shall pay to such other party one-half of the then value of the entire structure of such additions, extensions or rebuilt wall, or so much thereof as it may use, including the pile or other foundations or structures and coping; but if such additions, extensions or rebuilt wall, including the foundation thereof, shall be of greater thickness than is required by law for the building which said party who is to pay has erected or is erecting, then no payment shall be made for such excess of thickness.

(4). The cost of any necessary repairs made to any part of the then existing brick partition wall shall be borne by the parties hereto in proportion to the extent to which the same is respectively used by them.

(5). Either party may, in building upon its own land, erect a steel frame or concrete building, and in that event, if such building exceeds in height or length the brick partition wall then existing, shall build out to but no further than the division line above and in the front and rear of the brick partition wall then existing; but the walls of such building above, in front and in rear of the brick partition wall then existing shall be supported entirely by the frame of the building upon the land of the party erecting the same in such manner that no additional weight shall be imposed upon the brick partition wall then existing. Foundations for the support of such steel frame or concrete building may be placed in part under, or made part of the foundation of the brick partition wall then existing, but shall be placed wholly upon the land of the party erecting such building.

(6). In building a steel frame or concrete building, the party building the same may channel into the then existing brick partition wall, and any additions to or extensions thereof, for the insertions of the necessary beams, uprights or columns and beams resting upon said uprights or columns, provided that said wall is not thereby substantially weakened or its efficiency against fire is not impaired and the other party is not deprived in any material manner of the beneficial use of said wall, and provided further that the party so building shall leave not less than two inches of such brick wall or addition to or extension thereof on his own side of the division line. No use shall be made by either party of any wall erected by the other party above, in front or in rear of, the brick partition wall and supported by the steel frame or concrete building of the other party.

(7). The party erecting a new building or doing any work under this agreement shall comply with all the building laws of the City of Lawton; shall use good material and do all work in a proper and workmanlike manner and from his own side of the division line if the other side is built upon; shall carry up flues, chimneys and the like of the other party, adjacent to the new building, above the brick partition wall then existing, so as to leave the other party as nearly as may be in as good condition as before; shall place on land of the other party not exceeding one-half of the thickness of all foundations and footings to support the then existing brick partition wall, and during the process of the erection of any building or of doing said work shall protect and save from injury the other party, and shall fully make good all injuries which may be caused to the building of such other party, and shall indemnify such other party from any liability to his tenants and all other persons, both as to their real and personal property, caused by any act or omission in relation to the work herein described.

(8) Said parties mutually covenant for themselves, their respective heirs, successors and assigns, each to and with the other and his or its respective heirs, successors and assigns, to observe the above agreement; and that the covenant herein contained shall run with the land; and that no one shall be responsible except for his acts or defaults while owner.

COPY of Party Wall and Restricted Use Agreement
relating to land now vacant.

Hancock Registry of Deeds
Berwick, Ohio — July 5, 1930

Agreement between George J. Raymond of the first part and
Edward L. Pike and John K. Pike of the second part.

It is therefore hereby agreed that lot #2 upon said plan which
was bid off by said Moses and Eber shall and may be granted
to and taken by the said Galvin at the rate and upon the terms
upon which the same was bid off; it is further agreed that lot #4
which was bid off by said Galvin shall and may be granted to and
taken by the Moses and Eber Parker at the rate and on the terms
upon which the same was bid off. And whereas after such
exchange the line between #2 and #3 and the land between #4
and #5 will be dividing lines between the parties,

it is further agreed that whichever party shall first build upon
either of the lots adjoining said lines, shall build his partition
wall half on his own land and half on the land of the other party,
that the other party shall have full right to make equal use of
such partition wall for the purpose of building and whenever he
shall so use the same shall pay to the other party one half of the
value of such wall to the extent to which he shall so use the same,

it is further agreed that the said Raymond, his heirs or assigns
shall not erect any house or building on lots #1 and #2 nearer to
Essex St. than six feet and the said Raymond for himself, his
heirs and assigns as proprietors of said lots #1 and #2 doth hereby
grant to said Edward and John, their heirs and assigns as proprietors of lot #3 the privilege of having the said space of six
feet back from Essex Street kept open and free for air, light and
prospect together with the privilege at all times of opening
windows in the wall of any house which may be built upon

said lot # 3, through and over the said open space of six feet back from Essex Street, provided that every such window shall be furnished with a reversed blind made in one piece to be opened to a greater extent than a right angle with the wall of building in which said window is situated. Provided, however, that the said Edward and John are not to have the right of opening any window by virtue of this agreement nearer the ground than six feet from the first floor even or above the surface of the earth of any house that they may build or cause to be built on said lot #3.

INDEX

INDEX